INTERNATIONAL HARVESTER

FARM EQUIPMENT

PRODUCT HISTORY 1831-1985

Ralph Baumheckel & Kent Borghoff

Published by the
American Society of Agricultural Engineers
2950 Niles Road, St. Joseph, Michigan

About ASAE — the Society for engineering in agricultural, food, and biological systems

ASAE is a technical and professional organization of members committed to improving agriculture through engineering. Many of our 8,000 members in the United Stated, Canada, and more than 100 other countries are engineering professionals actively involved in designing the farm equipment that continues to help the world's farmers feed the growing population. We're proud of the triumphs of the agriculture and equipment industry. ASAE is dedicated to preserving the record of this progress for others. This book joins many other popular ASAE titles in recording the exciting developments in agricultural equipment history.

International Harvester Farm Equipment Product History 1831-1985
Editor and Book Designer: Melissa Carpenter Miller

Library of Congress Catalog Card Number (LCCN) 97-75110
International Standard Book Number (ISBN) 0-929355-86-5

Printed in the U.S.A.

Acknowledgments

Twelve years ago the American Society of Agricultural Engineers (ASAE) began publishing its photo history series of major American farm equipment manufacturers. *International Harvester Farm Equipment: Product History 1831-1985* is the fourth book in that series. The story of International Harvester spans well over 150 years. This single volume is not intended to cover the firm's entire business history or its massive product offering of farm equipment during those years. The goal is to record and preserve in one document some of the key events in the Company's development and to display and describe selected innovative, as well as traditional, farm and industrial tractors and equipment that contributed to IH leadership in the industry.

Over 600 photos and much of the reference material for text in the book are from the McCormick-International Harvester Company archives in the State Historical Society of Wisconsin (SHSW), located in Madison, Wisconsin. The SHSW received the formal archives of International Harvester's Farm Equipment Division and a massive collection of historical material in 1990 after the Division was sold to the Tenneco Corporation. This collection complemented the McCormick archives that were already housed at the SHSW. Management and support of this extensive collection is generously funded by grants from the Chauncy and Marion Deering McCormick Foundation.

Cynthia (Cindy) A. Knight, the archivist for the McCormick-International Harvester Collection offered much of her time, patience, and talent to facilitate the completion of the project. Her knowledge of, and dedication to, the IH archive material proved to be invaluable. Special assistance was provided by author and SHSW volunteer, Guy Fay.

Melissa Miller of ASAE did the layout and editing for the book. Her creativity, attention to detail, and sense of style with text and graphics are beautifully documented in the finished product. In particular, we will always remember her patience and understanding throughout this multi-year project.

Many IH retirees have loaned or contributed personal files, photos, slides, IH literature, and memorabilia for reference or inclusion in the book. One-on-one interviews, telephone conversations, and written communications have added detail and human interest to the document and extended the graphic coverage.

Central to development of the Harvest Mechanization and Axial-Flow chapters was Donald A. Murray, the retired IH Chief Engineer for Grain Harvesting at East Moline Plant. Mr. Murray shared his unpublished personal memoirs of his IH career with me and contributed over 1,000 slides and an extensive series of prints. This material will be contributed to the SHSW archives.

Other significant sources of reference material came from IH retirees Russ Poynor, Wil Ottery, and Rich Bromberek. Russell R. Poynor, ASAE past president and former General Supervisor of IH Product Planning Research, contributed material covering much of his International Harvester career. Mr. Ottery loaned numerous documents from his personal collection and several IH Farm Operating Equipment and IH Agricultural Equipment Reference Catalog binders dating back to 1943. Mr. Bromberek loaned a major share of the graphics and part of the references for text in the Industrial Equipment chapter.

In addition, at the risk of missing someone, the following have also made valuable, concrete contributions to the IH book project:

Charlie Albright, Bob Barrett, Jack Bauman, Chuck Boetto, George Boltz, Bill Borghoff, Len Buchholz, Bill Cade, Larry Cornelius, Russ Decker, Vedick Erickson, Ray Fischer, Ed Gaul, John Hamilton, Eldon Harden, Bruce Harrop, Richard Hennessey, Gordon Hirshman, Paul Hummel, Than Irwin, Otto Johnson, Pat Kaine, Vic Komuchar, Stan Lancaster, Don McAllister, Carmen Phillips, Paul Picot, Tom Scarnato, Harold Schramm, Herb Sullivan, Ralph Sutton, Ray Throckmorton, Terry Tracy, Mel (Melvin) Van Buskirk, Paul Wallen, Jim Wilkins, Art Williams, Bud Youle, Warren Zimmerman

- IH Equipment owners: Harry Lee, Kenneth Sayre, and Larry Eipers
- Deere & Company: Harold Hansen, Lyle Wade, and John Deere Inventor, Eugene Keeton
- Oliver Corporation: Roy Brandt
- Navistar International Transportation Corporation: Greg Lennes, Corporate Secretary

• Case Corporation: Dave Rogers, Eldon Brumbaugh, and Ray Heller

My co-author, Kent Borghoff, would like to specifically acknowledge the guidance and continued support of his father, former IH employee and Farmall collector, Bill Borghoff. His interest in the project was not only contagious, but essential to development of the initial chapters of this book.

My wife, Priscilla Baumheckel, entered every line of text into the computer and was a steady source of support through the obstacles and challenges associated with a work of this kind. She and daughter Carol Baumheckel, along with many IH retiree contributors, did the extensive proofing.

Hjalmar D. Bruhn, Agricultural Engineering Professor Emeritus at the University of Wisconsin, and his wife Janet offered their home as lodging during my 22 weeks of archive research in Madison. I especially enjoyed the wonderful conversations we shared about agriculture in the 20th century during the evening hours. The IH book research and writing project would not have been possible without their generous support.

Former employees travel miles to attend International Harvester Retiree Club meetings; farmers and other IH enthusiasts spend money and hours of labor restoring International Harvester tractors and equipment; non-farm people bring their families to Red Power Round Up events; all because the legacy of the International Harvester Company and its products lives on. We've written *International Harvester Farm Equipment: Product History 1831-1985* because of that legacy.

Ralph Baumheckel
Kent Borghoff

Photo Credits

Approximately two-thirds of the photographs used in this book were obtained from the McCormick-International Harvester Company Collection, State Historical Society of Wisconsin. Additional photographs were supplied from the personal files of the senior author, contributions from International Harvester retirees, and the IH Advertising Department files supplied by the Case Corporation. With completion of the book, this additional material was contributed to the State Historical Society of Wisconsin as a supplemental accession. All images in the book are the property of the State Historical Society of Wisconsin and cannot be reproduced in any form without the written permission of the State Historical Society of Wisconsin.

Copies of the photographs in the book are available for a fee from the Wisconsin Society by contacting:
The State Historical Society of Wisconsin
Visual Material Archives
816 State Street
Madison, WI 53706

Identify the image or images by book page number(s), location on the page, and image description.

Preface

For centuries the world grain crop was harvested by individuals with scythe and sickle. Other vital crops were planted, cultivated, and harvested by hand and with the use of horses and other animals in ingenious ways. In the early to mid-19th century, and perhaps long before, attempts were made to change these time-honored methods. It was in 1831 that Cyrus Hall McCormick demonstrated his reaper in the rolling hills of Virginia. On his first trip west, Cyrus saw vast quantities of grain going to waste on the fertile prairie for lack of labor to harvest it. After this he soon moved to Illinois to establish his reaper plant on the banks of the Chicago River.

Cyrus McCormick was a key figure in the highly competitive race to develop, manufacture, and market the machines that would revolutionize United States agriculture and help change the face of this young country into an extremely powerful and productive industrial nation. He operated as the McCormick Harvesting Machine Company until his death in 1884. His Company received many awards and medals of honor during his lifetime, especially in Europe.

After Cyrus McCormick's death, his company continued to grow under Cyrus Jr. and other family members. In 1902 the International Harvester Company was formed by the combination of the McCormick Harvesting Machine Company, Deering Harvester Company, Milwaukee Harvester Company, Warder, Bushnell & Glessner Company and the Plano Manufacturing Company. This great new venture expanded dramatically in North America and by 1905 began operations overseas. About this time the remarkable development of farm tractors began to really take shape and is most interestingly described by the authors in language and photos that clearly show how IH eventually became the world leader in farm tractors producing its 5,000,000th unit by 1974.

The authors tell the fascinating story of Cyrus Hall McCormick, the legacy that he left, and the firm that became International Harvester. The story is told with a unique insight obtained from an exhaustive search of the McCormick family history and International Harvester Company records located in the State Historical Society of Wisconsin archives. In addition, personal files and collections of pertinent material contributed to the authors by numerous former IH employees add a special insight This was indeed a labor of love on the part of Ralph Baumheckel and Kent Borghoff.

This historical treatise of a great American company spanning some 155 years is a must for everyone even remotely connected with agriculture anywhere in the world. Having served in executive management of IH, I am especially thankful that this wonderful product history has been preserved for us and many generations to come in this beautifully illustrated book.

J. Patrick Kaine
Retired Vice Chairman,
International Harvester Company

Table of Contents

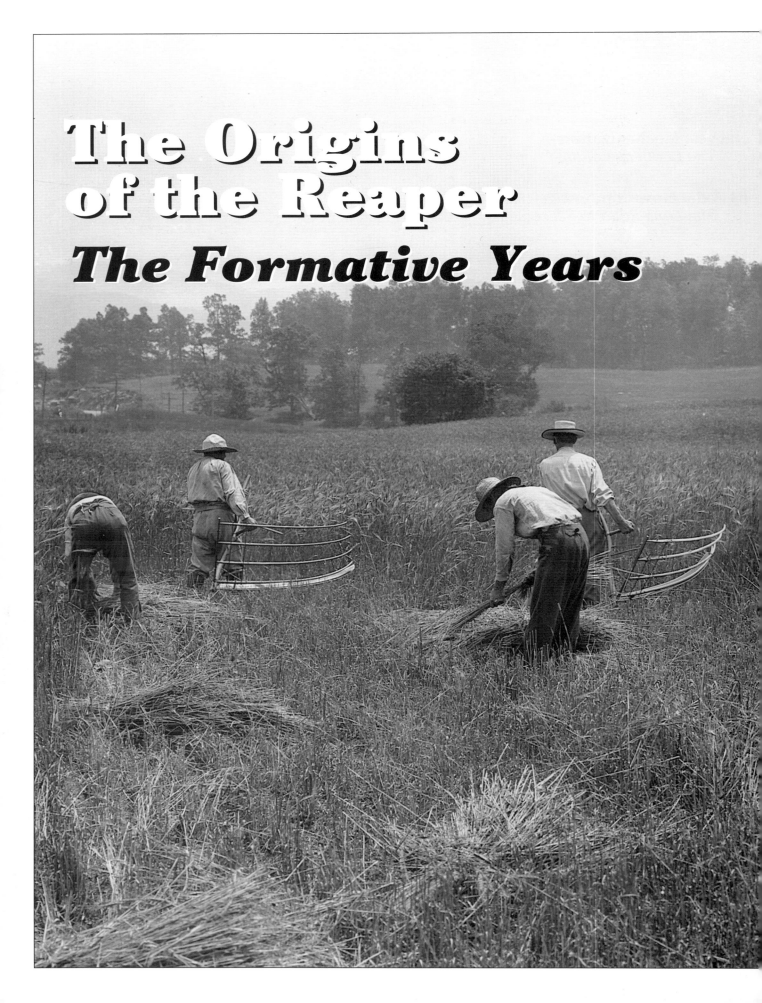

The Origins
of the Reaper
The Formative Years

President George Washington once said in 1794, "I know of no pursuit in which more real and important service can be rendered to any country than by improving its agriculture." At that time, improvement was sorely needed. Farmers throughout the world still depended on harvesting grain with the sickle, or reaping hook, which was essentially the same tool used centuries earlier. With it, a farmer could work the entire day and not cut an acre of wheat. The larger and more efficient cradle was used toward the end of the eighteenth century but despite the improvement, one harvester could only manage to cut 2 acres in a hard day's work. Estimates showed that the production of one acre of wheat, from plowing to seeding to reaping to threshing, required over 64 hours of labor. These demands necessitated that 9 out of every 10 Americans devote their lives to agriculture.

In 1831 Cyrus McCormick invented a practical reaper. In the years that followed, an entire industry emerged that was devoted solely to making agricultural production more efficient and easing the many burdens of the farmer. The invention and the industry forever changed the world.

work of six men. While some considered it a humbug, others were impressed with its work. But no one, including Cyrus McCormick, could have imagined the impact his machine would have on the future of agriculture.

Cyrus McCormick was experienced enough as an inventor to know that the reaper he displayed on Steele's farm was far from ready or capable of revolutionizing agriculture. McCormick's reaper, though successful in its trial run, needed modifications before he would even seek a patent. By the time this was done in 1834, McCormick had already received two other patents. The first was for an improved hillside plow that more easily turned all furrows uphill on a slope. McCormick's second patent was granted in 1833 for his self-sharpening plow where the shares of the implement could be turned over to wear the points equally on bottom and top. The reaper, though the greatest example, was certainly not the only evidence of McCormick's inventive mind.

Cyrus McCormick first turned his inventive genius to the problem of mechanically reaping grain at a very young age. His father, Robert McCormick, had attempted to solve the same problem for years.

The First Successful Reaper

The real significance of the event that took place on the John Steele's Virginia farm in July 1831 could hardly have been known to the few that witnessed it. On this hot summer day, Cyrus McCormick provided the first public demonstration of his latest invention: a mechanical reaper. In one day this new machine successfully did the

This painting depicts Cyrus McCormick walking triumphantly behind his reaper at its first public demonstration at Steele's Tavern, Virginia, in July 1831. The man raking the grain from the platform is Joe Anderson, the McCormicks' slave. Although the machine worked well, the excitement of this scene is most likely over dramatic; many observers remained skeptical.

Throughout his childhood, Cyrus watched as his father repeatedly experimented and failed. The difficulty in designing a machine that not only cut the grain but gently handled it after the cutting proved too much for Robert, and he finally abandoned his work in 1831, after 30 years of effort. Cyrus, however, was not yet ready to abandon the idea of mechanical harvesting. In fact, the complexity of the task seemed to inspire him.

Just six weeks after Robert's final failed attempt, Cyrus developed the machine that successfully cut the grain on Steele's farm in the summer of 1831. For decades, farmers and inventors across the world grappled with the problems that Cyrus so quickly solved. As Cyrus discovered, the key to a successful reaper was a combination of seven fundamental principles, each designed to address a specific problem. These principles, incorporated in McCormick's reaper were as follows:

Cyrus McCormick's father, Robert McCormick (left), spent many years trying to solve the riddle of mechanical harvesting. The machine he produced was considered by some to be the true "first" reaper. The debate stirred much dissension — especially within the McCormick family. But in reality, Robert abandoned his efforts as a failure. Cyrus (right) found inspiration in his father's efforts and created a far more workable machine.

1. **a divider** was used to turn the grain to be cut toward the blade.
2. **a reciprocating knife** with a straight, serrated edge to cut the grain. The back and forth motion tended to sever the stalk neatly without missing any of the grain.
3. **a row of fingers** or guards to support and hold the grain while it was being cut. This prevented the grain from slipping sideways or being flattened as it approached the blade. The fingers projected a few inches from the platform and each had a slit through which the reciprocating knife passed.
4. **a revolving reel** which lifted and straightened fallen grain and brought it against the knife and then laid the cut stalks on the platform.
5. **a platform** to gently catch the cut grain as it fell from the knife and hold it until raked aside.
6. **a front-side draft movement**, making it a machine to be pulled by the horses rather than pushed so paths could be straighter and corners turned more easily. The horses were placed on the stubble

side of the reaper so as not to damage the crop before it was cut.
7. **a master wheel** to carry the weight of the machine and furnish power to operate the reel and knife.

While these seven fundamental principles may seem simple when considered apart from the others, combining the principles to work harmoniously required the highest degree of perfection. The machine was anything but simple, and the mere presence of these principles by no means guaranteed a perfect reaper. But it was a start . . . and McCormick never stopped his pursuit of the perfect machine.

This rear view of Cyrus McCormick's original reaper clearly shows the elements that made it successful. The divider and revolving reel worked to gather the standing grain that was cut and delivered to the platform. The rake was a key piece of equipment used to sweep the cut grain to the side.

This close-up of the gearing mechanism on the original reaper shows how power was furnished from the master drive wheel to the reciprocating knife. The projecting finger guards kept the knife in line while also holding the grain in position to be cut.

Although the reaper greatly reduced the labor demands inherent in harvesting grain, several workers were still required to ride the horse, rake the platform, and bind and shock the grain. Eight acres was a good day's work for this crew.

In 1931 the American Society of Agricultural Engineers (ASAE) helped celebrate the reaper's one hundredth year by sponsoring a "Pageant of Progress" for harvesting machines. Over 1,000 interested engineers and educators gathered at Ames, Iowa, for the event. Among those attending the Pageant were Cyrus McCormick Jr., shown here kneeling at the platform of his grandfather's invention. J.B. Davidson, the first president of ASAE, and R.W. Trullinger, then acting president of ASAE, are the interested spectators to the left.

The Controversy

Cyrus McCormick's reaper was far from being the first to receive a patent. By the time a patent was awarded to McCormick in 1834, over 40 other inventors also held reaper patents. What's more, the principles upon which McCormick's patent were based were not wholly original with McCormick. Many of the principles were discovered earlier by other inventors. These facts made it easy for the competition to question McCormick's claim as inventor. The result was a debate that occasionally flared up in the agricultural press for the next several decades. The controversy seemed to capture the imagination of the rural population as several books, articles, and dissertations have been devoted to answering the question: Who really invented the reaper?

The answer to this question was not trivial at the time. Manufacturers who could claim their machine as "the original" possessed a tremendous advantage over the competition. The significance of the debate extended beyond mere business to include personal feelings and reputations. It may seem like an interesting historical sidelight today, but it meant everything to those that were involved at the time.

Certainly, not all agreed that Cyrus McCormick was the first inventor of the reaper. The earliest, loudest, and most persistent contention came on behalf of Obed Hussey. This former sailor and candlestick maker invented, built, and patented a successful reaper in 1833, one year before McCormick's patent was issued. As Hussey and McCormick both improved their respective machines and as competition between the two grew more keen, the debate became more hostile, more pronounced, and more significant. Farmers took sides.

Hussey wrote in 1855, "I can prove my reaper to have been entirely successful as early as 1833, while my friend McCormick was so unsuccessful between 1831 and 1834 that his father and family advised him to abandon his reaper . . . He sold no machines until 1840 and his machines were of no practical value till 1845, while my reapers had been perfectly successful for 12 years." Such was the basis of Hussey's claim as inventor.

Years later, a different case was made that ignored the claims of Obed Hussey and insisted that the true inventor of the reaper was not Cyrus McCormick, but his father, Robert. This contention is especially intriguing since it originated from Cyrus' brother and longtime business partner, Leander. As Leander's grandson later wrote, "My grandfather, Leander J. McCormick, who has supervised reaper manufacturing at the McCormick works nearly all his life, was deeply wounded by Cyrus' pretensions as inventor." To recon-

Obed Hussey, the rugged former sailor, competed with Cyrus McCormick for the claim as original inventor of the reaper. Hussey was also McCormick's only sales competition throughout the 1840s . His machine, pictured here, lacked the reel and divider that made McCormick's machine a success. As a result, farmers tended to favor the performance of McCormick's reaper for cutting grain, while Hussey's became the model for grass mowers.

cile the perceived injustice, Leander spent much time compiling statements and affidavits from family members and neighbors to support the claim.

The basic premise of this argument was that first, the machine that Cyrus patented was essentially the same as Robert's earlier design and second, Robert did not "abandon" his efforts to invent a practical reaper, rather, he had "given" the invention to his son, Cyrus, who then had the ethical blindness to lay claim to its invention. Leander found witnesses to corroborate the claim. One former neighbor swore to the following account: "I was working in the yard near [Robert] when I remarked to the old gentleman, 'Mr. McCormick, this is not Cyrus' invention; it is yours, is it not?' He replied at once: 'Yes, but I intend to give Cyrus the benefit of it.'"

What then can be said in defense of Cyrus' claim? While it is certainly true that Obed Hussey's machine was patented before Cyrus' and that his machines sold before those of Cyrus, it should also be remembered that Cyrus publicly tested his machine two years before Hussey even conceived his own plan. Also, the two machines were fundamentally different: Hussey's had no reel or side-delivery mechanism and was powered by two wheels as opposed to McCormick's single master wheel. In terms of reaping wheat, it was McCormick's machine that stood the test of time in the market, while Hussey's proved to be more aptly suited as a mower.

Regarding the contention that Robert McCormick was the true inventor, Cyrus later wrote in his own defense, "Robert McCormick, being satisfied that his principle of operation could not succeed, laid aside and abandoned the further prosecution of his idea." Further, Robert McCormick was later quoted as saying, "It makes me feel proud to have a son do what I could not do." More concrete evidence can be seen in the mechanical differences in the two machines. For instance, Robert's machine was propelled from behind whereas Cyrus' reaper was pulled from the front side. Also, Cyrus incorporated a reel and divider whereas Robert did not.

As history has produced little evidence that would convince either side of the validity of the opponent's claim, it seems sufficient to suppose that the truth lies somewhere in between. While it remains unclear whether Cyrus McCormick's reaper was the first invented, it was the first to incorporate the seven fundamental principles that became common on all major models for several future decades. It can also be safely said that his reaper was the first practical machine marketed on a large scale. In the final analysis, it was Cyrus McCormick that was the driving force behind the agricultural implement industry. On this fact, there is little dispute.

Making a Marketable Machine

When Cyrus McCormick demonstrated his reaper at Steele's farm in 1831, only a few people were present to witness the performance of the new machine. A similar demonstration just one year later attracted over 100 spectators. The word of the reaper was slowly spreading, and people wanted to come see for themselves. The site was a farm in the small town of Lexington, 18 miles away from McCormick's Virginia home. As the demonstration began, it soon became clear that McCormick's reaper was not up to the task. The machine rattled and jolted so badly as it was pulled across the rough and hilly field, that the owner could not bear to see his crop destroyed by this clattering machine. He soon ordered McCormick off his field. Many of the 100 spectators laughed and jeered. "Give me the old cradle yet, boys," said one.

But at least one spectator was impressed enough to offer McCormick another chance. "That field of wheat on the other side of the fence belongs to me," he said, "pull down the fence and cross over." McCormick openly welcomed the chance to redeem himself and his machine in front of the same, now hostile crowd. Because the second field was more level than the first, the reaper fared well, and cut 6 acres of wheat before sundown. As a whole, the day was remembered as a success, but McCormick must have not soon forgotten the feeling of presenting an inadequate machine to the public. Perhaps this explains why he waited two more seasons before seeking a patent, and eight more seasons before seeking a market. Cyrus McCormick knew the principles of his machine were sound, but improvements were nevertheless needed to make his machine more marketable.

Early Improvements

Cyrus McCormick's machine, as invented in 1831, was by no means perfect. Some of the largest problems were: the divider that extended to separate the standing grain from that to be cut had a tendency to uproot some of the tangled straws in its path; the reel that brought the grain to the knife was clumsy and unwieldy; the band that supplied power to the knife and reel would often slip, rendering the machine completely ineffective; the rim of the main wheel was too narrow and could easily sink in soft ground; and the space between the knife and fingers too easily clogged with weeds or particles of straw.

Cyrus made steady progress regarding each of these problems, to the point where he felt secure enough in 1834 to pay a $30 fee and apply for a patent. By this time, the reel was better supported and adjustable,

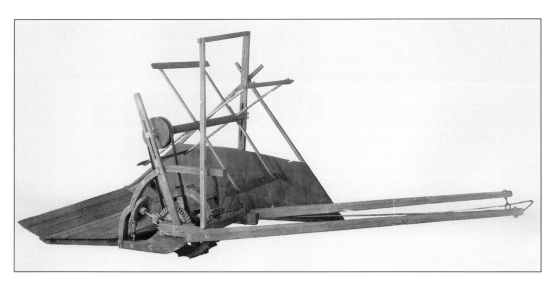

Although McCormick's machine represented a giant leap in grain harvesting technology, many improvements were needed before it could be widely successful. This view of the original reaper clearly shows some of its most significant shortcomings: the band that supplied power to the reel often slipped, the main wheel was too small to support the weight of the machine, and it was made almost entirely of wood.

and the finger guards were improved so that the motion of the knife would discharge any debris to prevent clogging. Other improvements continuously followed. By 1834, McCormick had his patent, and an article in the Lexington Union stated that the reaper, "promises to introduce much additional expedition and economy into one of the most expensive and critical operations of agriculture."

Delay and Distraction

Despite the fact that all seemed to be going well for McCormick and his reaper, in the next several years after 1834, his attentions became distracted. Strangely, little work was done on the reaper during this time, and it was seldom exhibited. Only speculation can offer reasons. Perhaps after 1834 Cyrus McCormick was still not satisfied with his machine and became frustrated with the constant attention that its improvements demanded. Perhaps also, he became aware of the limited possibilities of sale in Virginia, where recent crop failures and small, hilly fields made the reaper seem impractical. Clearly, developing a machine that nobody could afford would be a pointless exercise.

But considering McCormick's talents and personality, it seems unlikely that these were problems too great to overcome. More likely, his attentions were distracted by two other business matters. The first was a 400-acre farm that Cyrus received from his father in 1835. No doubt, managing this farm and making it profitable required much of Cyrus' time and energy. The second business matter that arose in this time was a venture in the iron furnace business.

Several years after the first successful demonstration, the reaper had still brought Cyrus McCormick no wealth. As a result, McCormick searched for prosperity elsewhere. The McCormick home in Walnut Grove, Virginia, was surrounded by rich sources of iron and many in the area became wealthy by erecting furnaces to process the iron. Cyrus sensed an opportunity. Although he was completely unfamiliar with the iron business, he secured the aid of his father and a neighbor and proceeded to establish and operate a small iron furnace business that was soon named Cotopaxi. For a period of time, McCormick prospered, but as the price of iron collapsed and the economy suffered through economic depression in 1837, McCormick soon found himself in over his head. Ultimately the business was a failure and Cyrus spent the next several years paying off the debts he incurred at this time. The best that could be said about the whole venture was that many business lessons were learned.

Returning to the Reaper

Having tried other avenues toward wealth, Cyrus again focused his attention on the reaper, this time with a determination to make it a commercial success. The new opportunity arose in 1839 when an intrigued farmer asked Cyrus to again exhibit the reaper on his farm. The improved machine performed well enough to please a large gathering of onlookers. Many of them wrote and signed testimonials that were soon published in local papers, but more significantly, after this exhibition, Cyrus McCormick sold his first reaper. Soon, the publicity from the event encouraged others to investigate the possibilities of harvesting by machine and two more sales were secured. It seemed as if, at last, Cyrus McCormick had found his path to prosperity.

But this was not yet the case. The first reapers sold performed poorly in the field. One of the first purchasers of the reaper was so entirely dissatisfied, that he put the reaper under an old shed at a tobacco house, where it stood until the shed blew down. Another buyer said, "it worked mighty bad at best." McCormick again worked to improve his machine.

Progress came quickly in the summer of 1841. Many critical parts that were made of wood, and therefore swelled when damp, were replaced with parts made of iron. The reel was again reinforced and supported. And most importantly of all, improvements were made in the cutting apparatus. The serrations in the knife that had all faced the same way, were now staggered every one and one-half inches. This seemingly simple change allowed the knife to cut the stalks, regardless of whether it was moving from right to left or left to right. The improved knife put less strain on the machine as a whole, and performance was considerably improved. Cyrus McCormick was now confident that this machine could be successfully marketed.

For once, McCormick's timing couldn't have been better. After the tremendous financial strain farmers endured in preceding years, recovery was on the horizon. Many farmers were eager to recover their losses. McCormick's reaper provided the means to that end.

Reaping Profits

Ten years had passed since Cyrus McCormick built and tested the first successful reaper, and still he had essentially nothing to show for his accomplishment. The 1830s proceeded to be a decade marred with frustration and failure. But the final abandonment of the iron furnace business in 1841 and the subsequent improvement of the reaper, transformed what was a slow start for McCormick into a soon-to-be booming business. Unlike the previous decade, however, nothing in the 1840s distracted Cyrus McCormick from capitalizing on this opportunity. McCormick knew he possessed a successful grain harvesting machine. He also knew how little that meant unless every farmer possessed the machine as well. To meet this end, McCormick developed business and marketing skills that perhaps even surpassed his skills as an inventor and mechanic.

Capturing the Farmers' Attention

Having successfully developed and demonstrated his new invention in 1831, Cyrus must have envisioned a clear path to financial success. But getting farmers who were typically unaccustomed to mechanical devices to understand and appreciate the new reaper proved to be no simple task. Advertising seemed to provide a solution. Although McCormick's first ad in 1833 solicited no response, he realized that this was an important way of informing and educating prospective buyers. Cyrus wisely perceived that for the reaper to become a success, advertising would have to play a central role.

In the meantime, methods of advertising developed as the reaper itself developed. The first advertisement that appeared in the *Lexington Union* was extensive for its

Improving the cutting apparatus must have occupied much attention of Cyrus McCormick and his slave, Joe Anderson. This picture attempts to recreate a typical problem-solving scene in McCormick's blacksmith shop. The anvil at the left was rediscovered long after McCormick had established his fortune in Chicago and became a valued relic to Cyrus and his company. A replica of this anvil has a permanent home on the grounds of the Case IH Farm Equipment Research and Engineering Center in Hinsdale, Illinois.

In 1847 a seat was added for the raker, and two years later, the driver also rode the machine. McCormick's reaper was also improved to cut a wider swath than the original. To accommodate these significant changes in weight, draft, and balance, a second horse was needed, and the main wheel was now significantly larger and made of iron.

Perhaps the most persuasive marketing technique was first used in 1842 when McCormick actually guaranteed that his machine would give satisfaction. If the machine did not cut 15 acres per day and save one bushel of wheat per acre, the farmer could return the machine for a full refund. This was indeed a bold and essentially unprecedented step — especially for the time. But the benefits were clear. As McCormick rhetorically asked in one advertisement, "If they perform as warranted to do, and if they will pay for themselves in one year's time, what tolerable farmer can hesitate to purchase?" Within three years, similar ads appeared in newspapers and periodicals from upper New York to Chicago. By 1847 McCormick was manufacturing 500 machines annually — impressive numbers considering his first machine was sold just five years prior.

Of course, newspapers and farm journals were not the only means by which McCormick advertised his machine. In fact, Cyrus began to find this sort of advertising increasingly inefficient as farmers began to take less notice of the increasingly common ads in periodicals. So to complement the traditional forms of advertising, McCormick also began to distribute circulars around the countryside and display posters in key locations such as the country store. But by far the most effective way to convince farmers of the value of the reaper was also by far the most risky: the grain cutting contest.

These contests were effective ways to sell reapers because they had all the appeal of a spectator sport. For weeks in advance, farmers anticipated these events that pitted leading reaper manufacturers against one another. Often, the reaper manufacturers would preface the event with attacks and counterattacks in the newspapers — anything to favorably bias the opinion of the spectators. On the day of the contest, spectators were treated to live bands, and free food and drink. Success in these contests could mean secured sales throughout the region for years. Each reaper manufacturer was well aware of this, and therefore sought to avoid the disaster of failure by employing specially-trained drivers and rakers on specially-made machines. Is it any wonder that editors of local papers typically announced the events with claims such as, "We may look forward to some 'rare fun' on the wheat field . . . much good always follows such a struggle for superiority." For both the farmers and the winners, this couldn't be more true.

time, using a full column to describe the principles of the machine. By the 1840s, however, Cyrus learned that more than a detailed description was necessary to be effective. So advertisements soon included a diagram of the reaper with numbers attached to the most important parts. A corresponding explanation of those parts appeared below the diagram. The simple advertisement was eventually embellished to the point where a contented, well-dressed rider was included on the machine which was pulled by a most handsome team of horses. Judging from these advertisements, one might think that suits, ties, and hats were the common farming garb of the day and that every field of wheat stood straight and tall!

But despite these glamorized scenes of the reaper in action, Cyrus McCormick always appealed to the common sense of the farmer. By constantly reminding the reader of the efficiencies inherent in farming by machine, McCormick aimed to make it clear that the reaper would quickly pay for itself, that buying a reaper cost less than not buying one, and that it was an economy and an investment — not a luxury. To convince readers of these facts, advertisements after 1841 most always included written testimonials from satisfied farmers that had already purchased the machine. Names and addresses were included with these testimonials so prospective buyers could easily make personal contact with the satisfied owner.

Supplying the Demand

Throughout the 1840s, the reputation of McCormick's reaper grew steadily. His aggressive advertising and winning record in reaper contests had produced the desired effect: an increasing demand for his reaper. Soon McCormick's greatest problem became not convincing people of the reaper's value, but simply producing enough reapers to satisfy demand. Even though Cyrus, his father, and two brothers continued persistently to build reapers at the Walnut Grove farm, other arrangements clearly had to be made.

With little capital to invest in a new manufacturing site or to hire additional workers, Cyrus had little other choice but to increase production by selling the rights to manufacture his patented reaper. The first arrangements of this kind were made in 1843 when McCormick sold the rights of manufacture to several agents in the Virginia area. One farmer for example, who used McCormick's reaper to cut 175 acres in an unprecedented eight days, was so impressed with the machine's performance that he paid $1,333 for the right to make and sell McCormick reapers to an eight-county region. These contracts not only provided McCormick with much needed capital, they also eased much of the manufacturing burden from McCormick himself. Cyrus was now free to leave Virginia and pursue markets elsewhere.

After the harvest season of 1844, Cyrus set off to explore the possibilities of selling his reaper in states farther west. As he traveled through New York and Ohio, he continued to secure contracts for the manufacture of his reaper and soon, his machines were operating in 10 different states. But by the time he reached the prairies of Illinois, Cyrus realized just how good the prospects for his reaper were. In one year, the flat, fertile land of that state produced over 5-million bushels of wheat. In fact, prairie harvests were so abundant and labor was so scarce that much of the crop was left standing in the fields. The prairies needed a mechanical solution to this problem. No one realized this more than Cyrus McCormick.

As McCormick pondered the possibilities of the western market, he also began to see the deficiencies in his current system of manufacture. The licensees that produced the McCormick reaper were not always as concerned with quality and reputation as was McCormick himself, and little could be done to prevent these manufacturers from taking "short cuts" in production. As a result, the reputation of the McCormick reaper began to slip. Cyrus, of course, had much more to lose by this trend than any regional manufacturer. The only solution, it seemed, was to centralize manufacture at one location where McCormick could personally oversee all stages of production. The location McCormick chose proved to be one of the most forward-thinking decisions of his career. The new home of the reaper was Chicago.

The decision to move to Chicago in 1847 was not as obvious as it may seem today. At that time, Chicago had only one paved street, a police force of six, and a population of 15,000. Other cities, like St. Louis and Cleveland were more mature, but in Chicago, McCormick saw possibilities, not limitations. Here, reapers could be manufactured and shipped east via the Great Lakes or south and west via the Mississippi River. But perhaps most importantly, Chicago was surrounded by the richest wheat-growing lands in the country. To McCormick, the choice was obvious.

To help amass the necessary money and credit for a new factory in Chicago, McCormick entered a partnership with C.M. Gray, a local businessman. This was to be the first of several partnerships over the next three years. The first reaper factory was a marvel of its time. It was a three-story, brick building that covered a 100- x 30-foot area and employed 33 men. Located on the north bank of the Chicago River, just east of the Michigan Avenue bridge, this was Chicago's largest factory. In its first year of operation, the McCormick Reaper Factory produced over 500 machines. Within 10 years, it employed 200 and produced 40 machines per day. As his business grew, contracts with outside manufacturers were allowed to expire and in 1850, McCormick bought out his partners for $65,000. Cyrus McCormick once again had complete control over his business.

A Sales Infrastructure Develops

Since the construction of the new factory, the weight of McCormick's concern had shifted from manufacturing problems to those of distribution. Farmers were ready to buy, and McCormick was ready to produce, but the connection had to be made. To remedy the problem, McCormick began to employ regular sales agents.

The job of these agents could not have been an easy one. The first task was to distribute advertising literature and canvass the most remote parts of a particular region, often while transporting a sample machine. Upon securing sales and receiving shipments from Chicago, agents would then set up the reaper and instruct the purchasing farmers on its operation. If the reaper ever broke down, it was the job of the regional agent to stock spare parts and provide any necessary field service. Finally, the agent had to make detailed reports to the central office and collect any unpaid notes.

The McCormick reaper factory was established in Chicago in 1847. For many years to come, McCormick and Chicago would lead the world in farm equipment manufacturing.

For this exhausting work, agents typically received a commission that ranged from 5 to 15 percent of the sales price which in 1849 was $120. The most motivated agents found this to be a highly lucrative line of work and could eventually hire assistants. This agency system continued to develop and by the mid-1850s, a network of agencies covered most of the United States and Canada; it would prove to be the backbone of the McCormick Company in the 1800s. International Harvester would realize similar benefits of this sales infrastructure in the next century.

McCormick's Other Genius: Business

In addition to his skills as a mechanic and inventor, Cyrus McCormick also possessed an able mind for business. In this sense, some of the practices he employed were at least as original as his invention of the reaper. McCormick was, after all, the first businessman of his time to issue a broad warranty for a manufactured product and the first to develop an aggressive sales system and efficient agency network. But perhaps most importantly, McCormick was first to recognize the importance of selling on credit. Since farmers rarely had the ready cash to purchase the reaper, McCormick realized at an early date that he could only sell a machine by waiting until it had paid for itself in reduced labor costs or increased crop yields. To buy a reaper, a farmer need only to initially pay freight charges. The balance was then paid in the fall or winter, after the wheat could be sold.

McCormick's personality helped to sell machines as well. One story tells of several farmers that were unable to pay the balance owed on their reapers because of a serious regional crop failure. At once McCormick rode out to the town and shook hands with each of the worried debtors and reassured them that the debt could be paid some other time. This simple act secured such a friendship and loyalty that McCormick machines were the only ones sold in that area for years to come.

Customer satisfaction became the basis of his successful business. Never before 1848, and rarely after that, did McCormick sue a purchaser for nonpayment of debts since this created the appearance of an adversarial relationship with the farmers, when McCormick wanted to establish just the opposite. When, for example, the 1853 reaper was equipped with a faulty gearing mechanism, McCormick sent each purchaser the necessary replacements, free of charge. In a day and age where the buyer was to "beware," McCormick took every possible step to secure the buyer's confidence, not his suspicion. For years to come this was the hallmark of Cyrus McCormick's company.

Challenges to Supremacy

Throughout the 1840s, Cyrus McCormick constantly sought to improve his original Virginia Reaper. As his machine evolved, so too did his business. Skillful marketing and manufacturing decisions enabled McCormick and his reaper to earn a reputation that extended well beyond the limits of Rockbridge County, Virginia. Having paid all debts from the Cotopaxi iron furnace fiasco, Cyrus finally began to establish some degree of financial security. But for McCormick, the road to success was far from complete. After all, the progress of the 1840s was due in part to the protection offered under the original reaper patent of 1834. McCormick indeed led the industry, but the industry lacked significant competition. If the patent protection expired, it would be an open question whether McCormick's supremacy would remain unchallenged.

The Unkindest Cut of All

In 1848, the patent McCormick had earned 14 years earlier was set to expire. Unfortunately for McCormick, much of the 14-year period of patent protection had elapsed before he had seriously begun to manufacture and market his reaper. In this respect, his preoccupation with the iron furnace business proved more than financially costly. Once he dedicated his business acumen entirely to the reaper business, only seven years remained on his most valuable patent. For McCormick, attaining a patent extension in 1848 became a top priority.

But the battle would not be easy. For as much as McCormick wanted the patent extension, others hoped to see it expire. Competing manufacturers, like Seymour & Morgan of New York, had much to gain if McCormick failed in his bid. As long-time licensed manufacturers of McCormick's Virginia Reaper, Seymour & Morgan could continue to produce a very similar model and save a $25 royalty payment per machine. Manufacturers therefore organized an effective counter-campaign by rallying the farmers against McCormick. Cyrus McCormick was soon the target of such cries as, "he has made enough money off the farmer!" and "one man is trying to impose a tax of $500,000 per year on the starving millions of the world!" Farmers were soon signing petitions against the claim for patent extension. McCormick, failing to understand how the farmers could so easily turn against him, considered this the "unkindest cut of all."

Ultimately, the Patent Board rejected McCormick's application for an extension of his reaper patent. In a statement concerning the Board's rejection, the Commissioner of Patents said of Cyrus McCormick, "He is an inventor whose fame . . . has spread through the world. His genius has done honor to his own country, and has been the admiration of foreign nations. But the reaper is of too great value to the public to be controlled by any individual, and the extension of the patent is refused."

The effect on the reaper business was all too clear. Until 1848, Obed Hussey was McCormick's only real competitor. Just three years later, over 30 manufacturers entered the field. In 10 years, the number was greater than 100.

The Reaper Industry Explodes

When the McCormick original reaper patent expired in 1848 and extension was subsequently refused, dozens of manufacturers, capitalists, and inventors freely entered the reaper business. At first, the new competitors produced machines that were very nearly identical to McCormick's reaper, but it wasn't long before these same competitors sought ways to actually build a better machine. Design improvements that reduced farm labor costs naturally resulted in increased sales. Such improvements were therefore pursued vigorously by the newcomers who wished to challenge McCormick and make a name for themselves. As a result, harvesting machinery entered a period of mechanical progress and innovation that would last for thirty years.

The first notable improvement to McCormick's original reaper was the addition of an automatic rake to sweep the grain from the platform, thus reducing labor demands by one half. The "sweep rake" was first patented in 1851, and soon manufactured by the firm of Seymour & Morgan. Marketed as the "New Yorker," this machine was the first popular self-rake machine, though scores of others soon followed. Having greatly underestimated the staying power of this machine, McCormick did not manufacture a competitive model for another 10 years. By that time, some twenty thousand self-rake reapers were in use.

The self-rake, like all reapers, was designed primarily for cutting grain; it inevitably proved inferior when used to cut grass. But as stock raising became more profitable in the mid-1800s, the demand for an effective grass-cutting machine became more pronounced. The first inventor to answer this demand was William F. Ketchum, who received a patent in 1847 for a separate mower that was designed exclusively to cut grass. Improvements soon came in 1854 and and 1856 when Cyrenus Wheeler and Lewis Miller established famous lines of two-wheeled, hinged bar mowers. The respective Cayuga Chief and Buckeye lines featured a cutting bar that could easily be raised to pass obstructions and adjusted to meet the various inequalities of the ground. Despite the instant popularity of these machines, McCormick would not build a separate mower until 1865.

In the meantime, the McCormick Company did focus some attention on the problems of cutting grass. As early as 1849, a mowing attachment was designed to complement the McCormick reaper. Although this combination reaper and mower, later known as the "Old Blue Machine," would sell thousands, it was clearly inferior to rival machines. By far, the most successful combined machine was designed by John H. Manny in 1851. The following year, William Whitley designed a combination self-raking reaper and mower that soon became a mainstay of a line of machines that bore the name, "Champion."

The challenge to the McCormick Company was clear. To remain at the top of the harvesting machine industry, the improvements of rival interests would have to be accepted and incorporated into various McCormick machines. Eventually, Cyrus McCormick realized this. But in the meantime, his attention, like that of all Americans, was diverted by the ravages of the Civil War.

Harvest Mechanization Takes Hold

The Evolution of an Industry

In the decade before the Civil War, American agriculture was advancing through an impressive growth stage. This is perhaps best illustrated by the fact that in the 1850s alone, over 600,000 new farms were created! Immigration, railroad expansion, and generous government land policies all contributed to this unprecedented growth. Naturally, new farms required new machines, and those in the business of manufacturing machines for this expanding market were rewarded handsomely. Cyrus McCormick, for example, first became a millionaire in this time period as annual sales of his reaper jumped from 190 in 1846 to well over 4,000 just 10 years later! Clearly, the reaper and mower industry was becoming a booming business.

Cyrus and the Civil War

Cyrus McCormick knew better than to expect this success to continue throughout the next decade. As the Civil War became increasingly inevitable, Cyrus was quick to perceive the threat to his business. It became impossible for McCormick to collect unpaid bills or unsold machines from southern states once they withdrew from the Union. This simple loss of property value to the confederacy neared $100,000. What's more, McCormick lost an important market as the South separated from the Union — continued sales in that region were impossible.

Not surprisingly, these economic considerations led McCormick to oppose the Civil War from the start. But McCormick had deeply rooted political convictions that also fueled his anti-war feelings. As a native Virginian and one-time slave owner, McCormick was convinced that emancipation of the slaves was simply not worth a Civil War. At all times he favored and actively pursued some sort of compromise to keep peace. But the time for compromise had passed, and McCormick found himself clinging to an ideology that

▱ In the competitive years that followed the Civil War, manufacturers would often use war scenes to stir emotional feeling of prospective buyers. This advertisement illustrates the battle of Gettysburg in 1863. The caption read, "The McCormick maintains the front rank in all contests on every field." Hardly accurate, the McCormick machine in the foreground is a twine binder — a machine not produced until nearly 20 years after the war!

McCormick and others developed these new machines and innovative sales methods to withstand the increasingly fierce competition. To be sure, only the strongest companies could survive the challenges of this new era.

was growing increasingly unpopular in the North. *The Chicago Tribune* labeled McCormick as a "rebel" and a "slave driver." An attempt to run for Congress in 1864 drew further criticism when the *Chicago Daily Tribune* opposed his bid and commented that, "all of the wealth which he has extorted from the loyal farmers of the West will not elect him." Comments like this must have been particularly difficult for McCormick to accept. For years, he had worked to establish an honorable reputation as a friend and ally of the American farmer. A loss of this goodwill would have been as ruinous to McCormick's northern sales as the formation of the confederacy was to his southern sales.

The Civil War's Influence on the Reaper

From every indication, it seemed as if the Civil War would wreak havoc on the industry Cyrus McCormick had worked so hard to establish. But in fact, just the opposite was true. Throughout the Civil War, the farm machine business proceeded as never before. In the years before the war, for example, there were an estimated 90,000 mowers and reapers in use in the North. By the end of the war, some five years later, that estimated number climbed to over 250,000. Furthermore, in this same time period, the amount of capital invested in the manufacture of farm machinery increased 300 percent! The Civil War, as it turned out, did anything but slow the successes of the 1850s.

The cause of such remarkable growth is rooted in the inherent labor shortage associated with war. As hundreds of thousands of men left the fields to fight in the army, the demand for labor-saving machines increased dramatically. In this respect, the reaper had no equal. One man with a self-rake reaper could cut 10 acres of wheat in one day — as much as five men working with cradles. Considering that the five grain producing states of the "old Northwest" supplied over 680,000 men for the union army, it is little wonder that the reaper found itself at home on over 75 percent of the farms throughout the war.

As the war continued, Cyrus McCormick realized this labor shortage was working to his advantage. While his political conscious desperately wanted a peaceful end to the war, he nevertheless realized that the war was good for business. Advertisements of the time reflect this awareness. McCormick consistently published testimonials that boasted the reaper's ease of use. Pictures illustrated that even boys and girls could operate the machine. The message was clear; if the men were off fighting a war, women and children could continue to operate the farm with the help of a McCormick reaper. Not only was the reaper presented as an easy machine to operate, but an easy machine to purchase as well. "One good crop" would be enough to repay the money borrowed to purchase the $130 machine. Farm owners responded to the advertisements; by the end of the war, McCormick was producing over 10,000 machines per year. Clearly, the Civil War affected the reaper.

The Reaper's Influence on the Civil War

Perhaps more impressive, however, is how the reaper affected the Civil War. Despite the labor shortage, the ability of the North to produce wheat continued unabated. One government official in 1863 noted, "that while all other crops show a deficiency, the wheat crop increased 50 percent in the last three years." Thus, the reaper played an important role in the war effort. As the Commissioner of Agriculture estimated in 1862, "each reaper released five men for service."

The North's ability to retain high levels of wheat production throughout the war is significant for other reasons as well. From the outset of the war, the Confederacy expected to establish friendly diplomatic, economic, and perhaps even military alliances with several important European countries. It was believed that much of Europe, because of its reliance on Southern cotton, would be sympathetic to the cause of the Confederacy. This, in fact, may have been the tendency in Europe were it not for an even greater reliance on American grain. Because of several poor European harvests in the early years of the war, the Union was exporting well over 30-million bushels of grain to Great Britain and France annually. It is also noteworthy that these exports provided a source of revenue for an otherwise cash-starved United States government.

Perhaps the influence of the reaper upon the Civil War was best summarized by Abraham Lincoln's Secretary of War, Edwin Stanton, when he stated, "The reaper is to the North what slavery is to the South. Without McCormick's invention, the North could not win and the Union would be dismembered."

In the final analysis, the Civil War provided the ultimate setting for the reaper to prove its importance to the American farmer and to the American nation as a whole. The impressive war record of the reaper convinced even the most reluctant farmers of the advantages of farm machinery. Whereas before the war reapers and mowers were becoming increasingly popular on America's farms, these machines became invaluable and indispensable after the war. The Civil War seemed to insure the permanence of harvest mechanization.

Ever Increasing Efficiency

The Civil War brought great acclaim to the reaper and its inventor. But during the war years, other machines had grown popular in their own right by offering features and improvements not yet available from McCormick. For years, the rival machines were dismissed by McCormick as "new fangled." Farmers, however, did not agree and McCormick was left with

Titled, "Back from the War," this McCormick advertisement is typical of the idealism used in advertisements of the day. Again, the machine pictured is not at all consistent with the time period. But the important role of McCormick machines in the Civil War was a theme consistently used in McCormick advertising for decades.

To "Old Reliable" represented McCormick's first efforts to compete in the self-rake reaper market. A mechanical rake was added to the machine to sweep the cut grain off the platform. Although a raker was no longer needed, a crew of four or five was still required to do the binding. $190 could buy one of these machines at the peak of its popularity, though price declined significantly as more technologically advanced machines were introduced.

little choice but to adapt. As a result, the Patent Virginia Reaper was changed and improved several more times, making it a machine desired by many, even well into the twentieth century.

The Old Reliable

Cyrus McCormick was finding it increasingly difficult for his original type of reaper to compete against the more efficient self-rake designs. In 1862, the ever-conservative McCormick finally responded by purchasing patent rights and building his version of the self-raking reaper, the Old Reliable. In a painful irony, McCormick was forced to pay over $60,000 in royalties to Seymour & Morgan, a firm that once paid for the privilege of producing his original reaper. Nevertheless, the Old Reliable proved to be a popular machine for several years, despite several shortcomings. The heavy, one-wheeled machine struggled on hillsides and in soft ground. Production of the "Old Reliable" ended in 1870, but was briefly revived again four years later as the "New Reliable" in response to cries for a less expensive reaping machine.

The Advance

Needless to say, improvements in the design of self-rake reapers continued throughout the industry. Samuel Johnston made great strides with his design that allowed the driver to control the rakes and discharge the cut grain at any time. Cyrus, with his business partner and brother, Leander, quickly realized that Johnston's innovation made the Old Reliable somewhat obsolete. In response, McCormick designers set out to create a competitive, two-wheeled, combined reaping and mowing machine that delivered the grain in amounts determined by the driver. Test runs of the new machine, later to be called the Advance, led one top executive to conclude that it was "as much ahead of our old Self Rake as light is ahead of darkness."

Designers immediately predicted that the Advance could become "the most popular machine that had ever borne the McCormick stamp." For a time, they seemed to be right. Over 3,000 were built in 1869, and the 6,000 supplied for the harvest of 1870 fell considerably short of demand. Production of the Advance soon taxed the old Chicago reaper factory to the limit and the McCormick brothers began to ponder the construction of a larger factory. The Chicago Fire of 1871 left little other choice.

The McCormick "Advance" succeeded the Old Reliable. The Advance was an attempt to combine the qualities of a good reaper and an equally good mower. Two wheels were used to make the machine more stable than the Old Reliable. And the reel was noticeably improved as well. The Advance sold extensively between 1869 and 1875 for about $195 complete.

PRIZE MOWER ON THE ROAD.

As seen in this typical advertisement of the time, the Advance could be converted to an effective mower, albeit with some difficulty. Even McCormick catalogs acknowledged that larger farms would be better served with separate mowers and reapers. Regardless, the Advance proved to be a popular machine of its day.

The Daisy

For farmers that did not desire a combined mower and reaper, McCormick again offered a separate reaping machine in 1882. The new Daisy Reaper was so named because designers were impressed with the machine's lightness, simplicity, and beauty. It soon became the most popular reaper on the market. In a time when automatic binders were claiming much of the market, there was still significant demand for machines, like the Daisy, that didn't bind the crop. As one catalog explained, "this reaper is in great demand on medium-sized farms for harvesting all kinds of grain, and it is especially well adapted for cutting oats, flax, and clover, where the gavels are to remain unbound until thoroughly cured and dried." The longevity of the Daisy was proof of its popularity and demand: it was built until 1934!

The Imperial

The next generation of McCormick reapers featured an iron frame. Otherwise, the new machine, called the Imperial, was similar to the Advance: it was a combination mower and reaper with a controllable rake. Advertisements later claimed, "the Imperial is the successor to the McCormick Advance, which was the first to lead the way in combining in one machine the qualities of a good reaper and an equally good mower." The Imperial reaper, however, was claimed to be "better, lighter, and more durable than any other that had ever yet been made." And because it proved effective in harvesting even the most difficult crops, it won immediate acceptance from farmers in every region. The production of 2,000 Imperials for the harvest of 1880 was pitifully short of demand; in subsequent years, production increased dramatically. The Imperial was manufactured until 1885.

THE McCORMICK IMPERIAL SELF-RAKE REAPER.

The McCormick Imperial was a direct response to the challenge offered by Samuel Johnston's popular self-raking reaper. With this design, the traditional reel had been replaced with a series of sweep rakes. More rakes allowed the driver greater control in sizing the amount of grain to be swept from the platform. An improvement over the Advance, the Imperial could be more easily converted to an effective mower.

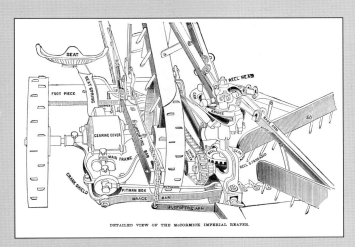

DETAILED VIEW OF THE McCORMICK IMPERIAL REAPER.

The frame of the Imperial was made entirely of iron and the gearing was enclosed to protect the machine from the effects of rain, mud, and dust. The rake heads acted as the reel and could be adjusted to automatically rake the grain at various intervals. The Imperial sold principally between 1880 and 1885. The price varied from $160 to $210, depending on the year and sales region. Typically, a 10% discount was given for cash payments.

Shortly after the introduction of the Imperial, the McCormick Harvesting Machine Company introduced the Daisy Reaper. For just $115, farmers found it difficult to resist the Daisy; its popularity soon enabled the McCormick Company to market the Daisy as "the Queen of the Reapers." Notice the ease with which the Daisy is shown to cut this downed grain.

The Folding Daisy—"Queen of Reapers."

The success of the Daisy had endured for many years, extending well into the age of power farming. By 1902 the Daisy had acquired an attractive color scheme. The machine could be raised or lowered to any desired height of cut and the four reel-rake heads enabled the driver to manipulate the amount of grain swept from the platform by using a simple foot pedal device — as this 1902 catalog stated, "so simple and yet so perfect."

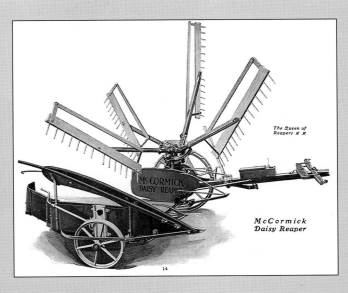

The Queen of Reapers

McCormick Daisy Reaper

McCormick Mowers and Droppers

Considering that William F. Ketchum developed a distinct grass cutting machine in 1847, and that the Cayuga Chief and Buckeye mowers steadily gained popularity throughout the 1850s, McCormick's entry into the market in 1866 was certainly overdue. Poor judgment was not as responsible for the delay as were other factors. Most importantly, the existing mower manufacturers had such a tight hold on so many patents, that it was long impossible for McCormick to produce a machine without facing almost assured infringement litigation. In the end this proved inevitable; entering the mower market eventually cost McCormick hundreds of thousands of dollars in shop rights, royalties, and infringement damages.

Fortunately for McCormick, the success of his mowers more than compensated for these staggering losses. By 1899, over 100,000 McCormick mowers had been sold, making the McCormick the most popular name in the mower market. Since it was first offered to the public, the McCormick mower was the subject of constant evolution and innovation. While the McCormick No. 2 Iron Mower sold by the thousands throughout the 1880s, it eventually gave way to the No. 3 Steel Mower, introduced in 1887. By the turn of the

Take care there, Bose, this is a McCormick Mower, it would mow you down like grass.

By 1887 the McCormick No. 3 Steel Mower had replaced the earlier iron models. The caption of this 1891 sales catalog is classic advertising of the day. At that time, the No. 3 sold for only $55; it was manufactured until 1899.

century, several mowers were offered, ranging from a one horse, "Little Vertical Mower" to larger models, like the "McCormick Big 4" which was designed to cut a swath up to 7 feet wide. McCormick's most popular mower at the time was the "New 4" which was claimed to "hold the record for neat, clean work, light draft, convenience, and quiet running."

To complement the rising popularity of its mowers, McCormick offered a related machine for a brief time. In 1880, the Dropper was introduced as a mower that was adaptable to reaping duties as well. The core of the machine was essentially the same as the McCormick iron mower but when converted to a reaper, it delivered the grain directly behind the cutter bar in sheaves sized by the operator. The demand for this machine was always limited, but according to advertising literature of the time, it was offered "principally to men who have small and hilly farms, or stock raisers who have large quantities of grass, but little grain to cut." The production of the dropper illustrates the aim of

THE McCORMICK IRON MOWER AT WORK.

In 1879 McCormick introduced the "McCormick Iron Mower." This mower featured a frame made entirely of cast and wrought iron and compared favorably in terms of strength and durability to many wood machines manufactured by the competition. Two steel knives were furnished with each mower, and farmers could choose between a 4-foot or 4-foot 3-inch cut.

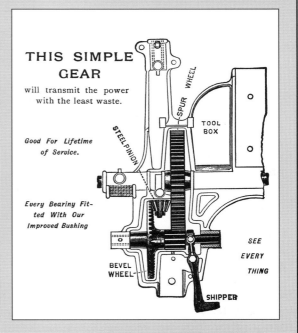

To help "Save the Hay," the No. 3 Mower featured an improved gearing mechanism which furnished more immediate power to the blade. McCormick advertisements called attention to the merits of this design, especially when compared to the competitors' machines, which could be drawn 5 inches before the knife would move.

McCormick Companies to provide for the different needs of all farmers. This tradition remained strong with the formation of International Harvester in 1902.

In the 1860s, the McCormick Company adjusted to the emergence of popular new machines like the self-rake reaper, mower, and combined reaper-mower machines. Through constant innovation and adaptation, the McCormick reapers and reaper-mower combinations remained not only competitive, but superior. For years they remained the most popular machines of their kind on the market. But despite this remarkable success, reapers and mowers soon became of secondary importance in the McCormick line. Harvest mechanization was about to take another giant step forward.

This 1898 photograph shows a McCormick No. 4 Mower at work on a farm in Avon, New York. Larger mowers like the No. 4 were pulled by two horses and were well suited to heavy grass, as seen here.

McCormick also offered smaller mowers, better suited for parks or farmstead lawns. Here a smaller McCormick mower, perhaps a Little 4, is shown at work on the grounds of the battle site at Gettysburg, Pennsylvania. Advertisements claimed that this maneuverable, horse-drawn machine "will be found on the lawn far more preferable than the cylinder lawn mower, and by the tilt it can be made to cut as close and leave as nice a stubble."

The mower on display at this home in Randolph, Iowa, is most likely a McCormick New 4 Mower. The New 4 was offered in a 4-and-a-half or 5-foot cut. Weighing 674 pounds, it was heavier than similar models offered by the competition yet lighter in draft. A similar model, the Big 4, weighed 800 pounds and could be equipped with cutter bars 6 or 7 feet long. Although production of the Big 4 ended in 1897, the New 4 continued to be popular until 1915.

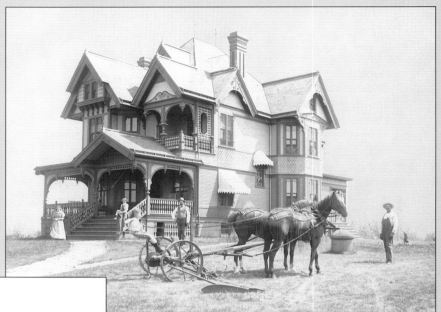

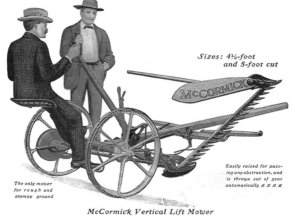

Sizes: 4½-foot and 5-foot cut

Easily raised for passing any obstruction, and is thrown out of gear automatically.

The only mower for rough and stumpy ground

McCormick Vertical Lift Mower
18

Vertical lift mowers were introduced to the McCormick line in 1896. Marketed as, "the only mower for rough and stumpy ground," it enabled the driver to simply pull a lever to raise the cutter bar and pass obstructions without stopping the team. As the cutter bar was raised over obstructions, the mower would be thrown out of gear automatically. Vertical lift mowers were offered in the same sizes as the New 4, while the Little Vertical Mower was a smaller version, equipped with a 3-and-a-half or 4-foot cutting bar.

The McCormick Dropper was built for a short time in the 1880s. Built to satisfy both mowing and reaping duties, each dropper was provided with one reaping sickle and two mowing knives. Also, two pinions were provided: a large one to give the reaping sickle a slower motion or a small one to give the mower knife a much quicker action. When used as a reaper, as seen here, the Dropper could not match the efficiency of a side delivery, self-rake machine like the Imperial or the Daisy.

THE McCORMICK FRONT CUT DROPPER.

The Foundations of an Automatic Binder

As McCormick's original reaper and succeeding self-rake reapers aptly demonstrated, machines that saved labor on the farm were destined for great success. Mechanics and inventors never lost sight of this, and continued the search for labor-saving advances. Realizing that further efficiencies in the cutting of grain would be difficult, attention turned to the labor involved in the binding of grain. The resulting innovations changed the harvesting machine business forever.

The Marsh Revolution

C.W. and W.W. Marsh, two brothers living near DeKalb, Illinois, were among the first to seek an alternative to the back-breaking labor involved in binding grain from the loose bundles that reapers left on the ground. Their resulting invention, patented in 1858, was the first successful hand binder offered to the public. Unlike earlier reapers, the Marsh Harvester elevated the cut grain over the drive wheel to a binding platform. This binding platform was designed to carry two men who would bind the grain as quickly as it was cut and elevated to them. By this method, the grain was tied in bundles before it reached the ground, saving a considerable amount of hard labor. Two men riding comfortably on the Marsh Harvester could bind as much grain as four men who otherwise had to waste time and effort walking and bending to accomplish their task.

Though sound in theory, the Marsh Harvester required several years of development before it could be marketed on a large scale. Early field trials were not impressive, and McCormick representatives reported that the Marsh Harvester was "a cross between a windmill and a threshing machine." Other manufacturers, however, realized the machine's true potential. George Steward, for example, invited the Marsh brothers to his implement factory in Plano, Illinois, to begin large scale manufacture. Other firms quickly bought rights to sell the new harvester. Those that did were soon rewarded with enormous success and popularity. Annual production increased from just 26 in 1864 to over 2,000 in just five years. By 1872, over 10,000 Marsh Harvesters were in the field.

The Marsh Harvester received much attention throughout the 1860s. Note how the grain is elevated over the main wheel to the binders' table. The Marsh hand binder was the first to apply the term "harvester" to a reaping machine. Soon "harvester" would be used synonymously with all grain binders.

McCormick's version of the hand-binding harvester, built between 1875 and 1883, was manufactured in two sizes, 5-1/4- and 6-1/4-foot cut. It also boasted a 9-inch wide drive wheel to support the weight of machine and prevent it from being mired down. Although sales catalogs claimed the machine was light in draft, a three-horse attachment was offered at additional cost.

McCormick representatives who kept insisting the Marsh machine would fail in heavy grain were forced to face the reality of the situation. Finally, after much deliberation, McCormick purchased necessary patent rights to begin production of a Marsh-type harvester in 1875. The delay cost Cyrus McCormick dearly in terms of prestige as a progressive manufacturer. Even with its impressive selling organization and customer loyalty, the McCormick hand binding harvester could not outsell its counterpart manufactured by an upstart firm named Gammon & Deering. Fortunately for McCormick, a new machine offered a chance for redemption; the wire binder soon made the Marsh Harvester a memory.

The Brief Reign of the Wire Binder

The Marsh Harvester not only reduced the amount of labor required to harvest and bind grain,

it became the foundation of further advances that led to a fully automatic binder. Wire binding devices were the first of such advances. By attaching a mechanical wire binder in the place of the manual binding platform, the binding process became fully automatic; a single driver could now cut and bind the crop. Because this advance further reduced labor demands, the wire binder quickly became the machine of choice in the late 1870s and early 1880s.

Although solutions to the problem of binding grain mechanically were sought as early as 1850, it wasn't until 1871 when a successful mechanism, using wire to tie bundles of grain, was patented. The Walter A. Wood Company, a long time rival of McCormick, immediately purchased the patent rights and began large scale manufacture. Similar patents were quickly acquired by other McCormick rivals, including D.M. Osborne and William Deering. But in this case, unlike the Marsh Harvester example, McCormick wasted little time and a careful study was immediately conducted comparing the merits of the many patents. In the end, McCormick judged the patent of Charles B. Withington to be superior. The rights to this patent were soon purchased and Withington was hired to work at the

Wire binders were the first successful self-binders and remained popular until a twine binding mechanism was perfected. The maze of gears, chains, and levers make the simplicity of McCormick's original reaper seem like a distant memory.

McCormick's Wire Binder used No. 20 annealed wire, which ran over 300 feet to the pound. As little as 2 pounds of wire could be used per acre. Two spools used on this machine fed two steel fingers which moved back and forth and twisted a wire band around each sheaf of grain. The crank at the driver's right hand made for easy adjustments for long or short grain.

McCormick factory to oversee production. After some years of experimenting and testing, the McCormick "Withington" wire binder was manufactured in quantity for the harvest of 1877.

The McCormick automatic wire binder was essentially the same machine as their hand binding harvester. Advertising literature simply explained that "the McCormick wire binder attachment is bolted in the place of hand binders' table and platform." Because the machines were in many ways identical, farmers that previously bought the Marsh-type harvester could easily update their machine by purchasing the separate wire binding device. This made the machine enormously popular and it soon outsold all competitors. Within the next few years, over 50,000 McCormick wire binders were at work in the fields.

Unfortunately for McCormick, wire binders soon fell out of favor with farmers. The problem was not in design or manufacture, for the machine performed impressively. Instead, farmers feared the metal wire would "poison" the grain and that pieces of stray wire would be eaten by livestock. Despite these objections and its short lived popularity, the wire binder represented an important step in the progress of harvest machinery development: The last manual labor requirement, the binding of the sheaves, was eliminated. One person with an automatic binder could reap and bind up to fourteen acres in one day.

The Supremacy of the Twine Binder

Automatic binders that used twine eventually replaced wire binders and became the grain harvesting machine of the future. Before this transition could take

place, however, several specific problems associated with using twine would have to be worked out by inventors and manufacturers. Foremost was the problem of developing a simple device that could mechanically tie a knot. Efforts in this regard date back to the 1850s and were met only with frustration. As the delicate problem continued to occupy even the most inventive minds, attention turned to the much simpler wire binder that required just a simple twist to secure the bundle. As wire binders began to fall out of favor with farmers, however, experiments with machines using twine began to show promise of success.

Appleby and Others

By far, the most common name associated with the development of the twine binder is that of John F. Appleby of Whitewater, Wisconsin. Appleby was regarded by many as an inventive genius, and for good reason. According to popular legend, Appleby first conceived the the idea for a workable knot tying device while watching a small puppy tangle himself in a leash. He began experiments with the "Appleby Knotter" as early as 1858 and postponed them only to serve in the Civil War. When he returned from service, he devoted most of his time and energy to the development of a wire binder. His efforts to this end were rewarded with a patent in 1869. In 1874, his efforts again focused on development of a twine binding device. Working in the shops of Parker & Stone, a firm that later became identified with the Milwaukee line, Appleby made steady progress. By 1878, Appleby had a successful machine and a patent. He immediately made 115 machines for Parker & Stone and sold an exclusive license to Gammon & Deering of Plano, Illinois.

Similar progress was being made in Rockford, Illinois, by an equally talented inventor, Marquis L. Gorham. Although Gorham began experimenting with binding machinery at about the same time as Appleby, he was able to secure a patent in 1875 — three years before Appleby. Thus, when most firms began to align themselves under the protection of the Appleby patent, it actually appeared that Gorham had legal priority to the invention. If the courts found this to be true, the manufacturers of the Appleby device could be the defendants of endless litigation. The McCormick firm wisely purchased the rights to manufacture both the Appleby and Gorham twine binders and by so doing, insulated themselves against future losses in court.

The McCormick Twine Binder

The first McCormick twine binder reached the market in 1881 and featured elements of both the Appleby and Gorham devices. Advertising the merits of the new twine binder must have been difficult because until 1882, McCormick still offered both the Marsh-type harvester and the wire binder. Appropriately, the 1881 advertisement for the twine binder read, "we place it on the market for the season of 1881, and expect it will meet with the favor of our patrons wherever it is introduced. Notwithstanding the popularity of our wire binders, and the faultlessness of their work, we appreciate the demand that has arisen for a twine binding machine." Indeed, a demand had arisen.

Buyers immediately made the McCormick twine binder the most successful machine on the market. The McCormick Company retained this claim by constantly improving the machine. In the early years, it was made almost wholly of wood and iron. By gradually incorporating steel, the machine became stronger and lighter. By 1885, the machine was advertised as the McCormick Steel Harvester and Binder. Subsequent

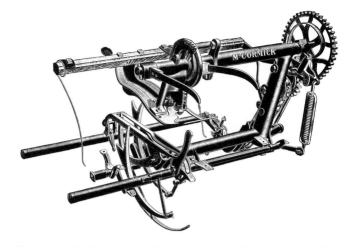

The twine binding mechanism on the new binders received the grain and held it until enough for a bundle was gathered. At that point, the bundle was compressed and the twine was wrapped and knotted around the center. Finally, the bundle was discharged to the ground. McCormick sales literature justifiably boasted that their binding mechanism was "a masterpiece of mechanical skill in automatic binding."

improvements in elevator and binding devices kept customers loyal to the McCormick design.

The twine binder quickly became the foundation of the McCormick line for many years to come. Other machines were relegated to secondary importance. Even the reaper suffered an identity crisis at this time. A catalog referred to the reaper by saying, "This machine, of course, is in no sense a rival of the self binder, but fills a place among farmers . . . who cannot afford a McCormick binder, yet feel they must have a McCormick machine." With annual sales of the McCormick binder reaching 66,000 by 1898, it is easy to see why it received the bulk of the company's attention.

A single rider aboard McCormick's first twine binder could conquer a large field of wheat. Scenes like this convinced even the most skeptical farmers of the merits of automatic binders. Although prices of these early models were high — around $350 — they fell continuously and dramatically due to intense competition among manufacturers.

This illustration in an 1884 catalog must have caught the eye of many prospective buyers. Titled, "Harvest Scene in Dakota" the caption read, "Twenty 8-foot McCormick Harvesters and binders at work, cutting and binding a crop of 8,700 acres of small grain, on the farm of Rand & Brown, Grandin, Red River Valley, Dakota."

Significance of the Twine Binder

Such remarkable success was not at all unique to the McCormick Company, however, as each of McCormick's leading competitors was producing successful machines under its own trademark. Many smaller companies, however, fell by the wayside as production complexities and costs were far greater for the twine binder than any previous machine. In the 1890s, the twine binding harvester had more capital invested in its manufacture than any other machine in the world, except only the steam engine.

Because of the success of the twine binder, and because many smaller companies could not compete in its manufacture, only about a dozen of the largest companies enjoyed the sales benefits of the most popular machine in farming history to that date. The biggest companies therefore became bigger — and more powerful. A competition for sales was brewing that soon erupted into a full scale war. This harvester war would prove to be the greatest of many challenges in the history of the McCormick Harvesting Machine Company.

Even after nearly thirty years of constant development, this McCormick binder of 1909 looked essentially the same as first generation models. However, much of the infrastructure, including the elevator, frame, platform, and binding mechanisms, was significantly improved in that time. Notice the bundle carrier feature on this machine that enabled the driver to hold and then drop several bundles at a time, eliminating much tiresome gathering later.

Not even the dawn of tractor power altered the fundamental design of the twine binder. Here, a powerful new IHC tractor takes the place of three full teams of horses.

Challenges in a New Era

The Search for Strength and Supremacy

M.CORMICK LIGHT DRAFT MACHINES

THE McCORMICK LINE :
Binders,
Reapers,
Headers,
Mowers, Rakes,
Corn Binders,
Huskers and Shredders,
Knife Grinders,
Binder Twine.

The Greatest Line of Harvesting Machines in the World

The ability to respond to any sort of challenge was a strength that helped Cyrus McCormick establish the world's most successful farm machinery business. In the past, he faced challenges in areas ranging from the courtroom to the marketplace. But Cyrus McCormick was faced with a new sort of challenge in 1871 when a great fire swept through the heart of the Chicago business district. With the Reaper Works totally destroyed, the continued development of the McCormick company had reached a critical stage. Yet as with so many other challenges throughout his business life, Cyrus McCormick responded with courage and determination. Somehow, both Cyrus and his company emerged from the rubble stronger than ever before. This increased strength proved to be the key to continued success in an era of new challenges.

The Fire and the Loss

McCormick's original Chicago reaper factory was constructed in 1847. At that time, McCormick produced and sold 500 reapers annually in a city with a population of barely 15,000. Over the next two decades, the manufacturer and the city both grew extensively — by 1870, annual sales of McCormick machines had grown to over 10,000 and the city's population exploded to 325,000. Together, the company and the city grew strong and at the heart of this growth stood McCormick's Reaper Factory.

Before 1871, nothing could seem to impede the progress of either McCormick or his city. But on the night of October 8, the Great Chicago Fire leveled the Reaper Works and over three square miles of the city that surrounded it. Over $188 million worth of property was destroyed and 94,000 people were homeless by the end of the next day. The city was in chaos and the progress that once seemed inevitable was now in question. After seeing $2 million worth of his property destroyed, the 62-year-old Cyrus McCormick contemplated retirement.

The harvest machinery business had come a long way since the early days of the reaper. As machines and product lines evolved, so too did distribution methods. For the first time, branch houses and dealerships, like the one seen here, displayed the latest models and offered knowledgeable sales help to buyers.

McCormick and others developed these new machines and innovative sales methods to withstand the increasingly fierce competition. To be sure, only the strongest companies could survive the challenges of this new era.

The Decision

Often in matters of great weight and concern, Cyrus would turn to his most trusted advisor, his wife, Nettie. The night of the fire, Nettie was at the McCormick home in New York. Upon hearing the tragic news, she immediately left for Chicago to see her husband and help him assess any future options. McCormick family tradition relates that Cyrus left the decision entirely with Nettie. According to this story, Nettie replied to Cyrus, "You have worked too long and too hard to let your business go to waste. You also have the goodwill of the nation, something no money can buy. The farmers still need harvesters and I do not want our son to grow up in idleness." Although this story may well be true, Cyrus probably needed very little convincing. By October 12, just four days after the start of the fire, the decision was made to reestablish production facilities in Chicago.

The decision seemed to energize Cyrus. He immediately ordered his subordinates, "Go at once to all the ports on the lakes and buy all the building material that is for sale! We are going to rebuild this city — rebuild it more magnificently than before. We are only waiting for the cinders to cool!" At the same time, a notice was issued to debtors, "We intend to put everything in operation again as fast as men and money can do it," and agents were ordered to rush in as much money as they could collect. McCormick's sense of immediacy was well justified: only 4,000 unsold machines remained in dealers' hands, and the harvest of 1872 promised to break all sales records. To meet this demand, production had to resume — as soon as possible!

Other manufacturers, including the J.I. Case Company of Racine, Wisconsin, offered to manufacture McCormick implements for 1872, but Cyrus clearly wanted no part of this offer. Instead, he opted to immediately erect a temporary facility on the grounds of the recently fallen reaper factory. This decision helped relieve demand until a larger, more permanent factory was constructed at a different location. Within months, the two-story "shed" was operating around the clock, producing over 3,000 machines for the next harvest. As one agent said at the time, "If the opposition think we are dead, they will find themselves woefully mistaken!"

The New McCormick Works

In reality, the Chicago fire had destroyed a somewhat outdated McCormick factory. With an annual capacity of 10,000 machines, and little room to expand, the future of the old Reaper Works was indeed limited. Even before the fire, tentative arrangements were made by the McCormicks to purchase 80 acres of land on Chicago's southwest side with the intent of eventually building a larger, more modern facility. The Chicago Fire made the tentative plans a certainty.

Ground was broken for the new works in the summer of 1872. Under the close supervision of Cyrus and his brother Leander, rapid progress was made. By February of the following year, the new McCormick Works was operational, and production at the old site forever ceased.

The new McCormick Works could hardly have been more impressive. The four original buildings covered an aggregate floor space of over 300,000 square feet and the prairie fields next to the buildings offered ample room for test fields and future expansion. Over 1,000 regular workers and even a full time fire fighting crew were soon employed at the new factory. But perhaps most impressive of all, the new facility more than doubled the company's annual production capacity.

Cyrus McCormick and his company thus emerged from the Chicago Fire with a firm commitment to the future. Although an era of new machines and new com-

petitors would soon challenge McCormick, the Chicago Fire strengthened his resolve and his ability to produce quality machines. McCormick could not have been better poised to face the challenges of the new era.

New Opponents Emerge

The Chicago Fire struck the McCormick Reaper Works at a time when grain harvesting machinery was advancing through an era of rapid progression and innovation. Self-rake reapers and combined reaper mowers gained ascendancy in the 1860s while the 1870s proved the supremacy of grain binders, first wire then twine. Such progress spelled opportunity for several relatively young manufacturers. Companies that were quick to recognize the value of these new developments flourished while more conservative companies were faced with almost certain failure. This was an era when many of McCormick's old rivals, such as Hussey, Manny, and Ketchum faded and many new opponents emerged. McCormick's name and reputation kept the

The interior of the McCormick Reaper Works was no less impressive than the outside view. Here, dozens of workers assembled gearing mechanisms and frame braces in the lathe and press room.

Judging from this engraving made in 1902, the decision to choose a new site with ample room to expand was well justified. The staggering growth of the McCormick plant in just 30 years is reflective of the world's ever increasing demand for mechanized farm implements during that time.

company on top throughout, but the competition's ability to quickly adapt new advances meant that McCormick's supremacy would be challenged as never before.

The Deering Harvester Company

McCormick's greatest challenge came from the machines that carried the Deering trademark. While Cyrus McCormick was developing the reaper. William Deering was acquiring some wealth in the dry goods business. In 1870, Deering invested some of his fortune with E.H. Gammon, an old acquaintance that had recognized the significance of the Marsh harvester at an early date and by 1869 had become a leading producer of the hand binding machine. Deering soon became a full partner and compensated for his lack of farm machinery experience with keen business sense and raw courage.

The Gammon & Deering partnership, one of the first to exploit the Marsh harvester, would forge ahead again in 1874,

with the production of wire binders. By 1879, when Gammon retired from the partnership, William Deering was sufficiently knowledgeable to capitalize on the greatest advance of the era — the Appleby twine binder. The very next year, while McCormick and others were still strongly advocating the benefits of wire binders, Deering had already experimented with, produced, and sold over 3,000 twine binders. As one associate later recalled, "The harvest of that year [1880] was a Waterloo defeat for the wire binders. Mr. Deering won a complete victory; he established twine binding machines as the grain

William Deering, with essentially no farming or engineering experience, nevertheless emerged as a leading farm implement manufacturer in a matter of just 10 years. Recalling the time just before he became a full partner with E.H. Gammon, Deering said, "At the time, I didn't know the appearance of our machine." It wasn't long, however, before his image became inseparable with the machines his company created, as this catalog cover illustrates.

By 1885, Deering advertisers could claim that their twine binder had been successful for six harvest seasons. Not even McCormick could match that claim.

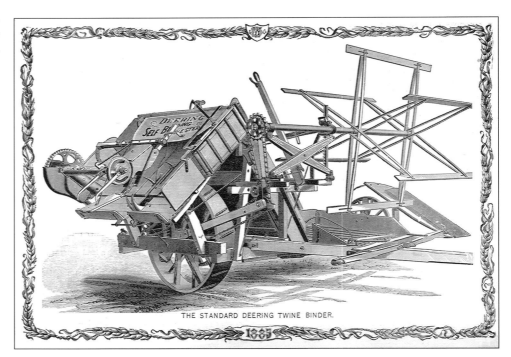

THE STANDARD DEERING TWINE BINDER.

harvesters of the time and of the future and himself as the acknowledged leader of the movement."

By 1880, Deering had taken another bold step. Having realized that the production facilities in Plano, Illinois, were growing increasingly inadequate, he ordered the construction of a huge new facility in Chicago. The threat to McCormick was all too clear. In just 10 years, William Deering became a leader and pioneer in an industry which he so recently entered. This success continued — eventually his company's sales and profits nearly matched those of the McCormick Company.

THE DEERING LIGHT REAPER.

While the popularity of the twine binder was the basis of William Deering's success, his company also offered a full line of grain and grass cutting machinery. Deering's mower (left) and light reaper (top) would rival similar McCormick machines for years to come.

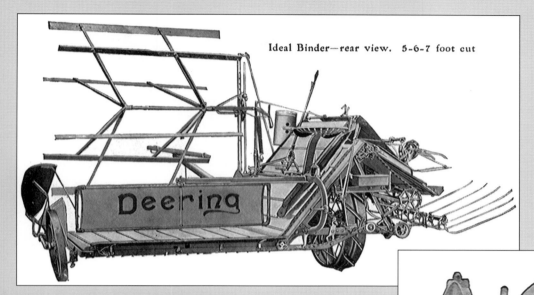

Ideal Binder—rear view. 5-6-7 foot cut

Deering's original twine binder had evolved throughout the 1890s and emerged the next decade as the Deering "Ideal" binder. Many thousands were sold by the time production was discontinued in 1937 — nearly 40 years after it was first introduced!

Since the introduction of the first successful twine binder, William Deering's firm had been identified as an innovative leader in the farm equipment industry. Such aggressive research brought more success to Deering in 1892 when a machine that used roller and ball bearings was first put on the market. Incorporated into the Deering Ideal, the natural result of this technology was a quieter, lighter draft machine. Once again, William Deering was forcing the industry to adapt.

The merits of the new ball bearing concept were introduced to prospective buyers through various forms of literature, including this 1896 catalog.

The Plano Manufacturing Company

As the initial home of Marsh Harvester production, Plano, Illinois, was rightfully referred to as "Harvester City." The manufacturing facility that first produced Marsh Harvesters for sale in 1864 was the same that attracted the investment interests of first E.H. Gammon and later William Deering. The Gammon & Deering firm produced machines in Plano until 1879 when Gammon retired and Deering began to build in Chicago. When the Deering move was completed a year later, the heart and soul of the once proud "Harvester City" no longer existed — the facility was abandoned.

The works at Plano remained idle until a former employee of Gammon & Deering, William H. Jones, realized the still awesome potential of the vacated plant. Revitalizing the old works also drew the interest of E.H. Gammon, who would provide the financial support that Jones so desperately needed. In 1881, under the leadership of William H. Jones, the Plano Manufacturing Company was incorporated and "Harvester City" was rejuvenated.

Plano machines quickly gained a reputation for their high quality and unique combination of innovative features. Unlike most machines, Plano mowers and binders utilized the chain drive principle to replace the more traditional gear drive mechanisms. Plano advertised that this feature made their machines "light running" and "less liable to get out of order." In addition, Plano binders incorporated a unique "friction clutch" that allowed the reel to turn back and avoid breakage if obstructions were struck. But the greatest selling feature of the Plano binders was the use of a flywheel. By storing power, this device minimized the inconsistent power demands of the knotting cycle and rough terrain.

Plano machines like the "Jones Lever Binder" and the "Jones

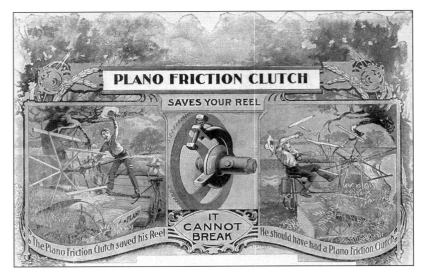

Like the Deering machines, Plano implements also boasted new and innovative features. The friction clutch, for example, was a feature unique to Plano machines. Dramatic advertisements, like the one shown here, made the benefits of such a device all too clear.

Chain Mower" had quickly gained a strong foothold in the farm equipment market. By 1893, William Jones was looking for a larger, more efficient facility to produce his machines. He soon found it in the Chicago suburb of West Pullman. While "Harvester City" was once again abandoned, Plano machines continued the same tradition of excellence.

"The sign of the satisfied farmer" was the slogan that typically accompanied Plano machines and advertising literature.

Still another point that differentiated Plano machines from the competition was the incorporation of a chain to transfer power from the drive wheels to the cutter bar. The Plano Manufacturing Company claimed that its chain-driven machines reduced friction and were more durable than competitors' gear-driven machines. The Plano sales department claimed that "noise and vibration are annihilated" with the Jones chain mower, shown here.

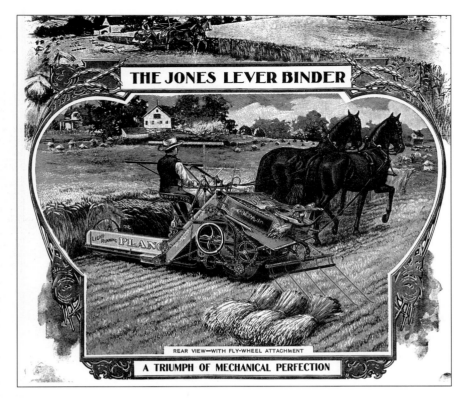

THE JONES LEVER BINDER

LIGHT RUNNING PLANO

REAR VIEW—WITH FLY-WHEEL ATTACHMENT

A TRIUMPH OF MECHANICAL PERFECTION

Plano binders could also boast of a fly-wheel attachment, seen here at the rear of the machine. According to sales literature of the day, "by storing up surplus power where the work is easy, the fly-wheel carries the machine lightly through the difficult places, and keeps the draft uniform."

The Champion Line of Harvesting Machines

Springfield, Ohio, ranked second only to Chicago in the production of farm machinery. A large reason for this ranking was the success of Champion machines that were manufactured there. The roots of the Champion line extend as far back as most any other manufacturer, except of course McCormick. In 1850 Benjamin Warder began the construction of reapers in a modest, water powered factory in Springfield. By purchasing patent rights from other manufacturers, Warder kept producing the most modern reaping equipment of the day. The self-rake reaper that Warder produced, for example, had antedated McCormick's "Old Reliable" self rake reaper by at least two years.

As Benjamin Warder was establishing himself in the reaper business, so to was William Whitely. In 1854, Whitely brought further fame to Springfield with the introduction of his combined self-raking reaper and mower, the first of its kind. The success

of this machine soon brought Whitely's firm in close competition with that of Benjamin Warder. This competition inevitably forced a compromise.

In 1867, Warder and Whitely agreed to pool their machine interests and patents. The output of this new consolidation was known as the Champion Line. According to the agreement, the still distinct firms would produce these machines and sell them in separate, non-competing territories. In 1887, however, the Whitely interest failed and the assets of the firm were taken over by Warder and his associates, J.J. Glessner and A.S. Bushnell. From that point on, the recently incorporated Warder, Bushnell & Glessner Company controlled all machines under the Champion name.

Eventually, Champion machines ranked third in production, behind only McCormick and Deering. This popularity was due in part to the strength of the Champion machines. This reputation began in 1874 when Champion was the first to use malleable iron castings on its mowers. A few years later, Champion reapers were first to use parts made of steel. By 1894, catalogs claimed that the Champion Harvester Binder was "the best and most durable machine ever made for harvesting grain." By setting standards that other manufacturers were forced to follow, the Champion line became a formidable contender in an era of the toughest competition.

Springfield, Ohio, was known as "Champion City" throughout the late 1800s. The Champion factory, located in Springfield, was one of the very largest of its kind in the world.

When it came to advertising, Champion was certainly as aggressive as any other firm. This catalog illustration carries the caption, "The Improved Champion Mower: President Harrison is the driver, and is comfortable and as safe on this mower's seat and has as complete control of these horses as if he sat in a buggy."

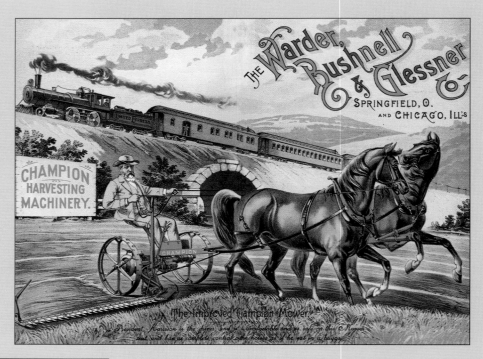

While the connection between the Champion line and President Harrison is unclear, the reference to mower safety is an obvious response to attacks on earlier designs of Champion mowers. For years Champion had stood by its design of a "rear-cut" mower, like the one shown on this rare 1869 Champion catalog cover. Competitors attacked these as unsafe — a driver could be thrown from the machine into the path of the cutting bar. Nevertheless, Champion continued to offer "rear-cut" mowers for at least another 25 years.

IN LODGED GRAIN.

Champion machines earned their reputation for strength and durability by being among the first to use components made of malleable iron and steel. Such strength enabled a driver to extend the reel, raise the platform, and tilt the cutting angle downward without weakening the machine. This agility was no doubt appreciated most in lodged or tangled grain, as seen here.

The Milwaukee Harvester Company

In the late 1850s, the partnership of L.H. Parker and Gustave Stone established a new factory in Beloit, Wisconsin, to manufacture hand-rake and self-rake reapers. The reapers manufactured in Beloit were unimpressive for many years. But in 1875, the Parker and Stone factory was home to an event that not only improved the fate of their business, but forever changed grain harvesting. In the Beloit facility that year, John F. Appleby began work on a full-sized twine binding harvester. The first Appleby binder of 1876 was successful enough to make only four more the following year. But by 1878, Appleby had built 115 twine binders in the Parker and Stone factory.

L.H. Parker and Gustave Stone wasted little time in adopting the Appleby patent for manufacture. As with Deering, this haste secured a significant advantage over more conservative manufacturers and practically

Although all Milwaukee machines included a logo that read, "The Milwaukee Leads," sales figures did not support the claim; Milwaukee sales consistently lagged well behind McCormick and Deering.

ensured future success. By 1884, the Parker and Stone partnership had evolved into the Milwaukee Harvesting Machine Company. This new corporation eventually claimed to have greatly improved the Appleby design by eliminating 91 pieces and producing a simpler, lighter machine as a result.

The Milwaukee Company had created a machine that claimed many followers. Deering, Plano, and Champion had also adapted to the many

The three generations posed near this Milwaukee binder are a clear reminder of just how much farming technology had progressed in the nineteenth century. The old timer seated on the platform had seen such progress in his lifetime; imagine the changes the youngster would witness in his lifetime!

changes of the era. As a result, each of these companies were poised to challenge McCormick's supremacy. In the closing years of the nineteenth century, other binder manufacturers, including Osborne, Keystone, and Buckeye joined the challenge. In succeeding years, these companies would do battle in one of the greatest competitive eras in farm equipment history. Later, each would contribute to the formation of one of the great manufacturing corporations in history: International Harvester.

The Harvester Wars

"Fierce," said Cyrus McCormick Jr.

"A bitter fight," offered John J. Glessner.

"Demoralizing," added William Jones of the Plano Company.

"Guerrilla Warfare," said a Champion executive.

The 20-year period of extreme competition at the close of the century had undoubtedly left a strong impression in the minds of these once bitter rivals. Although the twine binder had proven itself supreme it the 1880s, supremacy among the manufacturers of the machine was still an open question. During this time, the McCormick Company saw many smaller rivals disappear and several powerful new opponents emerge. The competition to produce and sell the new binders soon became a legend appropriately named, the harvester wars.

Causes of the Harvester War

Companies able to produce twine binders, though declining in number, were increasing in size. The newly constructed McCormick Works was only one of several gigantic manufacturing facilities. The makers of Deering, Champion, and Buckeye lines were rightfully proud of their sites as well. Such large production capabilities necessarily meant large economies of scale and wide marketing and distribution possibilities. As a result, supply had soon exceeded demand. In this atmosphere, the makers of farm machinery had to compete as never before to secure a share of the limited market.

Those doing battle in the harvester war soon realized that old methods of distribution were growing increasingly inadequate. Dealers that used to wait for business to come to them would now have to canvass the territory to help foster sales. These more active field agents, whether paid by salary or commission, faced intense pressure to sell machines. As a matter of survival, these agents were forced to compete aggressively for business.

The Industry Adjusts

Farm equipment manufacturers that did not adjust to the competitive market forces were doomed to fail. Declining prices were a vivid example of the changes that the industry faced. Binders that sold for $325 in

One result of the harvester wars was the use of more creative and aggressive advertising techniques. This is but one page of a 12-page booklet distributed by the McCormick Harvesting Machine Company titled, "Talking through His Hat." The poem takes direct aim at competing salesmen who try to entice otherwise loyal McCormick customers.

An' as I sit here on the fence an' look at my machines,
A bindin' grain an' cuttin' grass,—both mighty pretty scenes,—
I feel myself to rank as high as any 'ristocrat,
Because I'm seldom duped with talk that oozes through a hat.

An' when a Binder-Mower man comes here to talk with me,
An' says, McCORMICK doesn't lead, we simply disagree;
I tell him I have tried them all, first this one an' then that,
While all his talk is prejudiced, an' must come through his hat.

McCormick advertisements had come a long way from the simple printed testimonials of the early reaper wars. This novelty advertisement card cleverly answered the question, "which side of the fence are you on?"

1882 were reduced to just $110 by 1900. Often, these lower prices were accompanied by enticing credit terms. Time purchases of machines were extended to as long as four years. Cyrus McCormick later testified that a large portion of sales were made below list prices and that trade-ins were accepted at large values, even when they had no value at all. As far as the farmers were concerned, purchasing the most modern equipment had never been easier. A popular story of the time relates how one cash poor farmer wanted to purchase a new hammer and wrench; having no money, he bought instead a Milwaukee binder, all on time payments. Although he had no need for the binder, the tools and tool box that came as part of the deal were put to great use!

Such attractive prices and terms were made at great cost to the manufacturers. Profits were further sacrificed as advertising and promotion budgets soared. Scores of different pamphlets and brochures were printed and distributed to agents who in turn passed them on to prospective buyers. While some of these publications were simply catalogs that presented the features of machines in the company line, others were direct attacks on the machines of competing firms. "Novelty" items were also distributed, including calendars, postcards, date books, and almanacs. Each of these methods presented valuable opportunities to print lists of past achievements, awards, honors, and testimonials. The World's Fair offered the greatest opportunities for companies to impress the public. To attract attention, elaborate facilities were constructed to house machines and even gilded machine models. No expense was spared.

The World's Fair and International Expositions allowed harvester companies to demonstrate their best machines before a global audience. Naturally, favorable ratings were often shown off in the advertising literature of the day. Although this illustration is from a McCormick catalog, Deering catalogs offered a similar presentation.

The Battle in the Field

At the corporate level, every possible effort was made to sell machines, but agents in the field faced the toughest battles. Reminiscent of the reaper age, field competitions were common. For local agents, performance in these contests was critical to future sales. As a result, business ethics became secondary and preventing sales became as important as making sales. A McCormick sales agent realized this first hand at a local competition that put his binder against Deering and Champion machines. According to this agent,

"There were at least one hundred and fifty farmers there, and the Deering was the first to start. They had a brand new machine and four big gray horses, and the horses and the machine were decorated with little flags. But when the first bundle of tangled barley came through the binder, it choked and the bull wheel buried itself in the slippery soil and they were done. The farmer then drove our binder himself and was having no trouble. But the Champion dealer got a handful of straw and tried to put it secretly on our elevator chains, to prove his claim that our chains would pull grain out of our open elevator and wind it around the sprockets. I grabbed him by the neck and he fell down in the stubble. Then the Champion fellows started for me, but somebody got between us. They started to abuse the farmer, who was a big powerful man, and he struck the Champion dealer. His old father stopped the fight and they left in disgrace without having driven us from the field."

Stories like these were apparently not uncommon in the harvester wars. Some agents told of "wrecking crews" that were employed in certain districts to tamper with rival machines and create dissatisfaction with their performance. William Deering even placed claims of sabotage in newspapers and offered rewards of $100 if the culprits were caught.

Effects of the Harvester War

On the surface, it seems as if the only beneficiaries of the 20-year period of chaos and competition were the farmers. Lower prices and easier credit terms were of course welcome to any prospective buyer. But in the long run, the industry would benefit as well.

For example, when the market became saturated with the low cost binders, mowers, and reapers, the harvester companies were encouraged to design and offer new products that farmers needed. Innovation was key to success. In addition, the limited markets compelled harvester manufacturers to find new ways

THE McCORMICK AT WORK IN ASIATIC RUSSIA.

From a Photograph taken on the Estate of IVAN PLESHANOW, 120 miles east of Samara, Russia, who operates Five McCormick Harvesters and Binders, ALL DRAWN BY CAMELS.

The work of the McCormick Machines around the World and throughout the year NEVER CEASES.

Beginning in the harvester war era, manufacturers — McCormick especially — began to seek new markets to escape the cutthroat competition at home; by 1910 harvesting machines from America appeared throughout the world. Here, a McCormick reaper is displayed in a Russian field. The oddity of "camel power" made for an interesting advertising illustration.

to increase sales; the McCormick Harvesting Machine Company responded by establishing an impressive branch house system at home while seeking new markets abroad. Similarly, low prices and restricted revenues demanded that producers cut costs; to this end, Deering's company invested scarce capital in steel mills and coal fields. These efforts made companies strong enough to survive in a time when many others failed.

The harvester war ended in 1902 when five of the most bitter rivals agreed to combine their interests and form the International Harvester Company. The impressive strength of the new corporation was clearly derived from the strength of the companies that survived the demanding competition of the harvester wars.

Product Line Progress

Throughout this era of competition, each of the farm machine manufacturers faced a great deal of pressure to develop new or significantly improved products. Such innovation gave the respective manufacturers bragging rights, and a much needed selling advantage when many other things seemed so equal. As a result, great sums of time and money were invested to modify old machines and develop entirely new ones. Such efforts, however, did not insure success and many machines of this period were marked failures. Nevertheless, the 1890s were a time of significant product line progress.

Corn Machines

As early as the 1840s, inventors tried to improve the slow and laborious method of harvesting corn by hand. The only progress, albeit slight, was seen in the horse-drawn sled harvester. This crude machine incorporated stationary cutting blades and required two men to ride along to gather the cut stalks. The horses and sled were then stopped to put the fodder in a shock. Though an improvement over hand-cutting methods, much was still left to be desired.

McCormick and other large manufacturers eventually turned their attention toward the problem of harvesting corn. The competition to produce the first successful corn binder brought the needed capital and resources of the largest farm equipment manufacturers to the corn harvesting problem. Solutions quickly emerged. By the 1890s, several successful corn binders were on the market.

The first of these to come before the public was manufactured by D.M. Osborne & Company. It incorporated the basic principles found in corn binders for years to come: two gathering arms with endless chains

Throughout the industry, designs of corn binders incorporated the same basic elements; conveying chains gathered the stalks, engaged them past the cutting mechanism and rearward to the binding mechanism.

gathered the corn and passed it through a cutting mechanism to a binding attachment or an elevator.

Within two years, the Deering Company revealed its own corn binder. The product of over 10 years research and $200,000 capital investment, the Deering corn binder resembled the latest grain binders and could be modified to elevate the corn into a wagon. The success of the Deering corn binder was ensured when it impressed the Chicago World's Fair judges in 1893, despite difficult weather and conditions.

The McCormick corn binder also drew attention at the World's Fair. Unfortunately though, the attention was focused on its odd design and appearance rather than its impressive performance. The main difference between McCormick's machine and the others was that it was pushed by horses hitched behind the machine. Though sound in principle, the machine was significantly changed for the harvest of 1895.

Each of the companies that joined McCormick and Deering in the formation of International Harvester, namely, Champion, Milwaukee, and Plano produced corn machines under their own respective trademarks. This continued for several years after the merger until efforts were made to consolidate the lines. A 1914 IH catalog claimed, "Cutting corn by hand is rapidly becoming obsolete." With annual sales approaching 45,000, such a conclusion did not seem far off the mark.

The development of improved corn binders naturally increased the demand for improved husker-shred-

Whereas most corn binders of the day were vertical machines — meaning the corn was bound in an upright position — the Deering Ideal corn binder was unique in that it featured a horizontal binding attachment. Deering claimed this principle made the machine more simple and compact . . .

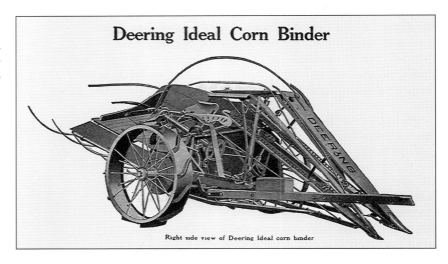

Deering Ideal Corn Binder

Right side view of Deering Ideal corn binder

. . . opponents were quick to show that the principle produced only "grotesque" results. This illustration was found in an 1898 McCormick sales catalog.

ders to process the cut and shocked corn. The first machine of this type, named a "corn husker and fodder cutter," was first produced by the Keystone Company in the 1880s. By separating the ears of corn from the stalk and subsequently separating the husks from the ears, the machine made quick work of a previously tedious task.

As with corn binder development, the McCormick and Deering companies each raced to market a husker-shredder machine of their own; and as with corn binders, competition produced progress. By the turn of the century, most every major farm

In this field scene, two McCormick binders operate in succession. For just over $100, corn binders proved to be cost-effective time-savers, but the bundles in the foreground show that much tiresome shocking or gathering still awaits.

In an attempt to further reduce the labor required to harvest corn, both McCormick and Deering offered a corn shocking attachment for their respective corn binders. The bundles were carried to a circular platform at the rear of the machine. When enough bundles were gathered on the circular platform, the driver stopped the team and turned the crank to hoist the shock. The central apparatus was then swung to place the shock into the cleared field.

☞ Producing labor-saving devices was a never-ending aim of any farm implement manufacturer. This corn shock loader was a curious device that, in the words of the advertising catalog, "solves the problem of getting shocks to the husker-shredder without drudgery." Up to six shocks could be raised with independent lifting devices. Once raised, they were easily carried to the husker-shredder site.

The corn shock hoist was yet another device intended to make corn harvesting more efficient. The purpose was to raise the corn shock from the ground to the feed table of the husker-shredder, thus eliminating much heavy lifting. Although each of these corn shocking devices seemed sound in principle, farm workers must have found them awkward to operate; the corn shocker, corn shock loader, and corn shock hoist never went into full production.

After 1923 the different International Harvester lines were consolidated into a single McCormick-Deering name. Naturally, design choices had to be made. In this case, the McCormick vertical-cut, right-hand design won out.

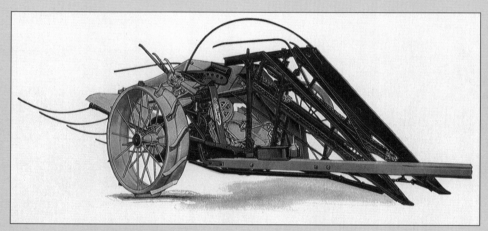

By 1923 International Harvester published catalogs that featured color illustrations. By this time also, machines carried visible IHC logos. These corn-binder illustrations reveal the differences between the Deering and McCormick models. The Deering binder, a horizontal-cut machine, is lower to the ground, yet wider than the vertical-cut McCormick design. Notice also the "left-hand cut" of the Deering machine. Most other manufacturers, including McCormick, produced "right-hand cut" machines.

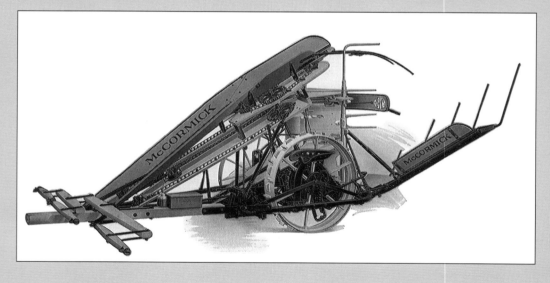

Aggressive advertising was responsible for educating farmers about the latest in agricultural efficiencies. Naturally, increased sales resulted. In this case a McCormick advertisement calls attention to the profitability of a husker and shredder.

A somewhat more attractive alternative to the corn shocking devices was the corn binder elevator. Nearly 12 feet long, the elevator would carry the bundles to a wagon being driven along with the binder, under the elevator. This field scene shows a McCormick corn binder and elevator in operation. Though extra farm hands would be needed to receive the bundles and drive the wagon, total manhours and much heavy lifting were greatly reduced by this process.

machinery manufacturer was producing its own husker-shredder machines.

Largely because of relentless marketing, farmers quickly became aware of the value of the husker-shredder. Advertisements claimed that 40% of the value of the corn crop was in the stalks; properly used, a husker-shredder made practically all of the stover available for feed. Farmers must have been intrigued by testimonials that claimed to process 20 acres of corn in one day and in the same time produce 40 tons of shredded fodder!

Even after the merger that formed International Harvester, such claims continued. Plano, McCormick, and Deering machines anchored the IH line for years. The largest machines employed 10 rolls to husk the corn and required at least a

20-horsepower engine. Because these giants were costly, manufacturers encouraged farmers in the same locality to pool their resources and jointly purchase a machine. Smaller, more affordable husker-shredders were also offered — the smallest was a two-roll husker-shredder manufactured by Deering. It required only 6 horsepower and had a capacity to process up to 250 bushels per day.

The Plano Manufacturing Company urged farmers to "turn corn stalks into coin" by using their husker and shredder. This cross section illustrates the essential operation of the Plano machine.

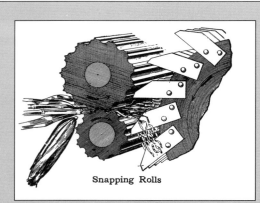

Snapping Rolls

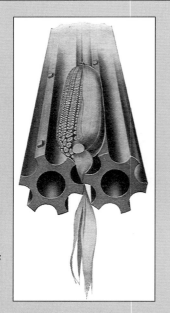

Although the specific component designs of the competing manufacturers varied somewhat, the basic process was comparable. Stalks would be placed on a feed belt and carried to snapping rolls (top) that separated the ears from the stalks. The ears would then pass to a series of husking rolls (right) and exit to a movable elevator.

This winter scene shows the typical operation of a husker and shredder, in this case, a Deering 6-roll model. A belt provided power from a tractor or stationary engine while workers loaded the stalks to the feed belt. The elevator carried the husked ears to an awaiting wagon and the blower pipe lifted the shredded corn fodder for storage. The fodder proved to be an economical and nutritional livestock.

For larger operations, manufacturers offered 8-roll and 10-roll outfits. While lower capacity models were typically purchased by individual farmers, these more expensive machines were commonly owned by custom threshing and shredding companies. This McCormick 8-roll machine featured a shredder head speed of 1,000 revolutions per minute to shred up to 100 bushels per hour.

In 1923, a deliberate effort was made to consolidate the many names under the International Harvester umbrella. It was at this time when many machines carried the united "McCormick-Deering" name; this 1923 McCormick-Deering husker and shredder proved no exception.

Grain Machines

The experimental efforts of McCormick and Deering led the companies to produce corn binders and husker-shredders at nearly the same time; neither company could make the claim of being "first." But the marketing importance of such a claim demanded that experimental efforts persist. Somewhat tardy in marketing the twine binder, McCormick was eager to reclaim the titles of "innovator" and "originator" in the area of grain harvesting machinery. Efforts to this end resulted in the development of odd machines that unfortunately succeeded only in being original.

Perhaps the best example was McCormick's ill-fated "Bindlochine" of 1892. The machine was designed to bind grain low to the ground, replacing the need to elevate grain over the drive wheel. By eliminating complicated elevators and aprons, the Bindlochine weighed less and created less draft for horses. Advertisements even claimed that the machine was "as neat as a toy." As expected, the Bindlochine catalog constantly reminds readers that the machine is the first of its kind — the product of the progressive McCormick Machine Company. But sales never matched the advertising rhetoric, and the Bindlochine was soon written off as a failure.

In the competitive harvester wars, any sign of progress helped to sell machines. However, the new features were often more stylish than substantive. This was certainly the case in the 1890s when McCormick attempted to market the first "right hand binder." Other makes, for various reasons, placed the cutter bar to the left of the main wheel. By moving the bar to the right side, McCormick had something different than the competition. The change was advertised as progress and it put other binder manufacturers on the defensive, but like the Bindlochine, the right-side binder brought McCormick no significant advantage.

A more appreciated advance in grain machines came with the development of the push-type harvester. Unlike conventional binders, these were pushed by the team of horses. The machine, operated as a header, was designed to cut the heads from the grain, instead of cutting all of the straw. The heads were then elevated to a wagon which traveled alongside the machine. Headers were also able to cut a much wider path than conventional binders, so an entire field could be harvested more quickly. To large western grain growers, these machines offered a quicker and lower cost alternative to the traditional binder. When a binding mechanism was used in place of the elevator, the machine was known as a header-binder. McCormick, Deering, Plano, and Champion were all significant manufacturers of these push-type harvesters before the formation of International Harvester.

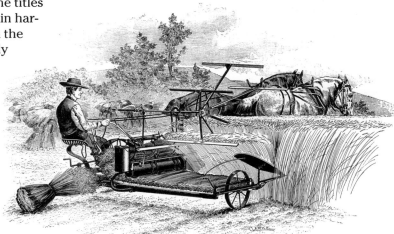

While the competitive harvester wars produced new machines like corn binders and husker-shredders, new versions of old machines were also common. McCormick's "Bindlochine," produced only in 1892, attempted to simplify the traditional binder design by eliminating the need to elevate the grain. As beneficial as innovative new designs were to manufacturers, gimmicks that did not catch on proved very costly. In this case, the Bindlochine proved too light for effective work — McCormick's reputation suffered as a result.

McCormick again attempted to gain an edge over the competition in 1898 by offering binders with a "right-hand" cut. McCormick advertised this as "The herald of a new era of grain binders." Indeed, the machine seemed sensible — after all, mowers and reapers had evolved to "right-hand" cut designs and teams were therefore used to turn to the right. But opponents criticized the fact that "right-hand" cut meant awkward "left-hand" lever operation. Sales of the McCormick design never eclipsed traditional designs so McCormick was forced to offer binders in both right- and left-hand cut models.

Auto Mower

The product line development and expansion of both the McCormick and Deering companies seemed to be more similar than different throughout the 1890s. Both companies experimented with and marketed corn binders, husker-shredders, and header-binders at about the same time, so neither company was able to gain a conclusive engineering victory. But a new era was dawning, and the stakes were rising. The emergence of the gasoline powered engine seemed to beg for an application to agriculture. Engineers for both McCormick and Deering did their part to respond by experimenting with a self-propelled auto mower. Again, the race for preeminence was under way.

The Deering Company gained an early advantage in 1891 when it developed its own engine. The next year, the 6-horsepower, two-cylinder horizontal engine was mounted on a Deering mower. Experiments continued for the next several years.

FIRST FARMER — Well, young man, I see that it's a new right-hand McCormick, and you look as if you were glad that you took my advice. There is none equal to the McCormick,

Though progress at the McCormick Company was comparatively much slower, an important step was made in 1894, somewhat unwittingly, when the company hired an 18-year-old machinist named Edward A. Johnston. The young Johnston's genius was soon apparent and by 1896, Johnston was employed by the McCormick Company as an inventor and designer. When the McCormick Company developed its first gasoline engine in 1897 and a two-cylinder vertical engine a year later, Johnston wasted little time in applying this to power a unique McCormick auto mower.

By the time of the 1900 Paris Exposition, both companies had displayed their own versions of an auto

In the 1890s harvester manufacturers began to add push-type harvesters to their ever-increasing product lines. These machines excelled in large western fields, like this one in Spokane, Washington. This McCormick harvester is equipped as a binder.

This photograph shows the optional heading elevator that could be used in the place of the binding attachment. Cutting the heads only and eliminating the binding process saved much harvesting time. Using the header elevator attachment necessitated the use of an accompanying wagon to gather the cut heads and transport them to a central location. This crew is working with a 1912 Deering model.

Turning a corner with a push-type harvester and team of six horses must have required patience, practice, and skill.

mower. But it was Edward A. Johnston and the McCormick Harvesting Machine Company that received first prize. That same year, Johnston built a second auto mower. All indications seemed to show that the age of power farming had begun with McCormick machines leading the way. But in reality, the power farming revolution was still years away. The McCormick and Deering auto mowers proved to be no faster than conventional horse-drawn mowers and demand for the still unproven machines was quite tentative. Nevertheless, the commitment of these companies to the design and production of the auto mower was a true foreshadowing of the power farming revolution that was still to come.

Clearly, the 1890s was an era when the product lines of harvesting machine companies, especially the McCormick and Deering Companies, made considerable progress. Though some products introduced in the 1890s failed to capture the imagination of farmers, others were soon found indispensable. The manufacturers that survived the harvester wars realized the importance of growth and expansion. With this mindset, several leading manufacturers agreed to combine their resources and form the International Harvester Company. Growth and expansion would proceed as never before.

McCormick responded to the Deering challenge by producing a competitive version of the auto mower. In this photograph, the genius behind the McCormick auto mower, Edward A. Johnston, poses aboard his invention. Johnston's design won first prize at the Paris Exposition in 1900. This two-cylinder motor had a transmission that functioned through tension supplied by a chain and roller. In contrast to the Deering design, the McCormick used a lever to steer the front wheel.

Perhaps the most foresighted advances in the competing product lines were seen in the development of the auto mower. The Deering Company proudly led the way with this self-propelled machine that could travel a whopping 1 meter per second!

Competitors Unite
The International Harvester Company

The International Harvester Corporation was launched in the summer of 1902. Five companies, once fierce rivals, finally agreed to work together in cooperation. The consolidation included the following companies:

McCormick Harvesting Machine Company
Deering Harvester Company
Warder, Bushnell & Glessner Company
    (makers of Champion machines)
Plano Manufacturing Company
Milwaukee Harvester Company

Reaching this point was not easy, but by calling a truce to the harvester war, the manufacturers could increase production efficiencies that ultimately benefited not just the owners, but the farmers as well. The combination that first was the source of much suspicion later created the deepest loyalties for generations to come.

Reasons for Organization

To the five companies that formed International Harvester, merging was simply a matter of survival. The competition of the harvester wars was devastating the industry, and the company executives knew it. John J. Glessner of the Champion line recalled, "In the harvester business, there was a competition never known in any other business in the world. It was a bitter fight between everybody to get business and to get the better of your competitor. We did everything we possibly could to prevent our neighbor from making a sale." W.H. Jones of the Plano Company concurred, "We had to [combine] or wind up the business. If we had not, we would have thrown all of our men out of employment. The best thing to do was to get rid of the fierce competition." The creation of International Harvester was the only clear alternative to the otherwise ruinous harvester wars.

When competitors united to form the International Harvester Company, new frontiers became accessible. The young corporation was able to invest unprecedented amounts of capital in the development of machines that would open the door to an era of power farming. These new products would then be offered to an ever-expanding global market. These catalog covers, for example, illustrate how the new line of tractors, wagons, and portable engines were marketed not just in the United States, but across the world. In terms of innovative machines and global markets, International Harvester set standards by which other corporations would be judged throughout the twentieth century.

But the combination proved to be more than just a means of survival, for it could offer other advantages as well. Prior to the merger, the fierce competition and the resulting cutthroat prices meant a scarcity of capital. This lack of capital stifled what the owners saw as opportunities to increase production and realize many economies of scale. The company leaders knew that by combining interests and limiting the wasteful competition, investment capital would become more abundant. The benefits of this were twofold. First, the foreign markets of Europe and Asia could more vigorously be pursued, thereby offering outlets for greatly increased production. Second, costly raw material sources could be secured thereby cutting costs by avoiding payment of excessive prices to the iron, timber, and steel interests.

Cyrus McCormick described the benefits of consolidation in a letter to his mother, "it seems like a wise, prudent, safe business move . . . large economies in operation could be made by working in harmony instead of by fighting each other as we are now doing." Clearly, the many benefits of consolidation were all too obvious to the owners in the industry. For years they attempted to combine their interests; but for years these efforts ended in frustration. Bringing together five fiercely independent interests would prove to be no small or simple task.

Previous Attempts

A study of the 20 years before the formation of International Harvester reveals a strong desire on the part of the harvester men to cooperate and consolidate but an even stronger desire to remain independent. Although each of these previous attempts to consolidate would ultimately fail, each must be considered a step toward the eventual successful formation of International Harvester.

Prior to 1890, several cooperative efforts revolved around the concept of fixing prices. But these loose agreements did not prevent the harvester manufacturers from pursuing their own interests. As a result, the market conditions were not influenced to any significant degree.

A significantly more complicated attempt to unite the manufacturers of twine binding machinery took place in 1883. Cyrus McCormick went to a meeting of independent interests in Niagara Falls to discuss the possibilities. But this, like many other attempts in succeeding years, seemed doomed to failure. Nettie Fowler McCormick, the wife of the inventor noted simply, "We cannot go into a partnership like that. For we would practically be tied hand and foot. We will go it alone." The next year, Cyrus McCormick passed away. The business in this delicate time was carried on by his son, Cyrus McCormick Jr.

By 1890, merger discussions were nothing new. As Cyrus McCormick noted in his book, *The Century of the Reaper*, "The records of 1885 are full of accounts of meetings called to consider consolidation and adjourned with nothing done." For the McCormicks, there was still not enough to gain by entering a combination with smaller interests.

Finally, a consolidation effort seemed to succeed. The formation of the American Harvester Company seemingly changed everything. McCormick, Deering, and 17 other harvester interests joined in this amalgamation, the purpose of which was to divide markets, consolidate operations, and fix prices. The efforts toward these ends went remarkably far. Upon actual incorporation on November 19, 1890, the new company chose Cyrus McCormick as its president, and William Deering as chairman and treasurer. Agreements for the transfer of property were executed and some employees were notified that their services would no longer be needed. American Harvester seemed to be off and running.

But this too, like all previous attempts was doomed to fail. Expert legal opinion suggested that the consolidation was "contrary to law and public policy." Furthermore, American Harvester was launched with no operating plan and no operating capital. The Deerings and McCormicks were quick to pick up on the many flaws of the new corporation. Nettie Fowler McCormick had misgivings from the start; she especially did not want to see the McCormick name submerged in the new company. Finally, Cyrus McCormick and William Deering shared a brief conversation. As told in *The Century of the Reaper*,

> The two Chicago men were sharing a hotel parlor, where late at night, McCormick was pondering the situation. As he sat alone, the door to Deering's room opened. Clad only in his nightshirt, the old gentleman walked in and stood before the fireplace, his hands locked behind his back, and his fine face grave with concern.
>
> "McCormick," he said at last, "are these other fellows trying to make the two of us carry water for them?"
>
> "It looks that way to me!"
>
> "All right, let's go home and call it off."
>
> "I agree," said the younger man — and both went to bed and slept soundly for the first

time in nights, secure again in the unimpaired possession of their own sound companies.

American Harvester died in January 1891, only a few weeks after it was formed. The competition of the harvester wars continued to rage.

The failure of American Harvester, however, did not discourage continued efforts to solve the costly problem of competition in the harvester wars. On different occasions, the McCormicks negotiated a possible buyout of the Deering firm. Another plan called for each of the two companies to retain control of its own business but with a large minority interest in the other. For various reasons these plans failed. In the end, neither side was willing to surrender control. And still the harvester war continued to rage.

The Complexities of Combination

"If only the Deerings and McCormicks could get together," J.J. Glessner said, "the rest would be easy." Clearly, the smaller harvester manufacturers like Glessner's Champion line, were eager to see the two giants call an end to the ruinous competition of the era. But this was precisely the problem: the Deering's and McCormick's could not get together. As the attempts before 1902 had shown, their mutual rivalry and suspicions were greater than their desire to join forces.

The task of combining forces seemed to get even more complicated in 1900 when the "trust-busting" president, Theodore Roosevelt, took office. A combination of harvester interests would be an easy and desirable target for Roosevelt to attack since such a move would clearly win support from farmers across the country. But the goal of combination never escaped the harvester kings. Both the Deerings and McCormicks now realized that in order to negotiate the differences between the two families and to navigate the threatening legal complexities, an outside negotiator would be needed.

Upon the advice of John D. Rockefeller Jr., the McCormicks contacted George W. Perkins of the firm of J.P. Morgan & Company. The Morgan firm had established an impressive record by organizing other combinations, most notably that of U.S. Steel — a billion dollar deal. Both the McCormicks and Deerings showed a trust in Perkins that they had not previously shown in each other. Perkins was the skillful outside negotiator both sides had been seeking. As a result, negotiations in the summer of 1902 proceeded at a most rapid pace.

Amalgamating former rivals into one huge enterprise, the Morgan firm traditionally assumed positions of command to resolve internal personality and policy conflicts. Certainly in the case of McCormick and Deering, there was much to resolve, so as negotiations progressed, the role of Perkins and the Morgan firm grew. In the end, Perkins eventually selected all the officers and directors of the new company, appraised the value of all amalgamated properties, and even selected the name "International Harvester." The Morgan firm, initially called on as a negotiator, became a permanent interest in the new company. The result was satisfactory to all. In three weeks, Perkins did what could not be done in the previous 20 years. Cyrus McCormick later said that George Perkins was the most brilliant negotiator he had ever met.

By July 28, 1902, the preliminary terms of the merger were settled; the McCormick, Deering, Plano, Milwaukee, and Champion lines combined to form the International Harvester Company. Control of the new company would, for a period of 10 years, rest in the hands of a three member "voting trust" consisting of Cyrus McCormick, Charles Deering, and George Perkins. This arrangement gave Perkins the authority to resolve the inevitable differences in opinion between McCormick and Deering. McCormick also took over the duties of president while Deering assumed responsibilities as chairman of the board.

By consolidating the five largest producers of harvesting machinery in the country, International Harvester was valued at $120 million and had under its control over 90% of the nation's trade in grain binders. The once fierce competitors were now united and poised to offer the most advanced machinery to meet the increasing needs of farmers in the twentieth century.

A new corporation meant new trademarks. The "I.H.C." symbol would serve as the company's trademark until 1945, when the more modern, block IH was adopted.

International Harvester of America: The Early Years

In a legal sense, the International Harvester Company was formed on July 28, 1902. The real identity of the new corporation, however, would take years to establish. What sort of corporation would International Harvester become? The owners pursued the answer cautiously while the farmers waited anxiously.

An Alliance of Rivals

Farmers seemed to have every reason to be anxious. By 1902, the American public had already been exposed to, and had grown wary of, the formation of trusts. In the past, these trusts had demonstrated the power to eliminate competition and control prices. What would prevent the new Harvester trust from doing the same and betraying the promise of lower prices and enhanced innovation? Furthermore, the intense competition throughout the harvester wars had fostered deep loyalties among the customers of each respective firm. In the absence of such

The principal agents in the formation of International Harvester were sons of the harvesting pioneers. Cyrus Hall McCormick Jr. (left) and Charles Deering (right) together successfully launched the new corporate juggernaut.

competition, what would become of the individual product lines?

The owners had questions of their own. What about the dangers of discord among the now united but once fierce competitors? The McCormicks and Deerings especially wondered if the new corporation meant a sacrifice of the tradition, pride, and and independence associated with a family-owned and family-named corporation.

In response to these numerous concerns, the new board of directors, at the first meeting in August 1902, passed a resolution that would help define International Harvester for much of the next two decades. The decision was made to conduct the manufacturing operations of the original vendor companies as separate divisions and independent units. The heads of the respective divisions were authorized to conduct the business of the several divisions along their "own lines." Although this arrangement seemed to sacrifice some possible economies of scale, it did allow the respective interests to retain some independent control. A further justification was given by the company sales committee:

> We believe that so long as there is competition it is desirable for the company to maintain five selling organizations for the purpose of getting the largest amount of effort from the greatest number of local agents without expense to the company, and for the purpose of utilizing in its own business as much as possible of the local agency material rather than permit any of it to become available for competitors.

Each division of the newly formed International Harvester Corporation strove to maintain its own identity through distinctive trademarks and slogans as shown with this McCormick logo (ca. 1910) and this artwork from a 1903 Plano catalog. Association with the larger parent company was gradually worked into the product catalogs.

almost as if no merger had taken place at all. It was at least conceptually possible for one town to have five International Harvester dealers — one for each of the somewhat independent product lines.

For the years immediately following the merger, business was conducted as if the companies were simply an alliance of rivals, rather than a complete consolidation.

As far as the farmers were concerned, this arrangement meant very little recognizable change. Each of the five companies continued to offer the same grain harvesting equipment as before the merger, namely, binders, twine, and hay and corn harvesting equipment. The dealers in each town continued to offer the same brand names and compete,

The IHC logo took much longer to appear on actual farm machinery. In fact, this Titan tractor appeared in the fields at about the same time as the IHC trademark on these Deering binders. This scene truly reflected the changing times.

Separate divisions meant continued competition among the divisions. A Champion catalog printed just after the merger reassured the loyal customers, "Champion machines have features of construction that are distinctly Champion." But even though competition remained, and even though the lines continued to differentiate their products, the tenacity of the "harvester wars" was clearly over. Catalogs that used to claim superiority over other brands appeared to mellow somewhat with statements such as "The Champion machines for this year are built in strict accordance with modern harvesting machine requirements" and "All Plano products are modern and up to date, constructed of the best materials attainable . . . and built to give satisfaction."

Toward a Complete Line

Despite the retention of five distinct product lines, the International Harvester management never lost sight of one significant purpose for consolidation. In the words of Cyrus H. McCormick, "to enlarge the business and make a greater success of the business by building more machines and especially, different kinds of machines." Company executives referred to the pursuit of "different machines" in terms of establishing a "new line" of farm equipment. The products that characterized the new line, such as harrows and hay tools complemented the traditional "old line" pursuits of the five recently merged companies. International Harvester did not remain a combination of companies devoted primarily to the manufacture of mowers, binders, and reapers for long. The addition of new machine lines made the International Harvester line complete.

Many reasons help explain Harvester's otherwise uncharted venture into new product lines. First, the company wanted the claim of being able to service every purpose of the farm — to be able to offer something for every farmer. Significantly, no other company at the time could come close to making this claim. Second, the market for harvesting equipment had become oversold in the years of the harvester wars. In addition, wheat acreage and production

simply did not expand in the first 15 years of the new century. Since growth could not depend solely on the sale of harvesting machines, it would have to be sought elsewhere. Third, it was believed that diversification would remove the seasonal character from the harvesting machine business and provide employment on a year-round basis to the thousands of Harvester factory employees and dealers. For these reasons International Harvester continued to expand.

Building the complete line was not easy — it required the efforts of the International Harvester management for nearly two decades. These efforts included the purchase of companies that enabled International Harvester to enter the markets for products like tillage and haying tools. In other cases, exclusive selling agreements were arranged that allowed Harvester to market products like seeding machines and plows. But perhaps the most impressive strides toward complete line development were made as a result of Harvester's own devotion toward research and product innovation. In these different ways, the full line began to come together. By 1918, the new line had matured and the goal of a complete line was realized.

Entering the Tillage Line

The new line pursuits began in earnest with the purchase of D.M. Osborne & Company in January 1903.

At the time of its acquisition, Osborne was easily Harvester's largest rival. Once ranked third in the production of harvesting machines, D.M. Osborne & Company was clearly smarting since the formation of

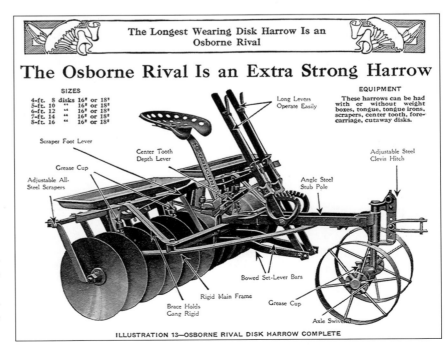

An exceptionally versatile and rugged disk harrow, the Osborne "Rival" was a welcome addition to the International Harvester line. Though useful in rough ground, the forecarriage and weight boxes seen here were only offered as options at extra expense.

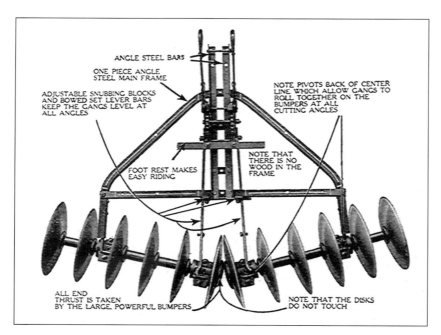

ANGLE STEEL BARS

ONE PIECE ANGLE STEEL MAIN FRAME

ADJUSTABLE SNUBBING BLOCKS AND BOWED SET LEVER BARS KEEP THE GANGS LEVEL AT ALL ANGLES

NOTE PIVOTS BACK OF CENTER LINE WHICH ALLOW GANGS TO ROLL TOGETHER ON THE BUMPERS AT ALL CUTTING ANGLES

FOOT REST MAKES EASY RIDING

NOTE THAT THERE IS NO WOOD IN THE FRAME

ALL END THRUST IS TAKEN BY THE LARGE, POWERFUL BUMPERS

NOTE THAT THE DISKS DO NOT TOUCH

The "bumper" disk harrow was a clever response to the problems of "end thrust" inherent in most disk harrow designs. Rather than stressing the frame and bearings, "bumpers" were designed to roll together and thus absorb the end thrust. This feature made the harrow lighter in draft and increased its overall durability. International Harvester offered several brands of "bumper" disk harrows, but this Osborne version again seemed to be most popular.

McCormick trademarks. By the time the full line was complete, International Harvester offered farmers an impressive array of brand-names in harrows and other tillage equipment. Keystone, Columbia, New Southern, Cotton King, Corn King, and New Zealand were important names under the International Harvester umbrella in the first part of the twentieth century.

Harvester's success in this new line endeavor can be seen in the sales figures from the period. In 1909, for example, International Harvester produced over 50,000 disk harrows, approximately 26% of the total market. In just two short years, production of disk harrows shot up to over 83,000 for over 49% of the total market! No doubt, product quality and lenient two-year payment terms helped account for the meteoric increase. But probably more important was the growing realization of the disk harrow's value to the average farm. It was effective before plowing to cut up crop residue like corn stalks and weeds and after plowing to pulverize the soil and prepare the ground for spring planting. Some special disk harrows, like orchard harrows, were particularly suited to cultivation as well.

the International Harvester Company. The owners were very anxious to dispose of their interests. Harvester quickly obliged. By taking over its operations, Harvester increased its capacity to produce binders, mowers, and reapers by about 35,000 machines per year. Osborne's location in Auburn, New York, further opened the East Coast and overseas markets to the influence of International Harvester. But perhaps most importantly, D.M. Osborne & Company produced an impressive line of tillage equipment, including disk, peg-tooth, and spring-tooth harrows. Osborne had produced over 52,000 harrows the year it was acquired.

Harrows

The purchase of the Osborne Company was an important first step in developing the new line of farm equipment. But the development of the tillage line was by no means complete with the acquisition of one company. In a few short years, harrows were also being produced under the Deering and

In addition to beautiful scenery, this photograph features a Deering double disk harrow. The front disks were complemented with a tandem attachment of "cutaway" disks that further pulverized the soil and leveled the ground with its "in throw" action. This design saved a great deal of time by eliminating the need to "lap half" and go over the same ground twice in opposite directions.

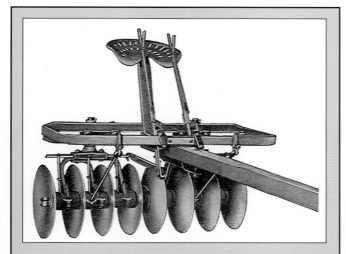

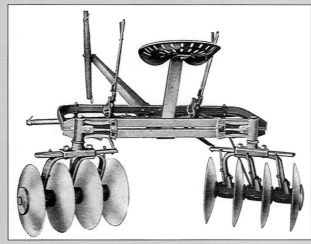

The New Southern and Cotton King brands of disk harrows were popular because of their simplicity and adaptability to cultivating purposes. The gangs were designed to be easily tilted, separated, or reversed to throw the dirt toward or away from the center. Extension standards were available upon special order for cultivating tall crops.

To complement the popular disk harrows, International Harvester also offered a wide variety of spring-tooth and peg-tooth harrows. The Culti-packer also enjoyed a brief period of popularity as an effective implement for pulverizing the soil.

Despite the popularity of disk harrows, the spring-tooth design was more flexible and therefore better suited for harrowing rough and stony ground. The sulky riding attachment on this Osborne harrow was an optional feature many overworked farmers could not pass up.

Unlike spring-tooth harrows, the peg-tooth design was designed less for pulverizing and more for smoothing and leveling the soil. Notice the curved teeth in the corners of each section; these were designed to be quickly converted to "runner teeth" for easy transport. Identifying this 1913 photograph is not easy — it is labeled as an Osborne, Deering, and McCormick outfit.

Here, a spring-tooth harrow is seen working in in conjunction with an Osborne Rival Disk harrow. The center tooth of the disk harrow was a popular feature that eliminated the ridge otherwise left between the gangs.

This McCormick harrow combines the benefits of both spring-tooth and peg-tooth designs for one easy operation. The fresh pinstriping seems to indicate that this harrow has not seen many hours in the field . . . yet!

Tandem rollers, like the International Harvester Culti-packer, were popular ways to pulverize the soil and leave behind a number of fine ridges. In time, farmers learned of the problems associated with "packing" the soil and use of the Culti-packer became limited.

A Developing Line of Hay Machines

What the purchase of Osborne had done for Harvester's tillage line, the purchase of Keystone would do for the haying machine line. On September 6, 1905, the property of the Keystone Company of Sterling, Illinois, was transferred to the International Harvester Company. Although the Keystone harvesting machine equipment line had a somewhat questionable reputation for quality, the hay tool line was excellent. Because of this, International Harvester soon discontinued production of Keystone harvesters and mowers; Keystone hay tools, however, were marketed for years to come.

Actually, Harvester's development of hay machines antedates the acquisition of Keystone. Hay rakes had been an important farm implement almost as long as the mower. By the 1890s, there were over 60 manufacturers of this hay tool — including the five companies that would merge to form International Harvester. In 1902, the combined companies of International Harvester had sold over 160,000 rakes, approximately 67% of the total market. What's more, the subsequent acquisition of Osborne increased these numbers significantly and added an all-steel hay tedder to the IHC line.

The purchase of Keystone further complemented this line by adding a side-delivery rake and a windrow hay loader. As a 1903 Keystone catalog accurately stated, "The first machines of this character ever placed upon the market were built in Keystone shops." With nearly 15 years experience in producing side-delivery rakes and 30 years experience manufacturing hay loaders, Keystone was certainly a reputable and welcome addition to the International Harvester family.

In subsequent years, International Harvester continued to develop its line of hay machines. Soon, sweep rakes, hay stackers, and hay presses became regular features of the International line.

Hay tedders and hay rakes entered the product lines of various harvester companies in the 1890s; with the formation of International Harvester in 1902, these became the foundation of further advancement in haying machines. This Osborne hay tedder featured six forks to stir the hay, thereby assuring a more uniform curing.

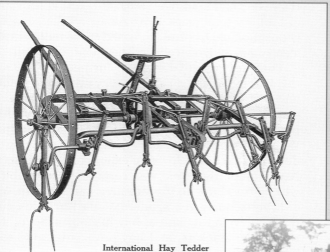

International Hay Tedder

This eight-fork hay tedder, though featured in a Milwaukee product catalog, was one of the first implements to carry the "International" name. The shape of the tines and motion of the crankshaft ensured a consistent lifting motion through the hay. On every tedder, forks were placed outside the wheels so tedded hay would not be mashed down on the next pass.

Dump rakes like this Milwaukee design were first produced by the leading harvester manufacturers in the 1890s. Significantly improved over earlier standard rake designs, the "dumping" action was initiated by either a foot- or hand-lever mechanism. This enabled farmers to gather the hay into windrows or a central field location to in turn be pitched onto a wagon.

The Keystone Company made a great advance in the 1890s with the development of a side-delivery rake. The great advantage of the side-delivery design was that it could be operated continuously, without stopping to dump collected hay. Another advantage of side-delivery rakes, like this Osborne model, shown here, was that the hay was gathered in continuous windrows. This made for much simpler gathering — especially with the advent of hay loaders, like the ones shown on the opposite page.

The usefulness of side-delivery rakes ensured their place in the International Harvester product line for many years. For 12 years before this 1935 photograph, the various makes and models were consolidated into a single McCormick-Deering nameplate. The left-hand design of this rake created windrows on the raked stubble, not on top of the swath.

A sensible complement to the side-delivery rake was the windrow hay loader. These machines elevated the hay from the windrow to an awaiting wagon, thereby eliminating tiresome lifting by hand. Keystone loaders were the first ever sold on the market and had established a reputation for quality and durability. International Harvester capitalized on this by acquiring Keystone in 1905.

At some point, International Harvester marketed hay loaders under the names of Keystone, Osborne, and International. Consolidation efforts in the early 1920s simplified the name game and all International Harvester hay loaders carried the McCormick-Deering mark, as seen here.

Keystone claimed that their machine was the "simplest loader made." Amazingly, there were no gears on this machine! The gathering drum not only gathered the hay, but also drove the elevator, resulting in a light draft machine that "never required more than two horses to pull." Such simplicity was also reflected in the price; in 1906, a 6-foot loader cost only $45!

The Keystone Gearless Hay Loader

For a time, rake-type loaders were also popular. The advantage of this design was that a load could be gathered from either the swath or windrow. The design of the shafts enabled the rake heads to move in a long, elliptical motion. This way, the rake heads would raise and lower at the proper time, eliminating any damaging choppy movement.

To move hay from the windrow or swath to a stack or press, International Harvester also offered a complete line of sweep rakes. The No. 4 model, shown here, was a four-wheeled, rear-hitch, push-type design. The pencil pointed teeth were nearly 8-feet long and capped with metal tips to prevent wear.

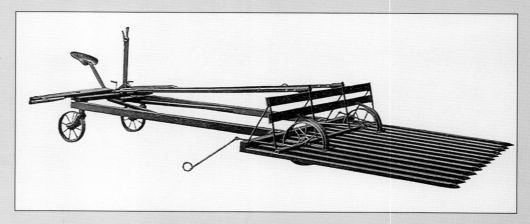

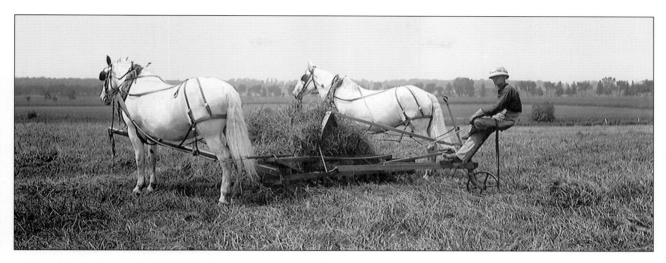

Model designs of the International sweep rake varied based on the number of wheels used and the hitch location for the horses — either side or rear. This photo shows an International No. 2 rake, with three wheels and a side hitch arrangement. The lever at the driver's right hand controlled the positioning of the teeth.

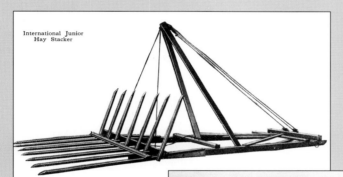

Gathering the hay with a sweep rake was one thing, but stacking it was another matter entirely. For this purpose, International Harvester offered a series of affordable hay stackers. In 1904, a farmer could purchase this International Junior Hay Stacker for just $25. It is shown here ready to receive a load from a sweep rake

Once loaded, two horses powered a lifting motion and the load was literally thrown onto the stack. In this scene, a side hitch sweep rake has delivered a load of hay to the International Junior that is in the process of delivering a load to the haystack. The two horse team in the background to the right is furnishing the power. Little wonder these stackers were classified as "overshot" stackers!

For a more controlled delivery to the haystack, a swinging hay stacker was also offered. Here, the team to the left has delivered the hay to the stacker while the team to the right waits to provide the power necessary to lift the stack.

Once raised, the operator could manually swing the entire stack in either direction by means of the lever behind the center of the "A" frame. The heavy stakes seen here were provided with a sledge at no additional cost. This stacker could deliver hay as high as 25 feet!

By 1911, engineers at International Harvester found a way to combine the merits of a sweep rake and stacker into a single unit. Lifting power for this machine was provided by the main wheels. The lifting cable wound around a drum in the center of the axle that operated by means of a friction clutch. Once the load was elevated, the driver could choose to set it down on top of the stack and back away or simply release a lever and dump the load. Both operations were controlled by the main lever in front of the driver's seat. The operation of this machine must have been an awesome sight!

Within five years after its formation, International Harvester began to produce a series of hay presses that quickly became very popular since baled hay was more easily stored on the farm and more easily transported to cities where no hay was grown. The simplest machine was this one-horse pull power hay press. This machine featured a 14- x 18-inch bale chamber and could make bales that weighed up to 90 pounds.

With the acquisition of Osborne and Keystone, International Harvester made great strides toward reaching its goal of developing a complete line of farm equipment. With new capacities for manufacturing tillage and hay tools, International Harvester was clearly becoming more diversified. The real expansion, however, was still to come.

In this scene two men are loading the hay into the bale chamber while another worker ties the bales. The baling wire and tied bales can be seen to the right. In one 10-hour day, this press could bale as much as 8 tons of hay.

A two-horse pull-power hay press was also offered for greater capacity. Bales were compressed by means of a compound lever and a toggle joint plunger. In this way, a 500-pound pull on the sweep could give 76,800 pounds of pressure in the bale chamber! Advertisements claimed that the $170 cost of this outfit could be quickly regained by shipping the baled hay to an urban market.

As gasoline-powered engines emerged they were soon incorporated into the design of the hay press. When not in use, the engine could be disconnected and used for other purposes. In 1912, the motor hay press was equipped with a 3-horsepower IHC gasoline engine. For additional cost, a 4- or 6-horsepower engine could be substituted.

It didn't take long before the International hay press was applied to duties far removed from the farm. Like hay, scrap and garbage proved far more manageable when baled!

Expansion through Innovation

The addition of tillage implements and hay tools proved to be merely the start of the huge diversification necessary to build a complete product line. International Harvester continued to aggressively acquire farm equipment manufacturers. By 1905, both the Minnie Harvester Company of St. Paul, Minnesota, and the Aultman-Miller Company of Akron, Ohio, had also joined International Harvester.

But purchasing companies was not the only means by which International Harvester developed its complete line. A certain pride was taken in the products that were instead developed as a result of research and innovation. In its annual report, the management at IH would repeatedly stress, "The Company, in pursuance of its established policy, maintains a skilled force of inventors and designers for the purpose of producing new devices and improvements in type, design, or construction of its products." Such a commitment to engineering and innovation paid huge dividends to the International Harvester Company. As a result, entirely new products were developed and added to the "new line."

Twine

It seems ironic that twine, a product seemingly so simple, would receive so much attention from Harvester's team of inventors and engineers. But in reality, much development in this area was needed. The success of the twine binder in the 1880s had made high demand for binder twine a certainty. At the time, binder twine was made from imported manila and sisal fibers. The problem was that these fibers were simply too expensive. If a cheaper source could be found, both the producers and farmers would benefit.

William Deering can be credited with blazing the trail toward a solution. His company was the first of the harvester manufacturers to build a mill for the production of binder twine from imported fibers and the first to experiment with alternate sources of fiber. By the time International Harvester was formed, no suitable alternative to manila and sisal was yet found, so the new company continued the research. Many experiments were conducted, all geared toward finding a suitable low-cost alternative. Fibers of paper, wire grass, and straw were all tried, but found unacceptable.

Finally, after repeated efforts, a suitable alternative to manila and sisal was thought to be found: American grown flax. Here was a material that had been tested as stronger than sisal and could be produced at a much lower cost than either sisal or manila. International Harvester accordingly made a strong commitment to

ENOUGH DEERING BINDER TWINE made in a single day to reach around the world with 3,500 miles to spare.

The average length of all DEERING TWINE made during 1898, as shown by inspectors reports, was as follows:

KIND		AS ADVERTISED				ACTUAL LENGTH			
PURE MANILA	650	FEET	TO	THE	POUND	654	FEET	TO THE	POUND
MANILA	600	"	"	"	"	602	"	"	"
STANDARD MANILA	550	"	"	"	"	552	"	"	"
STANDARD	500	"	"	"	"	501	"	"	"
SISAL	500	"	"	"	"	503	"	"	"

Prior to the formation of International Harvester, the Deering Harvester Company led the industry in both research and production of binder twine. This page from an 1899 catalog reflects the pride that Deering had in these efforts.

the production of flax twine. The plant that once produced Minnie Harvesters in St. Paul, was geared to the production of several thousand tons of flax binder twine for the 1906 harvest. A separate corporation, the International Flax Twine Company, was even established to oversee production.

Unfortunately, the years of research and development in this case were ultimately unsuccessful. In a few short years, the production of flax twine was discontinued, as it proved to be both a grasshoppers delight and a commercial failure. The use of manila and sisal fibers would endure. Nevertheless, the commitment of International Harvester to the production of twine is nothing less than impressive. After all, at one point about 20 million miles of binder twine was used annually in the United States alone — International Harvester accounted for nearly 65% of this production.

Although the attempt to market flax twine ultimately failed, International Harvester never stopped trying to find ways of helping farmers to reduce their costs. As a result, International Harvester continued to research and develop new products. Each new

For a short time after the merger, it seemed as if flax would be the low-cost alternative to imported manila and sisal fibers. This belief led to the creation of a subsidiary named the International Flax Twine Company. The logo for this ill-fated company looked much like the more familiar and longer lived IHC logo.

innovation eased farmers' lives while, at the same time, increased their profits.

Cream Separators

An excellent example of this innovation can be seen in International Harvester's development of cream separators. The recently invented centrifugal separator offered obvious advantages to the tedium and waste of skimming milk by hand. Realizing this, Harvester engineers began to develop their own model in 1904. Within one year, "The Cream Harvester" was being marketed to farmers across the country. One early advertisement claimed, "Butter fat left in the skim milk is practically money thrown away. Save the money by saving the butter fat. The Cream Harvester will do it." Enjoying some success, The Cream Harvester was given the new name, Dairymaid. Other International Harvester models soon followed, including Bluebell, Lily, and Primrose. A second generation of cream separators was then sold under the McCormick-Deering name.

To make space for the manufacture of these new machines, the decision was made to move the production of all Milwaukee Harvesting machines to the McCormick plant in Chicago. The Milwaukee plant then became the home for International cream separators and other new line products as well. With the successful production of cream separators, International Harvester had shown it could meet the needs of farmers, not only in the field, but around the homestead as well.

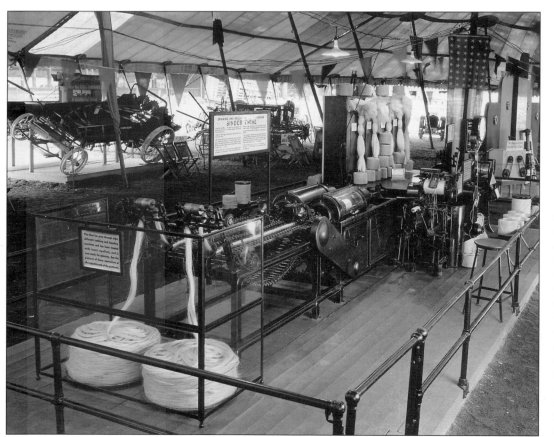

Despite the failure of the flax twine industry, International Harvester continued to boast of its ability to produce more twine than any other supplier. This 1935 exhibit displays some of the machinery required to produce a ball of twine. Such equipment was no less complicated than the machines used to produce the most advanced harvesting implements.

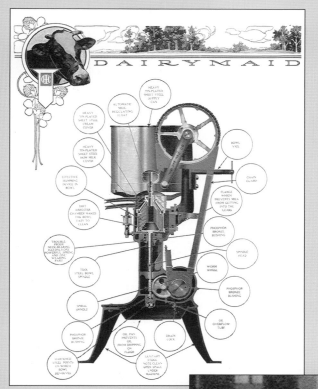

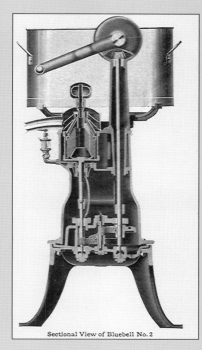

Sectional View of Bluebell No. 2

To complement the Dairymaid design, the "Bluebell" was introduced in 1906. Unlike the chain-driven Dairymaid, the Bluebell transmitted power from the crank to a vertical shaft. The friction clutch in the gear nest enabled the gears to keep turning even when the handle stopped. The friction clutch also gave the operator the option of pumping the handle. This feature was especially valuable when initiating the motion of the separator.

The Cream Harvester had evolved into a model that carried the name "Dairymaid." This sectional view identifies the essential working components.

By the time International Harvester cream separators bore the McCormick-Deering name, the design incorporated the use of ball bearings. This photograph was part of a 1929 catalog. The caption read, "Slow crank speed and four ball bearings make the McCormick-Deering the world's easiest turning cream separator." This was certainly a good thing since the capacity of the No. 6 had reached 1,500 pounds of milk per hour!

With the introduction of the Lily and Primrose models in 1911 and 1913, respectively, the older Bluebell and Dairymaid designs began to be phased out. Customers were given a $15 credit for trading up to the newer models. Lily and Primrose cream separators were offered in four sizes, ranging from the No. 1 model with a capacity of 350 pounds of milk per hour to the No. 4 with a capacity of 850 pounds per hour. Naturally, the price increased with the capacity. While the No. 1 only cost $65 in 1921, the No. 4 cost $95 that same year. Electric motor attachments, seen here powering a Primrose No. 4, were offered at an additional cost of $45 or $55, depending on whether a DC or AC motor was desired.

THE I. H. C. GASOLINE ENGINE

If a farmer expects to make money by using a power producer, he must have the most practical and economical one on the market. He must use the one that has produced profit for scores before him. Such is the I. H. C. gasoline engine.

The I. H. C. engine is designed specially to meet the requirements of the up-to-date farmer. It has few working parts, all of which are easily accessible. It does not require any time to get ready, only one turn of the fly wheel being necessary to start the engine. The time consumed by other kinds of power in getting ready is spent by the I. H. C. in working. Other excellent features of the I. H. C. engine are the small fuel consumption and the fact that it does not require an engineer. These features alone should recommend it above all other kinds of power.

International Harvester Company engines are made in the following styles and sizes:

Horizontal } Portable { 4, 6, 8, 10, 12, 15 and 20 horse power.
           } Stationary {
Vertical—2 and 3 horse power.

Call and let us show you many more good points of the I. H. C. engine.

This space is mortised to set in your name and address.

Advertisements for International Harvester's new line of gasoline powered engines made it clear that a new era of power farming was under way. Similar advertisements would claim that these engines were so simple, safe, and economical that "it is only a question of time when they will be in general use."

Stationary Engines

International Harvester's attempt to help farmers through product innovation reached a critical stage in 1904 with the development of the gasoline powered stationary engine. Here was a device that would ease the handling of crops as well as lighten the load around the house. Other machines such as hay presses, corn shellers, feed grinders, cream separators, and even washing machines could all be powered with the new line of International Harvester engines. With so many diverse applications, these engines quickly became a popular part of the International Harvester line.

Although a staggering variety of models and sizes were offered, the International line of engines was dominated by the names Famous, Mogul, and Titan. Like the manufacture of the new cream separators, these gasoline engines were primarily produced at the Milwaukee Works. Mogul engines were sold exclusively

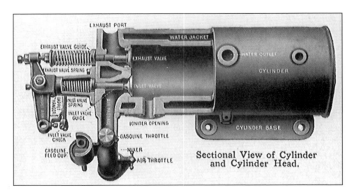

Sectional View of Cylinder and Cylinder Head.

This sectional view shows the general construction of the cylinder and cylinder head of an International Harvester horizontal engine. Advertising material called special attention to the ample room between the cylinder and jacket walls for circulation of cooling water. Horizontal engines were initially offered in 4-, 6-, 8-, 10-, 12-, 15-, and 20-horsepower sizes.

by McCormick dealers while Deering dealers offered the Titan name. Famous engines were often similar — sometimes identical — to those engines bearing the Titan name. Famous engines however were not exclusive to any one division of International Harvester. Therefore, these engines tended to be the most popular of all those carried in the International Harvester line.

Efforts to consolidate these various names began in 1917. That year, International Harvester introduced the Type M series of engines to replace the Famous, Mogul, and Titan names. The Type M engines dominated sales

The sturdy vertical engine was offered in 2- and 3-horsepower sizes. Included as regular equipment were a muffler, galvanized steel cooling tank, an electric battery, and even an oil can. A gas tank and two lengths of pipe to install the tank outside the building were also provided, free of charge. The 1904 price for this 3-horsepower outfit was $150.

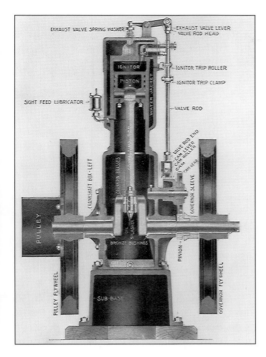

The cooling tank attachment was designed to drain easily — an obvious advantage for winter operation when the water would have to be drained after each use to prevent freezing when the engine was idle.

This cutaway view of the vertical engine reveals its essential working components. Notable features included a hit-and-miss type governor, a speed regulator, and a splash system of lubrication. A 2-horsepower model weighed 883 pounds and could reach a maximum of 450 rpm.

The 20-horsepower horizontal engines weighed 6,470 pounds! Little wonder that International Harvester offered "portable" models mounted on trucks for easier transport. Notice the seat and footboard for the driver. These larger engines required 1 gallon of gasoline per horsepower to run for 10 hours.

Working Side of Portable Engine.

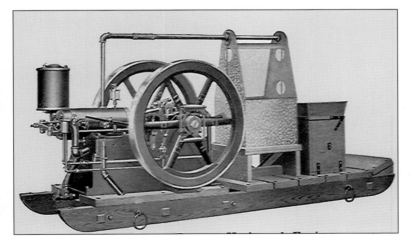

The "Famous" brand of International Harvester engines was essentially identical to other IHC stationary engines except a gasoline tank was incorporated in the base of the engine. This was not standard on other models because of safety restrictions by the National Board of Fire Underwriters. Notice this 6-horsepower engine is mounted on a sled for more manageable transport.

-Where is the engineer?
-Where is the fireman?
-Where is the coal wagon?
-Where is the water cart?
-Where is the smoke?
-Where are the dangerous sparks?

You don't have these annoyances, dangers and expenses with a gasoline engine. That's why the gasoline engine is the best power for the farmer.

KEEP ABREAST OF THE TIMES

Secure an I. H. C. engine at once. Don't delay. Farmers everywhere say that the I. H. C. engine can't be beat for an ever-ready, practical, economical power producer.

They are built in sizes from 1 to 25 horse power — one to meet every requirement on the farm from churning to threshing.

I. H. C. engines are made in the following styles and sizes:
Vertical — 2 and 3 horse power.
Horizontal (Portable or Stationary) 4, 6, 8, 10, 12, 15 and 20 horse power.
Call today and let us show you the reason why you should not be without an I. H. C. engine.

This space is mortised to set in your name and address

As seen in this advertisement, the portable engines were ideally suited for powering threshers or huskers and shredders. Safety and simplicity were constant themes of engine advertisements of the day.

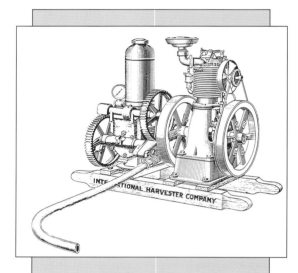

Famous engines were also offered for more specialized applications such as this 4-horsepower sawing outfit (left), 2-horsepower pumping engine (above), or 2-horsepower air cooled spraying outfit (top).

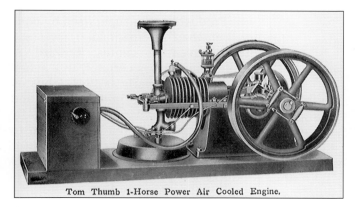

Tom Thumb 1-Horse Power Air Cooled Engine.

For less demanding applications, International Harvester offered the "Tom Thumb" 1-horsepower engine. The convenience of this engine made it extremely popular; not only was it smaller and lighter than other models (still over 250 pounds!) but it also featured an air cooling system that cooled the cylinder by a blast of air from a fan belted to the flywheel. The spark plug was mounted on top of the cylinder for easy cleaning or replacement.

for the next 20 years until the Type L series was launched. As horsepower needs grew, International Harvester shifted to the production of 4- and 6-cylinder power units.

Engine power was ideally suited to replace the otherwise tedious operation of a cream harvester. The Titan Jr. 1-horsepower engine shown in this enhanced photograph was produced in limited quantities from 1915-1917.

This era of engine production clearly illustrates International Harvester's commitment to product line progress through innovation. Such innovation helped make power farming a reality.

Motor Trucks

International Harvester's development of power farming equipment would have been incomplete had the company not also built trucks to enable farmers to get their produce to market faster and more economically. To this end, the company aggressively sought a way to enter the truck business.

The Aultman & Miller Buckeye Company, located in Akron, Ohio, had enjoyed for many years a considerable reputation. A letter within the Harvester organization reveals, "The Buckeye selling organization will market a certain number of Buckeye machines each season by reason of the prestige of the Buckeye machines and on account of the standing that a good many of the dealers have in the country." Because of certain financial difficulties within the Buckeye Company, however, International Harvester was able to become a controlling interest in the struggling firm. By 1905, the takeover was complete. Soon the Buckeye line of harvesting equipment was dropped entirely, despite its solid reputation. Clearly,

In an effort to consolidate the Mogul, Titan, and Famous brands, International Harvester offered the Type M series beginning in 1917. The 1.5-, 3-, 6-, and 10-horsepower Type M models incorporated kerosene carburetors and and as seen here, were ideally suited for line-shafting applications. These popular engines helped bridge the gap to the development of larger 4- and 6-cylinder power units.

This 1911 version of International Harvester's Auto Buggy is shown with the optional top folded down. The acetylene lamps, horn, and flare boards were standard equipment. With its 7-gallon fuel tank, this 20-horsepower Auto Buggy could cruise for up to 100 miles.

International Harvester had bigger plans for the factory in Akron, Ohio; in 1907, the Akron Works was equipped with the latest and most modern machinery for the manufacture of auto wagons and passenger cars.

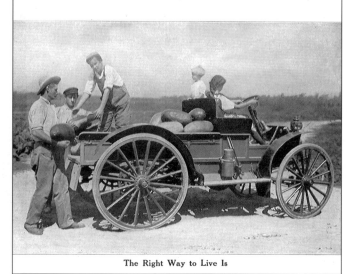

The International Harvester Auto Wagon was designed to meet many diverse needs. As seen here, the panel box body could carry up to 800 pounds of freight. If the need arose, however, an optional rear seat and full top could be added to make the Auto Wagon a passenger vehicle very much like the Auto Buggy.

Production was supervised by none other than International Harvester's own inventive genius, Edward A. Johnston. He was certainly well suited to the task. As early as 1898, Johnston made his own automobile and attracted considerable attention by driving it along the roads of Chicago, to and from the McCormick Works. Under Johnston's supervision, the Akron Works was producing over 4,000 auto-powered vehicles by 1910.

The first successful production vehicle acquired the name "Auto Buggy," probably because of the uncanny likeness to the buggies of a previous era. The greatest difference, of course, was the 2-cylinder, air cooled engine that was mounted on the chassis. The Auto Buggy was soon joined by the somewhat more rugged Auto Wagon. With a capacity to travel 20 miles per hour while transporting a ton of cargo, farmers must have agreed with an early advertisement for the Auto Wagon, "The right way to live is to make your work a pleasure." Together, the Auto Buggy and the Auto Wagon represented the start of an impressive truck division.

For a brief time, International Harvester also produced passenger automobiles. In addition to a sporty, two seat roadster called the "Runabout," a more sophisticated touring car, the IHC 30, was also produced. Despite some impressive features, International passenger car production proved to be short lived. The future clearly rested with trucks.

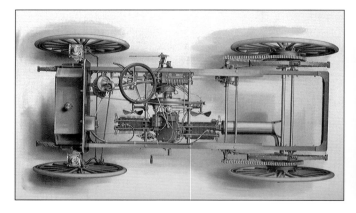

A top view of the Auto Wagon chassis reveals many of its working features: the steering column, clutch, and hand brake are located on the right side of the vehicle, while the starting crank is on the passenger side; the two-cylinder, four-cycle, air-cooled engine is placed at the center of the chassis for even weight distribution and two chains powered the rear wheels. The Auto Buggy chassis was identical except for a more rounded hood.

Advertisers at International Harvester capitalized on the diverse capabilities of the Auto Wagon. The Singer Sewing Machine Company realized that the high wheels and optional chains made the Auto Wagon ideally suited for iced urban streets. As a passenger vehicle, the Auto Wagon was rugged enough to cross most any terrain. By the way — is that Teddy Roosevelt riding in the passenger seat?

"This car is the fullest realization of construction, comfort and beauty." Such was the claim of the advertising catalog for the IHC "30" touring car. With roomy seats, split windshield, first-class leather, carpeted rear floor, pneumatic tires, and 4-cylinder engine, the IHC "30" was clearly targeted for the more uncompromising driver. Unfortunately, the public was not yet ready for such extravagance — the IHC "30" was only produced for two years, beginning in 1910.

As demand grew for greater load capacity and more power and speed, International Harvester responded with a new series of trucks, beginning in 1915. With a 145-inch wheelbase and 4-cylinder engine, these trucks had a capacity of 1 1/2 tons. The low wheels made these vehicles better suited for highway transportation.

In 1915, International trucks were significantly redesigned. The original high wheeled design of the Auto Buggy and Auto Wagon was abandoned forever as speed, horsepower, and payload capacities increased. This new series of trucks became so popular that soon more International trucks were being sold in urban markets than in rural ones. International Harvester was no longer strictly a farm equipment company.

International trucks were in such demand that the facilities at Akron, Ohio, soon became inadequate. In 1921, truck manufacture began at the Springfield Works, previous home of the Champion line of harvesting equipment. Just two years later production began at the Fort Wayne Works, a plant designed specifically for truck manufacture.

With annual production of over 15,000 motor trucks, it seemed obvious that the truck line of International Harvester could become a mainstay of the company .

Realizing the Goal

The executives at International Harvester must have been satisfied with the success that accompanied the new line ventures. From tillage implements to motor trucks, farmers everywhere seemed to be buying International Harvester products. The success and popularity of new line machines was due to a combination of product quality and corporate reputation. Another key factor was the efficient and well-established dealer network IH had established throughout the country. Farmers realized and appreciated that International Harvester parts and service were as easily accessible as International Harvester machines.

Since the earliest years, the company strove to offer a complete line of equipment to farmers across the world and progress toward this goal was being made. Catalogs that once offered only binders, reapers, and mowers had grown to include many types of farming and homestead equipment. But a complete line demanded the addition of even more machines. To farmers, this meant a wider selection of quality, reputable products. To International Harvester, this meant more acquisitions, more research and development, and more exclusive selling arrangements. Though a complete line must have seemed elusive at times, it was a goal that would benefit both the company and the people it served. And so the efforts continued and machines were added until the goal was realized.

Wagons

Even with the growing popularity of the motor truck, it took a considerable amount of time before it claimed to replace the farm wagon. These affordable, dependable wagons that helped with the hauling of goods

First manufactured in 1845, Weber wagons established a reputation that nicely complemented the original members of the International Harvester family. Known for years as the "King of All Farm Wagons," the Weber wagon boasted attractive colors and pinstriping.

were a business necessity to most every farmer. Because of this, farm wagons were also a necessary addition to International Harvester's new line.

International Harvester entered the farm wagon trade in earnest in 1904 with the purchase of the Weber Wagon Company. Like other new line pursuits, Harvester's wagon line began with the purchase of an

All Weber wagons were built in both standard and wide track sizes. The 60-inch wide track had been the norm in the wagon industry until automobiles, with a universal 56-inch tread, began to carve up the muddy country roads. The wide track, seen here, therefore typically encountered a rough ride. As autos became more popular, the 56-inch track became the standard.

One unique feature of Weber wagons was pitched as the "safety first" swivel reach coupling. This enabled the wagon to endure severe twisting and jolting. This feature obviously saved much in repair costs and the driver faced less risk of being thrown from the wagon.

existing, reputable company. This purchase enabled Harvester dealers to immediately offer an established and respected name in the farm wagon trade. Weber Wagons were soon joined by other names including New Bettendorf, Columbia, Sterling, and Buckeye. The development of Harvester's farm wagon line continued in 1906 by converting existing manufacturing facilities. In this case, the manufacture of Plano harvesting equipment was moved to the Deering Works in Chicago and the vacated Plano factory in West Pullman, Illinois, was then retooled to the production of farm wagons. Through acquisition and conversion of existing facilities, International Harvester quickly became an important player in the farm wagon business, producing nearly 60,000 annually.

Manure Spreaders

In a similar fashion, International Harvester wasted little time establishing itself as a leading producer and distributor of manure spreaders. By 1911, over half of the manure spreaders sold in the United States carried an IHC logo — an amazing accomplishment considering International Harvester had offered this line for just six years! Like other new line machines, such remarkable growth was the result of a familiar pattern: established companies were acquired and existing factories were converted.

Arrangements with the J.S. Kemp Manufacturing Company in 1905 enabled International Harvester to purchase one plant for the manufacture of manure spreaders and lease another. The former was located in Newark Valley, New York, while the latter site was in the town of Waterloo, Iowa. Both sites produced the popular Kemp Twentieth Century brand of spreaders. Furthermore, by moving the manufacture of Plano harvesting equipment to the Deering Works, enough space was created in the West Pullman factory for manure spreaders as well as wagons. West Pullman, as

NO WONDER HE'S ANGRY

You, Mr Farmer, have no doubt had the experience as is shown in the above illustration. There are few farmers who have not. Smeared from head to foot; wagon all plastered with manure; corn stalks sticking to the fork to be pounded off on the side of the wagon box. These conditions alone ought to be enough to make you buy a manure spreader. If you had a chance to get rid of this most dreaded work of the farm, besides doubling the value of your barnyard manure, wouldn't you take it? The Cloverleaf manure spreader offers you such a chance. It will double the value of your barnyard manure as a fertilizer as well as relieve you of the dirty work of spreading by hand from a wagon.

The Cloverleaf spreader is made of the best material, is easy to operate, is light in draft, and anyone that can drive a team can use it.

Call on us and we will be pleased to show you the advantages of owning a Cloverleaf manure spreader.

This space is mortised to set in your name and address.

What an advertisement! In 1908, it probably wasn't difficult to capture the attention of farmers that were fed up with the task of spreading manure by pitch fork. Machines that eliminated this most dreaded chore met with immediate popularity — little wonder!

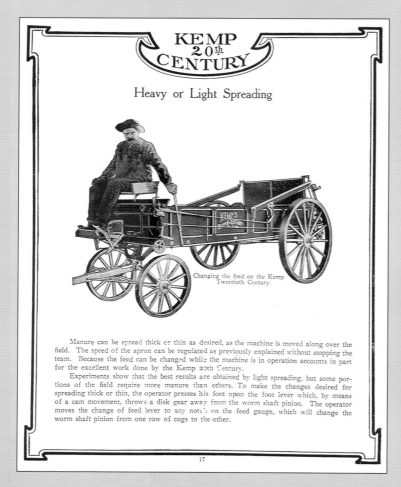

KEMP 20th CENTURY

Heavy or Light Spreading

Changing the feed on the Kemp Twentieth Century.

Manure can be spread thick or thin as desired, as the machine is moved along over the field. The speed of the apron can be regulated as previously explained without stopping the team. Because the feed can be changed while the machine is in operation accounts in part for the excellent work done by the Kemp 20th Century.

Experiments show that the best results are obtained by light spreading, but some portions of the field require more manure than others. To make the changes desired for spreading thick or thin, the operator presses his foot upon the foot lever which, by means of a cam movement, throws a disk gear away from the worm shaft pinion. The operator moves the change of feed lever to any notch on the feed gauge, which will change the worm shaft pinion from one row of cogs to the other.

17

Advertised as the "first practical manure spreader built," Kemp's 20th Century featured conveniences that were frequently copied in later years. The front wheels were small and spaced closely together for tight maneuvering; a lever placed within easy reach of the driver regulated the degree of spreading; and the end gate could be conveniently lowered or raised, depending on whether the manure was being loaded or spread.

Another improvement was the wide-spread feature located behind the beater. Available for both Corn King and Cloverleaf models, these disks could spread a path of manure up to 10-feet wide. The width of the spread could be controlled by the wings located at the side of the device. With this attachment, unloading time was greatly reduced.

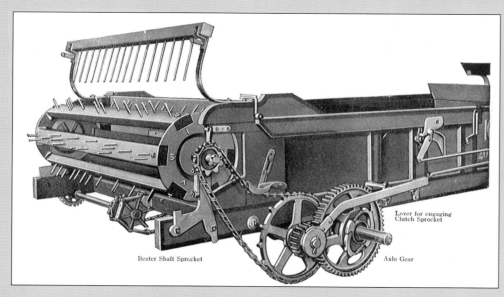

Beater Shaft Sprocket

Lever for engaging Clutch Sprocket

Axle Gear

This view of Kemp's 20th Century manure spreader shows the essential working components. Six wooden slats with uniquely arranged steel teeth served to thoroughly pulverize and distribute the contents of the spreader. Power for this beater was furnished by a large gear, seen here, on the right-rear axle.

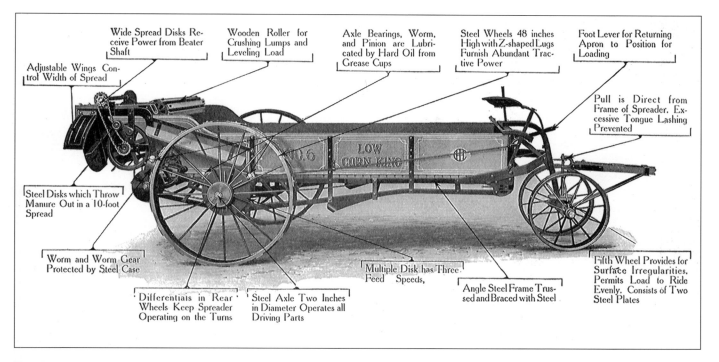

Wide Spread Disks Receive Power from Beater Shaft

Wooden Roller for Crushing Lumps and Leveling Load

Axle Bearings, Worm, and Pinion are Lubricated by Hard Oil from Grease Cups

Steel Wheels 48 inches High with Z-shaped Lugs Furnish Abundant Tractive Power

Foot Lever for Returning Apron to Position for Loading

Adjustable Wings Control Width of Spread

Pull is Direct from Frame of Spreader. Excessive Tongue Lashing Prevented

Steel Disks which Throw Manure Out in a 10-foot Spread

Worm and Worm Gear Protected by Steel Case

Differentials in Rear Wheels Keep Spreader Operating on the Turns

Steel Axle Two Inches in Diameter Operates all Driving Parts

Multiple Disk has Three Feed Speeds,

Angle Steel Frame Trussed and Braced with Steel

Fifth Wheel Provides for Surface Irregularities. Permits Load to Ride Evenly. Consists of Two Steel Plates

By 1914 the design of manure spreaders had changed substantially. As seen with this Corn King model, manure spreaders were built lower to to the ground to ease loading. Notice also the added wooden roller near the beater to further pulverize and level the load.

a result, became the home of Cloverleaf and Corn King manure spreaders.

The demand for these machines was exceptionally high. Few other machines could claim to reduce labor by 50% while increasing crop yield by as much as 20%. In an effort to meet this high demand, a portion of Champion Works was also allotted for production of manure spreaders. Starting in 1908, manure spreaders with the International trademark were manufactured at this location.

The introduction of the McCormick-Deering manure spreader around 1923 made the designs of older spreaders a distant memory. Offered in a 50- or 75-bushel capacity, the McCormick-Deering featured an all-steel frame and a tapered box that was wider at the rear to prevent lodging as the load moved toward the beater.

Corn Machines

Prior to the formation of IH, the McCormick and Deering companies had already begun to successfully design and market corn machines; the corn binder and husker-shredder had appeared in each company's catalog in the years preceding the merger. These machines were therefore considered a part of the "old line." However, once the newly formed company had made its commitment to the development of "new line" products, the number of specific corn machines offered to farmers increased dramatically.

The stalk cutter, for example, was added to the International Harvester line in 1912. Both single-row and two-row cutters were available. For years, the simplicity of the horse-drawn cutter appealed to farmers who needed to prepare stalk ridden land for

The usefulness and simplicity of the stalk cutter made it an easy addition to International Harvester's new line of equipment. This stalk cutter is equipped with a seven-knife head — the nine-blade version cost only $25.50 in 1914.

The Keystone Company, acquired by International Harvester in 1905, was the first company to widely produce a corn sheller. In 1880, Keystone produced a model called the Pony Sheller. Keystone's design was so successful that few changes were necessary over the years; in fact, in this 1923 steel frame McCormick-Deering version closely resembled its wood frame Keystone ancestor.

plowing. By using the stalks for fertilizer value, crop yields increased substantially. Stalk cutters provided the most suitable alternative to burning the stalks.

Away from the field, numerous machines were offered to process the corn crop. Corn shellers, a longtime speciality of the Keystone Company, remained in production at the Keystone Works after the company had been acquired by International Harvester. Early models were operated by hand and were capable of shelling 200 bushels per day. With the advent of power farming, later models when belted to gas-powered engines could process over 600 bushels per hour!

Feed grinders and hammer mills were of great value to the educated farmer in the early twentieth century. Though neither could be considered an implement of necessity, both were certainly implements

Corn shellers, like so many other farm implements, were readily adapted to gasoline power sources for greater capacity. This International No. 2 corn sheller required only 4 horsepower to shell as much as 150 bushels per hour. When tractor belt-pulley driven, as shown here, capacity increased. The 1921 price for this outfit was $175.

The No. 10 corn sheller was the largest machine of the era. With a capacity of up to 600 bushels per hour, this machine was best suited for the largest of farms or community cooperatives.

Feed grinders were added to the International Harvester line in 1909 and could come equipped with several labor-saving features. Notice this farmer is using a chute to run the corn from the bin into the 10-inch Type B feed grinder and an elevator to lift the ground corn to storage. This model required approximately 10 horsepower to grind up to 50 bushels per hour. A smaller 8-inch model was also offered for a 1923 price of just $34.25. The addition of a feed grinder on a farm saved much time and expense of transporting feed to a nearby mill.

Several observers endured the cold winter day in Madrid, Iowa, to observe this feed grinder in action. This dealer in Madrid must have been very active as similar scenes in different years and with different equipment appear throughout the archives.

Sometime in the late 1920s or early 1930s, hammer mills that pulverized the grain became an alternative to feed grinders. The McCormick-Deering No. 1-A hammer mill could handle up to 40 bushels per hour.

For just $190 in 1914 a farmer could purchase an International Type B ensilage cutter. This machine required at least 15 horsepower to reach its capacity of 16 tons per hour.

People came aboard their International trucks and Weber Wagons to witness first hand the benefits of this McCormick-Deering hammer mill. Dating back to the era of the reaper, demonstrations like this were a sure way to stimulate sales.

This 1935 scene shows a McCormick Deering No. 12-A ensilage cutter at work. The power source is a McCormick-Deering W-30 tractor.

of economy. In the feeding of livestock, the use of feed grinders and hammer mills greatly increased livestock feed efficiency.

The benefits of silage were likewise becoming increasingly recognized in the early 1900s. Silage made use of the otherwise wasted corn stalks while proving economical livestock feed. Silage made use of the entire corn plant and provided an economical feed for many classes of livestock. International Harvester designed and produced its own line of ensilage cutters to offer farmers for over three decades.

Plows

In 1909, Cyrus McCormick made a revealing comment:

> *For some years our traveling men and our agents had been pressing us very strongly to go into the plow business, but we had up to the present time strongly declined such a policy . . . but of course if the plow people went into the harvester business we might find ourselves drawn into the plow business.*

For many years, both the John Deere Company and International Harvester were cautious about entering into direct competition with each other. In a meeting with Cyrus McCormick in 1909, the Chief Executive Officer of Deere & Company, William Butterworth, confessed that Deere "knew nothing about the harvester business and had no wish to enter it." Butterworth later wrote in 1912,

> *It would be the height of unwisdom to attack the International Harvester Company, which has at least $7.00 to our $1.00 in working capital . . . A serious fight with them will mean a serious depletion of our profits, maybe their absolute curtailment, thus endangering our dividends, the passing of one of which would very seriously affect its market price and do great damage to our credit. The theory that because the Harvester Company may go into*

> *the plow business, we should go into the harvester business and so start a fight with them, seems to me to be most unwise. I would avoid a fight with them as long as possible."*

But the executive committee at Deere did not agree with Butterworth. One member wrote that, "to conserve what we have, we must aspire to get more." This mind-set would prevail at Deere. In the summer of

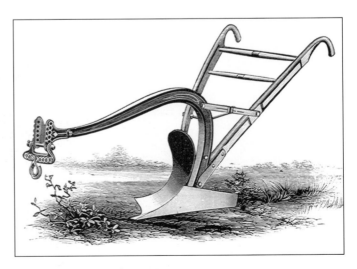

Manufactured in Canton, Illinois, since 1840, Parlin & Orendorff plows had secured a reputation as being among the best on the market. The Canton Clipper model, seen here, could be furnished with a steel beam and depending on the size cost from $14.75 to $21.50.

This Parlin & Orendorff Scotch Clipper model is turning over 16 inches of virgin sod.

The Canton Clipper Tricycle was advertised as the "most successful, popular and best plow ever placed on the market." Since the wheels carried the weight of the furrow, these plows were remarkably light in draft, despite the added weight of the rider. A complete assortment of plow bottoms to suit most any soil type and condition were available upon special order.

1912, ground was broken for a new Deere & Company harvester plant in East Moline, Illinois. Clearly, the time had come for International Harvester to enter the plow business.

International Harvester had already made separate contracts with Parlin & Orendorff and the Oliver Chilled Plow Company in 1909 and 1910, respectively. But these contracts concerned only the manufacture for sale in Canadian markets. The well-developed domestic selling organization of these plow companies and others, especially Deere & Co., prevented International Harvester from more fully entering the domestic plow business for another several years.

This busy scene is set in Ontario, Canada, and is actually a junior boys plowing match. The standard equipment for each contestant was a McCormick-Deering No. 407 walking plow. The McCormick-Deering name was offered to complement rather than replace the successful P&O models.

Parlin & Orendorff's Diamond sulky plow enjoyed remarkable longevity. First offered at the turn of the century, production of this model lasted until the 1940s!

The Parlin & Orendorff name remained even as the McCormick-Deering name was added to the line of plows. This particular plow was Little Chief sulky and in this illustration, carried an "F" series bottom.

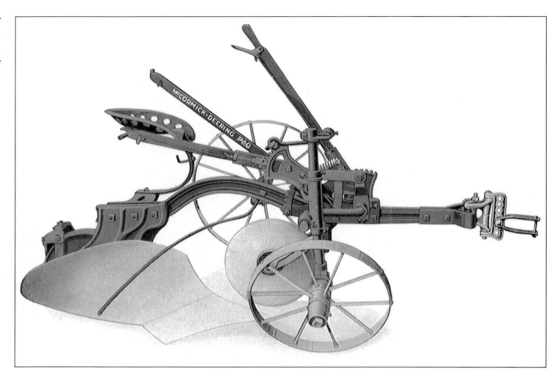

"Full Plow Line for Harvester Company" was the proud headline of *The Harvester World* in May of 1919. On May 7 of that year, International Harvester announced the purchase of the plant, line, and business of the Parlin & Orendorff Company of Canton, Ohio. The article exclaimed, "There is no doubt that there is a general feeling that the management has thus completely and in a most effective way carried out its promise to provide the sales organization with a full line of plows."

Much evidence seemed to support this claim. At the time of acquisition, P&O was the oldest and third largest plow manufacturer in the country. In addition, the newly acquired company had strongly established lines of tillage implements to complement the existing

Like Parlin & Orendorff, the Chattanooga Plow Company offered a full complement of walking and sulky plows. But perhaps most intriguing was this design: the reversible disc plow. The team, seat, and disc all turned in one sweeping motion in order to throw a furrow to the right in one direction and to the left in the opposite direction. The reversible disc plow was especially useful for hillsides where the furrow could be constantly thrown down hill.

Harvester tillage line. In fact, the P&O tillage line would largely replace other International Harvester lines of tillage equipment.

A few months later, International Harvester bought the Chattanooga Plow Company. A Harvester executive stated, "This purchase was made for the sole purpose of completing our Company's plow line with a chilled plow of the highest excellence and reputation. Now, with Chattanooga chilled plows and Parlin & Orendorff steel plows, we feel that we enter this department of the farm implement business on a broad and sound manufacturing basis."

By 1919, the Company was able to boast, "by these purchases, the Company has rounded out its list of products with an essential farm implement not heretofore manufactured by it." It is interesting to note that while at its formation in 1902, the International Harvester Company manufactured only nine kinds of machines, 17 years later the "International Line" consisted of 54 separate classifications. The goal of establishing a full line seemed finally complete.

Reaching to New Frontiers

At the same time International Harvester was working to establish its complete line of farm equipment, impressive gains were being made in other areas as well.

Vertical Integration

William Deering realized that for his company to survive the harvester wars, he would need to secure every possible advantage. To sell machines at a lower price than the competition and still realize a profit, production costs had to be lowered. To this end, the Deering Harvester Company began to purchase and lease properties rich in iron-ore and coal. In addition, steel mills and blast furnaces were acquired in South Chicago. By controlling raw materials, Deering could control his own raw material prices; as a result, product prices could be lowered. The foresight William Deering demonstrated in integrating his company vertically would eventually be of great benefit to the International Harvester Company.

In 1907, International Harvester organized a subsidiary company under the laws of the state of Wisconsin to handle the production of these raw material sources. The new company was launched as the Wisconsin Steel Company. Under its immediate control were the 200 acres of the Hawkins and Agnew iron ore mines on the Mesabi Range in northeastern Minnesota. Together, these mines produced over 700,000 tons of ore annually. In addition, Wisconsin

Steel took control of the blast furnaces and steel mills in South Chicago, originally acquired by Deering. To fuel these mills, over 22,000 acres of coal lands originally bought by the Deering Company were also transferred to Wisconsin Steel.

Wisconsin Steel was an enterprise that was nothing short of impressive. "THE HARVESTER" was the name of the company's new steamship, purchased in 1911 to carry the ore from the mines in Minnesota to the steel mills in South Chicago. The South Chicago facility employed over 1,500 people in 1912 and by 1919, was producing over 350,000 tons of steel — far more than International Harvester could alone consume. The surplus was therefore sold to outside interests for a considerable profit. Throughout World War I, Wisconsin Steel was contracted by the government to help with the manufacture of explosives. The new subsidiary was so impressive that the Federal Bureau of Corporations concluded, "This feature of integration in the International Harvester Corporation is a great feature of its strength."

With the success of the Wisconsin Steel Company, it might be easy to overlook Harvester's other efforts to secure raw materials. Also of great significance were its interests in the timber industry. Here again, a subsidiary company was organized, the Wisconsin Lumber Company. Its chief assets included over 81,000 acres in Missouri and Mississippi and also saw mills in Missouri and Arkansas. Further integration was achieved when International Harvester acquired a sisal plantation in Cuba to provide material necessary for manufacturing twine.

By controlling necessary raw materials to meet much of its own demand, International Harvester was able to avoid buying such materials on the open market. As a result, profits remained within the company rather than being distributed to other producers. Vertical integration was equally important in that International Harvester was always assured of getting quality materials, never of poor quality or short supply.

Establishing a complete line and full integration of production were vital to the strength and success of International Harvester in its first two decades. Additional strength and diversity would be derived from the continued pursuit of foreign markets and the construction of manufacturing facilities in foreign countries.

Harvester Becomes International

The tremendous sales potential of Europe and other foreign markets had been realized by the harvester manufacturers for years. Cyrus McCormick himself had started efforts to enter these practically untouched

The new Hamilton Works facility in Ontario, Canada, was initially large enough to supply much of the Canadian and French markets. Located on Lake Ontario, this property remained one of the highest volume producers in the entire International Harvester fold.

markets as early as 1851 with the display of his reaper at the London Exhibition of Industry. In subsequent years, the McCormick Company steadfastly pursued and attained a rising influence abroad. With the formation of the International Harvester in 1902, foreign sales eclipsed the $10,000,000 mark, constituting roughly 20% of the company's total sales. Continued growth was, of course, desired and expected by company management.

But in the early 1900s, this was becoming increasingly difficult to accomplish. Foreign countries erected high tariffs to protect their respective industries at home. Realizing the threat to their growing sales and influence in foreign markets, Harvester acted swiftly. In a seven-year period, from 1903-1910, manufacturing facilities were either purchased or constructed in several foreign countries. Such a move was not without risk, but it was essential to avoid the rising import duties. As a result, Harvester's foothold in foreign markets was maintained and even strengthened.

The first of International Harvester's new foreign manufacturing facilities was the plant in Hamilton, Ontario. Construction of this 775,000-square-foot plant began in 1903 on 118 acres of land the Deering's had purchased before the merger. That same year, the subsidiary company, International Harvester of Canada, was organized. By 1904, the Hamilton Works had produced its first machines, and just six years later over 136,000 machines, including binders, mowers, rakes, cultivators, drills, and manure spreaders were being manufactured in Canada.

The success of the Hamilton Works inspired similar efforts in Europe. In 1906, International Harvester began manufacturing at its first European plant in Norrkoping, Sweden. This relatively modest venture initially

employed only 245 employees and had an annual capacity of 20,000 machines, most of which were mowers and rakes. In 1910, two new European factories

The Harvester Building on South Michigan Avenue in Chicago, Illinois, served as the corporate headquarters for International Harvester in the critical years of the early twentieth century.

commenced manufacture of International Harvester machines — one in Croix, France, and the other in Neuss, Germany. While each plant initially produced about 45,000 machines per year, they were both clearly built with the future in mind; each had an ultimate production capacity of nearly 200,000 machines!

International Harvester's annual report in 1909 explained the company's next move in Europe, "The growth of the Russian trade in the past and the assurance of Russia's great future as an agricultural country has made it desirable to manufacture there at least a part of the requirements for the Russian harvest. A large plant comprising 40 acres has been purchased at Lubertzy, near Moscow." Soon, in addition to mowers and gas engines, the Lubertzy Works was producing the "lobogrieka," a type of reaper particularly designed and suited to Russian agriculture.

Harvester's commitment to foreign manufacture was initially a remarkable success. The world's demand for modern agricultural machinery was now being met by International Harvester. By 1911, foreign sales accounted for no less than 40% of Harvester's total business. The new manufacturing facilities were largely responsible for this remarkable growth. These same foreign factories in addition diversified International Harvester and provided a greater stability and security against crop failures.

The brilliant course plotted by Harvester's management was not without obstacles, however. The greatest came in 1914 with the outbreak of war in Europe. The Croix Works in France was immediately threatened and eventually overtaken by the German military. Before the war was over, the factory's equipment, tools, and materials had been wholly removed or destroyed. At the factory in Neuss, Germany, the situation was little better. Although production continued under German authority, International Harvester retained no control and realized no profits. The factory in Russia, however, was under the greatest strain. Torn apart by World War I and Communist revolution, the market for harvesting machines collapsed. Harvests were only 40% of what they once were and hunger was so widespread that the draft animals that once pulled Harvester machines were being slaughtered for food. Remarkably though, the Communists did not immediately nationalize and take over the Lubertzy works.

After the war, International Harvester, like everybody else, began to rebuild. The first steps were taken at the Croix Works in France which was completely reequipped at staggering costs. The status of the Neuss Works in Germany was in question. Located in the occupation zone, International Harvester was not able to formally retain control of the facility until June 1920. The Lubertzy Works did not fare so well. In 1923, International Harvester closed the facility due to low demand and the restricted supply of raw materials. Just a year later the Communist government finally nationalized the factory. Of course, International Harvester received no compensation and as a result had to bear the $2.2 million loss.

The inclusion of the word "International" in the company's name could not have been more appropriate. Regardless of these setbacks and others, International Harvester continued its commitment to foreign manufacture. This commitment would again be tested in the worldwide depression of the 1930s and an even more devastating world war of the 1940s. The fact that International Harvester would persevere and emerge from these times of crisis with its leadership unscathed is perhaps the truest tribute to the strength of the corporation and the products it manufactured.

The Croix Works covered 51 acres in the northern section of France. For years, this facility served as the principal European source of mowers and binders. Despite being threatened by two World Wars, the Croix Works remained a leading supplier of farm equipment for the entire European market.

The International Harvester Company
A New Direction

International Harvester Company made a major change of direction in 1906 with the sale of its first gasoline traction engine. The Company was well positioned to enter this young market because it was already established in the manufacture of stationary gasoline engines. The market for gasoline traction engines was small; less than 250 units were estimated to have been produced in 1905. At that time, Hart-Parr of Charles City, Iowa, held a dominate position and was thought to account for half of the market. However, changing farm economics and large-scale farming of the U.S. and Canadian western prairie signaled a need for gasoline-powered machines to pull large plows and implements, not just self-powered transport for engines intended primarily for belt work. The time was right.

After careful review of various options, IHC management chose to enter the gasoline traction engine business by contracting with the Ohio Manufacturing Company of Upper Sandusky, Ohio, to mount slightly modified IHC stationary engines on the Morton friction-drive truck. S. S. Morton built a gasoline powered "tractor" in 1899 at York, Pennsylvania, and received patents in 1902 and 1903. Morton consolidated his interests with the Ohio Manufacturing Company in 1904.

The truck developed by Morton provided frame, transmission, axles, wheels, and steering. The truck had all the components needed for a field-ready traction engine, except the engine. (The term tractor had not been coined at that time.) Installing the IHC horizontal, single-cylinder, open crankcase, stationary-style engine completed the package. The engine had a hit-and-miss governor and battery and coil ignition. Except for the crankshaft, the engines were the same as the stationary units, less sub base. Like the stationary units, cooling water was pump circulated around the cylinder and then sprayed onto a tent-shaped wire

screen for evaporative cooling and collected in the catch tank for recirculation.

Tractive power was engaged or disengaged by moving the roller-mounted engine. Moved to the rear, the 12-inch diameter paper drive pulley on the engine crankshaft contacted and friction drove the 50-inch diameter, cast-iron drive wheel. To reverse the unit, the engine remained in the disengaged or forward position, and a toggle-operated, friction idler roller was wedged between engine pulley and drive wheel. This simple drive system made it easy to install

This friction drive, early Upper Sandusky-produced IHC tractor was beautifully restored to operating condition.

engines from various manufacturers on the Morton truck and that is exactly the route taken by the Ohio Manufacturing Company.

IHC shipped 14 gasoline traction engines from 1906 production to various geographic areas where demand was thought to exist. Response was so positive that plans were made to produce 200 units for 1907. To accomplish that level of production, it was necessary to begin production at the Akron Works, in Akron, Ohio, in addition to Upper Sandusky. As further evidence of commitment to the new venture, E. A. Johnston, who headed tractor experimental work, and his department were transferred from the Keystone Works to the McCormick Works in February 1907 and by October they were transferred again, this time to Akron.

The friction-drive transmission system was not really satisfactory for plowing; so, a gear-drive transmission was developed at Upper Sandusky. One 15-horsepower gear-drive gasoline traction engine, called Type "A," was shipped from that location in 1907 along with 153 friction-drive units.

Eight Models of Tractors, Three Manufacturing Sites, and Quadrupled Production

For 1908, a 20-H.P. Type "A" gear drive with 56-inch drive wheels on stub axles and a 20-H.P. Type "B" gear drive with 64-inch drive wheels on a continuous axle were added to the model mix. (When horsepower was used in the advertised name of an IHC tractor, it was usually shown as H.P.) The only difference between the Type "A" and Type "B" gear drive was the drive wheel diameter and axle design. The IHC "Famous," horizontal, single-cylinder gasoline engine powered both units. Only two 12-H.P. Type "A" gear-drive units were built; however, the following year the design evolved into a two-speed, Type "A" gear drive with only friction reverse and three were produced. During the next three years, a total of 62 of these low horsepower, friction

Field experience quickly demonstrated that the friction drive power transmission of the first tractors was not suited to drawbar work. By 1908 the Type "A" and Type "B" gear-drive models were added. The IHC 20-H.P. Type "B" gasoline tractor graphic was later modified to illustrate the IHC two-speed 20-horsepower, kerosene-gasoline version of the Type "B".

reverse tractors were manufactured. Production ended in 1912.

The Type "A" and "B" gear-drive tractors were manufactured at Upper Sandusky along with four models of friction drive for total production of 247 at that location. The Akron Works came on line with 321 of the then current friction-drive models. The Milwaukee Works — the source of the IHC engines — manufactured 100 friction-drive models. Total production of 668 tractors was over four times that of the prior year. The rapid growth demonstrated IHC's commitment to the tractor business and the ability of its sales organization to sell a new product in a new market even though advertising was minimal. The *International Guide* for 1908 devoted 88 pages to IHC products but only one half-page to the four sizes of friction-drive tractors. Two years later the last 11 friction-drive tractors were produced at Akron and the following year all tractor production ended at that location.

The year 1908 also marked the start of the Winnipeg Motor Contest held in Winnipeg, Manitoba, Canada. The need to plow and till the great prairies of the Canadian Western Provinces made Canada the largest tractor market and tractor interest was high. Kinnard-Haines took first place and International Harvester received second place. Hart-Parr, who was the industry sales leader at that time, was not a factor because its unit was over the 7-ton weight limit and not permitted to compete.

Contests were used to educate farmers on the benefits and performance of this new tool — the farm tractor. Winners at these events were not bashful

In May of 1909, a decision was made to develop a 20- and 25-horsepower tractor similar to the new-type 45-horsepower in time for the Winnipeg contest in July. After 40 days of "furious" effort, the tractors were ready for a short test and loading on a railroad freight car for the trip to Winnipeg. The rush had been so great that the tractors were still being painted on the rail car while the train was under way. Unfortunately, the tractors that resulted from this frantic effort did not win any gold medals.

about advertising their successes. The following photo and text are an International Harvester Company example:

This crowd was following the International tractor at Amiens, France.

"In the Farm Motor Contests held at Brandon, Manitoba, International tractors won three medals.

"In the plowing contest held at Aurora, Illinois, September 18, 1909, the International tractor won the loving cup offered by the Wheatland Plowing Association.

"These successes in Canada and the United States were crowned by the victories of International tractors in the plowing competition which took place in October, 1909, at Amiens, France, which was open to all comers and all nations. In this contest an International tractor won the cash premium of 2,000 francs offered by the Automobile Club of France, for the tractor doing the best work. In addition, a diploma of honor and two gold medals were awarded the company.

"The conditions of this competition were the most severe ever imposed in any contest. The tractor was required to work two consecutive days without stopping a single instant. An International tractor performed this task under the most difficult conditions, to the entire satisfaction of the special committee appointed by the Automobile Club.

"The tractors winning the prizes in all of these contests, both at home and abroad, are not "de luxe" engines built especially for these trails. They are every-day stock engines such as are delivered to purchasers."

Following the European contest successes, the Company began exporting two tractors a month from Tractor Works.

The chief engineer for tractors in the Gas Power Engineering Department recalled how in the spring of 1908 the company hired a man to design and build a new type of tractor. The design of the 45-horsepower engine was not typical of the time: It was a twin-cylinder, twin-crank design with removable cylinder liners, tight crankcase for pressurizing the intake charge, ran on kerosene, and had a throttling governor. The truck was all-gear drive with automotive-type steering. All of the previous International Harvester tractors sold had bolster and chain steering like the steam traction engines. In fact, the general truck design and overall appearance of gasoline traction engines in that period was not greatly different from the steam powered units.

The Birth of Two Great Tractor Trade Names: Titan and Mogul

Experience during 1908 and 1909 with the new engine style for the 45-horsepower tractor and similar 20- and 25-horsepower tractors resulted in their redesign to the commonly used hit-and-miss governor system. When these gear-drive tractors went into production at Milwaukee, Wisconsin, in early 1910, they

The wide expanse of the Canadian prairie was well-suited to the early tractors and interest in tractor plowing contests was high. The IHC Reliance Type "D" shown here in Canadian competition would carry the trade name Titan by the end of 1910.

This archive photo has the following caption, "International 20-horse power type C tractor pulling five 14-inch bottom plows. Working with all levers adjusted." This Milwaukee Works-produced gear-drive tractor with friction reverse would become the Mogul Type "C" in 1911.

were called Type "D" and at first carried the trade name "Reliance." By December 1910 the IHC Type "D" tractors were called "Titan" and one of the industry's great tractor trade names was launched. Titan 25-H.P. Type "D" production jumped from only 52 units in 1910

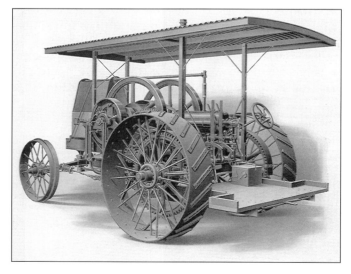

This 12-horsepower, friction-reverse Type "A" tractor was the smallest built at Upper Sandusky, Ohio. The IHC "Famous" single-cylinder engine had a 7-1/2-inch bore x 12-inch stroke. The tractor weighed 9,000 pounds. This tractor series became kerosene-gasoline models in 1913. A year later they were equipped with Titan oil engines and became IHC Type "A" and Type "B" oil tractors.

to over 1,000 the following year, along with a smaller but significant increase in Titan 20-H.P. and 45-H.P. Type "D" tractors.

The new IHC tractor business experienced two major events in 1911: (1) Four new tractor models introduced with the name "Mogul" and launched a second great IHC tractor trade name; and (2) the new Tractor Works production facility at 2600 West 31st Boulevard in Chicago, Illinois, came on line with two of the Mogul tractor models. During the year, the Akron Works ended tractor production. Industry tractor sales grew to approximately 7,500 units and IHC accounted for over one-third of the total.

During the same period a line of gear-drive 12-H.P. and 15-H.P., two-speed Type "A" and 20-H.P., two-speed Type "B" tractors were developed for production at the recently purchased Upper Sandusky Works. Three tractors of this family were produced in 1910 and 10 were made in 1911. However, the following year saw 271 of the two-speed Type "A" and Type "B" gear-drive tractors manufactured along with seven 12-H.P., two-speed Type "A" versions with friction reverse for a total of 278 units. This made 1912 the peak year for Upper Sandusky tractor output with the 20-H.P., two-speed Type "B" accounting for over half of the production. This family of International gasoline tractors became kerosene/gasoline tractors in 1913. The following year they were equipped with Titan oil engines.

An attractively bound 30-page booklet published in 1914 called *IHC Two-Speed Oil Tractors* pictured the three models of two-speed Type "A" and Type "B" tractors in 32 field scenes and commercial locations from New York to North Dakota. The first page listed

IHC Type "B" 20-H.P. two-speed oil tractor

The IHC 20-H.P. Type "B" two-speed oil tractor had the same basic design as the Type "A" except for: a live rear axle in place of stub rear axle; 64-inch diameter rear drive wheels in place of 56-inch diameter rear drive wheels; and a cab and canopy in place of a canopy only.

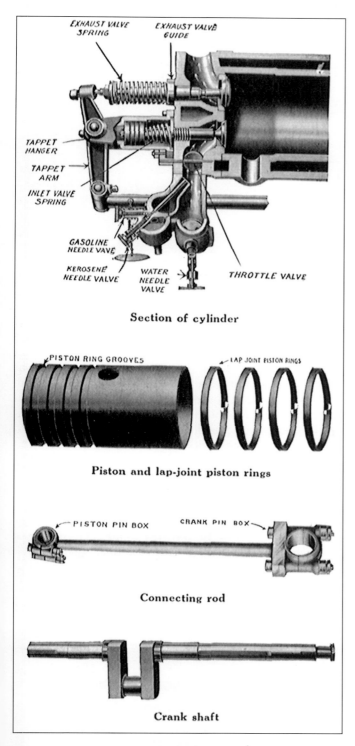

EXHAUST VALVE SPRING
EXHAUST VALVE GUIDE
TAPPET HANGER
TAPPET ARM
INLET VALVE SPRING
GASOLINE NEEDLE VALVE
KEROSENE NEEDLE VALVE
WATER NEEDLE VALVE
THROTTLE VALVE

Section of cylinder

PISTON RING GROOVES
LAP JOINT PISTON RINGS

Piston and lap-joint piston rings

PISTON PIN BOX
CRANK PIN BOX

Connecting rod

Crank shaft

Detail of Type "A" and "B" engine parts from literature illustrations:

Cylinder Cross-Section — Only the exhaust valve is opened by positive cam and tappet action. The spring-loaded intake valve opens only by pressure differential.

Piston and Rings — Center located wrist pin and four lap-joint rings.

Connecting Rod — Drop-forged, steel rod equipped with phosphor bronze bushings.

Crankshaft — "IHC crankshafts are all forged from solid open hearth steel billets without welds of any kind."

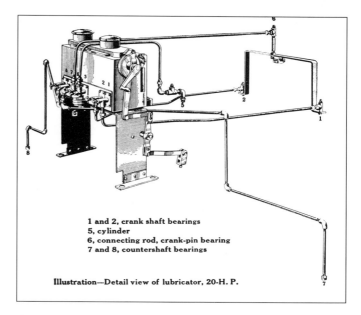

1 and 2, crank shaft bearings
5, cylinder
6, connecting rod, crank-pin bearing
7 and 8, countershaft bearings

Illustration—Detail view of lubricator, 20-H. P.

Open crankcase design required continuous power lubrication of key engine moving parts as shown in this mechanical oiler. Counter-shaft bearings were also power lubricated. Other shafts had compression grease cups or simple oil holes for lubrication.

20 advantages these tractors offered compared to steam traction engines. One of the most desirable features, second gear or fast speed, was promoted for hauling loads to and from town. Every element of the tractor's construction was shown in photos and drawings and described in great detail from the double gear drive to the length of the axle bearings to the material used in the fuel pump plunger. This in-depth explanation of the tractor and engine components served two purposes. First, the engine detail illustrated parts that were similar to, or the same as, those found on stationary engines and would look familiar. Second, most farmers had little or no mechanical experience so the detailed explanation helped in the necessary education process. In spite of the promotion of IHC Type "A" and Type "B" tractors from Upper Sandusky, Titan and Mogul tractors from Milwaukee and the Tractor Works came to dominate IHC tractor production. In 1917 the last five 2-speed Type "A" tractors were manufactured at Upper Sandusky.

Fifty-six companies claimed to be in the gasoline/kerosene tractor business in 1910; however, only about half of them had commercial machines for sale. Several new firms entered the tractor business that year; the most significant entry was the Case

As stated in the literature caption, this IHC 20-H.P. Type "B" oil tractor was on the road to the elevator. Type "A" and "B" two-speed gear-drive tractors had the advantage of a 3- to 3-1/2-miles per hour "road speed" for hauling and transporting.

Threshing Machine Company. IHC expanded its export business interests by shipping its first tractor to Russia.

The Winnipeg Contest entered its fourth year in 1911 with the addition of a kerosene class and inclusion of an over 40-horsepower class in response to the demand for larger tractors. IHC won first in the small tractor class — there was only one entry — and they won second prize in the medium class. The first tractor demonstration in the United States was part of the Omaha Corn and Land Show; American farmer interest in gasoline/kerosene tractors was growing. The following year marked the end of the Winnipeg Contest.

Tractor Works and the Mogul

An employee transferred from the Akron Works related his arrival in Chicago in March 1910. He "found the boys manufacturing tractors in a little shed near the McCormick Works on Blue Island Avenue." E. A. Johnston was sent to Chicago as superintendent of the new Tractor Works to lead this small operation that would become a major manufacturing facility. The two-cylinder opposed, 9-inch bore x 12-inch stroke, 45-horsepower tractor Johnston had developed at Akron Works went with him to Chicago. This was the first large tractor produced at Tractor Works and carried the IHC Mogul 45-H.P. gasoline tractor name; literature described it as follows:

Engine — Opposed double cylinders are used on this tractor. This insures perfect balance and maximum power.

Cylinders — Cylinders and jacket walls are cast integral. Ample space is given to allow free circulation of the cooling water.

Cylinder Heads — Bolted to cylinder. The water jackets of the head and the cylinder register.

Valves — Poppet type, ground in their seats and held by springs. Valves and seats may be removed by loosening only one bolt and without removing cylinder head or disturbing any con-

How do you effectively use the pulling power of a 1911 tractor if you do not have tractor implements available? You modify and use your horse-drawn tools. You add weight to your tandem disk harrow and set it to cut deeply; you string three tillage tools together; and you add a person's weight to the roller-mulcher. In time, implements designed for tractors found a ready market.

Photo of an IHC 45-horsepower Mogul gasoline tractor owned by John McQueen, Kirkland, Illinois, pulling two, four-furrow plows. The tractor drive wheels were equipped with 12-inch tire extensions.

nection. The inlet valve check keeps intake valves automatically closed when the exhaust valve is held open in cases where speed is above normal. Insure fuel economy.

Governor — Spring governed, fly-ball type.

Starting — A relief cam relieves the compression when starting the engine. This makes starting easy.

Piston — Trunk type, extra long, turned and carefully ground to size. Provided with lap-joint piston rings.

Connecting Rod — Drop forged, carefully machined to size. Provided with a divided box on the crank end and adjustable split babbitt bushings for the wrist pin bearing.

Crankshaft — Forged shaft of liberal proportions and turned to exact size.

Main Bearings — Special high grade babbitt, reinforced with stiff metal grid. Machine finished to gauge, of liberal length and thickness, and extra heavy.

Fly-Wheel — Provided with split hub, keyed to the crankshaft and clamped by means of bolts running through the hub.

Gasoline Pump — Plunger type, ball valves, operated from cam shaft. No escape of gasoline past the plunger.

Mixer — Nozzle inside of air pipe. Controlled by needle valve. Fuel is atomized before it enters the cylinder. Mixer is provided with overflow pipe to carry excess fuel back to the tank.

Ignition — Make and break ignitor. Spark control is convenient to the operator. Electric current from batteries and Auto Sparker.

Oiling System — Includes two separate systems. Mechanical oiler for truck and pump oiler for engine. Mechanical oiler furnishes oil for the three countershafts and the two main driving gears. Oil is supplied to engine by means of a pump which sprays oil into the crankcase and lubricates the crankshaft, connecting rod, cylinder, and cam shaft. Oil returns to oil tank for continuous use.

Speed Regulating Device — Provides for a variation from 200 rpm to 375 rpm.

Mounting — The engine is mounted on a substantial steel channel frame. The sills of this frame are reinforced in the rear by the manner in which the axle is secured. Extra heavy axle castings are used. The base of the engine is securely bolted to steel channel sills. The front axle is arched and trussed by two heavy steel rods. The rear axle is 5 inches in diameter and is continuous — extending through both drive wheels. The weight of the frame is so distributed that maximum tractive power is produced.

The first version of the IHC Mogul 45-H.P. tractor had a two-cylinder opposed 9-inch bore x 12-inch stroke engine and two-speed forward, friction reverse, gear-drive transmission.

By 1914 the Mogul 20-H.P. and 25-H.P. Type "C" single-cylinder tractors had reached full development and saw its last year of production. The friction reverse system is shown in the center of the graphic. Advantages of friction reverse were promoted with statements such as, "It may be thrown in (reverse) while the machine is moving without danger of stripping gears; in fact, it could be used as an emergency brake." The funnel-top filling pipe is conveniently located at the rounded corner of the main frame. The flywheel driven Auto Sparker has a similar handy location.

Field reports from the first year's experience with the Tractor Works Mogul 45-H.P. gasoline tractor indicated a number of areas needed strengthening and resulted in practically a redesign. By the fall of 1912, the fuel was changed to kerosene, the bore increased from 9 1/2 to 10 inches, and the rating changed to 30-60-horsepower. Production record summaries in the archives show the Mogul 30-60-H.P. still listed as a Mogul 45-H.P. until 1917,

This graphic shows the IHC Mogul Jr. 25-H.P. kerosene tractor as produced in 1912.

the last year of production. Record keeping was a bit more relaxed than the rigorous demands of today.

Building a factory in 1910 to manufacture tractors was a bold move by IHC; however, production plans were quite conservative with a goal of only six tractors per day when production began in 1911. Popularity of the Tractor Works-built Mogul 45-H.P. and Mogul Jr., 25-H.P., resulted in an increase to 12 per day. By the end of 1912, added facilities and a third shift made possible 14 tractors per day. Mogul availability was augmented by Mogul 20-H.P. and 25-H.P. Type "C" tractors from Milwaukee Works.

The year of the big tractor was in 1912 and IHC was well represented. Milwaukee Works produced 728 of the large Titan 45-H.P. Type "D" tractors and the Tractor Works, now in its second year, produced 1,052 Mogul 45-H.P. tractors that by the end of the year became the

This impressive cross-section of a Mogul 30-60-H.P. kerosene tractor appeared in two versions for promoting this largest of the Mogul tractor line. The forward tank is for fuel and the larger rear tank is for water to serve the ever-thirsty evaporative cooling system. A version of this graphic with large-print component descriptions formed a three-page center fold in a 1913 Mogul tractor sales booklet.

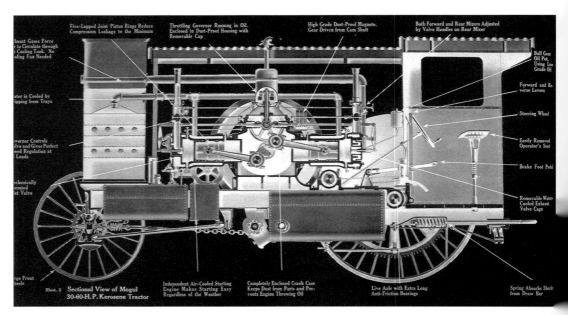

Dirt and gravel roads in the early part of the 20th century required work and maintenance that seemed never ending. The Mogul 45-H.P. and Mogul 30-60-H.P. tractors were well suited to meet the demands of the job.

Milwaukee Works engines like this Mogul Jr. 25-H.P. kerosene/gasoline model were readily adapted for tractor applications with few modifications.

Mogul 30-60-H.P. In each case, these large models also had higher production than any other model at each Works. With 17 models in production at three plants and ranging from 12 to 60 horsepower, there was no clear understanding of where the market was going.

In addition to the Mogul 45-H.P. and Mogul 30-60-H.P., Tractor Works produced the Mogul Jr. 25-H.P. The name Junior helped distinguish this tractor from the Mogul 25-H.P. Type "C" models produced at the Milwaukee Works that belonged to a totally different tractor family. Literature from 1912 shows a unique round stack on the Mogul Jr. 25-H.P. cooling tower and a flat belt-driven water circulation pump. A gear forward, friction reverse transmission drove 72-inch diameter wheels on a live axle. Literature from 1914 shows the Mogul Jr. 25-H.P. equipped with the traditional, rectangular cooling tower in place of the round stack and an under-frame, chain-driven, water-circulation pump in place of the over-frame, flat belt-driven pump.

Certain Mogul tractors had a unique differential lock-up provided on the left drive wheel. A cast lug keyed to the end of the axle could be bolted to the cast hub of the drive wheel through a hole provided in the hub. If the tractor mired down and spun out, it would have been helpful to have an assistant who could help get the bolt holes lined up and the bolt shoved in place. Convenient or not, this was a useful feature when required.

The Continuing Battle

Competition between the individuals who came from the Deering side of the Company and those who came from the McCormick side of the Company before the merger continued for decades — it even showed up

The Mogul 45-H.P. was one of the first tractors produced at the Tractor Works in 1911. It was later upgraded to the Mogul 30-60-H.P. The Grand Prize was awarded the Mogul 30-60-H.P. at the San Francisco Exposition in 1915 and IHC recorded the success with a color illustration in a large catalog.

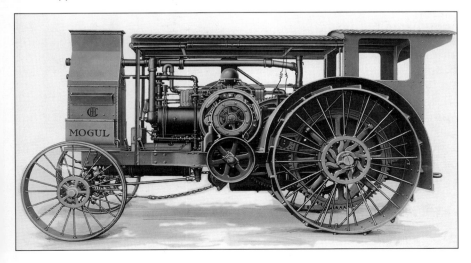

This is a rate photo of the Steward tractor, Mr. Steward came to the Deering Company with the Marsh Harvester acquisition. He must have had considerable stature within the Deering part of IHC to have gained enough support for them to build 20 of these prototype tractors in 1913. For drawbar work the tractor operated in the reverse direction.

in tractor designing. During 1913, Deering Works produced 10 of the lightweight Steward tractors and two Waite tractors. This was no doubt, in part, a response to the small, highly successful Bull tractor introduced by the Bull Traction Machine Company of Minneapolis, Minnesota. Photos of the Steward, "I.H.C. Light Tractor" reveal the engine mounted over the drive wheels and a long wheelbase that provided room for attaching a three-furrow moldboard plow under the frame. This geometry transferred part of the plow draft to the drive axle for improved traction. Decades later the concept of weight transfer found a more practical application in the three-point hitch, Fast Hitch, and Snap Coupler among others. The guide wheels and operator were in the rear. However, for drawbar work the tractor operated in the opposite direction and the operator was repositioned directly behind the drive wheels. The Deering people didn't get into the tractor business — their "friends" at Tractor Works had the upper hand. However, they did help establish the need for a lightweight tractor and promoted the bi-directional tractor concept that would dominate early Farmall experimental work.

A fascinating 1912 photo of a Milwaukee Works-developed product shows a clean looking, conventional design, four-wheel tractor. The 12-22-horsepower tractor engine had four horizontal cylinders positioned

with the crankshaft at right angles to the tractor axles. The valves were in a vertical position. It is doubtful that more than this one prototype was ever built. During this period there were about 100 firms experimenting with building tractors and they represented a wide range of design approaches; the best configuration was yet to be determined. The various components of the IHC organization were anxious to have their input to the direction the Company should take in tractor development.

Tractor Works Experimental Department developed the Mogul 20-40-H.P. tractor. The four-cylinder, horizontal engine mounted directly to the transmission case and the assembly formed the frame of the tractor. Ten of these tractors were produced from 1914 to 1915. Though not a commercial success, the configuration did represent the frameless design that would be incorporated in many future tractors.

The Growing Mogul Line

The next regular production additions to the Mogul line in 1913 were the Mogul 15-30-H.P. and Mogul 12-25-H.P. tractors. The Mogul 15-30-H.P. was an increased horsepower version of the Mogul 10-20-H.P. oil tractor. Each had make-and-break ignition, batteries to start, gear-driven magneto to run, and exhaust gas induced draft cooling tower. The chassis had a one-speed, double gear-drive forward, friction-reverse

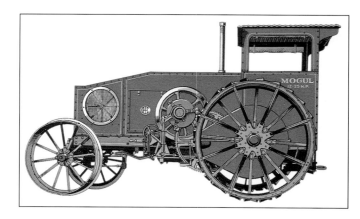

The new totally-enclosed engine compartment sets this unit apart from other IHC tractors of the time. Spring-mounted, automobile-type steering of the Mogul 12-25-H.P. was described as enabling "the operator to manipulate the tractor to the utmost nicety." (Underline is by the author.)

End views of the Mogul 12-25-H.P. oil tractor illustrate the trim design of this tractor and its automotive-type steering. Standard cab equipment included "side and rear curtains to protect the operator in bad weather." A removable seat was provided as standard.

install a bow protector on the front of the tractor for orchard use was strongly promoted. This lightweight Mogul 12-25-H.P. weighed "only" 10,000 pounds and in 1915 sold for $1,350 on 60- x 12-inch wide wheels. By enclosing all of the working parts, this design represented a functional approach to improved styling.

transmission. There were differences in front and rear wheels and overall tractor dimensions. Only 85 units of the Mogul 10-20-H.P. version were produced. The Mogul 15-30-H.P. essentially replaced the Mogul 10-20-H.P. in 1913 and 527 units were shipped over a three-year period ending in 1915.

The Mogul 12-25-H.P. tractor was quite different from the other Mogul family. The two-cylinder opposed oil-burning engine had two mixers, one for each cylinder, and jump-spark ignition. An auto/truck-type radiator and plunger-type circulating pump met the cooling needs. Steel gears of the two-speed, sliding-gear transmission ran in oil. A fully shielded, adjustable, double-chain drive conveyed power to the rear axle and eliminated the alignment problems associated with gear drives. The ability to remove the steel cab and

Special tire equipment offered for the Mogul 8-16-, 12-25-, 15-30-, and 30-60-H.P. tractors in 1915 included:

Regular 1-3/4-inch high, angled, side bar lug
Special lug — For the large tractors only — with
    center bar and double the number of side bars
Road lug with 4-3/8-inch wide flat face
Sand lug with 3-7/8-inch wide chisel point,
    3-7/8 inch high
Ice lug with 3-1/2-inch high cone shape

Mogul tractors of the period were equipped with cast lugs attached to a rolled steel tire. A system of buttons on the back of each style of full-width lug fit into the large part of a button hole punched in the face of the steel tire. Installed over the large holes, lugs were pushed back so the button locked in the small slotted part of the hole. The last lug was bolted in place to prevent the remaining lugs from moving out of position. The patented

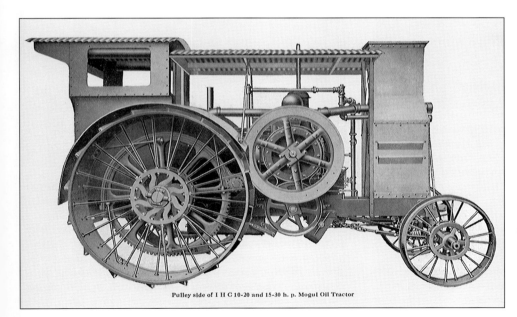

Pulley side of I H C 10-20 and 15-30 h. p. Mogul Oil Tractor

The Mogul 10-20-H.P. and 15-30-H.P. oil tractors are essentially the same except for horsepower. A single illustration is used for both and the general description is the same.

The 1916 Dallas, Texas show was a great place to demonstrate the features of this attractively styled Mogul 12-25-H.P. oil tractor including its 4-mph road speed. The friction drive, hand-crank starter is clearly visible under the flywheel. This "modern" tractor may seem crude by today's standards, but look at the state-of-the-art automobile in the background.

lug-mounting system was intended to make it easy to change the style of lug. Two rows of round holes were provided in each tire for adding special sand lugs or ice lugs. A special angle lug that extended beyond the rim could be purchased for the Mogul 8-16-H.P. tractor. This popular, and likely necessary lug, is shown in many Mogul 8-16-H.P. photos.

In spite of the new products, economics and the prospect of U.S. involvement in World War I brought lower Mogul production in 1913 and 1914. A major change in IHC tractors was about to take place with the pilot run of 20 single-cylinder Mogul 8-16-H.P. tractors in 1914. Tractor Works produced over 13,000 of these lightweight (4,920 pounds) low-cost tractors the following two years to meet the demand generated by the war. The tractor had two distinguishing features: First

The plow is direct connected to the tractor drawbar and can be raised or lowered by the operator to adjust plowing depth or to raise the plow out of the ground. This "semi-mounted" plow forecasts the time when hydraulic-controlled tractor hitches would make mounted and semi-mounted plows virtually the only type in use. This early Mogul 8-16-H.P. outfit has no stack on the hopper cooling system and no air strainer; it may have been an engineering test tractor since it was plowing close to a residential area. The archives have many photos of this Mogul 8-16-H.P. and three-furrow plow; however, they are marked, "Do not use, on account of three-bottom plow." Twenty-five percent more drawbar horsepower made the Mogul 10-20-H.P. a true three-bottom tractor.

This photo of a late model Mogul 8-16-H.P., after 1916, has the following note on the back, "IHC Tractor No.19 driven by T. F. Fuller loaned to the Chicago (Land) Bureau by IHC." The underlined word is not clear on the photo but could be either Land or Park. A reasonable guess would be the tractor is plowing small garden plots in Chicago to aid in the war effort. The sharp turning ability of the steering system design (as shown here) had real appeal to farmers with small fields and narrow head lands.

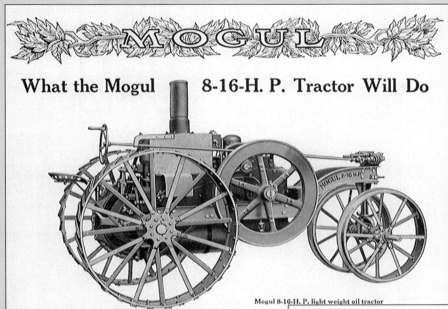

Mogul 8-16-H. P. light weight oil tractor

Literature stressed the fact that, "The rear wheels carry only 3,500 pounds, and with extension tires the weight per square inch on the ground is 10 pounds, which is approximately only half the weight (per square inch) of the average horse." What could this lightweight tractor do? The Mogul 8-16-H.P. could plow, work orchards, pull two binders, grade roads, as well as power threshers, hay balers, or silo fillers. There were attractive field scenes in the literature to prove it.

The Mogul 8-16-H.P. oil tractor power plant was described as, "Four cycle, single cylinder, slow speed oil burning engine of extremely simple construction." The headline read, "Most Power for Weight and Money Ever Offered."

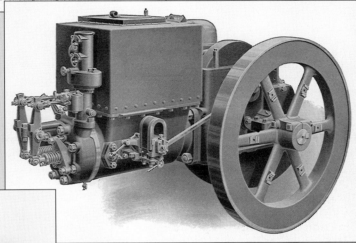

The 1915 literature for the Mogul 8-16-H.P. oil tractor asked, "Could there be anything more convenient than this tractor? Spring seat with foot rest on right side, giving operator a clear view of furrow, with steering wheel directly in front, speed levers and mixer within easy reach."

Described as a, "Simple, Easy to Operate, Two-Speed, Many Purpose Small Farm Tractor." This two-speed, sliding-gear transmission, increased horsepower version of the Mogul 8-16-H.P. was a worthy successor.

was the 35-gallon water-filled hopper for engine cooling that made it closely related to the thousands of smaller hopper-cooled engines on farms across the country. Second was the Mogul 8-16-H.P. planetary transmission. Introduction of a planetary transmission into an IHC tractor required extensive explanation in company literature. It was frequently described as the "simplest type of transmission that can be used." The transmission provided a 2-mph forward speed and a slower reverse.

The Mogul 8-16-H.P. would evolve into the higher horsepower Mogul 10-20-H.P. with two-speed sliding gear transmission in place of the planetary transmission. It never hit the high production levels of the Mogul 8-16-H.P. it replaced because of timing in the marketplace and the advent of two significantly superior products in this horsepower class from IHC. Production ended for the Mogul 10-20-H.P. in 1919 and with it the nine-year reign of the Mogul trade name came to an end.

International Harvester located, purchased, and restored a Mogul 8-16-H.P. tractor. The unit was used at the Hinsdale Research Farm as part of a new product introduction.

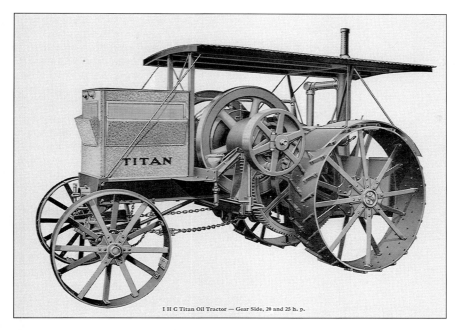

I H C Titan Oil Tractor — Gear Side, 20 and 25 h. p.

Powered by the IHC "Famous" single-cylinder engine with special oil mixer, the Titan Type "D" tractors were both simple and rugged. Eight-inch steel channels were the basis of the 20-horsepower frame while 10-inch channels were used for the 25-horsepower frame. The highly recognizable, rectangular evaporative water cooler box made it easy to identify these early Titan tractors. The slow speed — 240 to 290 rpm — engine had an 8-3/4-inch bore x 15-inch stroke for the Titan 20-H.P. model. The bore was increased to 10-inches for the Titan 25-H.P. version.

sales leader and restored Tractor Works to number one.

IHC Titan 20-H.P. and 25-H.P. tractors were similar except for horsepower and width of wheel face; they were advertised in the same booklet. Literature covered every component of the IHC Famous engine in great detail including the kind of material used and the degree of finish achieved. Simplicity and ease of operation was always stressed. One statement in the 1913 booklet is especially interesting, "All the parts are numbered and are easily removed, so by giving these numbers, duplicate parts guaranteed to fit as accurately as the originals can be quickly obtained." Since parts books of that day were a far cry from today's exploded-view references, such a system would have been a real service.

Reference to "duplicate parts, quickly obtained" is quite germane because of how IHC used the strength of its dealer organization and branch house network against smaller, less established competitors.

The Tractor Works Mogul 45-H.P. tractor had a two-cylinder, horizontal opposed engine that made the tractor 228 inches long. The more compact Milwaukee-built Titan 45-H.P. and later Titan 30-60-H.P. tractors had horizontal engines with the two cylinders side by

Milwaukee Works and Titan

Milwaukee Works was well established as a stationary and portable engine manufacturer and supplier of engines for IHC's Upper Sandusky and Akron, Ohio tractor plants when they built their first 100 tractors in 1908. The Titan trade name was introduced in 1910 with 20-, 25-, and 45-horsepower sizes of Type "D" tractors. The following year saw over 1,000 of the Titan 25-H.P. Type "D" model produced. No Titan tractor model would come close to this kind of volume until five years later when the flagship of the Milwaukee line, the Titan 10-20-H.P. two-cylinder model, would hit 2,248 units in the first full year of production in 1916. Popularity of the Titan 10-20-H.P. kept Milwaukee Works the IHC tractor volume leader from 1917 until 1921 when the success of the International 8-16, four-cylinder vertical, became the Company's tractor

I H C Titan 45 h. p. Oil Tractor, gear side

This IHC Titan 45-H.P. oil tractor engine had a gear-driven Bosh magneto and fly ball governor. The convenient gasoline and fuel oil filler funnels with lids and brass gauge strainers were located under the letter "N" in the name Titan. The engine could burn kerosene, distillate, solar oil, gasoline, or naphtha.

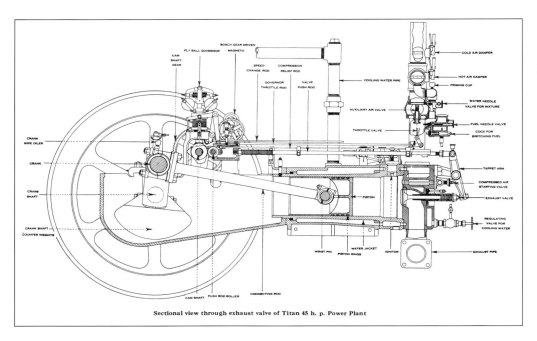

FLY BALL GOVERNOR
CAM SHAFT GEAR
BOSCH GEAR DRIVEN MAGNETO
SPEED CHANGE ROD
COMPRESSION RELIEF ROD
GOVERNOR THROTTLE ROD
VALVE PUSH ROD
COLD AIR DAMPER
HOT AIR DAMPER
COOLING WATER PIPE
PRIMING CUP
WATER NEEDLE VALVE FOR MIXTURE
AUXILIARY AIR VALVE
FUEL NEEDLE VALVE
THROTTLE VALVE
COCK FOR SWITCHING FUEL
CRANK WIPE OILER
CRANK
CRANE SHAFT
CRANK SHAFT COUNTER WEIGHTS
PISTON
TAPPET ARM
COMPRESSED AIR STARTING VALVE
EXHAUST VALVE
REGULATING VALVE FOR COOLING WATER
WRIST PIN
WATER JACKET
PISTON RINGS
IGNITOR
EXHAUST PIPE
CAM SHAFT
PUSH ROD ROLLER
CONNECTING ROD

Sectional view through exhaust valve of Titan 45 h. p. Power Plant

The removable, wet cylinder liner can be seen in this IHC 45-horsepower Titan oil tractor power plant cross section. This large, two-cylinder engine was started with compressed air; the starting valve was located just above the exhaust valve. The crank end of the connecting rod was lubricated by a wipe oiler supplied from the mechanical 10-feed oiler.

were for the compressed air starting system; the air supply tank was between the frame rails directly over the front axle. Gasoline and fuel oil filler funnels with lids and brass gauze strainers were at waist high level for easy filling.

IHC Titan 20-H.P. and 25-H.P. convertible, kerosene, gasoline, road-roller tractors were modified basic Titan 20-H.P. and 25-H.P. tractors. They were single-cylinder, single-speed, gear-drive tractors developed for this special application. The standard front truck was replaced with a bolt-on, frame-extension arch with pivot for the four-segment front roller. Slip-over, full-width, tire bands converted the standard rear drive

side; that made them only 192 inches long. The resulting 3-foot shorter Titan with auto/truck steering was a better balanced and more maneuverable tractor. The original Titan 45-H.P. tractor developed in 1908 through 1909 had a progressive engine design that incorporated removable cylinder sleeves and a tight crankcase with transfer port so crankcase compression could be used to obtain greater cylinder efficiency. The mixer had a throttling governor and burned kerosene. Directly after this tractor was demonstrated at Winnipeg in 1909, the decision was made to convert it back to the simpler, more common, hit-and-miss governor system.

When the IHC Titan 45-H.P. oil tractor went into production it had a two-cylinder horizontal, 9-inch bore x 14-inch stroke, 355-rpm, 45-horsepower engine. This tractor was the largest Titan when it was introduced in 1911. The "make-and-break" ignition and "hit-and-miss" governor along with pump and tank cooling made this tractor easy to understand and operate. Simplicity was important as farmers who had little experience with machinery began to replace their horses with tractors. The fully enclosed engine compartment had a removable metal cover. Small pipes at the front of the tractor

The open doors on the front of the tractor cooling box on this IHC Titan 45-H.P. tractor show the ready access to the "self-starting devise." The single-cylinder, 1-horsepower, air-cooled engine and air compressor combination supplied an air storage tank located under the frame, over the front axle. For starting, compressed air was piped to the left-side cylinder through an automatically operated valve. Note the rugged, narrow tread, automobile-steer front end in this 1913 graphic. The front wheels were equipped with extension tires.

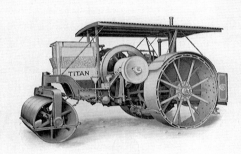

IHC TITAN

KEROSENE-GASOLINE

20 AND 25-HORSE POWER CONVERTIBLE ROAD ROLLER-TRACTORS

INTERNATIONAL HARVESTER COMPANY OF AMERICA
(INCORPORATED)

CHICAGO   U S A

Basic Titan 20- and 25-horse-power, single-cylinder, single-speed, gear-drive tractors were modified for this application.

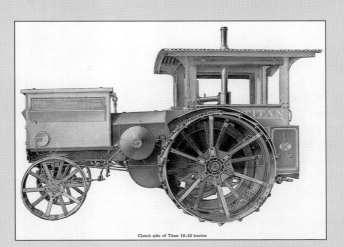

Clutch side of Titan 18-35 tractor

This clutch-side graphic shows the full sheet-metal enclosure of the engine compartment, clutch, and counter-shaft gear on this Titan 18-35-H.P. oil tractor. The large model name, Titan, striping and IHC logo add a touch of class. Rear drive wheels are quipped with 10-inch extension tires that bolt to the wheel hub and the tire. Drive wheel and extension both are reinforced on the edges by small channels bent in and riveted on the edge.

IHC TITAN OIL TRACTORS

Construction of Titan 18-35-H. P. Oil Tractor

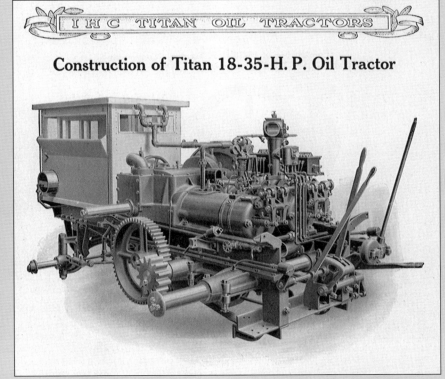

This 1915 graphic clearly shows the cast-iron, dust-tight crankcase of the Milwaukee built engine. The enclosure was a "new and exclusive feature." A graphic like this helped convey the rugged construction of IHC engines and frames along with the size of bearings, shafts, and gears. It also illustrated the complicated collection of parts and plumbing of such a "modern" tractor engine.

wheels to rollers. The Titan 25-H.P. convertible road roller weighed over 28,000 pounds. Farm-type front trucks could be bolted on in place of the roller for hauling or field use. The effort to expand the market with a dual purpose machine ended like most similar efforts, not too successful. After three years, only 80 were built.

Three interesting tractor projects occurred at the Milwaukee Works in 1912. First, was the start of the Titan 20-H.P. and 25-H.P. convertible road-roller project. Second, they built one Titan 30-H.P. Type "D" tractor that was never put into production. Third, two prepro- duction Titan 18-35-H.P. Type "D" tractors were assem- bled and were followed by almost 250 more tractors over the following three years of production.

The problem of tractor engines and dirt was just being recognized; so, the Titan 18-35-H.P. "power plant with cast-iron, dust-tight, crankcase for protecting the piston and cylinders, crankshaft, etc. from dust" was an important advancement. Throttle governor, two- speed transmission, and auto-type steering added to the list of improvements.

Even though the Titan 18-35-H.P. had 10 less belt horsepower than the top-of-the-line Titan 45-H.P., it was still a large tractor. Two years after the last one was built, IHC no longer built a tractor over 30 horsepower; it was a transition tractor.

The Milwaukee Work's Titan 45-H.P. tractor was introduced in 1910 and remained the horsepower leader until 1915 when a new mixer and other changes increased its rating from 45 to 60 horsepower even though it kept the 9-inch bore x 14-inch stroke and 355 rated rpm. Starting was changed from compressed air to a 1-horsepower, air-cooled gasoline starting engine. Once the little engine was started, its friction drive wheel was engaged to drive the main engine flywheel by means of a lever-operated eccentric bearing. Ignition was still "make-and-break" with bat- teries to start and a gear-driven magneto to run. The highly recognizable, large rectangular Titan evapora- tive cooler box remained a part of the new tractor. A pair of truss rods appeared under the main frame. The Titan 45-H.P. now became the Titan 30-60-H.P. tractor. The next big change for the Titan 30-60-H.P. oil tractor was replacement of the evaporative cooling system with a fan-cooled, automotive-type radiator and cen- trifugal circulating pump.

Export markets were good for IHC. To help promote the Titan 12-25-H.P. four-cylinder, 18-25-H.P. twin- cylinder, and 30-60-H.P. twin-cylinder, an advertising headline stated, "Around the World with the Titan Tractor" and the spread showed scenes from, "Germany, Russia, Canada, Porto [sic] Rico, Cuba, Argentina, Australia, Turkestan, Roumania [sic],

The intent tractor operator was doing a quality job of plowing with the Titan 18-35-H.P. oil tractor and five-furrow plow. The intake air heater jacket around the exhaust pipe is clearly seen in the front left corner of the cab. The good plowing indicates the tractor was up to full power; so, the intake air must have been warmed just right to vaporize the kerosene fuel and deliver maximum output.

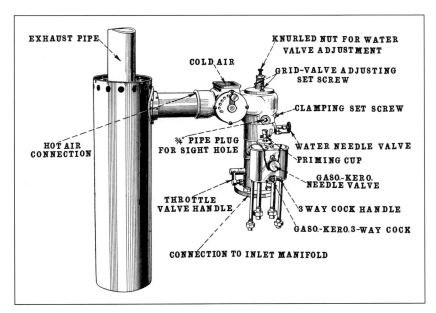

EXHAUST PIPE

COLD AIR

KNURLED NUT FOR WATER VALVE ADJUSTMENT

GRID-VALVE ADJUSTING SET SCREW

CLAMPING SET SCREW

HOT AIR CONNECTION

¾" PIPE PLUG FOR SIGHT HOLE

WATER NEEDLE VALVE

PRIMING CUP

GASO.-KERO. NEEDLE VALVE

THROTTLE VALVE HANDLE

3 WAY COCK HANDLE

GASO.-KERO.3-WAY COCK

CONNECTION TO INLET MANIFOLD

"One of the strong features of the mixer is the perfect control of the air supply to the mixer and the automatic supplying of water when operating on low grade fuels." The Titan 30-60-H.P. Oil Tractor Kerosene Mixer instructions continued with these statements, "By means of the knurled nut at the top of the grid valve, adjustments can be made for controlling the water inlet valve. The fuel cup is of our standard two-compartment type with a throw-over valve between the cups thus allowing instantaneous change from one fuel to the other." It noted that, "the two set screws on top of the mixer are for close adjustment of the air inlet grid valve. These should be adjusted as to allow the engine to run under no load <u>without racing, giving muffler shots, or backfiring</u>." (Underline is by the author.)

France and selected states in the United States." The "confident" closing banner read, "Titan Tractors are used in every Civilized Country." I believe there were a few countries in 1915 that might not agree. But, this was advertising in the early part of the Twentieth Century.

Help for Cold Climate Titan 30-60 H.P. Owners

Instructions for starting and operating the Titan 30-60-H.P. kerosene twin-cylinder tractors includes the following cold climate advise in the 1916 owner's booklet:

"In the Northwest or other cold climates where starting is difficult, heating the cylinder has been found to greatly overcome this trouble. The safest way to warm the cylinder is by the use of hot water, which may be done in the following manner:

Close the globe valves and open the drain cocks under the cylinder heads; remove plug at top of large water pipe leading from the cylinders to the cooling tank; pour two or more pails of hot water through this pipe and allow first pailful to run out of drain cock. The second pailful may be allowed to stand in the cylinder jackets some minutes, or until the cold iron has taken up most of the heat of the water. The engine should then be started easily.

The object of closing the globe valves under the cylinder heads during this heating up, is to keep the water out of the pipe leading to the pump to avoid freezing."

Comment: It's easy to forget how "simple" and convenient things were in the good old days.

Operators of a big Titan oil tractor, or most other tractors at that time, needed to use their eyes, ears, and sense of feel to adjust the engines for peak performance. By watching the color of the exhaust, listening to the sound of the power stroke, and responding to vibrations good or bad, the skilled person could achieve maximum engine performance and avoid possible engine damage from detonation. With the introduction of the throttle governor for kerosene mixers, new "automatic" features were added that made tractor operation less of an art. It was a step in the right direction, but there was a long way to go before engines essentially controlled themselves.

The Titan 12-25-H.P. oil tractor had a four-cylinder, horizontal, L-head engine with enclosed dust-tight crankcase. The cylinder heads were cast in pairs and could be removed without disturbing other parts, "so valve service was easy." Ignition was jump spark (spark plug) type with power from a gear-driven, impulse magneto, so starting batteries were eliminated. Engine lubrication was by a new design automatic, force-fed oiler with 12 feeds. The valveless, mechanical oiler could force feed oil at "2,000 psi at any temperature." The belt pulley friction clutch was controlled by a lever in the cab. A belt-driven pump circulated cooling water through the forward-facing, fan-cooled, vertical-tube radiator. All of these features plus a short wheel base and automobile-type steering made this a truly innovative new tractor. The 12-25-H.P. rating was about the only thing that related this tractor to its single-cylinder Titan Type "D" predecessor.

Lighting for night plowing or hauling was one of the few options available. A kerosene headlight was offered that could be mounted on the right front corner of the cab (probably marginal at best). On the other

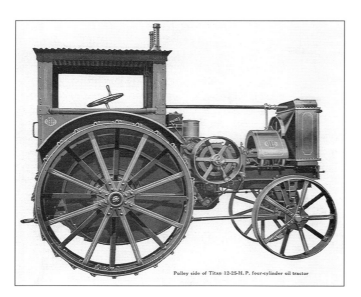

Pulley side of Titan 12-25-H.P. four-cylinder oil tractor

Rated at less than half the horsepower of the big Titan 30-60-H.P., the Titan 12-25-H.P. oil tractor did share a family resemblance. The four-cylinder, 575-rpm, horizontal, jump-spark ignition engine and two-speed transmission made it totally different from the 335-rpm, two-cylinder horizontal, "make-and-break" ignition, single-speed transmission of its Titan big brother.

Extension tires for increasing flotation under wet conditions were offered to match the particular drive wheel tire. Optional slip-over tires were available for traveling over paved roads or for equipping tractors that would be used only for belt work.

The almost universal option was the IHC friction clutch pulley that bolted directly to the engine flywheel. The three-shoe clutch could be engaged by pushing in on the hand wheel or disengaged by pulling out on the hand wheel. The assembly was available in a range of sizes to match engine horsepower, rpm of the engine, and rpm requirements of the machine being driven.

Development of the Titan 12-25-H.P. started two years before the conservative first production of 13 in 1914. Field results must have been good because Milwaukee Works produced 196 the following year. The four-cylinder, horizontal, L-head 12-25-H.P. engine was converted to value-in-head, the horsepower was increased and the resulting tractor was named the Titan 15-30-H.P. Production of 511 tractors in 1916 launched the new Titan 15-30-H.P. kerosene tractor.

hand, an optional acetylene gas headlight was available for the Titan 18-35-H.P. and 30-60-H.P. tractors that would surely have been a big improvement. The gas generator used for this headlight was "the same as the IHC motor truck generator that had been used for many years with great success."

The two-speed forward and one-speed reverse transmission had a dust tight case, and all gears and the differential ran in oil. Bearings, however, were outside the case and lubricated from a central, mechanical, force-feed oiler that served only the transmission. What appears to be excessive shaft overhang on the output shaft was not a problem; frame-mounted bearings next to the small sprockets supported the transmission and carried the load.

Titan 12-25-H.P. tractor rear axle — Because the rear axle was chain driven, it could be spring mounted and was said to be, "built like a Pullman car." The angle iron and hook bolt chain take-up device shipped with each tractor is shown installed. Steel spacer plates positioned the rear-axle bearing in the guide. Plates were shifted rear to front, or vice versa, to set proper chain tension. Drive chains were to be cleaned with gasoline once or twice each plowing season and then placed in hot tallow until the chain was warm and tallow had penetrated each joint. Oil from the crank-case drain was piped to each chain.

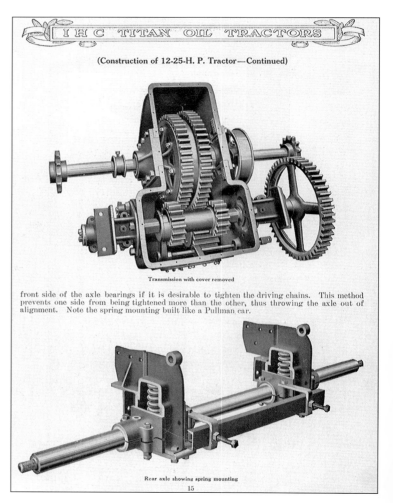

IHC TITAN OIL TRACTORS

(Construction of 12-25-H. P. Tractor—Continued)

Transmission with cover removed

front side of the axle bearings if it is desirable to tighten the driving chains. This method prevents one side from being tightened more than the other, thus throwing the axle out of alignment. Note the spring mounting built like a Pullman car.

Rear axle showing spring mounting

15

The clean, carefully lined tractor in the photo displays a large International Harvester Titan 15-30-H.P. burning kerosene sign. It must have been prepared for a parade, sales promotion, or management review. The building in the background is probably Milwaukee Works.

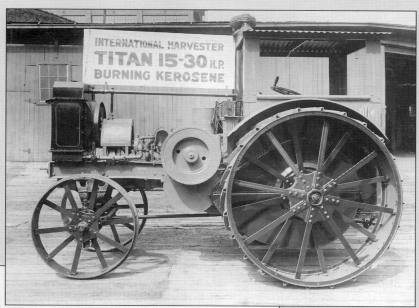

Demonstrations were a popular way to sell IHC tractors. Perhaps the second person in the cab is the prospective customer for this four-cylinder, Titan 12-25-H.P. oil tractor.

This new "EC" version of the Titan 15-30-H.P. tractor reflects a need to simplify and reduce cost. The bevel-gear drive for the radiator fan has been replaced by a direct-drive belt system. Further simplification and cost reduction resulted in production without a cab. Other changes included tall intake and exhaust pipes

To promote winning the San Francisco Exposition Grand Prize in 1915 with the Titan 15-30-H.P. tractor, a large, colored, advertising print was circulated. The caption read, "Four-Cylinder Power Plant — Operates on Kerosene — All Working Parts Enclosed — Automatically Oiled — High Tension Magneto — No Batteries." The brief caption said it all. This was truly a new kind of Titan tractor.

For 1917 the Titan 15-30-H.P. kerosene tractor became the International 15-30 kerosene tractor. The graphic on the front of *Instructions for Operating* was the same as the Titan model but the Titan name was gone. To balance the work load, two-thirds of International 15-30 production was shifted to Tractor Works in 1918. The following year, all production for this tractor was at Tractor Works and continued there until the last production in 1921.

Big Markets and A Little Titan

When Milwaukee Works-built tractors acquired the trade name Titan in 1910, the label was very appropriate. The age of the big tractor was just beginning, and with a large Type "D" tractor rated at 45 horsepower at the top of the line, to call these tractors Giant or Titan was both descriptive and effective. However, by 1915 when the little Titan 10-20-H.P. tractor was introduced, IHC and the industry had recognized the need for smaller, lighter, more maneuverable tractors in the under 20-horsepower class. In fact, the Mogul 8-16-H.P. tractor, introduced the year before, was now the Tractor Works volume

The caption read, "Look Bill, What Dad Bought for You." As the little song says, "How you gon'na keep 'em down on the farm, after they've seen Paree?" IHC took the approach that a new tractor would be one of the best answers.

leader with over 5,000 produced. Production of the Titan 30-60-H.P. tractor ended in 1917 and with it the end of IHC tractors over 30 horsepower for more than a decade and a half.

Production of U.S.-built tractors took off in 1918 in response to the demands of World War I, and over 132,000 were produced by U.S. manufacturers. The Titan 10-20-H.P. was positioned just right and 17,675 were manufactured that year. Production of Titan 10-20-H.P. tractors alone were 250 percent more than total production at Tractor Works. No single IHC model of tractor had ever been close to such high volume. These impressive production figures continued through 1920 with record production of 21,503 Titan 10-20-H.P. tractors. During the 1915 to 1922 production run, Milwaukee Works produced 78,363 of these very popular Titan tractors.

The October 1918 issue of *Tractor Farming* devoted many columns to the important role IHC tractors played in the war effort at home and overseas. The Titan 10-20-H.P. kerosene tractor was the featured contributor. A clever cartoon carried the title, "New Traffic Cop on the Job;" a sign board stated, "Pershing needs the gas, don't waste it, save it, USE KEROSENE;" the caption

This innovative little tractor, the Titan 10-20-H.P., had a two-cylinder horizontal, valve-in-head engine with gear-driven high tension magneto for jump-spark ignition. The mixer was designed so water was admitted in proportion to the air intake flow. Automotive-type steering had enclosed worm and sector drive coupled with a narrow tread front axle for "easy," sharp turning capability. The closed cooling system used a steam impulse, thermosiphon system to circulate the water. Transmission and differential ran in oil. Final drive was by two exposed chains to rear drive wheels on a dead axle.

This photo (of tractor serial number TV 39712) is from a series of photos taken near the factory. The tractor is equipped with fenders that extend down to the operator's platform. That feature, along with a water bath air cleaner, carburetor, and a 15 percent increase in engine rpm that increased travel speed the same amount, were incorporated in the later TY Series Titan 10-20-H.P. tractors.

read, "On gasless Sundays, autos, trucks and most tractors are held up by Uncle Sam, while a Titan gets the right of way — it burns kerosene."

A column headed, "The Titan was a Pershing Patriot," relates how during World War I a clever War Savings Stamp (W.S.S.) salesman got a farmer to calculate a $132.25 savings from using his Titan kerosene tractor versus one that burned the more expensive gasoline. The W.S.S. salesman sold the farmer that

amount of War Savings Stamps and told him he was helping General Pershing by saving gasoline needed for the war. A good salesman takes any advantage he can get!

Issue after issue of *Tractor Farming* during 1918 and 1919 were filled with "reasons" to buy a kerosene tractor and help the war effort. After the armistice, the reasoning changed. Farmers were told that to keep sons on the farm when they returned from the army, the farm should have modern tractor equipment. After operating tractors and engine-powered equipment in the army, their sons would likely have no interest in staying on the farm and driving a team of horses or mules. The economic value of a tractor compared to horses was given as another reason farmers should purchase a tractor. The cost savings were essential if they expected to survive the post-war decline in commodity prices.

The post-war depression hit in 1921 and U.S. tractor production dropped to one-third of the prior year. To make things worse for IHC, the very low-priced Fordson tractor accounted for about half of that seriously depressed market. That year International 8-16 tractor production exceeded the little Milwaukee Works Titan 10-20-H.P. for the first time. Titan 10-20-H.P. production ended in 1922.

Tractor Price Wars

The massive drop in the 1921 U.S. tractor market was devastating for all manufacturers, especially the smaller firms. Rather than take necessary cuts in production, the Ford Motor Company cut the price

The International Harvester archives contain literally thousands of motion picture reels, black and white and color, silent and sound, along with today's video format. The Company was a leader in using movies for marketing and for training. The service was called the Chart, Slide and Reel Division. Today, we would call the man with the pencil in this scene a product manager; the job hasn't changed. As in this photo, it's essential to get everything perfect so nothing detracts from the product or the message. At the same time, producer/directors and camera men with "wonderful" creative ideas must be kept focused on communicating to prospective farmer purchasers.

This Watertown, Wisconsin scene of a Titan 10-20-H.P. kerosene tractor and New Racine 24x40 thresher reminds us of the importance of belt-power applications. This late model Titan 10-20-H.P. kerosene tractor had a carburetor and water air cleaner.

(already low) of its Fordson tractor by $165 to $625. In response, IHC made mid-year cuts as follows:

Titan 10-20-H.P. reduced from $1,200 to $900
International 8-16 reduced from $1,150 to $900
International 15-30 reduced from $2,300 to $1,750

In spite of the depressed U.S. market and falling exports, IHC management had the courage and foresight to release to manufacturing the new 10-20 for production two years later. This tractor was similar in design to the new International 15-30 that had just started production with 199 units. These were totally new, four-wheel tractors that would become the McCormick-Deering 15-30 and 10-20 in 1923 and set a new standard for the industry.

Not satisfied with 50 percent of the U.S. market, Ford cut the price again in 1922 by $230 and the price of a Fordson tractor became $395. It would appear this price was well below cost and some observers suggest the strategy was to use the financial resources of the Ford Motor Company as a way for Henry Ford personally to get at his old nemesis — the senior International Harvester Company management.

To counter the second Ford price cut, IHC took the lead and immediately lowered the International 8-16 the same amount as Ford to a new price of $670. The Titan 10-20-H.P. price was reduced $200 for a final price of $700. Since these prices were still substantially higher than that for a Fordson tractor, IHC took advantage of their position as an implement manufacturer and offered a free two-furrow P&O plow with the purchase of an International 8-16 tractor and a free

International 8-16 $670

With 2-bottom
Plow Free

(Tractor and Plow
f. o. b. Chicago)

Per terms announced
Feb. 3, 1922

Free Plow Offer Extended to May 20 to Offset Late Spring Season

HEAVY rains, cold weather, and a tardy spring have delayed tillage and planting. **Now** you must put extra power and help to work to make up for lost time. Even though you did not intend buying a tractor this spring, it is probable you will find in the International 8-16 tractor plowing outfit the answer to your big problem.

The Harvester Company's Free Plow Offer was originally advertised to close on May 1, as that is ordinarily the end of the heavy tillage season. But after weeks of delay thousands of acres remain untilled, and an unexpected need has developed for International tractor power.

For this reason the Harvester Company has instructed us to extend the Free Plow Offer until May 20. Until that date you can buy an International 8-16 tractor from us at the present low price, and you will receive free a P & O 2-bottom plow, or a tractor disk harrow, as outlined in the original Free Plow Offer announced February 3, 1922.

Your best way out of the present difficulty is good tractor power. Come in and see us about an International. Every hour saved now means dollars at harvest time. Get your International now, and you will benefit from the extended Free Plow Offer.

The second time prices were drastically cut on the Fordson tractor, IHC responded with a similar reduction in the International 8-16. But, this time they added the free plow program. A similar price reduction and free plow program was offered on the Titan 10-20-H.P. tractor.

three-furrow plow with the purchase of a Titan 10-20-H.P. tractor. The Harvester Company told their dealers, "This price cut and special offer uncovered a million new prospects over night! The barrier is down! The time is short! Get the orders!"

Massive price cuts by the tractor manufacturers coupled with problem weather in the spring of 1922 and prospects for better commodity prices, all combined to generate a greatly improved market for tractors. As a result, the excessive tractor inventories built up after the war quickly disappeared and production gradually expanded. Ford built 101,898 tractors and still dominated the market in 1923 with a 76-percent market share. Since IHC got 9 percent of the market, the remaining 73 tractor manufacturers had to divide up the remaining 15 percent; these were still tough times in the tractor business.

IHC published a booklet titled, *Internal Combustion Engines and Tractors* in 1918. Without naming the brand, it describes the heating, wear, and inefficiency of Fordson's worm-gear transmission. This design shortcoming and other problems finally began to take

its toll; Fordson sales fell from the 1923 peak and by 1928 Ford stopped tractor production.

One factor that kept the Titan 10-20-H.P. viable during the tough post-war years was continued improvement. The metal canister air cleaner filled with combed lambs wool was replaced with a more efficient and easier to correctly service water-bath air cleaner. Another significant change was replacement of the kerosene mixer with a modern carburetor to automatically meter the correct proportion of kerosene fuel and water, depending on load.

Automobiles, Trucks, and Tractors

The automobile and the motor truck were making a major impact on American transportation by 1917. Likewise, the tractor was beginning to change the way America farmed. Technical progress taking place in these two industries was represented by the Society of Automotive Engineers (SAE) and the Society of Tractor Engineers. Recognizing their many areas of common interest, the two organizations combined in 1917;

International 8-16 kerosene tractor, an open invitation — This center section of a two-page advertisement appeared in the heat of the price war with the Fordson tractor. It listed "37 jobs Internationals are doing for others." Detail graphics and descriptions of nine of these International 8-16 jobs surrounded the center photo. Two statements in the list of reasons why it does its work so well are of particular interest:
"BOTH REAR wheels are drive wheels." This would be a direct reference to the Big and Little Bull tractor competition that had only one drive wheel.
"CENTRALIZED CONTROL — All levers are conveniently located. Speed changes and steering mechanism similar to construction used in automobiles." The Society of Tractor Engineers and the Society of Automotive Engineers had recently merged and the incorporation of automotive technology in tractors was considered a marketing advantage. With throttle lever, spark advance, and retard lever along with the kill switch all mounted on the steering column just below the steering wheel, reference to automobile design was justified.

however, the name SAE continued unchanged for the new unified organization. Ten years earlier, in 1907, the American Society of Agricultural Engineers (ASAE) had been founded at the University of Wisconsin in Madison, Wisconsin. Over the decades these two organizations would cooperate, and sometimes compete, in establishing standards for tractors and agricultural equipment. Future decades would find technology moving freely between industries regardless of the nature of their product. Automotive engineers contributed some progressive ideas to, and speeded many improvements in, tractor development, but some of the concepts were not necessarily well suited to the sustained, full-load operation required of tractors. Over time, the differences in application got straightened out.

A proud manager of this attractive Columbia, Tennessee, farm wrote the IHC Nashville Branch House in response to a visit by one of the Company agents. His testimonial recorded that the International 8-16 Kerosene Tractor and two 7-foot Deering binders, "cut eighty acres of wheat within thirty hours, using 30 gallons of kerosene and about 5 quarts of cylinder oil. The total cost per acre being about eleven and three-fourths cents for fuel." His letter closed with, "The tractor gave no trouble whatever while at work, and I don't think any other make of Tractor could do the work any better than the International. I am well pleased with the results and can highly recommend the Tractor to other farmers." IHC made extensive use of such testimonials.

A New Product for Tractor Works

In 1917, Tractor Works made a preproduction run of 38 International 8-16 kerosene tractors. The use of International in place of Mogul was a major change. In addition, the letters H.P. behind the 8-16 horsepower rating was gone. The Titan 10-20-H.P. from Milwaukee Works was the sales leader and the Tractor Works

Mogul 8-16-H.P. and 10-20-H.P. needed to be replaced. The International 8-16 proved to be the right answer.

Configuration of the International 8-16 tractor was truly innovative. No firm documentation exists, but observation would lead one to believe the radiator mounted over the flywheel in the middle of the tractor and the down-sloping hood had its roots in a similar component arrangement used in IHC trucks. The result was a novel, two-plow tractor that was the Tractor Works volume leader until it was replaced by the totally different McCormick-Deering 10-20 in 1923.

First production International 8-16 kerosene tractors had vertical, 4-cylinder, 4-inch bore x 5-inch stroke, value-in-head engines with removable cylinders and three crankshaft bearings. Rated at 1,000 rpm, it would be considered a high speed tractor engine. Three forward speeds of 1-3/4, 2-1/4, and 4 mph provided a plowing speed, a tillage speed, and a useful transport or hauling speed. This tractor had three distinct model changes during the production period that ended in 1922. The most

This June 1918 photo of first production tractors shows the interesting exhaust location and minimal fenders. Tires are equipped with the essential angle lugs that extended beyond the rear tires. This International 8-16 kerosene tractor was on the E. V. Babcock Farm, Valencia, Pennsylvania.

visible changes were replacing the air strainer with an efficient water air cleaner, relocating the exhaust to the rear, and eventually supporting the fuel tank on sheet metal side sheets in place of supporting straps. Changes in exhaust and intake manifolds accommodated an Ensign 1-1/4-inch-type JK carburetor for starting on gasoline and operating on kerosene. Cooling was by "thermosyphon" circulation and a flat-belt driven fan that exhausted out both sides of the fan enclosure.

Tractor Power Take-Off, An IHC Commercial First

The concept of a tractor power take-off shaft to power mounted or trailing implement has an interesting history; however, International Harvester Company is recognized as the developer of the first commercial application to a regular production tractor. The International 8-16 deserves recognition here because Tractor Works Decision No. 451, dated March 29, 1919, provides for 50 power take-off shafts for this tractor. Application of the power take-off (PTO) was extended to the development of the new International 15-30 with a pencil note on a September 28, 1920, Milwaukee Works decision. The decision to offer the PTO as special equipment for that tractor was later confirmed on February 14, 1921. The new International 15-30 was the first tractor submitted for Nebraska Tractor Test that was equipped with a power take-off. During development of the Farmall, power take-off capability was specified in the release to production of 20 tractors known as the "heavy" Farmall on April 20, 1922, and 25 of the tractors known as the "light" Farmall on

Early PTO Development History

The first recorded effort to drive a harvesting machine from a traction engine is a 1885 *Farm Implement News* published graphic showing a push reaper propelled by a steam traction engine and chain driven by the same unit. The combined machine was said to have been shown at the Paris Universal Exposition in 1878. A more practical application of tractor power to an implement was demonstrated by Mr. Albert Gougis of Anneau, France in 1906. This small manufacturer of agricultural implements constructed a very serviceable tractor and equipped it with a power shaft for operating a drawn McCormick binder. The French farmers were not ready for an expensive tractor with a PTO; so, today it resides in the Museum Institution Agronomique in Paris. The Gougis family says representatives of the International Harvester French Company were invited to a demonstration of the tractor and PTO-driven binder and recognized the commercial possibilities. Even then it took 14 more years before the timing was right for marketing a PTO-equipped tractor.

March 27, 1923. International Harvester recognized the significance of the tractor PTO and speeded its acceptance by developing implements like the power-driven binder and mower to utilize the new capability.

With approximately 100 U.S. manufacturers claiming to be in the tractor business during the 1920s, there were designs and configurations of every kind on paper, and many were reduced to prototypes. Tractor Works experimental tried their hand with an International 8-16 based, four-wheel-drive "skid-steer"

Release of 50 power take-off shafts for the International 8-16 tractor brought about extensive testing and development and possibly some sales of power-shaft operated mowers and binders; so, the photo may or may not be purely experimental.

Tractors and Farmerettes

Major military conflicts typically bring major changes in society and World War I was no exception. Farming in the second decade of the Twentieth Century required lots of horses and manpower — the war created a shortage of both. International Harvester had an answer for the first challenge; replace animal horse power with tractor horsepower. One solution to the manpower shortage took the form of women power. Women who joined the Women's Land Army received training in tractor operation; the Illinois Division received their IHC tractor training on a farm near Libertyville, Illinois. Participants in the program were frequently called "farmerettes." Women have always stepped forward to perform necessary tasks, traditional or non-traditional, in times of crisis or need, but they usually didn't receive a special name. Historians have noted that women and boys were credited with operating the McCormick reaper to harvest the critical Midwestern wheat crops during the Civil War. Those grain harvests contributed to the economic and political strength of the North.

The military needed man – the country needed tractor operators. Into the vacuum stepped trained and totally capable women. This photo was likely taken in the fall of 1918 when four members of the Women's Land Army, "Farmerettes," came to Grant Park, along with their IHC tractor, to help prepare for the Chicago War Exposition.

tractor. The manager of Gas Power Engineering recalled that, "One unit was in use near Aurora, Illinois, for so many years that needed repairs became a problem for us to supply — yet we could not persuade the owner to part with it." (This is an excellent example of why the industry generally will scrap prototype or field-test machines unless they are totally serviceable in spite of protests from farmers who hear about these "perfectly good" machines not being offered for sale.) He concluded with, "Expense of manufacture and patents on the differential steering were deciding factors in the conclusion not to manufacture it." Decades later the right configuration of this concept would spawn an entire industrial loader-tractor product line.

The Search for Power Plant Reliability

Rapid expansion of the number of tractors on farms during the post World War I period brought with it recognition by the industry that tractor engines of the day lacked mechanical reliability. The

manager of Tractor Works engineering related in an ASAE paper how the "problem of engine <u>cylinder</u>, <u>ring</u>, <u>valve</u>, and <u>bearing</u> wear from dirt entry, became so acute a trouble to the tractor industry that in approxi-

This IHC Tractor Works experimental steam-powered tractor was built in the 192

mately 1920, we developed and built a uniflow type steam engine and a fully enclosed condensing system for the boiler needs to have ready *if the internal combustion engine could not be made durable*." (Italics are by the author.) Fortunately, IHC engine development progressed rapidly; the steam tractor remained only an experiment.

Searching for New Markets

Gas Power Engineering at Tractor Works took advantage of the short wheel base and close-coupled design of the International 8-16 to explore some interesting possibilities. One experimental tractor had front and rear wheels of equal size and steered by differential braking. A second experimental version had three axles with smaller, equal size wheels and steered the same way. The age of the ski-steer tractor was a long way off and these tractors never became more than interesting experiments. A third experimental tractor was equipped with full crawler-tractor tracks. All of the experiments incorporated the mid-mounted radiator and fan located over the engine flywheel and the forward sloping hood that distinguished the International 8-16 from other tractors in the line. True crawler tractors would eventually become a major product line for the Company.

In an age when many heavy-duty trucks had hard rubber tires, it is logical for IHC to equip a tractor that way. This version of the International 8-16 would be a good answer on hard roads or around a factory. This early model does not have the cooling fan vents along the side of the radiator. Instead, the air is exhausted through the forward-facing louvers on the side of the engine compartment.

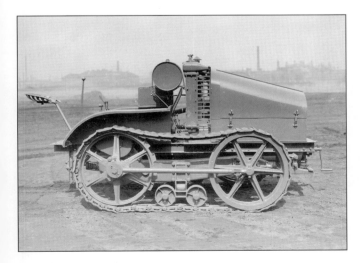

The compact design of the International 8-16 kerosene tractor made it ideally suited for experiments like this crawler version that called for a short wheel base.

Here is an experimental 1920s International 8-16 based skid-steer tractor.

Nineteen years of production with only minor improvements is a record match by few tractor designs; the McCormick-Deering 10-20 was the right tractor at the right time. This rugged two-plow tractor survived good markets and bad. In spite of competition from the Company's own Farmall, 215,793 McCormick-Deering 10-20 tractors rolled out of the Tractor Works in Chicago by the end of this impressive production run.

A Bold Move in Tractor Design

IHC production of tractors over 30 horsepower ended in 1917. Management recognized that tractors of the future must be smaller, lighter weight, and more versatile than current production tractors. Furthermore, they must have a significantly higher level of mechanical reliability and require less routine maintenance. The future IHC tractor must be a totally different design than the recently introduced four-cylinder, horizontal-engine powered International 15-30 chain drive or the current, successful Titan 10-20 and International 8-16. They made a decision, and a new tractor development program began in 1917.

Design of the new International 15-30 gear drive incorporated a vertical, four-cylinder, 4-1/2-inch bore x 6-inch stroke engine with many modern features. This engine had an innovative crankshaft supported on a large ball bearing at each end. A stronger, close-coupled crankshaft design made it possible to eliminate the center bearing.

Two chassis for the new International 15-30 gear drive were tried in 1918. One was a large, cast-iron transmission case attached to a channel frame front end. A second was a one-piece, cast-iron frame that extended the full length of the tractor. After two years of testing both designs, the one-piece, cast frame was selected for the new tractor. The full-length, one-piece frame would become the trademark of a highly successful family of IHC standard tractors.

By 1921 the post-war depression was having a serious impact on U.S. agriculture in general and the farm machinery industry in particular. Export sales of IHC

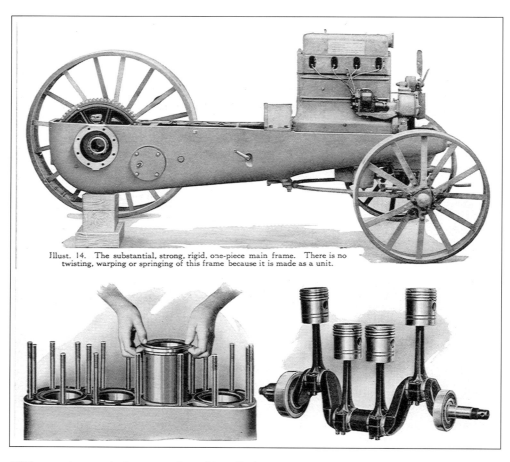

Illust. 14. The substantial, strong, rigid, one-piece main frame. There is no twisting, warping or springing of this frame because it is made as a unit.

With one-piece main frame, replaceable cylinders, and ball-bearing crank shaft, the McCormick-Deering 10-20 and 15-30 tractors represented significantly different tractor designs from the competition. IHC promoted the efficient, quality production capability of Tractor Works in photos and articles for customers and Company personnel alike. An example is a photo showing the special machine that could simultaneously drill 28 holes in the top of McCormick-Deering 10-20 and 15-30 tractor main frames.

This familiar photo of a McCormick-Deering 10-20 tractor provided a good view of the large water air cleaner and air intake stack with extension. Only a few years prior, very little consideration had been given to providing engine combustion air free of service-life robbing dirt. Additional engine driveline design improvements resulted in this tractor and the companion McCormick-Deering 15-30 setting a new standard for mechanical reliability and reduced routine maintenance.

Innovation is Great, But it Can be Risky!

The engine in these two new McCormick-Deering tractors had an innovative crankshaft supported by large ball bearings at each end. The high-strength design of the crankshaft made it possible to eliminate the traditional center bearing. Advertising and marketing continually search for at least one distinctive, new engineering advancement to promote. When they learned about the new engine they did an impressive job extolling the benefits of the exclusive, two-bearing crankshaft in McCormick-Deering

tractors and implements fell drastically. A great market was to be had: Less than 4 percent of U.S. farms had a tractor and only 2 percent had a truck; but, the farmer customers had neither cash nor willingness to invest in tractors and farm equipment. The poor economy and seemingly high tractor prices even gave the Horse Association of America an opportunity to escalate their anti-tractor propaganda. To make things worse, the tractor price wars destroyed profits and half of the tractors produced were Fordsons. This was a tough time to introduce the new International 15-30 gear-drive tractor. Challenges not withstanding, introduction proceeded.

Testimony to IHC management confidence in the superiority of the new International 15-30 gear-drive tractor design and further confidence in the future is shown by their 1921 manufacturing release for production in 1923 of the similar 10-20 gear-drive tractor. The Milwaukee Works <u>new</u> International 15-30 gear-drive tractor was renamed the McCormick-Deering 15-30 in 1923. This was the year of introduction for the smaller version of this design produced at Tractor Works; the new tractor was named the McCormick-Deering 10-20. The new tractor had a smaller 4-1/2-inch bore x 5-inch stroke engine, was 14 inches shorter, and weighed over 2,000 pounds less than the McCormick-Deering 15-30.

Wheel diameter and tread width along with other external dimensions were different in order to achieve a balanced design. Because the two tractors had the same general appearance and shared the same basic design, a single piece of literature was used to promote both tractors.

Customers were not totally convinced the two bearing crankshaft with ball bearings at each end used in the engine of the new McCormick-Deering 10-20 and 15-30 was reliable; it was too different. Engineering must have convinced management that the new design was highly reliable, because IHC issued this amazing life-long warranty on the two-bearing crankshaft and on the crankshaft ball bearings.

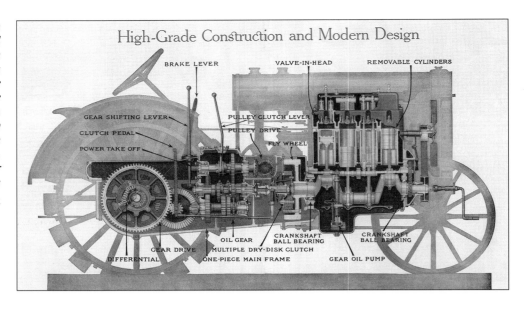

Because of the similarity of the 10-20 and 15-30, literature used the same illustrations to describe them with the exception that a full side view of each was usually included. Nothing helped convey the extent of modern design features incorporated in the new McCormick-Deering tractors like a highly detailed cutaway. Provision for the optional power take-off shaft is called out at the rear end of the pulley drive shaft.

10-20 and 15-30 tractors. However, a major share of prospective customers remained skeptical. To assure farmers that this design was the "best possible construction for a farm tractor," IHC offered a life-long guarantee on the two-bearing crankshaft and crankshaft ball bearings. Part of the warranty said, "never before has a manufacturer given such a far-reaching guarantee on the bearings and crankshaft of a tractor." A dealer commented on this unusual warranty as follows, "Very few of the crankshafts ever broke. We replaced a lot of bearings after years of use, on an exchange basis after the old warranty had been forgotten." Life-long guarantee or not, the "Old Faithful" 15-30 and 10-20 tractors had a long and successful production run.

Innovation of the tractor power take-off, on the other hand, may have had investment risk, but the PTO did not require special assurances to the farmer; its advantages were quite self-evident. IHC had another advantage. As a leading manufacturer of corn pickers, ensilage harvesters, corn binders, grain binders, and mowers, they designed these machines to utilize PTO tractor power; the Company could provide a proven tractor-implement package.

History of the Nebraska Tractor Testing Laboratory at the University of Nebraska, Lincoln, Nebraska, records the McCormick-Deering 15-30 as the "first tractor tested (Test 87) which was equipped with a PTO as standard equipment." Actually it was an option but it was standard in the sense that provision for it was designed into the basic tractor. The high location of the McCormick-Deering 15-30 PTO eventually gave way to a lower and more practical location as the industry moved toward standardization.

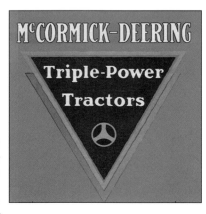

Drawbar power, belt pulley power, and power take-off power: McCormick-Deering triple power tractors delivered all three. When the McCormick-Deering 15-30 was tested at Nebraska in 1922, it became the first tractor tested which was equipped with a PTO as factory equipment. The clever Triple-Power promotion helped publicize IHC leadership in making the tractor PTO a commercial option. Advertisements closed with the admonition, "See that the tractor you select has a power take-off."

Mud on the tractor drive wheels indicates this was a wet harvest, and that is when ground-drive binders had problems or didn't work at all. The clearly visible PTO shaft on this McCormick-Deering 15-30 tractor tells us this farmer had the right combination of equipment to get the grain-binding job done in spite of the weather.

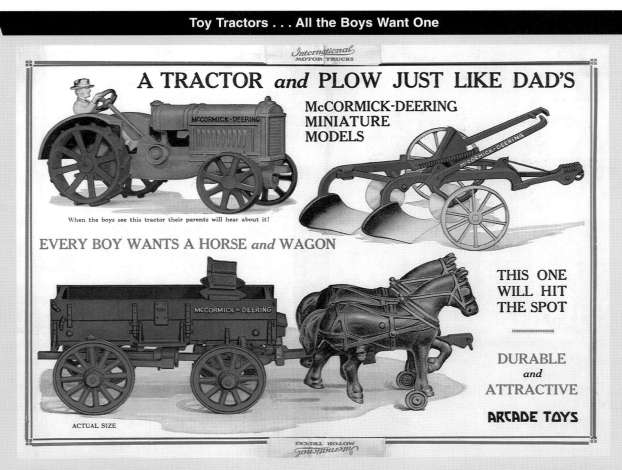

International MOTOR TRUCKS

A TRACTOR *and* PLOW JUST LIKE DAD'S

McCORMICK-DEERING MINIATURE MODELS

McCORMICK-DEERING

When the boys see this tractor their parents will hear about it!

EVERY BOY WANTS A HORSE *and* WAGON

McCORMICK – DEERING

THIS ONE WILL HIT THE SPOT

DURABLE *and* ATTRACTIVE

ARCADE TOYS

ACTUAL SIZE

Promotion for these toy tractors read, "When the kiddies see the McCormick-Deering toy tractor they invariably want one — consequently the older folks learn more about McCormick-Deering tractors; good advertising for the dealer at no cost." These wonderful 7-1/2-inch long, painted, cast-iron toy tractors cost the dealer 37.5 cents each in dozen lots; f.o.b. Freeport, Illinois. Tractors on disk wheels and rubber tires cost 48 cents each. Dealers were told these great little tractors regularly would retail for 75 cents to $1.00.

They came packed in paper boxes, one dozen to a case. *What a treasure two or three original cases of these toys would be today.*

It would take years before the industry realized that many little girls like toy tractors too! IHC didn't stop with cast-iron toy tractors; they offered a plow, miniature wagon with a team of horses, a thresher, and a "Red Baby" truck with a tiny winch that raised the dump bed.

Secrets of Tractors with Long Life Cycles

McCormick-Deering 15-30 and 10-20 tractors have impressive life cycles. The McCormick-Deering 15-30 was introduced as the <u>new</u> International 15-30 from the Milwaukee Works in 1921. Two years later it was named the McCormick-Deering and in 1928 a record 35,525 were manufactured. When production ended in 1934, over 157,000 of these tractors had been built during the 14-year life cycle. The McCormick-Deering 10-20 has an even more impressive history. Initial production at the Tractor Works began in 1923 with 7,117 units. Volume built rapidly until the 1929 peak of 39,433 tractors were produced. When production ended in 1939, over 215,000 McCormick-Deering 10-20 tractors had been built during the 17-year life cycle. This record was achieved during the time when IHC's trend-setting Farmall family of tractors was recording impressive production numbers as well.

The long life cycle of these tractors can be attributed to having been reliable, modern concept tractors when they were introduced. Furthermore, they were improved with advancing technology of the times. For example: The water-type air cleaner was replaced with an oil-bath air cleaner; the Dixie 46-C magneto was replaced with the International E4A magneto; an oil

With the purchase of Parlin & Orendorff in 1919, IHC acquired a proven, successful line of plows and tillage implements. Teaming the Little Wonder two-bottom plow with the popular McCormick-Deering 10-20 tractor made a smooth working outfit for this Stoughton, Wisconsin farmer.

filter and fuel strainer were added to the engine; and many less obvious design and manufacturing improvements. The McCormick 10-20 basic engine was unchanged throughout its 17 years of production. The McCormick-Deering 15-30 experienced a significant change in 1929 when cylinder bore was increased from 4-1/2 inches to 4-3/4 inches — the stroke remained the same at 6 inches — rpm was increased from 1,000 to 1,050 and thermostatic water temperature control was added. These changes and other engine modifications resulted in Nebraska Tractor Test results of 22.78 horse-

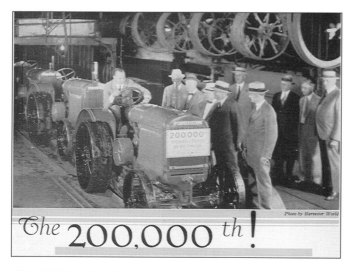

The 200,000th!

With IHC Vice-President Cyrus McCormick Jr. at the wheel, the 200,000th McCormick-Deering 10-20 rolled off the end of the Tractor Works assembly line on June 4, 1930. During the final stages of Farmall development in 1924 there had been great concern that the new tractor would destroy the market for the McCormick-Deering 10-20. This proud day proved that wrong — six years after the Farmall introduction, these two different tractors both enjoyed strong demand.

power drawbar and 36.15 horsepower belt, and it became a four-plow tractor under most conditions.

As a result, this tractor was frequently called the McCormick-Deering 22-36 to reflect the increased horsepower. To others it was still the improved horsepower McCormick-Deering 15-30. Additional updating of the two tractors included optional generator-powered electric lighting, comfortable cushion seat, and low pressure pneumatic rubber tires.

Building Blocks for Three New Markets

Confidence in the engine and driveline of the McCormick-Deering 10-20 led to simultaneous introduction of the agricultural tractor and the industrial version in 1923. This was the first new market. The McCormick-Deering industrial 10-20 had a lower profile and disc wheels with hard rubber tires. Production numbers were modest the first two years but increased to 1,300 by 1926. Output continued to increase until it hit 4,607 in 1929; this was the year that the industrial Model 20 replaced the original. Gas Power Engineering photos in the archives record many prototype industrial tractor products that were never put into production. The potential size of this market was being recognized. This modest start in industrial tractors eventually grew into a major industrial equipment product line.

Farm equipment export was always an important part of IHC's total business. The highly regarded, highly reliable McCormick-Deering 10-20 and 15-30 tractors were popular export products.

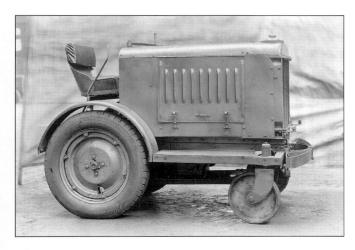

This interesting, little caster wheel, differential steer, industrial tractor is one of many Tractor Works Gas Power Engineering photos with no description. The name suggests it might have been a tractor developed around McCormick-Deering 10-20 components by a non-employee named Slonninger, and engineering was making an evaluation. Or, Mr. Slonninger may have been an engineer in the Gas Power Department who either had the idea or the assignment to develop the prototype.

The second new market resulted from the 1928 decision to build 200 track-laying attachments for the wheel-type 10-20 and 15-30 tractors. Production began that fall and 472 were reported in the 1929 Tractor Works year-end results. These new crawler tractors were marketed under the trade name TracTracTor and the identification lasted through several new generations of crawler tractors. Again, this was the foundation of what would someday become the International Harvester Construction Equipment Division.

The third new market was application of McCormick-Deering 10-20 and 15-30 engine and drive-

This attachment for the McCormick-Deering 10-20/15-30 tractors was developed by the Moon Track Company of San Diego, California. No one could have imagined that just 40 years later American astronauts would leave man-made "moon tracks" on the celestial moon.

trains to a broad range of products manufactured by other firms. IHC had sold stationary engines to OEM (Original Equipment Manufactures) before but marketing of virtually the entire tractor was a new opportunity. In future years, major groups within the Company would be established to build OEM sales around International Harvester Company-manufactured products from disk blades and ball bearings to complete engine and drive-train assemblies like the original McCormick-Deering 10-20 and 15-30 OEM sales.

Launch of the McCormick-Deering 10-20 farm tractor in 1923 was accompanied by a preproduction run of 23 low-profile versions on hard rubber tires for the industrial market. By 1927 when this photo was taken, over 1,800 of the Industrial 10-20s had been produced. Commercial deliveries like the nine tractors shown here were essential for achieving growth in this new market.

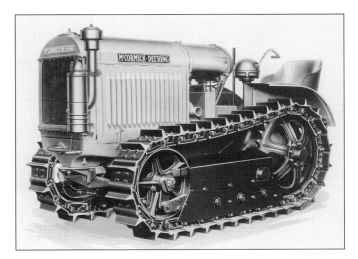

*IHC's **TracTracTor** entry in the small crawler tractor market was described as having, "The rugged and powerful engine, one-piece main frame, simple yet rugged single-plate clutch, gear drive, etc., exactly like those in hundreds of thousands of McCormick-Deering tractors in use throughout the world." Engine features were described in great detail and closed with this interesting statement for a tractor manufacturer, "The highest standard of automotive practice is maintained in the factories where McCormick-Deering engines are manufactured.*

The First Farmall

An Unlikely Beginning for a Tractor Farming Revolution

Take a look at the Kodak photo of the first experimental, all-purpose tractor developed and demonstrated by the IHC's Gas Power Division in 1915. The first reaction is, why did it take eight years of development before the basic Farmall concept evolved? The reaction is logical enough, but it must be remembered: Everyone with farm or farm equipment industry background today benefits from decades of tractor development experience and history. The International Harvester Company tractor pioneers were working in an environment that had, until a short time before, been dominated by heavy, high-horsepower tractors that closely resembled their steam engine predecessors. Introduction of the successful Mogul 8-16 H.P. tractor in 1914 and the Titan 10-20 H.P. tractor in 1915 had demonstrated the need and market potential for smaller, lower-priced tractors for the very large number of small to medium size farms. However, these more flexible tractors could still not totally replace the horse because they were not suited to row-crop cultivation.

The industry attempt to solve the problem focused on a two-part approach: Conventional tractors for drawbar, PTO, and belt pulley work; and horses or motorized cultivators for the remaining job — row-crop cultivation. An Ohio farmer developed the Universal cultivating tractor, incorporated the Universal Tractor Company, and by 1914 had manufactured and sold 150 units from the Columbus, Ohio, facility. When the International Harvester Company showed no interest in purchasing the Universal Tractor Company, it was sold to the Moline Plow Company.

The IH Motor Cultivator

The Company developed their own motor cultivator and put it on the market in 1917. The International Harvester Motor Cultivator was a three-wheeled design with two wheels in the front that supported the mounted, push cultivator and a pair of closely-spaced, pivoted drive wheels in the rear. The steering was unique. When the unit was headed down the row, the powered steering wheels at the rear were locked in the center or straight ahead position. Small corrections in steering and corn-hill dodging were made by the operator pushing on either the right or left foot pedal. The pedals moved the cultivator gangs and the two large front wheels to guide the unit; the effort required could be great. When the cultivator was lifted, the steering unlocked and the steering wheel could turn the pivoted driving wheels for very quick turns at the end of the row. The pivoted engine and drive wheel

Moline Universal, Avery, and other motor cultivators were on the market in 1917 when International Harvester rushed their entry to the field so it could compete in area demonstrations. Weights were added to the steel-fabricated front wheels in an effort to reduce the tendency of the machine to tip over. These wheels were soon replaced with cast-iron wheels.

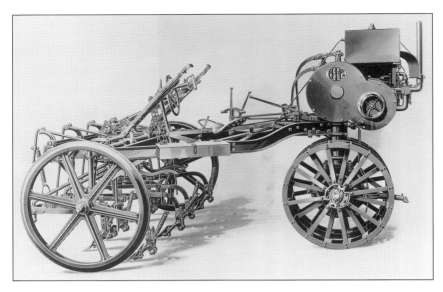

This enhanced photo was used in 1917 International Harvester motor cultivator literature.

design of the motor cultivator was claimed to, "put the weight over the drive wheels to assure ample traction, eliminate the need for a differential, and make it possible for the motor cultivator to turn within its own length." However, this configuration was top heavy and the drive wheel geometry would actually contribute to overturn. In an effort to increase traction, drive-wheel extensions became standard.

Production delays in the spring of 1917 reduced the original 300-unit production plan to 100-actually produced, and 48 tractors were shipped by late June. As a result of the production delay, only 31 motor cul-

tivators were retailed; since changes and improvements were needed, all were recalled.

For 1918, the IHC motor cultivator was made 50% heavier and the drive-wheel tread increased 4 inches. Manufacturing actually produced 301 units, but again they were shipped late. Literature stated, "A strong drawbar is part of the regular equipment and is provided for attaching harrows, drills, seeders, land packers, land rollers, and other implements that could be handled by four good horses." The little 12-horsepower Le Roi engine really wasn't up to that task even if the machine geometry had been right. It was not a drawbar machine, it still would tip over easily, it didn't work on hillsides or contours, and two units were required before horses could be eliminated. In an effort to make the motor cultivator more useful, experimental binder, sweep-rake, and mower attachments were developed. These efforts were not successful because the motor cultivator configuration was not right to serve as the "power unit" of a universal harvesting system; that industry development would come 30 years later.

To be economical, the International motor cultivator needed to be used for tasks other than cultivation. The literature caption under this photo read, "A simple, reliable drawbar hitch is provided for attaching disks, drills, seeders, peg harrows, etc. to the International Motor Cultivator." Unfortunately, the little 12-horsepower LeRoi motor had insufficient power to properly handle the 7-foot, horse-drawn style disk harrow in the photo or similar drawbar work.

The International motor cultivator is pictured in cornfield end rows with the drive wheels positioned for a sharp turn. Ability to turn in the length of the machine was a major sales feature. The spade-type handle "spinner" on the steering wheel was a big help in cranking around the engine and drive wheel assembly. Turning with an implement attached to the drawbar hitch was surely a herculean task. The belt pulley, on the other hand, found many useful applications on farms of the period.

One effort to utilize part of the motor cultivator development was a self-propelled binder. Hopefully, engineering learned something from the experiment because this was not the right answer.

Time and money invested in the short-lived, motor cultivator manufacturing and marketing project was not a total loss. Knowledge acquired in the field helped direct the experimental department's future motor cultivator efforts. Photos from 1919 show prototypes with a stronger frame, direct connected steering linkage, power lift capability, and three different PTO systems. This design facilitated front-mounted attachments such as binders, mowers, seeders, and corn binders as well as cultivators.

As farm economics improved during World War I, interest in motor cultivators increased. The Moline Plow Company improved the Universal and by 1919 marked 6,000 units. That year they showed their machine at the Blue Mound, Illinois, demonstration along with IHC and four other companies. By this time, International Harvester management recognized their motor cultivator product design was plagued with problems and shortcomings and their cost was too high. The profit margin was small in spite of a list price of $652.50 compared to Avery at $540. As a result, a decision was made in 1919 to sell off the remaining motor cultivator inventory and end production. It was a wise and timely decision; motor cultivators soon became history. Fortunately, that decision did not end continuing work by the New Work Committee, E. A. Johnston, and other far-sighted individuals on projects that would lead to an all-purpose tractor. Furthermore, a system requiring two "tractors" to accomplish what one unit should be able to do was not valid and they knew it.

In an effort to improve traction, a track-laying system was developed to replace the pair of close-spaced, open-tread rear drive wheels. A photo shows the track-layer version in the field with a front-mounted corn binder and bundle elevator attachment. Another photo shows the track-layer machine with a frame-mounted, two-furrow plow. This approach still was not suited to plowing or tillage.

In the spring of 1920 a major change took place in motor cultivator experimental design. The engine was rigidly mounted transverse to the rear frame and delivered power to a differential at the front. Right and left differential drive shafts powered chain drives to the widely spaced, cleated, drive wheels. Steering was

Bert R. Benjamin of McCormick Works designed the low down binder attachment for the experimental motor cultivator shown here in 1919. The Victory Liberty Loan sign on the side of the building is a clear reminder of America's participation in World War I. The use of straps with wood blocks on the header in place of the traditional cotton canvas is further evidence of war shortages.

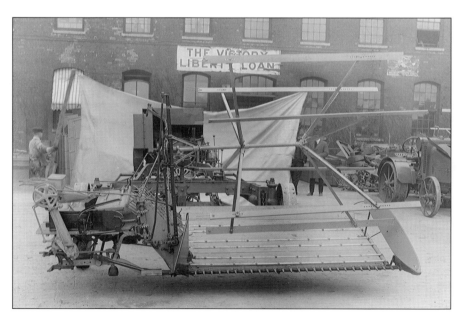

The wide front-wheel tread and deep front opening of the crawler version of the motor cultivator was well suited for many different harvesting attachments including this corn binder with bundle loader. This motor cultivator, like the other experimental versions, never went into production.

This 1919 photo shows the first and only attempt to direct connect a plow to the motor cultivator. Even if the heavier engine and crawler track combination could generate adequate traction for a two-bottom plow, excessive side draft from the plow's off-center location would have created serious problems.

This side view of the 1920 experimental cultivator tractor clearly shows the chain drive from the differential to the two lugged front wheels. The operator's seat can be seen squeezed in between the engine and the differential just above the side-mounted, power-lift spiral and just below the transmission driveline.

This experimental motor cultivator or cultivator tractor developed in 1920 was a radical change in construction. It had two wide-track drive wheels in front which were chain driven from a differential.

achieved through differential braking. This configuration improved performance of front-mounted attachments like an experimental sweeprake, double-bar mower, corn binder, etc.; however, the steering system did not provide the quick, accurate response needed for the front-mounted cultivator.

Reverse Operation is a Move Forward

By the fall of 1920 the transverse engine design demonstrated a different application. It was operated in the reverse direction. The engine and guide wheel

Dual sickle-bar mowers were mounted on the front of this 1920 version cultivator tractor . The mowers were another example to demonstrate the many uses for the experimental cultivator tractor.

An October 15, 1920 photo records a significant event in the long road to final development of the Farmall tractor. This cultivator tractor is pulling a corn binder and for the first time is shown operating in the reverse direction with a draft load; the guide wheel is in front and the drive wheels are in the rear.

Forecasting the Future?

One of the great photos in the archive collection from this period shows the track-layer version of the motor cultivator equipped with a PTO-driven, front-mounted corn fodder harvesting system. The unit is standing in front of what appears to be a guard shack at either Tractor Works or McCormick Works with a line-up of men in suits and hats standing in front of the little building. Could this be the New Work Committee? The fascinating part is the operator who is also in a dress suit and hat. He is seated under a large umbrella with one hand on the steering wheel and the other hand holding a telephone to his ear. Was this just a first-class, staged joke? Did he actually make a phone call? Are the lines from the pole on the machine to the little building something just drawn in on the photo? Could it be this engineer was trying to demonstrate that some day the wireless communication age of the 1920s would advance to such a high degree that farmers on tractors in the field would carry on telephone conversations with someone back at the house, in another machine, in the office headquarters, or around the world? How wonderful it would be if the archives contained a record of what actually was talked about that day. Maybe it's more interesting for us to just imagine.

were in front with differential-driven, wide-spaced drive wheels in the rear. A November 1920 photo records this application with the unit pulling a loader equipped corn binder and a wagon receiving the fodder bundles. In later designs, this configuration would become the forward direction.

Another experimental tractor demonstrated the basic principals of an all-purpose tractor: The guide wheel was mounted at the front and differential-driven drive wheels were at the rear. A worm and large sector provided easier, more accurate steering. The single steering wheel located in front provided for a front-mounted cultivator that could be better guided to keep on the row. Cables attached to the sector actuated right or left drive-wheel brakes to assist in making sharp turns. The formerly crosswise engine was mounted in line with the center line of the tractor. The power take-off was located in the traditional position. For reverse operation, the operator's seat pivoted around the base of the perpendicular steering column. Reverse operation accommodated mounted grain binders or other crop harvesting machines. Cranking was done through a bevel gear set located on

This bi-directional, or reversible, tractor pictured in November 1920 moved the project several steps closer to the final Farmall configuration. Engine cranking was done at "A."

The bi-directional or reversible tractor of 1920 grew into a heavier, more refined design during 1921. A totally-enclosed drop axle drive replaced the chain drive. Open-style steel drive wheels were replaced with a completely new design. The engine was bolted to massive transmission and final drive castings that included the power lift, power take-off, and belt pulley.

the side of the tractor. Only one tractor was built.

Alex Legge, president of the IHC, was very supportive of continued experimental work to develop a true multipurpose tractor. He was not always impressed with what he saw from engineering, but he seldom made specific product suggestions. One time, however, he asked about a rear-mounted cultivator, and engineering promptly responded. The

One of the benefits of the reversible tractor was self-propelled harvesting capability. IHC history always made the grain binder top priority in any application of the all-purpose tractor. Corn cultivation and wheat harvest usually came together; with this system, the cultivator could stay on the tractor.

Mounting the cultivator on the front of the tractor nearly in line with the guide wheel gave good steering response for keeping on the row. The offset operator had excellent visibility for accurate cultivating. In the photo, the left row is equipped with rotary plant shields while the right row is equipped with standard flat, metal plant shields; it looks like engineering was making one more side-by-side comparison.

Operating in the "forward" direction, the bi-directional tractor could accommodate either a front-mounted or a rear-mounted cultivator. The time was yet to come for the rear-mounted cultivator.

This 1921-1922 photo came from Bert R. Benjamin's personal file. In 1954 the generally accepted father of the Farmall forwarded this and several other photos to the archives in IH World Headquarters. It is of particular interest because the archives have so few photos of early experimental Farmall tractors with plows. The tractor is equipped with the full-width, adjustable-height draw bar that became a standard Farmall feature. The flat steel drive wheels equipped with overhanging lugs would also become the wheel design of choice.

A Trade Name is Born

Names were solicited for the new multipurpose tractor and one submitted was FARM-ALL. Records of the Gas Power Division recorded the words "Farmall Tractor" on November 10, 1919. The "tractor" being described may have been a long way from the final Farmall configuration, but the term made a clear statement about what a multipurpose tractor should do. The name Farmall was regularly used by engineering after 1919. (New Work Report No. 530, January 25, 1921, used the name Farmall.) The trade name Farmall was not registered until July 17, 1923, or authorized by the Naming Committee until February 5, 1924.

1921 result looked workable, but neither cultural practices nor farmers were ready for such a "radical" idea. It would be several decades before rear-mounted cultivators would become a practical reality.

President Legge wisely insisted that whatever form the multipurpose tractor took, it must look like a tractor and furthermore it must accommodate plowing as well as cultivating. Photo documentation makes it clear, the experimental department was following his directive.

Basic Elements of the Farmall Cultivator

In the spring of 1921, the bi-directional tractor guide wheel was located forward of the radiator and the tractor could be equipped with a long-drawbar, front-mount cultivator. Front mounting the cultivator with the front shovels nearly in line with the hub of the guide wheel was a major milestone in Farmall development. Steering the tractor now affected the quick cultivator response required to "dodge" plant hills that were out of line. By autumn the cultivator incorporated a pivoted design so the frame and gangs could be shifted laterally through action of a linkage to the steering column and dodging ability was further enhanced. Cable connection

The IHC Research Farm at Hinsdale, Illinois, was the site of a front-mounted cultivator demonstration in 1921 on a reversible "heavy" Farmall tractor. The tractor was not the right answer, but the cultivator design became a central factor in the success of the final Farmall.

from the steering gear to each brake assisted in making short turns. These two cultivator concepts and brake assisted turns represented significant advances in the development of the Farmall.

Provision for cultivator frame shifting and differential braking were part of the Farmall system for decades. Front-mounted cultivators remained the standard until chemical control of weeds in the row made rear-mounted cultivators practical; however, chemical weed control was several decades in the

future. Most successful corn growers check-row planted their fields and cross cultivated. Even careful check-row planting did not result in precise placement of all hills. So, when cross cultivating, the ability to "dodge" out-of-line plants had always been seen as a design requirement for all cultivating systems: horse-drawn, motor cultivator or an attachment for the new Farmall.

Twenty bi-directional or reversible "heavy" Farmall tractors were produced and shipped to various Midwest locations in the spring of 1922. A 3 3/4-inch bore x 5-inch stroke, 1,200-rpm kerosene engine powered the 3-speed, 3,500-pound tractor. Power take-off and power lift were standard. The Tractor Works decision releasing these tractors stated, "This is a new type of machine, and the limited quantity is placed to determine the real need for such farming equipment." Five tractors were placed in the Chicago area so they could be closely followed.

Bert R. Benjamin had been in charge of experimental work at McCormick Works since 1916. About half of his time had been spent directing attachment development for the motor cultivator and the multipurpose tractor. In October 1920, Benjamin wrote Mr. Legge

Notes on the back of the print say this 1922 bi-directional, or reversible, tractor was operating an experimental "Farm All" (note: two words) Power Drive Binder on the H. B. Utley Farm at Downers Grove, Illinois. Mr. Utley was an IHC executive whose farm was close to the Company's Hinsdale Research Farm and his land was frequently used for test work. Utley's farm was a commercial operation and the experience gained there had practical value.

This photo shows a bi-directional or reversible "heavy" Farmall tractor.

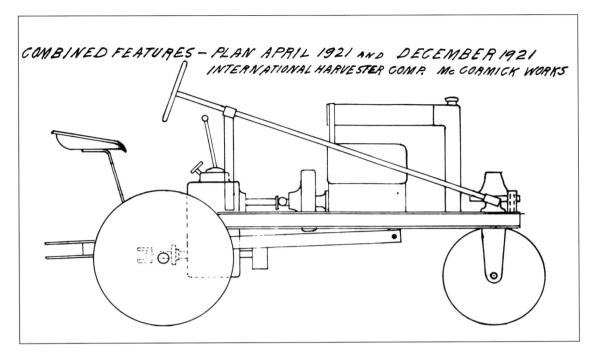

COMBINED FEATURES — PLAN APRIL 1921 AND DECEMBER 1921
INTERNATIONAL HARVESTER COMP. McCORMICK WORKS

While Tractor Works under E. A. Johnston was developing the bi-directional, or reversible, all-purpose "heavy" Farmall tractor, McCormick Works Experimental under Bert R. Benjamin was developing cultivators and implements to work with that tractor. Benjamin succinctly analyzed the problems encountered with the all-purpose "heavy" tractor design and proposed his all-purpose "light" tractor ideas to management.

proposing a bi-directional tractor that would completely replace horses. He had been collecting data on farming methods of the day and had developed a clear understanding of what a multipurpose tractor must accomplish. Benjamin is credited with the idea that, "When we were building attachments to fit a tractor we were not getting anywhere in particular, but when we started building a tractor to meet the requirements of the attachments we began to forge ahead."

Two Approaches: The "Heavy" Farmall, The "Light" Farmall

Farmall development was conducted at Tractor Works under the direction of E. A. Johnston. Bert R. Benjamin's directing of attachment development for the Farmall at McCormick Works kept him close to the total program. A McCormick Works sketch titled "Combined features-plan April 1921 and December 1921" shows a forward-only operating tractor with engine and single guide wheel in front and drawbar to the rear. This is not a complete layout for what became known as the "light" Farmall but it indicates that the Experimental Work Department at McCormick Works had firm ideas about the direction Farmall development should take. Features of a "lighter" Farmall were presented to the New Work Committee in January of 1921 and approval given for developing two of these units for test. For the 1922 test season, 20 of the reversible or bi-directional "heavy" Farmalls complete with cultivators, push binders, etc. were approved for production.

Field response from these test units in the spring of 1922 was not particularly encouraging. Even the few supporters of the Farmall program began to lose heart.

IHC Conversions for Fordson Tractors

An innovative proposal for an all-purpose tractor approach is revealed in a May 28, 1921, letter from Bert R. Benjamin to Company President, Alex Legge. He wrote, "If we take a Fordson tractor, which is said to be a satisfactory plowing rig, combine the two front wheels into one so that it will go between the rows, raise the rear axle, and set the wheels out to straddle the rows, we will then have combined, first, the same plowing outfit, second, a cultivator such as you saw at Hinsdale. This can be made and sold to the farmer for $700. No two separate machines of the same plowing power and the same cultivating power could be sold for less than $1,200. We believe that either this Company or Ford will soon be putting out the modified form of Fordson outlined above. It seems important that Ford does not take the lead on this, because the farmer is looking for this machine and there is a good chance to sell eighty percent of the trade and make a profit for the farmer instead of a loss." The Fordson attachment concept was developed to the point of a filed and issued patent, but the attachment was never put on the market; Fordson got 50 percent of the tractor business in 1921 compared to 25 percent for IHC. Was this strictly a defensive move?

This all-purpose "light" tractor was developed under the leadership of Bert R. Benjamin who was in charge of the McCormick Works Experimental Department. Following a demonstration of this tractor at the Hinsdale Research Farm on July 24, 1922, the New Work Committee decided to definitely abandon the "heavy" Farmall in favor of the "light" Farmall.

. . . A Turning Point in Farmall History

A July 19, 1922, photo records the "light" Farmall which is sometimes called the high frame or high side-rail Farmall. It incorporated virtually all of the basic features and components of 1923 Farmall production tractors. One radical change from prior designs was a pair of closely spaced guide wheels mounted on a single steering column in place of the yoke and single guide wheel design of all prior Farmalls.

The "light" Farmall was now ready for management review and on July 24, 1922, the new tractor was demonstrated on the Harvester Research Farm at Hinsdale, Illinois. After seeing the new "light" Farmall at work, Mr. Legge, president of IHC, indicated he was satisfied that some progress was being made. He added that, "The small machine which Mr. Benjamin had brought out was a big improvement." However, he stipulated that the Farmall must be a light one and must be able, above all, to cultivate corn and handle row crops.

Following the demonstration of the "light" Farmall tractor at the Hinsdale Research Farm, the New Work Committee decided to definitely abandon the "heavy" Farmall in favor of the "light" Farmall developed under the leadership of Bert R. Benjamin of McCormick Works. This critical decision started the International Harvester Company on a tractor development program that would lead to IHC domination of the tractor market and bring radical change to tractor designs throughout the industry.

By July 29, 1922, the New Work Committee stopped work on the "heavy" Farmall. This decision represented a major shift in direction and highlights what may have been a very intense political and ideological struggle between the two main players in the Farmall development project.

A. E. Johnston was in charge of the experimental department at Tractor Works where the motor cultivator and early Farmall development work was done.

Bert R. Benjamin was superintendent of the experimental department at McCormick Works where the attachments for the motor cultivator and early Farmalls were developed. These two men appear to have evolved significantly different concepts for the Farmall tractor. Since Benjamin did not have control of development at Tractor Works, he tried to influence the direction through persuasion, letters, and memos. After the Benjamin concept "light" Farmall was well received at the Hinsdale demonstration and development stopped on the "heavy" Farmall, it would seem reasonable to assume that the political battle came to a head. Whatever the true situation, senior management made the decision to transfer B. R. Benjamin to the City Office (The Corporate Office) and he was assigned the duties of "coordinating all of the work in connection with the Farmall and Farmall machines."

Who Deserves Credit for the Farmall Tractor?

Notes on the Development of the Farmall Tractor is an unpublished paper written by C. W. Gray prepared for the patent department and dated September 15, 1932. He gives significant credit for development of the Farmall tractor to Bert R. Benjamin. The archives contain an eight-page memorandum dated June 20, 1934, from A. E. Johnston to Mr. Gray's superior, A. C. Seyfarth, regarding the copy of the notes Johnston received on November 7, 1933. Mr. Johnston's memorandum is a scathing, detailed rebuttal of Gray's document. He recited year by year the accomplishments he and his department had achieved on the Farmall and other projects. The content of the memo is best summed up with his opening statement, "It is indeed unfortunate that such a document containing so many errors and misstatements should ever have been compiled." He delivered the memorandum in person. A. E. Johnston states, and we would surely agree, "In connection with the development of most of our products over a long period of years, and this is especially true of the Farmall and its attachments, the ideas and suggestions of a large number of engineers are involved; consequently, it is difficult to place individual credit where it belongs." Rightly or wrongly, Bert R. Benjamin's promotion to the City Office and being named Farmall coordinator made him the person most recognized as the key person in the success of the Farmall development program.

Not everyone agreed with the decision to stop work on the "heavy" Farmall and concentrate on Benjamin's "light" Farmall, but a firm decision had been made. In fact, test work being conducted on the 17 bi-directional, "heavy" Farmall tractors in the field was brought to a halt. There is no recorded evidence that A. E. Johnston and his Tractor Works people did not cooperate fully with the new plan.

With firm direction and Bert Benjamin's leadership, development of a marketable machine moved rapidly. Photos of the Farmall in February of 1923 look very much like the 200 full production tractors manufactured in 1924. Control of cost and weight were always paramount. The air cleaner was a long pipe with a flannel intake cover. The exhaust was a tall, straight pipe. The steering pedestal in front of the radiator does not provide arms to actuate lateral movement of a front-mounted cultivator or differential braking; that was soon to change. Two months later, photos show the steering column modified to accommodate both brake-assisted steering and cultivator frame shift; the front-mounted two-row cultivator is also shown. Accomplishing so much in such a short time indicates that everyone on the team was excited about getting the new "light" Farmall ready for test and early production.

Manufacturing was fully committed to producing the successful McCormick-Deering 10-20 tractor and made it clear they could not build the 25 preproduction

This photo shows the clean, well-balanced design of the Farmall prototype. The "light" non-reversible Farmall design was ready on February 16, 1923, just seven months after the critical decision of July 1922 to abandon the bi-directional, or reversible, "heavy" Farmall.

This April 1923 engineering shop photo records successful installation of the previously developed lateral movement cultivator and shows cables for actuating the differential braking system.

Farmalls approved for 1923; they would have to be built by the Engineering Department. Of the 26 Farmalls actually produced, seven were sent to different outlying company territories so broad experience would be gained. Three each were placed on the Hinsdale experimental farm and the Insul farm at Libertyville, Illinois. The remaining tractors were located on the near-by Aurora territory or close to Hinsdale. All tractors were followed closely, because a major decision on this new Farmall concept would soon need to be made. Fate of the all-purpose tractor program would rest on the performance of these 26 units.

Experience with the carefully followed 1923 preproduction tractors identified mechanical and design problems that needed attention, but the performance of the concept was positive.

Changes needed for 1924:
- Increased rear axle diameter
- Stronger, single-piece front bolster
- Improved drawbar
- Rolled tube main frame rails
- Strengthened bull gear housing
- Flat front wheel tire
- Kerosene tank capacity increased from 10 to 13 gallons
- Special equipment for specific sales areas

Farmall field experience was summarized in October and the reports were good; "In every case the purchaser or user had been most enthusiastic on the operation of the machine." Now, what do you do for next year?

The Vice President of Sales was concerned about the impact of a large number of Farmalls on the sale of the all-important McCormick-Deering 10-20; he recommended only 100 machines be produced for 1924. Edward A. Johnston had the vision to state that, "If the 10-20 tractor is to be killed, it is better for us to do it

than wait for somebody else to do it." Since he and President Legge were more committed to the project, they recommended production of 200 Farmalls if too much excess cost did not result from the increased production. A manufacturing order for 200 Farmalls and cultivators was entered. Conservatism still ruled where other attachments were concerned, only 10 Farmall mowers and 10 Farmall corn planters were scheduled for production.

1924 Farmall Production at Tractor Works — A First Hand Report

The senior author had the unique opportunity in 1994 to interview and tape record the personal recollections of Kenneth J. Sayre. This 91-year-old farmer and agricultural engineering graduate related how he had been hired by International Harvester in 1924 at 50 cents/hour to test drive, help assemble, and break-in the first 200 Farmalls produced at Tractor Works. Following are the experiences he shared:

"In December 1923 I went to Chicago and applied for work at the I.H. Tractor Factory at 24th and Western Avenue. They soon called and hired me to test and break in the first run of 200 Farmall Regular tractors. These tractors were built in a small corner of the huge 10-20 factory. The man in charge of the experimental department was named Critic, and he was well named. He was a hard driver and required quality work.

This 1923 preproduction Farmall had a lateral shift, front-mounted cultivator. Since the Farmall did not have a power lift system, the cultivator depth and lift was controlled by a pair of inward canted levers. Long counterbalance springs helped the operator to manually raise the cultivator.

"Farmall tractors were built on three sets of saw horses. First the frame rails were laid over two horses and all of the components were bolted to the side rails. The engine came all assembled. Transmissions and rear axle assembly were put together on benches at one side of the work area.

"I think there was one foreman and two workers besides myself. They tried to finish two tractors every day but did not always make it. I did very little work on assembly, as I was kept busy breaking in the tractors in the big yard in back of the factory. I had to run each tractor around the lot for three hours dragging a 10-20 rear wheel fastened to the drawbar with a log chain. This made the tractor work a little. When it snowed 3 or 4 inches deep I could not pull the wheel as there were no lugs on the smooth steel rear wheels; I was continually getting stuck. I was instructed to turn sharp left and right so as to pivot the inside wheel and see that the turning brakes were properly adjusted and the brake cables set at the right

This Farmall power take-off mower represents one of the strengths of the Farmall program; implements were specifically designed to match the new tractor. Since it was directly mounted to the tractor drawbar in a trailing position, the unit could cut square corners. Like the all-important front mounted cultivator, the Farmall mower was designed, developed, and manufactured at the International Harvester McCormick Works and is pictured in front of the office.

tension. Wheel trouble developed on the first tractors. The hubs cracked and failed. The engineers finally made a heavier cast-steel hub which didn't break. The only other major trouble I remember was with the differential spider gear thrust washer. The first washers were steel on steel; they cut out at once. Then came steel on bronze washers; these were better but still didn't last long. Finally they used a ball thrust bearing on each side and the trouble stopped.

"By the time they had built about 100 tractors, most of the bugs were eliminated. After I had driven each tractor a minimum of three hours and Mr. Critic okayed it, I drove it to the paint department to be painted. The tractors I drove did not have the tall intake and exhaust pipes, these must have been installed by the dealer; they were really noisy. If there was a tractor painted and ready, I drove it back to the shipping dock and drained the radiator as they did not use antifreeze. If there was no painted tractor to return, I walked back to the workplace. I discovered a shortcut through the drop forage plant. It was a welcome place as it was always very warm there and I was always cold. Chicago is the coldest place on earth in winter as it is so damp when the wind blows off of Lake Michigan. The drop forage plant fascinated me as it was a spectacular sight to see a white-hot billet of steel pounded into a crank shaft in a matter of a few seconds. The showers of sparks looked like a fireworks display. I never stayed there long as I was generally behind in breaking in the next tractor. When the thrust bearings were replaced I had to break in the differential again to be sure it was okay. This took another hour or two.

"When I wasn't running a tractor I helped with assembly. Mostly I lined up the clutch shaft with the flexible coupling under the U-shaped steel shield in front of the transmission case. A dial indicator was used to check the alignment and shims were placed, generally under the rear motor mounts if the engine was low and under the front if it was high.

"One interesting facet of the 10-20 factory was the engine break-in department. This was a large room with some 30 or 40 D.C. electric motor/generators. A 10-20 engine was hooked to each generator with quick hookups for exhaust, water, and gasoline. First the engine was run by this motor to break it in. After the proper time, the engine was fueled and it turned the generator. Thus the gen-erators furnished enough current to run the ones which were breaking in the newest engines. The whole unit was self-powered.

"In early May we finished the 200 tractors and I was sent to Libertyville for a short time. When that job ended, I was told to go back to the factory for a new assignment. As I was fed up with Chicago's climate and smog, I resigned and returned to my father's farm where I lived until, at age 84, I moved to town."

In 1991, Mr. Sayre attended the Rock River Thresheree and had the pleasure of seeing an original 1924 Farmall Regular owned by Mr. Harry Lee of Elnora, Indiana. It was an exciting day for Ken Sayre to be "reunited" with the Farmall he had driven 67 years earlier.

How Do You Market the New Tractor Concept?

In order to market the 200 Farmalls, a price needed to be established and the Vice President of Sales recommended $825 for the Farmall tractor and $88.50 for the cultivator. Since the 200 units were mostly hand built, the cost would be high and the suggested tractor price would result in a loss. The price, however, was part of the introduction strategy. By fall it was sug-

A June 1924 photo of one of the first 200 production Farmalls shows the McCormick-Deering Farmall and patent pending stencils on the fuel tank and main frame of the tractor. The patent pending statement had real meaning because engineering and the Patent Department were actively trying to protect the inventions embodied in the new Farmall tractor and related implements. This casual product identification is in keeping with a low-volume production run of a new product assembled on wooden saw-horses in a corner of the big Tractor Works facility. The smiling operator is likely an engineer — could it be Bert Benjamin? — happily posing with three helpers on the product he had worked so hard to make a reality.

Mr. Charles Urfer demonstrates the versatility of the 1924 Farmall Regular and 10-foot McCormick-Deering power drive binder on his farm near Des Moines, Iowa.

gested that the Farmall price should be increased to $950 to "test the market."

The first Farmall produced carried Serial Number QC501 and was retailed to a customer in Taft, Texas. Bert Benjamin followed this tractor carefully and returned to Chicago convinced of the need for a four-row Farmall cultivator. By June, a four-row cultivator was tested at Hinsdale. By July, 111 Farmall tractors had been retailed and the balance were being heavily demonstrated. Nine of these 1924 production Farmalls were sold in Texas which supported the plan to place the new Farmalls in areas that were not prime McCormick-Deering 10-20 tractor territory.

Experience with the 200 Farmalls produced in 1924 resulted in a list of improvements for 1925. Most of these changes strengthened or simplified various components. Two very significant changes were replacing the tall intake pipe and flannel-covered, banded ball with a Pomona air cleaner and replacing the tall, open exhaust pipe with a muffler.

The Farmall results in 1924 were encouraging. The Vice President of Sales returned from a field trip con-

The Farmall tractor mowing fairways at the Aurora Country Club, Aurora, Illinois, in this 1924 photo does not carry the name Fairway. The Fairway tractor with 8-inch wide front and 16-inch wide rear tires would not be released until 1929.

This first 1924 Farmall tractor (Serial Number QC503) and cultivator sold was purchased by Roy Murphy, Forestdale Farm, West Burlington, Iowa. In 1945, the Company bought back this tractor and restored it for the big post-World War II Product Introduction at Hinsdale. The proud, original owner must have installed a 1925 Pomona air cleaner on his 1924 tractor in place of the tall intake pipe and flannel covered inlet used on the first 200 Farmall tractors.

These Farmall tractors were coming down the production line for 1925. Replacing the tall intake pipe and flannel strainer with a Pomona air cleaner, shown here, and adding a muffler in place of the long, straight pipe were two of the more significant improvements over the first 200 Farmalls built in 1924.

vinced the Company should build 500 Farmalls for 1925. Others were more conservative and the schedule set in the fall of 1924 called for 250 Farmalls for the following year; the more optimistic estimate proved more nearly right; 870 Farmalls were produced and sold in 1925. Wisely, the Council did not say the Farmall product was ready for export.

In the spring of 1925 Mr. Legge, president of IHC, showed enough confidence in the Farmall that he didn't feel it was necessary to spend money on a national advertising program. Dealer advertising was limited to a four-side, fold-over mailer. The cover stated, "FARMALL POWER — A New Development" and the inside headline read, "A Few of the Jobs the Farmall Does Better Than Any Other Power." Photos illustrated the Farmall drilling, checking, and cultivating corn, mowing hay, pulling a corn binder, and powering a tractor grain binder. Belt power for threshing and sawing wood was also shown. Graphics stressed the 7-1/2-foot turning radius and 30-inch rear axle clearance of the Farmall. In keeping with management policy, no horsepower figures were given. Rather than leave a questionable void, the specifications read:

> *Belt Horse Power, suitable for 20-inch threshers fully equipped or average-size ensilage cutters.*
>
> *Drawbar Horse Power, pulls two 14-inch bottoms in average conditions.*

Texas Success for 1925 Farmalls

Nine IHC management and product test group people check out a 1925 Farmall tractor and four-row planter in San Angelo, Texas. Was this demonstration of one-man operation of a four-row planter and Farmall tractor a farmer development or an engineering experiment? The archives give us no clue. The most significant person in the picture is the last one on the right. He is Bert R. Benjamin who was in charge of the experimental department at McCormick Works when he proposed the "light" all-purpose tractor that became the production Farmall. Texas owner quotes helped market the new Farmall.

"I've been feeding ninety head of mules but never again; there goes my fifth Farmall."

"My wife uses a nickel's worth of ice per day and the drippings from the ice box is more than ample for the Farmall."

"Well, I'm buying my second Farmall today. When I bought my first last spring I was afraid it would give me considerable trouble as it looked spinderly [sic], but there has not been a cent spent on it, and it pulls as well today as it did the day it was delivered to me."

The primary sales technique was to place a Farmall with a farmer prospect for his use for a week or ten days. When the dealer or company man would make the return trip to pick up the demonstration tractor, the user would usually agree to a purchase rather than let the Farmall leave the farm.

Another reason for restricting Farmall advertising was that Company management continued to be concerned about reducing demand for the very important new McCormick-Deering 10-20 and 15-30 tractors. Territory sales managers were frequently reminded not to let down on promoting the Company's bread and butter tractors just because they had something new in the Farmall.

The Ronning Patent

A possible complication arose for the Farmall and front-mounted cultivator in 1925. IHC was threatened with an infringement suit based on the Ronning patent. A six-page analysis by the Patent Department summarized with a final opinion that the Ronning patent did not read on the Farmall tractor cultivator construction. Rather than fight and possibly loose, the Company decided to contract for a license. They paid A. G. and Adolph Ronning of the Ronning Machine Company, Minneapolis, Minnesota a $25,000 cash advance and $1.00 per Farmall tractor starting May 1, 1926, and throughout the 10-year life of the contract. Correspondence in the archives covers the negotiations and records the payments made each six months. An interesting January 1935 settlement entry says 262 tractors returned to the Works. Were they reworked and shipped again in a different pay period? There is no further explanation.

Fordson Tractors Dominate the Industry

During the period from 1918 to 1928, the Fordson tractor from Ford Motor Company became the tractor sales leader. Fordson tractors would easily tip over backward resulting in operator death or injury. Strange looking, rear projecting fenders — which incorporated a tool box — attempted to solve the problem. The tractor had other design shortcomings that required careful maintenance and frequently resulted in hard starting. However, the product that

came to market had one outstanding feature: Price! Mr. Ford had the financial resources to buy market share if he chose; he did.

The Fordson was said to represent 76 percent of the total U.S. tractor market in 1923. Because of the size of the Ford organization and the use of automobile components in their tractor, International Harvester Company management understood they could not compete with the Fordson on price. The new Farmall provided a way to compete with a needed product innovation. Ford's share of the tractor market slipped to 64 percent by 1925 and continued to fall until Ford ended tractor production in America in 1928.

A New Home for the New Farmall

Activities during 1925 laid the groundwork for major growth in the Farmall program the following year. The Moline Plow Company tractor factory of Rock Island, Illinois, had been purchased by IHC in 1924. Now the major decision was made to tool this Tri-Cities (Quad City) plant for the sole production of Farmall tractors.

A fascinating quote from the Farmall Works booklet follows:

"This big manufacturing plant was not conceived in the spirit of the slow-moving, ox team age of the early nineteenth century — a little at a time — a building here and an extension there. It was made to order in all its detail all at one time, and when the big whistle sounded its first blast on that opening day in June 1926, it was a twentieth-

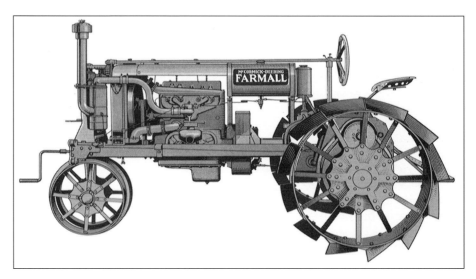

IH Farm magazine offered this color art rendering of the Farmall Regular as part of a "Portfolio of Antique Tractors in 1967." A letter from the IH Corporate Archivist states there were two different product identifications used on the Farmall Regular. The very earliest models had black letters, "McCormick-Deering Farmall" on the gray background color of the tractor. A later version of the Farmall Regular had decals with a black background and white letters like the artwork.

century plant that sprang into being. The opening of the Farmall Works marked the beginning of a new era for the American Farmer and helped to eliminate the horse as a beast of burden."

From Conservatism to Unbridled Optimism

Bert R. Benjamin's analysis of cotton production cost documented that the Farmall system could lower cost to $83.33 per bale compared to production with mules at $110 per bale. Better yet, production cost with a Farmall was less than the $95 per bale cost in Egypt and other foreign countries. With the Farmall, American cotton growers could compete on the world market.

In the South, demand for a four-row planter was documented along with the need for middlebuster attachments. These larger farms wanted to fully utilize the productive capacity of this new tractor. Fifty four-row cultivators were tested in Texas and the Central District.

Farmall demonstrations were held in the Nebraska territory. This was an area where International Harvester received very limited tractor business and was a good place for Farmall market expansion. Territory management was warned, however, about limited Farmall production capability. In August 1924, management finally agreed to schedule the Farmall for the Nebraska Tractor Test the following year.

By May 1925, the General Office sales manager was recommending having 1,000 Farmalls by the end of October. By the end of July an order for 2,500 Farmalls was placed for 1926. All estimates proved very conservative, because the results for 1926 were 4,400 Farmalls. To support the increased production, an expanded advertising program was initiated. The International Harvester Company publication *Tractor Farming* carried a feature article on the Farmall titled, "General-Purpose Tractor." The article said the "Much-talked of 'New Model' (is now) released to the whole United States."

Based on the growth in sales for 1926, branch house and district managers began to estimate sales of 6,500 to 7,500 Farmalls for 1927. Company President and long-time supporter of the Farmall, Alex Legge, very clearly stated his position, "Sometime around the first of the year (1927) we need to get up our courage and perhaps go to a bigger schedule in order that an accumulation of Farmall tractors can be made to meet what I feel to be a sure demand in the next year's cultivating period." He was right!

Production at the new Rock Island, Farmall Works had only reached 10 per day by October 12 and 20 per day by October 25, 1926; then a steady trend of rapid expansion began in 1927. Production was up to 25 per

THE FIRST PUBLICATION DEVOTED EXCLUSIVELY TO FARMING WITH TRACTORS

TRACTOR FARMING

Reg. U. S. Pat. Off.

Vol. 11.   Nos. 3 and 4   Chicago, March—April, 1926   Copyright, 1926 by International Harvester Company

After two years of very limited advertising, Farmall finally hit the front page of Tractor Farming. *The job of check-row planting in the picture was so well done the hills of corn even line up perfectly at a 45% angle.*

day by the third week of January and hit 30 per day ten days later. President Legge wired Chicago from California in April of 1927 and asked how long it would take to increase Farmall production to 50 per day. Manufacturing achieved Legge's 50 per day by May 16. By late August, acceptance in the field and confidence in the product prompted Legge to request 60 per day; he got his wish on November 14, 1927. Farmall demand was also supported with improved attachments and new products that would expand its usefulness. A new two-row mounted corn picker was under development.

The author's experience in product development and manufacturing leads to the following conclusion: By early 1927, many people in International Harvester middle and upper management must have gotten squarely behind the Farmall product and started early to plan for rapid expansion of production. To double tractor output in five months — mid January to mid May — is an impressive accomplishment.

Peter J. Lux, three-time Grand champion "Corn-King" winner of the 10-ear International Corn Show in Chicago, is pictured on his Farmall in 1926. The photo was part of a Tractor Farming *article recording how the "Corn Kings Praise Farmall" for its roll in producing the champion crop. Son Thomas Lux was the Junior Champion.*

The IHC Research Farm at Hinsdale, Illinois, 15 miles west of Chicago, provided an ideal location for operating experimental equipment like this Farmall Regular and 4-row mounted cultivator.

Farmall tractor success continued to challenge the Rock Island Farmall Works ability to produce. Following the 1927 accomplishments, manufacturing again almost doubled production. Output went from 65 per day in January 1928 to 125 per day the first week of June. Increases continued until Farmall Works produced 200 tractors per day on January 27, 1930.

The farm machinery industry has always been dominated by concern for development and marketing of tractors and achieving the desired tractor market share. This must have been as true then as it is now because the written record in the IH Archives says little about the important role cultivators, planters, corn pickers, and other vital attachments played in achieving the Farmall's rapid rise to dominance. Credit must also be given to the total International Harvester Company and its wide-spread dealer organization. On April 12, 1930, The International Harvester Company celebrated production of the 100,000th Farmall tractor. The occasion was described in *Harvester World* as follows, "Vice President Cyrus McCormick Jr. in the presence of Company officers, department managers, distinguished guests, and the tractor makers themselves, *a milestone in Farmalling* [sic] *of Agriculture* (italics are the senior author's) was most colorfully and impressively marked." By July of the same year, 1930, the Company recorded the production of the 200,000th McCormick-Deering 10-20 tractor.

Colorful "fans for hot weather" were offered to McCormick-Deering dealers and promoted for use as advertising at the fair. If the dealer's wife objected to promotions that featured the faces of pretty ladies, the likeness of a hunting dog could fill the bill. At 2 1/2 cents each, the price was right even in 1927.

143

To meet the farming requirements of differing geographic areas, machines like this four-row, front-mounted lister planter were developed for the Farmall Regular.

The first major Farmall milestone, the 100,000th Farmall, Farmall Works, April 12, 1930.

Confidence in the Farmall . . . Confidence in the Future

The celebration would be short lived. By the fall of 1930 the farm economy began a sustained decline that over the months and years ahead would impact the entire farm equipment industry and all of agriculture. The problems in the farm economy helped contribute to the long and painful depression in America during the 1930s. During this period, farsighted management had the courage to support expansion of the Farmall Regular into a family of tractors and initiate development of a totally new and different line of future Farmall tractors in spite of the doom and gloom.

In addition to the economic disaster of 1929, IHC now had a valid challenger to the Farmall for the first time; J I Case introduced their Model CC, General-Purpose, tricycle tractor. In response, the Company built their tractor sales campaign around the slogan:

If it isn't a McCORMICK-DEERING, it isn't a FARMALL

IHC introduced the new Farmall F-30 in 1931. The original Farmall had a two-plow rating; the new Farmall F-30 had a three-plow rating. Along with the 50 percent increase in capacity rating came a four-speed transmission and enclosed steering gears. This was the first of what would become a three-member, F-Series of model numbered Farmalls. Up to this time, with only one model, the name Farmall said it all.

Manufacturing records from 1932 show production of the new F-20 regular and narrow tread, the new F-12, and a narrow tread version of the F-30. This was also the year Allis-Chalmers introduced a production tractor on "air tires." The depression and a horribly depressed agricultural economy devastated tractor and farm equipment sales. To maximize sales of existing inventory, major promotion of the new products was held back. To promote the economics of tractor ownership, a one-year cost study of 156 McCormick-Deering Farmall tractors was publicized in *Harvester World*, "These Figures Show the Farmall Saves $6.72 per day Compared to 8 Work Horses."

The new McCormick-Deering Farmall F-20 had physical dimensions practically the same as the

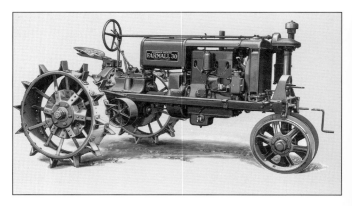

Harvester World *introduced the new Farmall F-30 with a full page in 1931. The headline read, "a 3-Plow Model of the Original FARMALL."*

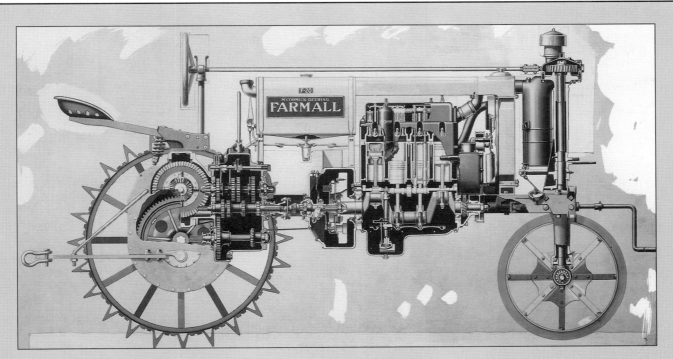

This line art graphic beautifully illustrates the rugged simplicity of the Farmall F-20. A combination of fuel economy, size, features, and price made this model the most popular tractor in the F-Series during its 1932 to 1940 production run.

The F-30 Farmall tractors came in regular, narrow tread, cane, and cane-regular versions as well as this cane high-speed model.

The proven design components of the Farmall F-20 and F-30 drive line helped earn these tractors a reputation for rugged dependability and performance that set the industry standard for all-purpose tractors.

Internal Expanding
Differential Brake—
9-in. diam.
1¾-in. face

4 Differential
Spider Pinions

Steel Casting

2 double-row
ball bearings
support differential
assembly

Ball Bearing

3 Ball Bearings
on Pulley Shaft

Double Ball
Bearing

Heavy Roller
Bearing

Pulley shaft construction permits
removing pulley and attaching cover
plate without disturbing adjustment of
bevel gear set.

original Farmall or Farmall Regular including the 3 3/4-inch bore by 5-inch stroke engine. Most of the Farmall Regular equipment and attachments would fit the new tractor. With rubber tires and the wheels turned in, a minimum tread of 68-inches was possible; with a special axle extension and the wheels turned out a maximum tread of 96-inches was possible. Significant changes were the four-speed transmission that provided two "very good plowing speeds" and a 10-percent increase in horsepower. The enclosed steering gear introduced on the F-30 was now standard on the new line including the F-20.

1934 price of a Model F-20 Farmall tractor (4-cylinder vertical) with friction clutch pulley, PTO, and steel lug wheels: **$895**

1939 price of a Model F-20 on rubber front and rear: **$1,190**

This black-and-white photo of a McCormick-Deering Farmall F-20 on rubber and an attractive, modest farmstead was converted to a color drawing, shown at right, that featured the identical tractor and plow, but the barn more than doubled in size and acquired a silo. At the end of the twentieth century, we do it with computer graphics.

This gray Farmall on rubber with red wheels is one of the last tractors with this color scheme before Farmall went all red in 1937.

A composition steering wheel in place of the original cast iron was a new feature for this McCormick-Deering Farmall F-20 with adjustable wide front axle attachment.

When F-20 production ended in 1939, 148,960 of these extremely popular tractors had rolled off the Farmall Works assembly line.

A Third Member of the F-Series Farmall Family

The new McCormick-Deering Farmall F-12 was a totally new tractor. Management and engineering had recognized that if you wanted a significantly lower cost, more economical tractor, you couldn't just make the original Farmall a little smaller, a little lighter, and reduce the horsepower. They did these things but also utilized large diameter rear drive wheels to make it possible to eliminate the external bull gear drop axle and still maintain the Farmall's reputation for rear axle crop clearance. To accomplish this, a totally new, three-speed transmission and final drive was required. Since the drive wheels were clamped to a rear axle that extended beyond the end of the rear axle housing, wheel tread adjustment from 44 to 78 inches could be achieved; this was a significant contribution to Farmall tractor application flexibility.

This McCormick-Deering Farmall F-20 was working with a 10-foot McCormick-Deering M4-type power drive binder. The merits of the Farmall tractor PTO were well established by the time this photograph was taken on the Grover Evans and Son farm, Kirkland, Indiana, in 1936.

The Farmall F-12 Transmission and Final Drive

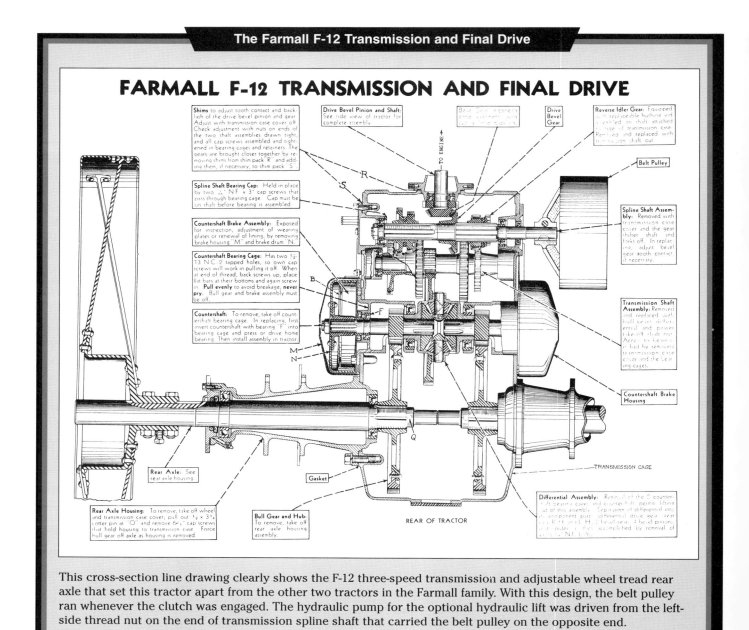

FARMALL F-12 TRANSMISSION AND FINAL DRIVE

This cross-section line drawing clearly shows the F-12 three-speed transmission and adjustable wheel tread rear axle that set this tractor apart from the other two tractors in the Farmall family. With this design, the belt pulley ran whenever the clutch was engaged. The hydraulic pump for the optional hydraulic lift was driven from the left-side thread nut on the end of transmission spline shaft that carried the belt pulley on the opposite end.

The new F-12 with its 3-inch bore by 4-inch stroke, valve-in-head engine was rated for one 16-inch plow or two 10-inch plows, two-row cultivator, two-row corn and cotton planter. Furthermore, even with all of the changes it looked like it belonged to the Farmall family. The new lower-priced tractor sold in the depressed economy of the 1930s for $500 to $600 depending on equipment. Fifteen "Quick Detachable" implements designed for the Farmall F-12 further complemented the tractor. This popular little tractor stayed in production until it was replaced with the similar F-14 in 1938.

The design of the F-12 easily accommodated the hydraulic power lift attachment that brought new operating convenience to this smallest of the new F-Series Farmalls. An external gear pump was mounted on the left side of the transmission case and driven from the nut on the end of the transmission spline shaft. The vane-type hydraulic actuator and lift arm assembly mounted on top of the transmission case under the operator's seat. The two-way control value, also under the operator's seat, provided for both up and down pressure.

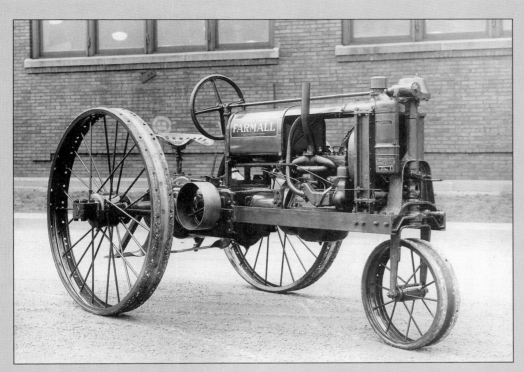

Since there were Farmall F-20's and F-30's already in production, engineering must have assumed a lower horsepower tractor would be named Farmall F-10; not so, the new tractor would be named Farmall F-12. Engineers don't think like marketers; marketers don't think like engineers.

Adding the one-plow Farmall F-12 and the two-plow F-20 to the three-plow F-30 in 1932 gave IHC an all-purpose lineup of tractors to meet virtually any need.

One Tractor Model — Two Different Engines

The first 25 Farmall F-12 tractors produced in 1932 had Waukesha, four-cylinder, L-head engines. This is the engine pictured in the Gas Power Engineering photo captioned F-10 Farmall tractor. It has the exhaust on the right side and a long, curved intake pipe leading to the air cleaner mounted on the right side of the radiator. In 1933, Farmall F-12 tractors Serial Number 600 to 608 had International Harvester-manufactured, four-cylinder, valve-in-head engines. The next F-12 tractors built were equipped with the original Waukesha engine. Late in 1933, starting with Serial Number 3034, the engine was changed again; and this time it was equipped with the same valve-in-head engine used earlier in the year. This became the standard engine with the air cleaner and exhaust both on the left like the two larger Farmall tractors; it looked like it belonged to the Farmall family.

One theory claims the Waukesha engine was used to save cost. Another theory claims that IHC wanted to aide the struggling Waukesha Motor Company. A third theory claims valve-in-head engines were in short supply or had a reliability problem in early 1932-1933. Maybe a note buried in the archives will tell us someday.

New Paint for Safety

Beginning November 1, 1936, all Farmall tractors were painted red. The stated reason was that red was considered a safety factor with so many Farmalls moving on public roads. In 1932 an IHC tractor sales department representative said his calculations showed that, "at least nine of every ten all-purpose tractors in the field are Farmalls." The color change moved IHC forever from the world of gray Farmall tractors to the world of "BIG RED!"

This traditional farm home in 1934 had the modern convenience of electricity thanks to the REA line in front of the house. The new Farmall F-12 tractor provided the owner with all of the benefits of modern rubber tractor tires. The diamond tread design of the rear tires identify them as Goodyear tractor tires.

The trim little F-14 equipped with fenders and rubber tires front and rear makes a most attractive unit in 1938. This kerosene-fuel version has a small gasoline tank used for starting; half of the tank projects above the hood line and makes it easy to identify the kerosene model. The control rod for adjusting the radiator shutters is clearly visible on the right side of the tractor.

Even though a dramatic new line of Farmall tractors would come on the market the following year, the improved F-12 was introduced as the F-14 in regular, wide front end, orchard, and fairway versions in 1938. The elevated steering wheel was a distinguishing feature. Update kits were available to convert Farmall F-12 tractors to the new F-14; they even included an F-14 serial number plate. An optional electric starter and light package was available; however, the engine ignition was still powered from the magneto.

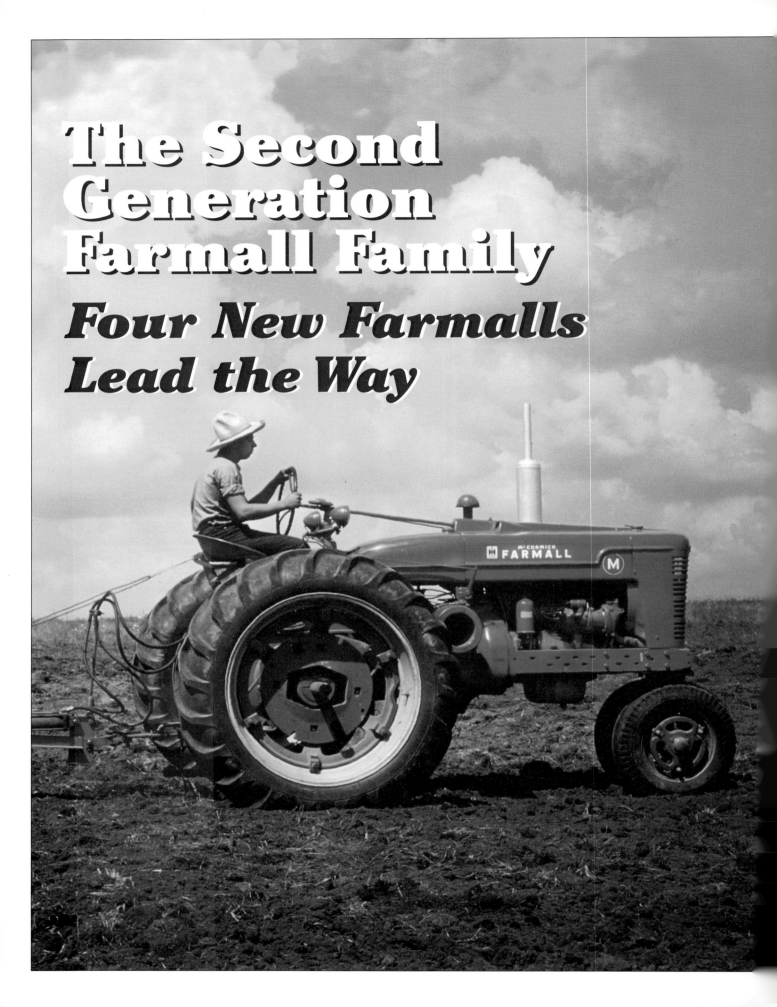

The Second Generation Farmall Family

Four New Farmalls Lead the Way

International Harvester not only weathered the economic depression years of the 1930s, the Company invested in developing a series of new products including four new Farmall tractors. These were not just improved Farmall F-14's, F-20's, and F-30's, they were totally new tractors; this called for a major introduction.

Literature Proclaimed:
A and B Small Size,
H Middle Size, M Large Size

First came the public introduction of the Farmall A on July 12, 1939, at the Tractor Works in Chicago, Illinois, where it was manufactured. Each branch house that had a potential market for Farmall A tractors followed up with local and dealer promotions for this smallest member of the new Farmall family.

Next came a formal debut of the new modern, high operator platform, row-crop Farmall H and M tractors on August 9, 1939, at Rock Island, Illinois. Farmall Works and the local Chamber of Commerce worked together to put on Farmall Day. It began with a luncheon for community leaders and the media, followed by a plant tour and product parade featuring the new tractors and matching size Farmall implements. The closing event attracted 15,000 employees and their families and other citizens of the area to the local high school stadium for a tractor and implement parade, music, and entertainment. Farmall Day featured the new Farmall Works-produced H and M, and also included the recently introduced Farmall A as well.

The influence of IH-retained industrial designer Raymond Loewy is easily recognized in this impressive looking Farmall 22 prototype tractor. Unfortunately, the fully enclosed side panel and grill did not end up in the final version. Did it look too much like a major competitor? Was the tooling and product cost too high?

A New Look for Farmall Tractors

In the late 1930s IHC management took a bold step for a farm machinery manufacturer; they commissioned the internationally known industrial designer, Raymond Loewy, to give the new Farmall tractors a distinctive, modern family appearance. The new IHC family styling also included the TracTracTor crawler tractors. Both of these product lines shared the same radiator grill design including the three silver stripes and three-dimensional Farmall or International name plate. In 1939 the IHC cream separator even received the Raymond Loewy design touch.

Tractor Power
Not Horsepower

The beautiful, multi-page, two-color literature that accompanied the 1939 introduction of the Farmall H and M tractors described the new Farmall H as, "the tractor for that large group of farms known as

Gas power engineering photos record this 1937 styling proposal for the new family of Farmall tractors. Note the vertical steering wheel typical of the original Farmall series.

The Farmall M, flagship of the new McCormick-Deering Farmall tractors, was introduced at the Rock Island, Illinois home of Farmall Works in 1939. Since the Farmall H and M shared a common wheel base and the same attaching points, mounted implements would fit either tractor. The tractors in both photos are shown with cultivator shifter levers extending from the front bolster.

The classic styling of this McCormick-Deering Farmall H tractor and its larger counterpart, both introduced in 1939, established IHC dominance in row-crop tractors for more than a decade.

average." The Farmall M, on the other hand, was described as a more powerful tractor. "It will pull three 14- or 16-inch bottoms under harder than average soil conditions at good plowing speed, pull a 9-foot double disk harrow, handle four-row planters and cultivators and three- or four-row middlebusters and listers and two-row corn pickers." Page after page of descriptive text never mentioned actual belt or drawbar horse-

power ratings. Since the days of the first Farmall Regular, there was resistance to stressing raw horsepower ratings. Rather, this line of tractors was promoted in terms of the size plow or implement it could pull and how many acres could be worked in a day. In fact, as late as 1946 the Farmall H was described as "doing the work of 4 to 8 horses or mules" and the Farmall M as doing "all the work on farms that in the days of horse farming required up to 12 horses." However, a specification chart on the back page did reveal the Farmall H to have a maximum drawbar pull of 18 horsepower and the Farmall M to have a maximum drawbar pull of 27 horsepower. These tractors were equipped with combination manifold for burning distillate or gasoline; the horsepower ratings were for distillate. The *Farmall System of Farming* published in 1945 took the same approach of describing performance rather than horsepower ratings. However the horsepower specifications of the 1939 introduction literature were replaced by ASAE and SAE Test Code ratings as follows:

	Farmall H	Farmall M
Max. belt horsepower (gasoline)	27.90	39.23
Max. belt horsepower (distillate)	24.34	36.70
Max. drawbar horsepower (gasoline)	25.50	34.44
Max. drawbar horsepower (distillate)	22.65	32.86

Steel-wheeled Farmall H and M tractors had four working speeds: 2 5/8, 3 1/2, 4 1/4, and 5 1/8 mph.

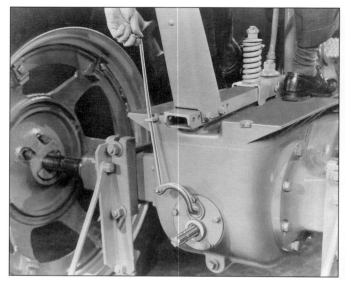

International Harvester pioneered the PTO in 1918. The Farmall H and M could be easily equipped with the transmission-driven PTO option shown in this 1939 photo.

This combination of the McCormick-Deering Farmall M tractor and McCormick PTO-driven power binder could get the job done in good conditions like this 1940 photo or in wet soggy conditions that would leave a ground-driven binder at the edge of the field.

Rubber tire equipped models had a fifth 16 3/8-mph road speed added to the basic four speeds. "This was a real time saver in getting to and from fields and hauling crops to town" said the literature.

Special transmission speeds were useful options added in 1945 for rubber-tired Farmall H and M tractors. For high-speed work with rotary hoes, harrows, and heavy road transport, a 7-mph fourth speed attachment could replace the regular 5-mph gearing. Also, an extra-low first gear could replace the standard low gear.

With the exception of a 1 1/2-inch shorter wheelbase, only minor variations in specifications occurred over the six-year period from 1939 to 1945. However, there was one major area of change. The shipping weight on steel for the Farmall H changed from 2,700 to 3,175 pounds. Shipping weight on steel for the Farmall M changed from 3,495 to 4,260 pounds. Running improvements and more standard equipment were obvious.

Direct-Connected Implements

The Farmall System of Farming included an extensive list of quick-attachable machines that would fit either the H or the M because they shared a common wheelbase and attaching methods. The 1945 offering of Farmall direct-connected machines included: moldboard and disk plows, bedders, tool bar middle-

busters, planters and listers, push-type middlebusters, two-row corn planters and drills, two- and four-row cultivators, forward-mounted planting and fertilizing attachments for cultivators, four- and six-row beet and bean cultivators, beet pullers, and bean harvesting

The Farmall Regular tractor was created to accommodate a front-mounted cultivator that would shift laterally as the front wheels were steered. The new McCormick-Deering Farmall H (shown here) and M tractors had the same capability but with vastly improved and simplified cultivators like this Farmall MH-221.

The IHC introduction of four new Farmall tractors in 1939 was coupled with an extensive offering of front-mounted and direct-connected implements. This Farmall No.11-38, four-row lister which directly connected to the McCormick-Deering Farmall M is a good example of the variety.

Tractorette? This young women might bristle at the name given to the women tractor drivers of World War I, but she's doing her part in 1942 for U.S. participation in World War II. Rubber tires, hydraulic power lift, electric starting, differential brake pedals, and greatly improved seating on this Farmall H made cultivating a lot more enjoyable for everyone compared to 25 years earlier.

attachments. The two-row Farmall No. 2-M mounted corn picker for the Farmall M tractor, capacity 16 to 20 acres per day, also made the list along with IH pull-behind equipment. Proper mounting was easy with the quick detachable "C" drawbar. Wheel tread adjusted from 44 to 80 inches on the Farmall H and from 52 to 88 inches on the Farmall M tractors.

LIFT-ALL . . . Something Absolutely New in Hydraulic Power Lifts

"The 'Lift-All' pump tucks away in 'the tractor main frame' out of the way. It is a complete unit and can be easily installed or removed," so read the descriptive literature. The pump was located directly behind the flywheel and was driven from the front end of the power take-off drive. Provision was made to lift the front section of the implement before the rear section raised, lift either side, or hold the implement at the desired working depth. It was stressed that the hydraulic cylinders were interchangeable with other Farmall implements.

"The cylinders are single-acting and leakproof," claimed the Lift-All literature; that is quite a statement. The cylinders employed a unique two-piece piston with an internal chamber and two check valves. The "leakproof cylinder" was described as follows: "Oil escaping past the piston is forced into the piston chamber and compresses the air in the chamber. When cylinder pressure is released, the compressed air forces the oil inside the piston back into the cylinder." Future single-acting cylinders would employ one-piece, solid pistons and vent the piston-rod end to the outside through a simple air filter.

The self-contained Farmall hydraulic Lift-All neatly fit in the tractor clutch housing and drove from the front end of the PTO drive. "Leakproof" single acting cylinders lifted front-mounted implements and could delay lift rear-mounted implements.

Literature said little about horsepower ratings. IHC rated the H at "two 14- or 16-inch bottoms (size depends upon soil type and plowing depth) — 9 to 10 acres per 10-hour day."

The floto oil screen was the floating type that supplied the oil pump from the top of the crankcase oil "thus supplying the engine with sediment-free oil."

The Farmall M, 3 7/8-inch bore x 5 1/4-inch stroke, and Farmall H, 3 3/8-inch bore x 4 1/4-inch stroke, replaceable cylinder sleeve engines were well engineered, carefully manufactured power plants that helped build a reputation of reliability and performance for the Farmall H and M tractors. That reputation has lived far beyond their 15-year production history. Production at Farmall Works stopped briefly on Monday morning April 30, 1951, to celebrate production of the one-millionth Farmall; then it was back to work to meet the schedule of 306 tractors per day.

Smooth, Four-Cylinder Power

"New Farmalls have the finest 4-cylinder gasoline-distillate engines ever built." To support the claim, some of the features of the new engines were listed:

- Valves in head
- Removable cylinder sleeves
- Tocco-hardened crankshaft
- Precision-type bearings (not the crankshaft!)
- Force-feed lubrication
- Floto oil screen
- Large air, oil, and fuel cleaners
- Extra large flywheels

By 1946, tractor identification lost the Deering name and acquired the new corporate symbol. The result was the IH McCormick Farmall H decal style shown here. The four-row, double tool bar HM-439 beet and bean cultivator shown here, and the similar six-row HM-639, are examples of the wide range of products included in the Farmall System of Farming.

This detailed cutaway of a 1940 McCormick-Deering Farmall M was an effective tool for telling the "inside" story of the outstanding features of the two new Farmall tractors introduced the previous year.

The two plow McCormick-Deering Farmall H tractor had more than adequate horsepower to handle this four-row McCormick-Deering drawn planter with fertilizer attachment. With the exception of the zero-pressure rubber press wheel tires and heavier frame, this tractor planter was similar to the horse-drawn planter.

This McCormick Farmall H and front-mounted HM-250 cultivator with hydraulic Lift-All is at work. Tractor and implement test and advertising photography was done on many DuPage County, Illinois farms — the county west of Chicago's Cook County — as well as the IH Hinsdale Farm. Several of these sites were farms owned by International Harvester management.

Rated as a two-plow tractor, this McCormick-Deering Farmall H is living up to its reputation.

Two-way plows are important in furrow-irrigated regions and other applications as well. This McCormick-Deering Farmall H did a good job for this western farm operation.

The Farmall H, M, and MD wide front axle adjusted from 57 to 81 inches in 4-inch increments. It provided a standard 90-inch wheelbase and an extended 100 1/2-inch wheelbase for front-mounted cultivators.

The extra power of the Farmall M was a real asset when pulling a PTO-driven forage harvester. The slow Weston (ASA) speed rating of the Kodachrome color film used in this 1940's photo was no doubt the reason this attractive farm scene was photographed static rather than with the forage harvester in action.

This mechanical lift plow and McCormick Farmall M tractor make a good "team." When farmers talk tractors, the number one topic is how many bottoms will she pull? How deep? How fast? Performance of the "M" was worth bragging about.

The design of the Farmall tractor made it adaptable to many kinds of jobs and farming practices in widely varied regions. This front-mounted, two-row middlebuster is a good example.

Loyal Users With Special Needs

International Harvester had a strong marketing presence in the South and South East. This included states like Louisiana that produced sugar cane on high beds. Special high-clearance Farmall "V" Series tractors had front ends and final drive drop axles that provided the needed under-frame clearance. The Farmall HV had 30 1/4-inch clearance under the front axle and the Farmall MV had 29 7/8-inch clearance under the rear axle. The added clearance was obtained at the rear by means of a roller chain driven counter shaft and axle assembly. Rear wheel treads of 60, 65 3/4, and 72 inches were obtained through changes in rim position. The Company provided Farmall cane tools to match the high-clearance Farmall tractors. Producers of other crops found the high-clearance "V" Series Farmall tractor the answer to their needs as well; however, sugar cane producers were still the primary market. IHC had served these same markets earlier with the Farmall Cane tractor in 1935 and the Farmall Cane Regular and Cane High Speed in 1938. Decades and several models later, the high-clearance tractor market demand dropped to such low numbers that IH stopped production.

The Super H and M Series

In response to the beginning of the horsepower race, the Farmall Super M, MD, MV, and MDV were

With 33 1/2 drawbar horsepower and almost 30 inches of clearance under the rear axle, the high-clear McCormick-Deering Farmall MV tractor was ideally suited for the tough demands of sugar cane producers. Equipped with a direct connected tool bar and adjustable disk gangs, the outfit could perform several different tasks in building, cultivating, and maintaining the very high cane beds.

introduced in 1952 with a 1/8-inch larger cylinder bore, aluminum pistons, and other improvements for increased horsepower at the same rpm. The Super Series extended to the Farmall Super H a year later with improvements similar to the Super M. Both Super Series tractors came with disk brakes.

Torque Amplifier, "TA" . . . An International Harvester First

The Farmall Super MTA and Super MD-TA introduced the exclusive IH Torque Amplifier (TA) in 1954. This major development in tractor transmission design was located in the clutch housing. It consisted of planetary drive with its own manually operated, single-disk clutch that drove the input shaft of the regular 5-speed transmission. When the TA clutch was engaged, the planetary was locked up and delivered a one-to-one direct drive. When shifted from direct drive to TA, the clutch released and the travel speed was reduced about 32 percent; pulling ability was increased almost 48 percent. The shift from direct drive to TA and back to direct again could be done at any time, in any gear and on-the-go. The TA provided 10 forward and 2 reverse travel speeds.

Independent PTO

International Harvester was the first manufacturer to commercially introduce a tractor power take-off system. In 1954 the Farmall Super MTA introduced a major IH improvement, the independent power take-off or IPTO. Power was taken directly from the engine flywheel to the rear of the final-drive housing for input to the IPTO assembly. It contained a planetary controlled by two separate band clutches. One band clutch stopped and started the IPTO shaft. When the

Pictured is an IH McCormick Farmall Super M. A 1/8-inch increase in cylinder bore and other engine changes provided increased horsepower for the 1952-1953 Super M/Super H Series tractors.

The added power and other improvements of the McCormick Farmall Super H and M were also made available in the high-clear "V" Series tractors. This photo shows the new design, high-clear front axle with relocated support rods on the IH McCormick-Farmall Super HV.

The McCormick Farmall Super MTA introduced the exclusive International Harvester Torque Amplifier "TA" in 1954. The innovative, planetary unit ahead of the transmission made it possible to reduce travel speed almost one third with shift-on-the-go convenience and to increase drawbar power about 48 percent. The number of forward and reverse travel speeds were doubled.

The Electrall "Bug Zapper"

In the wide search for new Electrall applications, Purdue University conducted tests of an Electrall-equipped Farmall 400 with a front-mounted boom and electric grids with UV lights to attract and kill crop damaging insects. One "zapper" panel was mounted on the adjustable height boom for each row middle. Ecologists would highly approve, but the experiment never went to market.

shaft was not operating, the other band clutch held the shaft and kept it from creeping. The ability of the IPTO to stop, start, or "power unplug" PTO-operated machines independent of tractor master clutch engagement was extremely useful.

Electrall

Since development of the first PTO, the advantages of the system were partially offset by the potential safety hazard. Conscientious effort by the industry to develop effective shielding standards helped greatly; but operator cooperation was required to achieve maximum protection. Furthermore, attaching or detaching a PTO driveline from the tractor could frequently be difficult. One trouble-free answer to tractor remote power transmission was the electric power cable.

International Harvester developed the Electrall system in cooperation with the General Electric Company. This new product was first

introduced on Farmall Super MTA tractors in 1954. The generator rested in a cradle-type bracket on the right side of the tractor. The generator was belt driven by a gear-driven pulley mounted behind and on top of the tractor clutch housing. The control panel had a three-phase outlet for powering up to a 10-horsepower motors (22-horsepower gasoline engine equivalent) as a PTO replacement on farm implements or other applications. A 220-volt single-phase outlet could be used as a backup if power was lost on the rural power lines. The 115-volt, single-phase outlet provided a handy source of remote power for a long list of small hand tools. Other generator versions could be installed in a pickup bed or mounted on a two-wheel trailer for easy PTO hook up to any two-plow or larger tractor.

The idea of tractor PTO-driven power generation did find commercial application, but mounting the generator directly on the tractor or replacing the PTO did not prove to be practical. Interest in tractor-driven generators for portable AC power did continue. In 1965 the

The McCormick Farmall Super MTA pictured here is equipped with the optional Electrall system. Electric energy from the tractor-driven generator is powering a McCormick 55W baler as a replacement for the PTO drive. The system was promoted for a number of other remote electric power uses. The most significant use, however, was for standby electric power at the farmstead in case of high-line failure.

There is nothing so new as an old idea! This 1930 IHC Gas Power Engineering photo predates the Electrall by showing a McCormick-Deering 10-20 tractor equipped with a large direct current generator; the photo is titled, "Electric Power Take-Off."

Marble Electric Company manufactured a one-point hitch, PTO-driven, 2,000-watt generator for Farmall Cub tractors that was offered for sale through the IH organization.

Was the Electrall a new idea? Not at all! Photos from IHC Gas Power Engineering taken in 1930 show a large General Electric direct current generator mounted on the front of a McCormick-Deering 10-20 tractor. The caption reads, "Electric Power Take-off."

IH Logo . . . The Fastest Form of Communication

Industrial designer Raymond Loewy impacted International Harvester in many ways in addition to tractor styling. However nothing was more significant

than the IH logo and his design of the prototype sales and service building.

For the logo, Loewy began with the decades old IHC circle and proposed new versions. This was followed by stylized, lower case ih ideas. Next came block letter combinations of I and H including a pictogram with a round circle dot over the I that looked like a man driving a Farmall tricycle tractor. Finally came the familiar red and black, block IH logo. It is recognized the world over. The significance of this IH logo is demonstrated by its inclusion, in slant form, in the combined Case IH logo (used by the Case Corporation after they acquired the IH Farm Equipment Division). Industrial design philosophy is correct, a truly great logo, like the block IH, is the fastest form of communication; one quick glance and the long, full history of "Big Red" products comes to mind.

A second area of major impact on International Harvester was the Raymond Loewy designed prototype dealer building. The instantly recognized, rectangular red pylon incorporated in these buildings was a unifying element that helped tie the entire 1,800 dealer and company store sales and service organization together. The prototype design worked well for new structures; incorporating it into dealership remodeling sometimes posed challenges.

The New "Small Size" Farmall Tractors

The small Farmall tractors were produced at the Tractor Works, in Chicago, Illinois, and had been introduced in 1939 ahead of the larger H and M tractors produced at Farmall Works in Rock Island, Illinois. The first small tractor was the Farmall A. It was a one-row, four-wheel type tractor with the seat offset to the right of the engine. With a front-mounted cultivator, this arrangement gave the operator an unobstructed view of the crop row. This outstanding feature rated the trade name Culti-Vision. The 3-inch bore x 4-inch stroke, 1,400-rpm engine developed 17.35 maximum drawbar horsepower running on gasoline. A distillate-gasoline version was available that included adjustable radiator shutters and

Starting in the mid-1940s, the block IH and central red pylon prototype building became the universally recognized symbols that stood for International Harvester and its products. Both of these trademarks were the creation of the internationally recognized Raymond Loewy industrial design firm.

The first of the new line of tractors introduced in 1939 was the Tractor Works-built McCormick-Deering Farmall A.

This McCormick-Deering Farmall A cross section view highlights the long, one piece, cast housing that enclosed the clutch/flywheel assembly and connected the engine to the transmission. This design was the subject of patent infringement litigation brought against IHC by the Allis-Chalmers Company.

heat indicator. The padded seat was supported on each side by leaf springs; it was adjustable fore-and-aft and the spring rate could be changed. The seat could be unlatched and tilted back so the operator could stand. The Farmall AV was introduced two years after the Farmall A and provided an additional 6 inches of crop clearance under the rear axle. An International A version was introduced at the same time.

The second small tractor was the Farmall B. It was basically the same tractor as the Farmall A but in a three-wheel configuration. The offset seat still provided the benefits of Culti-Vision in a tractor that accommodated a two-row, front-mounted cultivator. The rear wheel tread of the A adjusted from 40 to 68 inches. Rear tread of the Farmall B adjusted from 64 to 92 inches. To meet special needs, the Farmall BN provided rear tread adjustment from 56 to 48 inches. The Farmall B and BN came standard with a single front wheel. Double front wheels for easier driving were an option when row spacing permitted.

Cultivation was the number one application for the McCormick-Deering Farmall A. The offset engine placed the operator directly over the row being cultivated. IHC called their design Culti-Vision. This photo with lines added from the operator's eyes in a gradually widening "V" to the ground was used to highlight the excellent visibility and was featured in almost every Culti-Vision advertisement. The cultivator is a double tool bar A-435 vegetable cultivator equipped with knife weeders.

The small, relatively low priced, Farmall A, AV, B, and BN tractors and their matching direct-connected implements were in keeping with the International Harvester objective of mechanizing the small acreage, two- to four-horse or mule farm. In addition, they were excellent tractors for vegetable and specialty crop producers. They made good "auxiliary" tractors on larger farms. The popular A and B tractors were produced until 1947. Due to the war, none were manufactured during 1943.

"The Large and Small of International Harvester Tractors." The International Harvester TD-18 TracTracTor was introduced the same year as the four new Farmall tractors. Picturing the little McCormick-Deering Farmall A and the giant diesel crawler side by side highlighted the range of IHC products. It also illustrated their common industrial design features.

This McCormick Farmall A tractor is equipped with a one-row, A-138, belly-mounted cultivator that did not shift when the tractor's front wheels turned.

This McCormick-Deering Farmall A tractor works with a Farmall A-12 middlebuster and No. 72 blackland planting attachment. A larger Farmall tractor works in the background.

Pictured is a McCormick-Deering Culti-Vision Farmall A tractor pulling a one-furrow plow. A rock-shaft and linkage to the touch-control power arm lifts the plow.

This McCormick-Deering Farmall A is equipped with a direct connected mower. The belt pulley and power take-off option was supplied as a unit or as separate attachments.

The real Farmall A market. This farmer in Albia, Iowa, had a business in town. Using only the tractor power of the McCormick-Deering Farmall A — no horses required — he was able to farm the 60 tillable acres of his 80-acre farm in addition to the work in town.

The added drawbar horsepower of the McCormick Farmall Super A was a welcome plus with high draft load implements like this mounted plow.

"Farmall in the Ozarks" was the headline on this Farmall A story. The 21-year-old tractor driver won a trip to IHC Chicago as part of the "Youth in Business" program. After the trip, the local International Harvester dealer loaned the young man a McCormick-Deering Farmall A to make demonstrations around the county. Finally, his dad and two other farmers went together and purchased the tractor

This McCormick-Deering Farmall A tractor is pulling a horse-drawn potato digger that had the tongue shortened. It takes four horses, and one less man, to do the same work with the potato digger in the background.

The tricycle McCormick-Deering Farmall B was designed for cultivating two normal wide rows compared to the wide-front Farmall A that was designed as a one-row cultivating tractor in wide rows. To accommodate more narrow rows, the tractor was available in the Farmall BN version with an 8-inch narrower basic wheel tread. This is a 1940, enhanced photograph.

The young lady operator demonstrates the ease of operating the McCormick-Deering Farmall A Culti-Vision tractor equipped with Touch-Control hydraulic lift. This made plowing with the direct-connected Farmall two-way plow an easy task.

This McCormick-Deering Farmall B tractor was equipped with a front-mounted, two-row, Farmall B-221 shifting gang cultivator. The two-row, Farmall B-238 cultivator was belly mounted and did not shift.

IHC Canton Works, Canton, Illinois, was glad to try out the new McCormick-Deering Farmall B tractor with the Canton-built 5-foot tandem disk harrow.

IHC Richmond Works, Richmond, Indiana, was the area where this McCormick-Deering No. 110 check-row planter with fertilizer attachment was tried out on the new McCormick-Deering Farmall B tractor. The single front wheel shown here did not steer as easily as the double front wheels. Double front wheels could be set to 6 3/4-, 9 1/2-, and 12 3/4-inch treads for easier working on beds.

The Farmall B-236 front-mounted cultivator in this photo was raised and lowered by a pneumatic Lift-All that was powered by exhaust gas pressure.

Lift-All for Small Tractors

Farmall A and B Culti-Vision tractors were excellent cultivating units; but, this required manual lifting and lowering of the cultivator at the start and end of each row. To solve the problem with a low-cost method that required minimum tractor modification, International Harvester introduced the pneumatic Lift-All system for these two small tractors. When the operator pulled on the control handle, a pressure valve above the exhaust manifold closed and diverted exhaust pressure to the open control valve. That valve directed exhaust pressure to the large diameter, compared to hydraulic systems, cylinder to

actuate the piston. At the end of the stroke, the control valve closed and the pressure valve opened. The pneumatic Lift-All could also be adapted for lifting rear-mounted implements.

Farmall Goes Diesel

International Harvester had the distinction of producing the first diesel wheel-type tractor tested at Nebraska; it was the McCormick-Deering WD-40 tested in 1935. As the interest in the use of diesel fuel grew, International Harvester responded by introducing the Farmall MD in 1941. This was the same tractor as the Farmall M, but it was equipped with an IH-manufactured diesel engine.

The IH-built diesel engine started on gasoline and when the engine was warm, it was switched over to diesel operation. To start on gasoline, the changeover lever was moved to starting position. This reduced the compression ratio to 6 to 1, opened a valve allowing the carburetor to operate, and threw a switch to energize the ignition system for the spark plug in the auxiliary combustion chamber. The engine was now started on gasoline and allowed to warm up. Next the changeover lever was moved forward and the governor set to operating speed; this shut off the spark plug ignition and carburetor. When the valve to the auxiliary combustion chamber closed the compression ratio increased to 15 to 1 and the diesel injection pump began supplying diesel fuel to the engine; operation now was a true diesel cycle.

By 1947, when this photo was made, diesel tractors were becoming more widely accepted (an IH McCormick Farmall MD, full-diesel tractor is shown here). The IH "easy, all-weather starting" system helped overcome the cold weather starting problems associated with diesel engines of the 1940s.

They just couldn't wait! IHC had so many projects going after World War II that it took several years to get them into production. This display of a preproduction Farmall Cub plus one pull and eight mounted Cub implements was shown at a Hinsdale Demonstration in 1945. Production would not start until 1947.

World War II is Over!

Mobilization for the war effort converted International Harvester manufacturing facilities, like the rest of the nation, from peace-time products to material for the military. Government restrictions, allocations, and shortages kept farm machinery production of established products at a fraction of the demand. No provision was made for introduction and production of new products. The Company, however, was looking to the future and continued to invest in new product development and improvement. One notable exception to government restrictions was the International Harvester mechanical cotton picker introduced in 1942. As labor shortages in the South became critical and military needs for cotton grew, the government did allocate material to IH for building the new cotton picker.

The war was over, production was increasing, new products were coming, it was time to tell the world, "What's New, Here Now: What's New, Coming Soon." This was the theme for an October 13-19, 1945 static display, grand stand show, and test track product demonstration at the Harvester Hinsdale Farm. Editors of leading newspapers and farm magazines and educators and engineers from agricultural colleges had their chance to look at the new products along with IH dealers and company personnel. This was the first time preproduction machines had been publicly displayed; 65 experimental machines and three experimental tractors were shown. The Farmall Cub was the "experimental" product that received the most promotion including a News Release and a four-page literature piece. Public announcements at the demonstration said, "International Harvester will build a brand-new factory (for Farmall Cub production). Ground for the site of this plant, which will be known as Wood River Works, is now being broken." The southern Illinois plant across from St. Louis never happened! The following year, 1946, the Company purchased four manufacturing facilities including one at Louisville, Kentucky. The Louisville Works became the home of the Farmall Cub and the other smaller tractors in the line.

The Mighty Cub

"Engineered, designed, and priced to fit the needs of the small farmer, gentleman farmer, and a chore boy for the large farmer," was the way Louisville Works, "the largest tractor plant in the world," announced their new product in the lobby of a Louisville bank. The new plant started production on April 9, 1947, and 23 months later had built 135,000 small Farmall tractors. More than 65,000 of those were Farmall Cubs.

A Cub in *Size* but
A *Bear* for Work!

If you're going to introduce a new product in Hollywood, California, you can't do it right without the help of attractive young women. The four professional models supplied the required Hollywood glamour.

The IH McCormick Farmall Cub tractor and Cub one-bottom direct connected plow were great for small plots and truck gardens.

The 2 5/8-inch bore x 2 3/4-inch stroke, four-cylinder, L-head, 59.5-cubic-inch, water-cooled, Farmall Cub engine turned at 1,600 rpm. It developed a maximum 8.30 belt horsepower at Nebraska in 1947. The 1949 model produced 9.76 horsepower on its best test. This compact little IH-built engine would almost have a life of its own as it was modified and improved over the years for application in a long line of small tractors that included "Cub" in their model name. Ten reasons were given why "the Farmall Cub engine excels

in long life . . . power . . . pep and performance:" 1. Outstanding fuel economy; 2. Pressure lubrication; 3. Engine oil filter; 4. Positive crankcase ventilation; 5. Thermo-siphon cooling; 6. Heavy-duty crankshaft; 7. Thin-walled, babbitt-lined, steel-backed, replaceable bearings; 8. Variable-speed governor; 9. IH designed-and-built ignition; and 10. Filtered air and fuel supply.

Literature proudly proclaimed, "The Farmall Cub is a 4-in-1, all-purpose tractor designed and built to do easier, faster, and better, every job ordinarily handled

Cultivating tobacco was the kind of work where the IH McCormick Farmall Cub excelled.

This farmer was one of the McCormick-Deering Farmall Cub preproduction test cooperators. The equipment is a No. 172A one-row, runner planter with edge drop hopper and fertilizer attachment.

This Sylvania, Ohio farmer was one of several farmers who operated and evaluated 1946 preproduction Cub tractors. This photo made the cover of IH Tractor Farming *in the summer of 1947. The bottom of the photo included this statement, "To serve one-third of the Nation's farmers who are on small acreages and without tractors."*

By 1949, hybrid seed corn production had become a major industry. Self-propelled, high-clearance machines for transporting workers through the fields for detasseling were produced by a number of small companies. The basic IH McCormick Farmall Cub, less wheels, was an ideal power plant for the machines they produced.

by two or three horses or mules on the small farm, or truck garden and many auxiliary tasks on the large farm." It was a 4-in-1 because it could pull, push front-mounted implements, provide PTO power for implements, and belt pulley power for processing. Equipment using the 1,600 rpm PTO had to account for its non-standard speed of operation.

A dozen or more photos of the Cub performing a wide range of tasks were used in literature to document its versatility and showcase the broad line of implements offered for Farmall Cub tractors. They included the extensive offering of cultivators and their planting and fertilizing attachments that complimented

the Culti-Vision design. When the Farmall Cub no longer replaced horses and mules, the 4 1/2-foot Farmall Cub No. 22 side-mounted mower and its belly-mounted, rotary mower successors made the Farmall Cub, and the Cub tractors that followed, the grass-cutting leaders.

In addition to the start of tractor production at Louisville Works, the year 1947 gave the Company an opportunity to celebrate "Harvester's 100 years in Chicago." That autumn an exposition of old and new IH equipment in Chicago's Soldier Field "depicted agricultural progress of the last century."

Sales constantly searched for new uses for the "Cub." A special hitch turned this "Cub" into an airplane towing tractor.

Official introduction of the IH McCormick-Deering Farmall Cub tractor wasn't confined to just rural areas. This display is in a bank lobby in New York City, New York.

This Humbolt, Iowa farmer found another way for the IH McCormick Farmall Cub to take the place of a horse.

Farmall Cub Month

In the fall of 1948, International Harvester received coverage of Louisville Works ability to produce 2,200 tractors per week in a *Life* magazine feature article complete with a full-page color photo of large numbers of tractors in the yard and on railroad flat cars; it included the Farmall Cubs. As a follow up, the Company proclaimed February 1949 as Farmall Cub Month. It featured "a Farmall Cub movie, movie trailers for theaters, newspaper publicity, a poster, and a special store display built around a colorful giant-size Farmall Cub Bear, four smaller bears and a two-sided, teardrop-shaped display that fit on the tractor."

Two New Small Tractors

The Farmall Cub was introduced in 1947. Then in 1948 came the new Farmall C with 22.18 maximum belt horsepower and the new Farmall Super A, Super AV, and International Super A with 19.06 maximum belt horsepower to complete the tractor trio. Both four-cylinder engines had a 3-inch bore x 4-inch stroke. The

An IH McCormick Farmall Cub introduction in 1947 included this line of 15 tractors. Each tractor was equipped with a different Cub direct-connected implement.

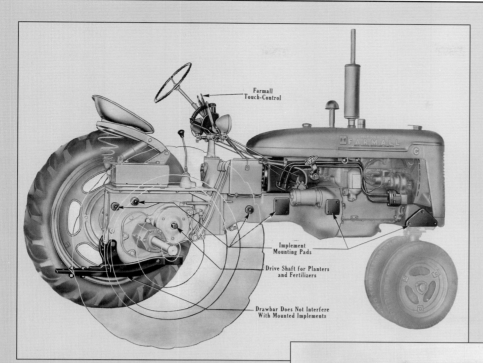

Farmall
Touch-Control

Implement
Mounting Pads

Drive Shaft for Planters
and Fertilizers

Drawbar Does Not Interfere
With Mounted Implements

IHC attention to mounted imple-ments is highlighted in this graphic calling out the six mounting pads on the IH Farmall C tractor's right side. The implements were easy to use with the live hydraulic Farmall Touch-Control System. The drawbar design and special stub drive shaft for planters and fertilizer units added to mounted equipment versatility.

This IH McCormick Farmall C tractor worked the field with a No. 8 Little Genius pneumatic tired plow with mechanical power lift.

This pair of IH McCormick Farmall C tractors are equipped with single front wheels. The two-row, front-mounted middle busters have planting and fertilizing attach-ments. IH provided an extensive selection of tractor-mounted equip-ment to meet the needs of widely varied farming systems.

The rugged cultivator parallel-linkage frame could handle 10- or 12-inch bottoms, 18- to 26-inch sweeps, and disk attachments. With 12 percent more power, the IH McCormick Farmall Super C could handle the job.

"C" engine turned 250 rpm faster, the chassis had a 10-inch longer wheel base, and the tractor weighed 395 pounds more than the Super A. In 1954, the Farmall Touch-Control hydraulics brought an important big tractor feature to these two smaller tractors. Touch-Control was a two-way hydraulic system that drove the power arms in both the lift and lower cycle. Selective control permitted independent operation of implement sections on the right or left side for the tractor and also front or rear. The engine-driven, gear-type pump made Touch-Control a live hydraulic system. A "slave" cylinder was used on trailing implements. Later, Touch-Control with a single power arm would be available for the Farmall Cub.

The Farmall C introduced a new shock-absorbing seat design. Improvement started with a wide, comfortable, upholstered seat. It was supported on a variable-rate, conical spring. Bounce was controlled by a double-action shock absorber. A latch permitted easy fore-and-aft seat position adjustment. This signaled the beginning of serious consideration of operator comfort in IH tractors and self-propelled equipment design that accelerated over the decades.

The Farmall C became the Farmall Super C in 1951. The engine bore increased 1/8 inch and the maximum

belt rating increased 2.6 horsepower. New, self-energizing double-disk brakes were part of a list of 17 improvements. In 1953 this tractor introduced the exclusive International Harvester Fast-Hitch.

Back up, Click and Go

 Two-Point Farmall Fast-Hitch . . . An International Harvester First

In 1953, IH held a major introduction at the Hinsdale farm for 77 new farm machines developed in the prior 770 days. Over 8,000 IH dealer representatives walked the Avenue of IH Progress and were told, "Back of this vast array of new equipment is an investment by International Harvester since the end of World War II of nearly 76 million dollars in new factory, tool equipment, research, engineering, product development and field testing." The Company was racing to meet post-war demand. But, the real star of the show was the new two-point, Farmall Fast-Hitch, "the revolutionary new automatic hitch for the Farmall Super C tractors, with a full line of 23 Fast-Hitch Implements."

Many "Hands" make light work — Teaming up a Farmall C and Farmall H with mounted cultivators would have cleaned the weeds out of this soybean field in short order.

This McCormick-Deering Farmall C tractor equipped with front-mounted, two-row cultivator was doing what the Farmall C did best; cultivate.

Implements like this high-wheel, rubber-tired hay rake designed for use with tractors is a light load behind this McCormick-Deering Farmall C tractor.

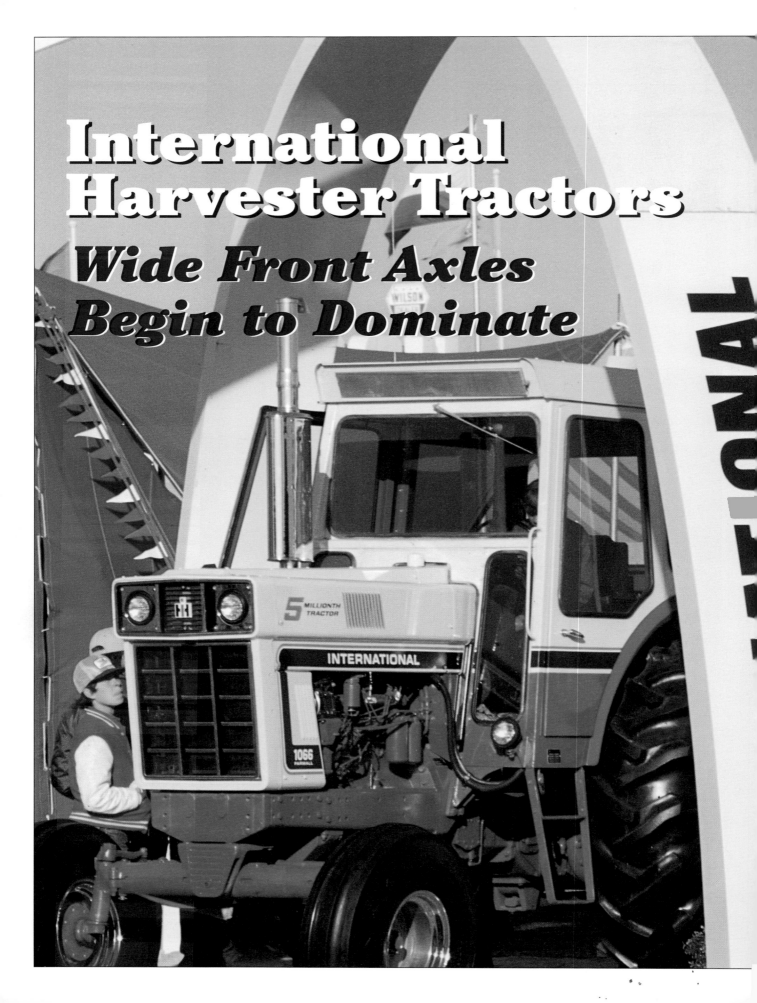

International Harvester Tractors
Wide Front Axles Begin to Dominate

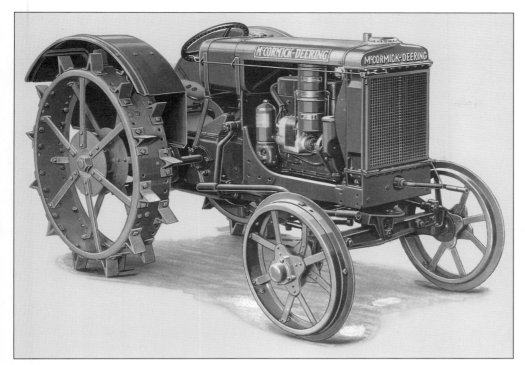

Production of the Farmall F-12 started in 1932. Two years later its 3-inch bore x 4-inch stroke engine and unique transverse transmission were utilized as components for the W-12, low-profile, wide front axle or standard-type tractor for non row-crop applications. The W-12, O-12 orchard tractor, and Fairway 12, all basically the same tractor, were produced at Tractor Works in Chicago from 1934 to 1938. When the higher horsepower F-14 replaced the F-12, the wide front axle tractors became the W-14, O-14, and Fairway 14. Tractor Works utilized the same basic components for the I-12 and later I-14, Industrial tractors. Eleven years of experience gained through the development and marketing of the Model 20 Industrial tractor was incorporated in these industrial "I" Series tractors. Production of this complete family of tractors ended in 1940 with the end of the "F" Series tractors. Tractor Works then became the source for the new Farmall A and AV, the Farmall B and BN, and the International-A.

Production of the Farmall F-30 made available its four-cylinder, 4 1/4-inch bore x 5-inch stroke engine for incorporation in the Milwaukee Works-built McCormick-Deering W-30. A preproduction run of 20 tractors was made in 1932. Production records of this wide front axle, four-wheel style tractor show a 1937 change involving the "SP" four-speed transmission providing 15-mph travel speeds and the "T" four-speed transmission providing 10-mph travel speeds. In addition, lower low gear and differential lock options were available.

When the McCormick-Deering W-30 was tested at Nebraska in 1936, it recorded 35.01 belt horsepower operating on kerosene. It was a true three-plow tractor and could supply the power needed for large tillage tools typical of the farming areas that preferred standard-type tractors.

This McCormick-Deering W-12 four-wheel style, wide front or standard tractor may have been a low horsepower unit, but it was put to good use in this small grain production operation. The operator would be required to unroll the canvas and cover the radiator before starting on gasoline and warming up and then switching to kerosene. When the engine was warm the canvas could be rolled up again and stored just above the hand-starting crank as shown in the photo.

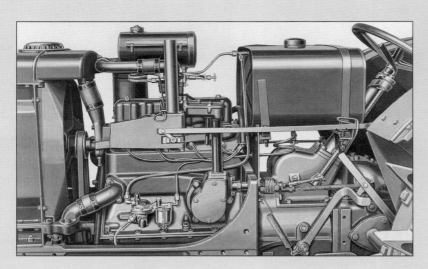

This W-14 tractor graphic shows the heat control for the "combination" manifold and the small gasoline tank for starting. The design is unique because half of the tank extends above the sheet-metal hood. That feature readily identified the non-gasoline fueled 12 and 14 Series tractors.

Locating the large air cleaner outside the tractor frame saved space and helped keep the short wheel base that was so important for this McCormick-Deering W-30 tractor and its massive cast frame.

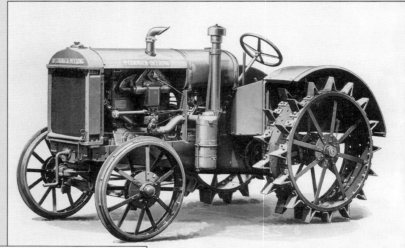

This pulley side view of a 1936 McCormick-Deering W-30 tractor shows the sheet-metal panel between the fire wall and the fender that helped keep "some" of the dirt off of the operator. This tractor is equipped with an optional air intake extension. The diamond shape tread on these 1936 tractor tires, and the familiar flag logo, identify them as Goodyear.

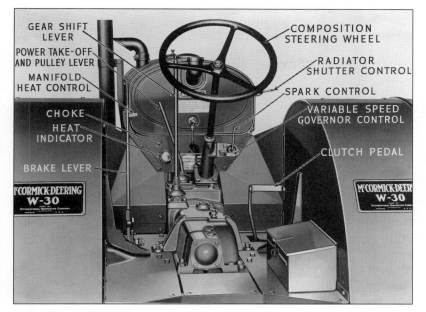

GEAR SHIFT LEVER
POWER TAKE-OFF AND PULLEY LEVER
MANIFOLD HEAT CONTROL
CHOKE
HEAT INDICATOR
BRAKE LEVER
McCORMICK-DEERING W-30
COMPOSITION STEERING WHEEL
RADIATOR SHUTTER CONTROL
SPARK CONTROL
VARIABLE SPEED GOVERNOR CONTROL
CLUTCH PEDAL
McCORMICK-DEERING W-30

The seat has been removed for a clear view of the McCormick-Deering W-30 tractor controls. Of particular interest is the clutch pedal located on the right and the single brake lever on the left that controlled both right and left brakes. The optional PTO was located directly under the operator's seat and installed where the plate with four cap screws is shown in the graphic.

The McCormick-Deering W-30 orchard version had the seat moved back and lowered to protect the operator from low branches. This alteration required that the steering wheel be lowered and repositioned, the clutch pedal moved toward the rear of the tractor, and the gear shift lever arm bent down and back. The basic low profile of the tractor, low inlet of the standard air cleaner, and full fenders completed the package.

The I-30 Industrial tractor was developed from the W-30 standard tractor. The new I-30 incorporated many of the features of the smaller Model 20 Industrial plus additional refinements. Attention was given to mounting allied equipment and supplying special modified versions for original equipment manufacturers (OEM). A partial list of Industrial tractor features and options included: solid or pneumatic tires, pintle hook drawbar, rear exhaust, water muffler, four-speed transmission, full reverse transmission, electric lighting and starting, air compressor for inflating tires, dual rear wheels, and narrow tread versions. International Harvester I-30 Industrial tractor production ran from a 1931 preproduction lot of 12 to total production of nearly 5,000. Production ended in 1940.

The need for more power to farm the larger acreage operations of the plains was met by the McCormick-Deering W-40. Like the other Milwaukee-built tractors, it had the one-piece, cast frame that extended from the radiator to the final drive. One significantly different feature of the "40" Series was the massive single bull-gear final drive. Since there was only one bull gear, the very heavy-duty differential was part of the single bull gear and directly drove each rear axle half. The "40" Series came in Model WA-40 gasoline, W-40 gasoline or distillate, and WK-40 kerosene. Later, the A and K designations were no longer used. This series was produced from 1935 to 1940. They were powered by a 6-cylinder, 3 5/8-inch bore x 4 1/2-inch stroke engine at 1,750 rpm. When tested in Nebraska in 1936, the WK-40 was listed as having a 3 3/4- x 4 1/2-inch engine. The tractor produced 49.76 maximum belt horsepower operating on distillate. This was a radical change from the 1/2-inch longer stroke W-30 engine that ran at only 1,160 rpm. Engine technology was changing rapidly.

The power generated by this new engine could seriously deflect the transmission case. The 1936 *Operator's Manual* gave detailed instructions for setting a set stud in the side of the main frame casting that limited transmission deflection and protected the bevel gear and bevel pinion.

This I-30 tractor replaced the Model 30 Industrial kerosene tractor built from 1930 to 1932. This gasoline-kerosene tractor was built from 1931 to 1940 and incorporated many of the features introduced in the Model 20 and Model 30 Industrial tractors. The spring-mounted "lazy back seat," down discharge muffler, and dual rear wheels are easily recognized industrial tractor features.

International Harvester developed an easy starting diesel engine that started on gasoline and when warm, automatically switched to true diesel operation. This engine, developed for the TD-40 TracTracTor crawler tractor, was incorporated in the WD-40, shown here, introduced in 1935. The WD-40 was "America's First Diesel Powered Wheel Tractor."

McCormick-Deering WD-40, the First Wheel-Type, Diesel Tractor Tested at Nebraska . . . An International Harvester Company First

The McCormick-Deering WD-40 was basically a W-40 equipped with a four-cylinder, 4 3/4-inch bore x 6 1/2-inch stroke diesel engine. This engine was the same one used in the TD-40 TracTracTor crawler tractor.

McCormick-Deering W-40 and WD-40 agricultural tractors were the basis for development of the International I-40 gasoline or distillate, IA gasoline, and ID-40 diesel industrial tractors; they were

This Gas Power Engineering photo from January 1938 reveals an impressively styled standard-type tractor called the WD-42. Like the equally impressive styling of the Farmall F-22 pictured in the Second Generation Farmall Family section, the fully enclosed engine sides would not be a part of the final design. The recognizable IH grille design would, however, become a part of the forthcoming new line of Farmall and Standard tractors that was introduced in 1939.

produced from 1936 to 1940. These tractors incorporated features similar to the International I-30 Industrial tractor.

The New "W" Series Standard Tractors

A year after introduction of the new Farmall line in 1939, the McCormick-Deering W-4, W-6, and WD-6 standard-type tractors produced at Farmall Works were introduced. Orchard O-4 and O-6 versions were also available. The "W" Series had cast front frames and angled steering columns like the previous standard-type tractors, but the grille and top line sheet-metal styling was almost identical to the Farmall H and M. Furthermore, they utilized the same Farmall H, M, and MD engines. They had a five-speed transmission housed in a single main frame transmission and final drive casting. IH had made significant progress in achieving a unified tractor line and family appearance.

The Milwaukee Works-produced W-9 and WD-9 tractors came on the market in 1941. They were equipped with the same four-cylinder, 4.4-inch bore x 5.5-inch stroke engine used in the T-9 and TD-9 TracTracTor crawler tractors. The five-speed transmission and differential were housed in one main frame casting while the dual bull-gear final drive was housed in a separate main frame casting that also incorporated the rear axle carriers.

To better meet orchard and grove needs, the OS-4 and OS-6 were introduced in 1944; a similar ODS-6 was added in 1947. The "OS" Series orchard and grove tractors did not include the extensive streamlined sheet metal of the "O" Series.

This IH McCormick W-4 standard tractor with its wide front axle and short wheelbase provided improved ride and steering compared to Farmall tricycle tractors.

The IH McCormick W-6 standard tractor pictured here was as much at home on large farms in the Midwest as in the Western Prairie. Hydraulic lift in place of mechanical lift was a much appreciated pull plow option.

The needs of another special market were met with the WR-9 and WDR-9 Rice Field Special tractors. In addition to the basic W-9 or WD-9 features, these tractors came equipped with hand-operated over-center clutch, decelerator, front drawbar, steel wheels with 6- x 4-inch spade lugs, and waterproof upholstered seat. A useful rice grower option was the rear wheel mud scraper, "easily adjusted," for scraping the center of the steel tire between the two rows of lugs.

Because of Farmall and "W" Series commonalty, when the Farmall H and M became the Farmall Super H and Super M, the standard W-4 became the Super W-4 in 1953 and the W-6 and WD-6 became the Super W-6 and Super WD-6 in 1952. Production of the Super W6-TA was in 1954 only. The Super WD-9 and Super WDR-9 were built from 1953 to 1956.

When the work's done here, this IH McCormick W-4 standard tractor equipped with a swinging drawbar attachment made sharp turns at the end of the field with drawn tillage implements an easy maneuver.

183

A pull on the trip rope of this McCormick WD-6 diesel standard tractor and the McCormick-Deering No. 39 two-bottom, two-way plow will start the roll-over operation. Another pull on the rope and the other set of bottoms are ready to enter the ground. Plow wheels and hitch automatically switch over to the correct position when the plow rolls over.

When the new "W" Series standard tractors were introduced in 1940, an orchard or grove version with fully streamlined cover was offered for both the W-4 and W-6 size tractors. These O-4 (pictured here) and O-6 models were intended for working in citrus groves and orchards with closely spaced trees that had low hanging branches. The rounded, perforated cowling in front of the steering wheel was optional equipment. In 1944, OS-4 and OS-6 models were introduced with fenders and without the streamlined cover. The ODS-6 orchard diesel tractor became available in 1947.

This IH McCormick WD-6 diesel tractor was advertised as a 3- to 4-bottom plow tractor. It is doing a first class job of plowing with this McCormick-Deering 3-bottom pull plow in sod.

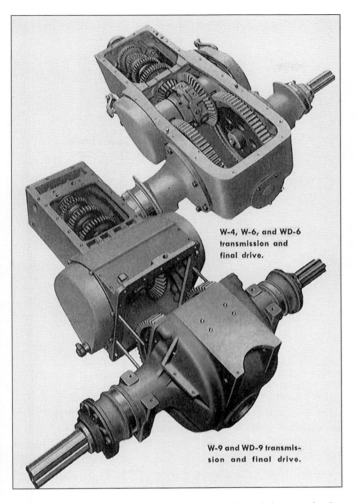

W-4, W-6, and WD-6 transmission and final drive.

W-9 and WD-9 transmission and final drive.

The W-4, W-6, and W-9 standard tractors shared the new look in IH tractor styling that conveyed a valuable positive image. However, these photos make it clear the Milwaukee Works-built W-9 and WD-9 tractors had totally different transmission and final drive designs than the Farmall Works-built W-4, W-6, and WD-6 standard tractors.

This International I-9 Industrial tractor equipped with dual-tires was towing a DC-4 aircraft at Chicago Midway Airport in 1948. It is representative of the five models of Industrial "I" Series tractors that were based on the similar McCormick "W" Series standard tractors.

New Industrial Tractors

The new "W" Series of three sizes and five models of tractors became the basis for a new line of "I" Series industrial tractors. The I-4 Industrial was built from 1940 to 1951. The I-6 and ID-6 as well as the I-9 and ID-9 were built from 1940 to 1953.

New, Number Series Tractors

Gone were the familiar letter names like Farmall H, Farmall Super MTA, and Farmall Super C. The year 1954 saw a new family of numerically designated models from the Farmall 100 that replaced the Farmall Super A to the Farmall 400 that replaced the Farmall Super MTA. Production ended for the Farmall Works-built W-4 and W-6 family and the new International 400 standard tractor replaced the Super W6-TA. To an army of loyal owners who grew up with the IH family of A, B, C, H, and M Farmalls, those tractors would never be replaced in their memory. One thing stayed the same; the newly styled Farmall Cub was still a Cub. In addition to the "New Distinctive Styling," each tractor had a number of mechanical or functional improvements.

This 1940 gas power engineering photo states, "W9 tractor with lighting attachment and rear wheel weights."

"Distinctive New Styling for Five New Farmall Tractors" — the Farmall Cub kept its name when the new models appeared. The restyled and improved Farmall 100, 200, 300, and 400 tractors composed the "Farmall Family" in 1954.

The new Farmall 100 had a more powerful engine, new single socket Fast-Hitch, and improved power train and steering gear. The new Farmall 200 offered the "exclusive" new, IH-developed Hydra-Creeper Drive with travel speeds as low as 1/4 mph. The new Farmall 300 and 400 had increased horsepower, new Fast-Hitch implement mounting, and the new live hydraulic power, Hydra-Touch implement control system. One, two, or three control knobs were functionally located to the right of the instrument panel.

Like its predecessor, the new Farmall 400 offered "TA" and independent PTO; the new Farmall 300 now could be equipped with these valuable options.

The International 300 Utility tractor came to market in 1955. This low profile, "all duty" tractor brought Farmall-type features like "TA," Hydra-Touch hydraulics, and independent PTO to a true utility tractor in the 35-drawbar horsepower class. The FOB factory list price was $1,957 with Fast-Hitch, tachometer, and one-valve Hydra-Touch hydraulics.

With the right wheel removed, the details of the Farmall 400 equipped with heavy-duty fast-hitch, hydraulic control of draft point, remote hydraulics, TA, and IPTO are quite clear.

This striking, low angle, Farmall 400 photo helped promote this largest of the new number series Farmall family of tractors.

The low profile International 300 Utility tractor made life a lot easier for the operator when he needed to get on or off the tractor to service the planter.

IH Red, White, and Blue . . . and Black

The new colors were not used exactly in that order. In the fall of 1956 the IH Product Identification Committee issued a decision informing the Product Committees that the new IH standard colors would be: Harvester Red, Harvester Blue, Harvester White, and Black Canyon Black. The Implement Cream color was discontinued. The decision contained recommendations for use of the new colors on seven models of tractors, the following is an example:

Farmall 300 and 400 Tractors (Introduced as the Farmall 350 and 450)

Basic color	— Harvester Red
Radiator grille	— Harvester White
Wheels	— Harvester White
Hood	— Harvester White decal under the name plate
Fast-Hitch	— Harvester Red
Drawbar	— Harvester White

General guidelines directed the Farm Implement Product Committee: Harvester Blue was to be used as a trim color. Black was to be used for cultivator standards and clamps, disk blades etc.

The decision stated that the change was in response to competitors use of brighter two- and three-tone colors. The result was a major change in the appearance of IH tractors and implements.

Fast-Hitch with Traction Control

The exclusive IH Fast-Hitch had recently gained hydraulic depth control for plows and similar implements; then, in 1957, the system acquired Traction Control. The new Fast-Hitch with Traction-Control was available for McCormick Farmall 230, 350, and 450 tractors plus the International 350 Utility tractor. The purely mechanical Traction Control used a system of linkages, a cam, and a notched Traction-Control handle that selected the proper amount of weight transfer. A Pilot-Guide mounted to the left of the instrument panel had two indicators. One indicator showed the relative amount of weight transfer and the other indicator showed the relative implement working depth. "Hinged Sockets" on the Fast-Hitch drawbar arms assured uniform work in uneven field conditions. All of this was accomplished with "no-power-robbing hydraulics."

A four-page, 1957, *IH Dealer Bulletin* gave detailed instructions for, "A simple, effective demonstration of how, New TRACTION-CONTROL FAST-HITCH puts power to better use." A Farmall 300 tractor with Fast-Hitch (old) equipped with three sets of rear wheel weights was hitched drawbar to drawbar to a Farmall 350 Traction-Control Fast-Hitch tractor with no wheel weights. With the 350 Traction-Control off, its tires spun. With Traction-Control on, the 350 pulled the

New models and new paint styling.— The participants in this family portrait of the new IH tractors are on the left : Farmall F-450, F-350, F-230, F-130, and Farmall Cub. On the right: International Cub, International I-130, I-350, I-450, and I-650.

This IH Farmall F-450D was equipped with the IH-manufactured diesel engine. The Farmall F-450 tractor was also available in LPG and gasoline versions.

300 backward with its brakes set or trying to pull forward.

A new three-point implement adapter was introduced for the same group of Fast-Hitch tractors. It came in two versions, depending on the tractor model. It was succeeded by a new heavy-duty three-point adapter.

IH Six-Cylinder Agricultural Tractors

Lester Larsen was engineer-in-charge of the Nebraska Tractor Testing Laboratory for nearly 30 years. He has written that by 1952, "the race for increased horsepower was heating up." The start of the decade saw suppliers, other than the major tractor manufacturers, selling add-on turbochargers, oversized sleeves and pistons, and other after-market products to increase engine horsepower. This frequently created problems because of the resulting unbalanced design.

International Harvester responded to the changes in the marketplace with the Super Series and followed with other horsepower-increasing improvements to the four-cylinder engine line for the succeeding two model changes. To achieve significant increases in horsepower in the larger tractors, six-cylinder engines were needed.

This photo shows a McCormick Farmall 460 tricycle tractor and two-row, front-mounted cultivator. Other 460 configurations included: Hi-Clear, Utility, Hi-Utility, and Wheatland.

The High Horsepower IH 460 and 560 Tractors

More power was needed and the answer was within the International Harvester organization. Versions of the TD-9 crawler tractors with its 3 11/16-inch bore x 4.39-inch stroke, six-cylinder diesel engine formed the basis for the new 560 diesel and gasoline engines. The gasoline engine had a 1/8-inch smaller cylinder bore. The 460 diesel and gasoline engines had the same bore as the 560 but had a shorter stroke. The 460 and 560 diesel engines were both equipped with glow-plug starting aids in the precombustion cup of each cylinder. These direct start diesel engines were a vast improvement over the previous IH farm tractor diesel engines that started on gasoline and then switched to true diesel operation. Since six-cylinder engines are inherently balanced compared to four-cylinder engines that are not inherently balanced, the new tractors exhibited "vibration-free power." These engines had forged camshafts supported on four replaceable bearings, and cylinders that were the replaceable dry type. Engine-oil-to-engine-coolant heat exchangers helped cool crankcase oil and extend engine life. These were great power plants.

Nebraska Tractor Test corrected results for the new McCormick Farmall 560 diesel were 58.67 drawbar and 62.60 belt horsepower; the gasoline results were 59.47 drawbar and 65.25 belt horsepower. The new McCormick Farmall 460 diesel results were 47.99 drawbar and 52.19 belt horsepower; the gasoline results were 47.24 drawbar and 51.63 belt horsepower. Both tractors were tested with LP gas engines. International 460 Utility models were tested on all three fuel types with equally good performance.

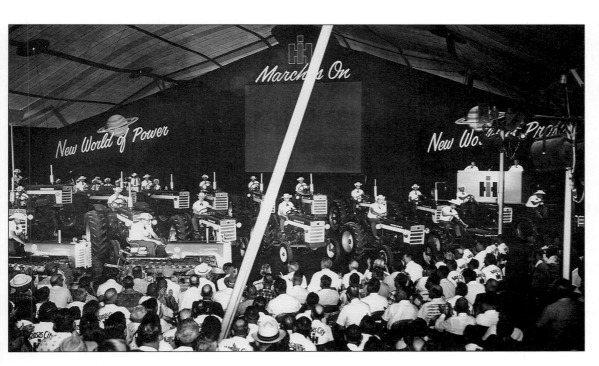

A big product launch for the "New World of Power" six-cylinder Farmall and International 460 and 560 tractors. The show included the full line from Farmall Cub to the TC-5 and TCD-5 crawler tractors.

Loaded with New Features

The new 460 and 560 tractors were not just increased horsepower older tractors, they introduced an impressive list of new features. The Hydra-Touch hydraulic system included Tel-A-Depth with follow-up-linkage for positive implement control. The hydraulic pumps were internally mounted and available in either 12- or 17-gpm sizes; they were driven live from the IPTO drive gear. One, two, or three valves were available. A separate 2.5-gpm pump supplied the totally new IH front bolster mounted, rack-and-pinion power steering unit. The steering wheel was repositioned to a more comfortable position like the International Utility tractors. Another operator pleasing feature was the upholstered seat with rear support. An optional foam padded, upholstered seat with deeper back rest was mounted on a double torsion spring suspension system. An improved IPTO was smoothly engaged by a new multiple-disk clutch drive. These truly new tractors combined features like these with traditional IH tractor features like TA and Traction-Control Fast-Hitch.

The tractor is a McCormick Farmall 560 with traction-control Fast-Hitch and two-point hitch drawbar that snapped in the hitch sockets.

The McCormick Farmall 560's rugged front frame and implement mounting pads were more than adequate to handle this five-row, front-mounted middlebuster.

Calendars, advertising, and product literature often used color artwork, like this McCormick Farmall 560 and McCormick-Deering baler example, to tell a story or fill a gap in existing photographic material.

Response From the Field

IH dealers and customers were pleased with the power, comfort, convenience, and performance of the new McCormick Farmall 460 and 560 tractors. However, warranty and management began to receive word of premature final drive failures from various parts of the country. In order to protect the reputation of the International Harvester Company, support the customers who purchased and the dealers who sold these tractors, a massive, $19-million field re-work program was initiated. In an effort to assist smaller dealers with such complex rework and assure proper installation of the package, centralized re-work stations were established. Unfortunately, this publicized the program and failed to secure the positive public relations benefit this extensive support of the customer's purchase should have achieved.

Today, some persons who were close to the actual field campaign indicate that senior management may have overreacted to the problem. The failures, though more than they should have been, came primarily from areas where local farming practices tended to reduce tractor wheel slip to almost zero and in turn generate significant overloads. A fix-as-fail program with greatly extended warranty might have been a better response.

The Total 1959-1960 IH Tractor Family

People in the farm equipment industry tend to think in terms of big tractors like the McCormick Farmall 460 and 560; however, the 1958-1959 tractor introduction covered not only the six Farmall tractors but three smaller International Utility tractors as well. The offering ranged from the 10-drawbar horsepower Farmall Cub to the 80-belt horsepower International 660. The I-660 was the largest tractor introduced and was the first IH agricultural tractor to be equipped with planetary drive on the outer axle. The International 660 was targeted for wheatland, rice farming, and industrial applications. Included in the family were the

Farmall 140, 240, and 340 plus the International Cub Lo-Boy; International I-240, I-340, I-460 Utility; and the International I-560 tractors. Hi-Clear and Hi-Utility versions for some models added to the offering.

A British Accent

International Harvester took advantage of their manufacturing facilities in England and imported the British designed-and-built McCormick International B-275 Diesel tractor starting in 1959. This low profile, 30.94 drawbar horsepower utility tractor offered a three-point hitch for Category I or II implements and mechanical weight transfer. Other key features were

The big tractor introduction in 1959 featured the new six-cylinder Farmall 460 and 560, but it included many other lower horsepower products like this Farmall 140 tractor.

By importing the B-414 diesel (shown here) in 1961, in addition to importing the B-275 diesel starting in 1959, IH quickly acquired tractors in this power class that had features requested by the marketplace. International Harvester plants in England manufactured both tractors.

differential lock, four-speed transmission followed by a Hi-Lo range transmission for 8-forward and 2-reverse speeds, live hydraulic power, constant running PTO operated by the single, two-stage clutch, and excellent under fame clearance.

Two years later, the McCormick International B-414 gasoline and B-414D diesel tractors were imported from England as well. Actually, the B-414 gasoline model tractor came to Louisville Works without an engine and was then matched up to a U.S. manufactured gasoline engine. The three-point hitch with hydraulic sensitivity provided position control with follow-up. High-clearance versions were available in both gasoline and diesel.

U.S. Built Tractors with Draft Sensing Three-Point Hitches

IH opened the decade of the 1960s with the 404 and 504 Series tractors with three-point hitches. The McCormick Farmall 404, International 404, and industrial International 2404 and International 2404 Lo-Boy were available with either gasoline or LPG engines. The Farmall 504 and Farmall 504 Hi-Clear were joined by the International 504, 2504, and International "Constructall" 2500.

These tractors used a torsion bar for their top-link, draft-sensing three-point hitches. Other new features included an oil cooler for the transmission and hydraulic oil, dry type air cleaner, and hydrostatic power steering.

Reverse Operating Farmall 460 Tractor

The personal files of the retired head of IH Farm Equipment Product Planning, Russell R. Poyner, contain a report of an Advanced Engineering Committee meeting held in the fall of 1958; the subject was, "The Reverse-Going Tractor and Implement Program." Attendees included senior Farm Equipment Division management. The meeting was held at the Hinsdale Farm to review the project and observe the experimental machines mounted on a reverse-going Farmall 460 tractor. Attachments for the Two-Way Tractor included:

- Loader
- 14-foot Mower
- Parallel Bar Rake
- Windrower
- Stalk Shredder
- Utility Harvester
- Forage Harvester
- Corn Picker
- Cotton Stripper

This plowing scene pictures a McCormick Farmall 504 with U.S. made top-link sensing, three-point hitch. The top link reacted against a torsion bar for load sensing.

This Advanced Engineering reverse-operating tractor was based on the Farmall 460. It was designed for mounting nine different attachments for operation like single-purpose, self-propelled machines.

This experimental, reverse-operating Farmall 460 tractor is equipped with a mounted forage harvester attachment.

never became a released product. Seven other advanced engineering projects were also demonstrated at the meeting. The unique one was a tape planter for planting single seeds at precise spacing in the row.

The World's Most Powerful, Four-Wheel-Drive Agricultural Tractor

Several small firms were building large, high-horsepower, four-wheel-drive tractors during the 1950s. These were intended primarily to replace crawler tractors in the Upper Midwest and West Coast regions. International Harvester initiated a program for an equal-wheel, four-wheel-drive tractor that would be larger than the current 80-belt horsepower International agricultural, rear-wheel-drive tractor and much larger than other two-wheel tractors on the market. The Frank G. Hough Company of Libertyville, Illinois, an IH subsidiary, built the first experimental tractor in this program for test in 1959; it was called the 4WD-1. When the Tractor Committee visited the test tractor, they realized it needed more horsepower; they considered a 4WD tractor with 125 to 150 engine horsepower. On this trip they saw the John Deere prototype four-wheel-drive articulated tractor under test with a reported engine horsepower over 200. That made the decision easier; IH would build a larger tractor.

The proposed 4WD-3, front- and rear-wheel-steer tractor was to be powered by a 300-horsepower IH, DT-817 turbocharged diesel engine and equipped with an eight-speed agricultural transmission or optional Allison "Torque Converter Transmission" with lockup. A confidential binder with complete text and photo description of the 4WD-3 was presented to the committee for approval in September of 1960; they approved. When introduced, this tractor would become the first IH agricultural tractor with a turbocharger.

After reviewing all aspects of the program, it was decided to proceed with development of the "two-way" tractor and various tools. In spite of farmer and industry interest in multiple power unit application at that time, the project

Photographed during test and development, this International 4WD-3 four-wheel-drive tractor was pulling a 40-foot, wing-type chisel plow with 18-inch sweeps working 8 inches deep. By the time it was introduced, it became the International 4300. The giant tractor delivered 214 drawbar horsepower in the 1961 Nebraska Tractor Test.

World's Most Powerful Four-Wheel-Drive Agricultural Tractor

10-Furrow
16-Inch Bottom Moldboard Plow
300 Engine Horsepower

When the giant 300-horsepower engine, four-wheel-drive tractor with Category IV, three-point "Fast-Hitch" and companion 10-bottom mounted plow were introduced in 1961, it had become the International 4300 four-wheel-drive tractor. These tractors were "stall-built" by the Frank G. Hough Company and contained a high percentage of purchased parts; this made them relatively expensive. Like John Deere, the Company found they were ahead of the market with such a large tractor; it took several years to retail the planned production.

A Glimpse of the Future

When International Harvester purchased the Solar Aircraft Company of San Diego, California, in 1959, one of their principal objectives was to develop turbine engines to power IH over-the-road trucks and large construction equipment vehicles. Development work was done on these applications. At the time of the acquisition, Solar had in production a small, 80-horse-power turbine engine called the Titan that weighed only 90 pounds. International Harvester engineering incorporated the Solar turbine into an experimental HT-340 research tractor. The beautifully styled, molded fiberglass body covered an impressive development in hydrostatic drive technology. Taming the 57,000 rpm output of the Titan was no simple task. The Solar gas turbine drove a variable displacement hydrostatic pump through a compact gear reduction. Output of the pump drove a pair of radial hydraulic motors, one in each rear wheel. The system provided infinitely variable travel speeds from 0 to 11 mph through a single lever control for both forward and reverse operation. The neutral position provided tractor braking.

Advances in diesel engine technology during the 1960 era indicated that modern diesel engines would likely become the future large tractor power source. This, combined with poor gas turbine fuel efficiency, resulted in no further IH gas turbine development within any of the three divisions. The project did, however, contribute to the rapidly growing body of hydrostatic transmission research information being accumulated by the IH Tractor Engineering Group. The HT-340 was a partial glimpse into the future of IH hydrostatic tractor models to come.

Charles Lindbergh — Titan — International Harvester

These three names have an interesting interrelationship. The "Spirit of St. Louis" airplane that Charles Lindbergh flew non-stop from New York City to Paris, France, in 1927 was built in San Diego, California. His

This is the Experimental International Harvester, gas-turbine powered HT-340 hydrostatic drive tractor. Neither gas-turbine engines nor hydrostatic drive systems were new, but combining them in an agricultural tractor was a completely new approach to tractor design. The HT-340's first public showing was at the University of Nebraska, Nebraska Power and Safety Day in 1961.

Three proud IH engineers show off "the inside story" of the experimental, gas-turbine powered, HT-340 hydrostatic drive tractor. They are, left to right: John R. Cromack, Carl H. Meile, and Ralph E. Wallace. The 90-pound Solar Aircraft built Titan gas-turbine engine and gear reduction package could develop 80 shaft horsepower. The tractor chassis shown here was developed to utilize just 40 horsepower of the gas-turbine engine output.

Farm Materials Handling Vehicle

Farm Equipment Product Planning proposed a multi-purpose vehicle for farm, commercial, and highway applications in 1959. The concept had farm tractor-type lug tires on the rear driving axle. The front steering axle had truck-type tires in a two-wheel-drive version. A four-wheel-drive version was also proposed. The chassis with offset cab was long enough to accommodate a bulk material box like a truck grain bed. The material box could be raised in front for unloading. The same hydraulic system would also be able to tip the material box a full 90 degrees and set the box on the ground. The material box would be stored in this perpendicular-to-the-ground position after it was disconnected from the vehicle. This made possible other attachments in place of the material box such as a fertilizer or lime spreader, manure spreader, self-unloading conveyor bed, and similar truck- and agricultural-type applications. A front-mounted forage harvester attachment would blow chopped material into a self-unloading forage box. A front-mounted conveyor would pick up hay or straw bales and deliver them to the rear box. A hydraulic crane was proposed to be mounted directly behind the rear corner of the off center half cab. Possible variations were extensive.

flight helped point the direction of future aviation. When International Harvester acquired the Solar Aircraft Company in San Diego, they acquired the building where Lindbergh's airplane was built. The same massive timber that framed the top of the hanger door in 1927 when the "Spirit of St. Louis" rolled out for shipment east was still in place when IH acquired the facility over 30 years later.

International Harvester used the Solar Aircraft Company Titan T62T gas-turbine engine in their pioneering research tractor, the HT-340. Starting in 1910, the Titan name on IHC tractors and engines established one of the Company's never-to-be-forgotten trademarks. Now, 50 years later the Titan name appeared on another International Harvester tractor power source. The HT-340 project did point the direction for future IH variable speed transmission development.

As a final tribute to Lindbergh's aviation accomplishment, the "Spirit of St. Louis" hangs from the ceiling of the Smithsonian Institution in Washington, D.C. In recognition of a unique contribution to agricultural tractor technology, the International Harvester HT-340 tractor, with its San Diego-built Solar Aircraft Titan gas-turbine engine, is also a part of the Smithsonian collection. Two pioneering products that share at least a partial common heritage.

International Harvester Hamilton Works, Hamilton, Ontario, Canada developed this hybrid truck/tractor prototype for on- and-off highway use in 1962. It would accommodate various detachable beds and material boxes on the rear and conveyor/loaders on the front.

The Fort Wayne Truck Division expressed interest in developing the farm material handler concept because it had many truck-like features. However, the short wheelbase, Jeep-like, Scout vehicle project took precedence, and their interest in the Farm Material Handler died. The Hinsdale Advanced Engineering Group looked at the project, but their docket was full. Hamilton Works, Hamilton, Ontario, Canada, with their own engineering group, saw this as a way to add a new product line to the Canadian operation. They developed a basic field prototype with removable, flair-side, self-unloading box. A photo of the Hamilton Works "Farm Hauler" with front-mounted bale loader-conveyor received exposure in various IH publications. Development of the original concept with all of its powered variations was not justified by the small size of the potential market; the project ended at the field prototype stage.

The only good way to convey all of the features and benefits of the totally new 706 and 806 tractors was to demonstrate, demonstrate, demonstrate!

Build 'Em Big and Build 'Em Tough

There was no question about it, the new IH 706 and 806 tractors had to have more horsepower than the major competition and they had to demonstrate proven, long-term reliability. Engineering met the requirements by designing a totally new tractor. Not only were the transmission and final drive gears, bearings, and shafts larger and stronger, the total

The year was 1963 and the new Farmall 706 and 806 tractors started coming off the Farmall Works assembly line. These two models marked the beginning of a whole new era for International Harvester agricultural tractors.

design was changed. One example was placing the bull-gear final drive in the axle carriers and bolting them to the outside of the rear frame. This afforded a stronger rear frame design and superior bearing support for the axle. In addition, this design provided for widening the bull gears to accommodate future horsepower increases without requiring major rear frame tooling changes. The list of design innovations and reliability improvements is long and impressive.

To make absolutely sure they had it right, product and test engineering cooperated in almost a full year of on-farm testing in widely scattered parts of the country where farmers and their hired hands worked the pre-production 706 and 806 hard and long. The IH Phoenix, Arizona proving ground was the headquarters for tractors tested by farmers in the surrounding irrigated areas. Engine oil samples and used oil filters were returned to the Hinsdale laboratory on a regular basis for analysis. Preproduction tractors were operated on the Hinsdale test track 24-hours a day. The results of 75,000 hours of on-farm testing resulted in over 40 changes to the 706 and 806 tractors before they went into production.

Engines for the 706 and 806 Tractors

The International Farmall 806 diesel was equipped with a new, direct-injected 4 1/8-inch bore x 4 1/2-inch stroke, six-cylinder, 361-cubic-inch displacement IH diesel engine that delivered 94.39 observed PTO horsepower. This new engine was designed specifically for the 806 tractor. The International 706 diesel was equipped with a direct-injected 3 11/16-inch bore x 4 25/64-inch stroke, six-cylinder, 282-cubic-inch displacement IH diesel engine that delivered 72.4 observed PTO horsepower. This engine had been proven in the International 660 tractor and IH TD-9 crawler tractor. Both engines were equipped with coolers for transmission and hydraulic oil plus two stage, dry-type air cleaners. Crank shafts were treated with the exclusive IH Elotherm journal and fillet hardening process.

New Features for 706 and 806 Tractors

The new four-speed transmission followed by a two-speed range transmission delivered 16 forward and 8 reverse speeds in torque amplifier TA equipped tractors. The driveline incorporated the exclusive new IH Dyna-Life clutch with metallic pads for long life. The transmission and final drive were pressure lubricated.

The new independent PTO had both the 540- and 1,000-rpm shafts in place so no changeover was necessary. Furthermore, the IPTO was a new design with a power activated clutch and 3-gpm hydraulic pump and control valve in a single, self-contained unit.

The power shift torque amplifier design was totally new. The limited capacity and lack of engine braking in the previous planetary system was gone. The TA in the 706 and 806 tractor consisted of a direct drive clutch and a TA one-way sprag clutch with a hydraulically actuated lock up clutch to prevent free wheeling in TA. The new design was so reliable that the same TA design concept was used in succeeding, higher horsepower tractors.

This International Farmall 806 tractor and five section spring tooth harrow were photographed at the IH Hickory Hill Farm and Photo Center. Because many of the fields were small, photos were taken from an elevated position to conceal actual field size.

The 706 and 806 tractors had a three-point hitch that introduced the torsion bar, lower link sensing system. Operator convenience was supported by hydraulically actuated, self-adjusting brakes and standard hydrostatic power steering. The deluxe, weight suspension seat was located ahead of the rear axle for added riding comfort. A clear operator's platform was achieved by moving the gear shift levers to the upper right of the steering column. The new location was great but hard shifting could result unless everything was adjusted perfectly. The next model solved the problem.

The new tractors were designed to accommodate two emerging trends: The standard Farmall 706 and 806 rear axles would accommodate dual tires and factory installed front-wheel-drive attachments were available.

A wide range of models accommodated the varied needs of customers across the country. The Farmall 706 Series was available in Hi-Clear, International, and Industrial International 2706 versions. The Farmall 806 Series was available in the same versions. In addition to diesel, the 263-cubic-inch displacement 706 engine was available in gasoline and LPG versions. The 806 could be purchased with the 301-cubic-inch displacement engine for gasoline or LPG.

The only good way to convey the rugged design of the new 706 and 806 tractors was to show cut-a-way components of the actual tractor. Similar cut-a-way modules for the differential housing, rear axle carriers, and hydraulic pedestal along with the clutch housing were featured at shows across the country.

The "Hydramatic" 706/806 Tractor

During the early development of the replacement tractor for the Farmall 560, the proposed 80- to 90-horsepower tractor design had a General Motors, heavy-duty, four-speed Hydramatic transmission. To accommodate this transmission, the clutch housing

No More New Tractors Until – – !

In the fall of 1963, the long-term manager of the IH Sales and Service Store at Mattoon, Illinois, called a meeting in his private office for his two agricultural equipment salesmen. The senior author was invited to attend. The manager said, "Gentlemen, I know how successful you have been selling the new Farmall 706 and 806 tractors; that is great! However, as of 7:46 this morning you can sell no new tractors until you sell one of the used tractors from the barter lot. It's one for one. Sell one used and you can sell one new." The salesmen were outraged; they had a notebook full of prospects for the new 706 and 806 tractors. The decision had been made. The seasoned manager knew there is more to a farm equipment business than just selling the exciting new products no matter how popular they may be. The used tractors began to move off the lot.

The International Harvester Farmall 1206 Turbo Diesel was the Company's first over 100-horsepower, two-wheel-drive tractor and the first turbocharged Farmall. The engineer in the photo is measuring the dB(A) sound level.

length was set at 27.915 inches. A prototype, automatic transmission Farmall tractor was built and tested. After the Hydramatic transmission was abandoned, the next major change in the development program was to increase the horsepower growth objective to 120 horsepower. To provide for this, the clutch housing was lengthened by 1.25 inches. The clutch housing that went into the production 706 and 806 tractors was precisely 27.915 plus 1.25 inches long. The ghost of "Hydramatic" still lived.

The Over 100-Horsepower Class

The Farmall 1206 Turbo Diesel gave IH their first two-wheel-drive tractor over 100 horsepower and their first turbocharged Farmall when it was introduced in 1965. This was basically a turbocharged 806 from the outside. However, the driveline had been re-engineered to fully account for the almost 18 horsepower increase in observed PTO output. In fact, during the development of the 1206 Turbo, some of the analysis suggested an area of questionable, long-term reliability. With the success of the 706 and 806 and their outstanding reliability, engineering, the tractor product committee, and senior management would not consider even a small calculated risk; the program was delayed. When the new tractor was introduced, it was right.

The Right Size

The International 300-engine horsepower 4300 four-wheel-drive tractor was definitely too large for the market that existed in 1961. The next IH four-wheel-

drive tractor with steerable axles front and rear was the International 4100 introduced in 1965. The tractor started out as an Advanced Engineering project rather than as a traditional development within the Tractor Engineering Department. With recognition of the market importance of this tractor, it was moved to a totally new engineering organization named Special Vehicles. The new group had a manager, a project engineer, and eight other professionals who represented all of the required disciplines for taking the International 4100 from concept to production. They accomplished their objective in only 23 months, and the merits of the self-contained, multi-discipline engineering group within the IH organization was proven.

This yellow International 4100, four-wheel-drive turbocharged diesel tractor demonstrated its drawbar capacity pulling a field cultivator. An optional factory installed cab was available.

The tractor market is more than just high horsepower units. The International 424 with three-point draft control hitch and a long list of standard features was a key IH entry in the 36-PTO horsepower class.

The "hottest" new 3-plow power from the greatest name in tractors

INTERNATIONAL 424

with Draft-controlled 3-point hitch • Differential lock • Hydrostatic power steering • 8½-foot turning radius • 8-2 transmission • Constant-running PTO • Choice of Gas or Diesel

All these features except power steering are standard on the all-new International 424. There's more comfort than you're used to in this size tractor. Better handling. Solid construction . . . ample evidence of more for your money. Before you buy any utility tractor, get details on an International 424—most exciting new tractor to hit the 3-plow market in 20 years.

The people who bring you the machines that work

The International 4100 was competitively priced because it was built under volume production conditions at Farmall Works and contained many current or modified No. 706 and 806 two-wheel-drive tractor components and tooling. It utilized the turbocharged six-cylinder, 429-cubic-inch diesel engine built by International Harvester and delivered 116.15 drawbar horsepower; it was the right size.

In 1967, new 28.1-26 tires, the largest cross-section width of any R1 or R3 tractor tire produced to date, became available for the 4100. A year later, an optional Category III, three-point hitch and 1,000-rpm independent PTO with two shaft sizes were offered.

New Swept Back Styling

Not just a swept back radiator grille for appearance but a swept back front axle for 8 1/3-foot turning radius made the new International 424 an excellent loader tractor, especially if it was equipped with the Forward-Reverse attachment. The handy, 31-drawbar horsepower tractor came with draft-controlled three-point hitch, differential lock, hydrostatic power steering, and constant-running PTO. The skid imported from the IH British Company had a BD-154 diesel engine. The gasoline version was the basic British skid less engine, with the Louisville Works-built and installed C-146 engine. To complete the tractor, Louisville would add radiator, grill, hood, front axle, power steering, electrical system, wheels, and tires to the skid.

Hydrostatic All-Speed Drive Tractor . . . An International Harvester First

IH expertise in hydrostatic power transmission dated back to IH Great Britain in 1955. The experimental HT-340 hydrostatic drive turbine tractor added to the knowledge base. The H-25 rubber-tired IH

Payloader with hydrostatic transmission was an industry first in its class and further contributed to IH hydrostatic transmission know-how. The Farm Equipment Division established another industry first with hydrostatic drive for IH 403 and 503 combines.

International Harvester introduced the Farmall and International 656 tractors in 1967 and they became the first hydrostatic tractors in the industry. Movement of the Hydrostatic 656 tractor Speed Ratio (SR) Control lever would provide any speed from 9 mph in reverse to 0 to 20 mph forward in HI range. (LO range was 4 mph in reverse to 0 to 8 mph forward.) Each range could be done without a clutch or shifting gears.

The International 656 tractor introduced the IH exclusive, infinitely-variable, hydrostatic drive power transmission technology. This I-656 hydrostatic All-Speed Drive tractor and PTO baler demonstrates one of the hydro's best applications. The tractor delivers full rated PTO rpm for the baler; hydrostatic drive delivers infinitely variable travel speed for the tractor to match changing windrow conditions.

How Does Hydrostatic Work?

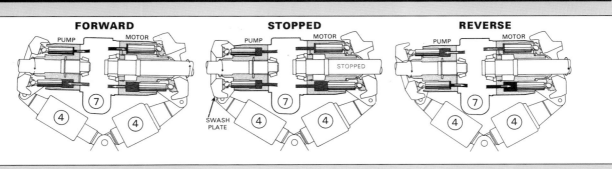

The swash plate controlled hydrostatic piston pump is directly connected to the tractor engine. When the operator moves the speed ratio (SR) control, the hydraulic powered servo cylinder (4) changes the angle of the pump swash plate. This changes the amount of high pressure oil flowing to the hydrostatic piston motor that is directly connected to the tractor final drive. The higher the volume of oil flowing to the motor, the faster it rotates, and faster tractor travel results. When the pump swash plate is in the neutral position, there is no pump output and the tractor stops. When the pump swash plate tilts past neutral, the oil flows in the opposite direction and the hydrostatic piston motor reverses and the tractor reverses. The hydrostatic pump and hydrostatic motor are mounted on the center section (7) that also provides the interconnecting, high-pressure oil passages.

The theory is very simple. However, it took IH engineers 14 years to develop hydrostatic components that were reliable and could be economically produced in high volume to meet the requirements of a competitive farm tractor transmission.

A Foot-N-Inch control was positioned where the traditional clutch would normally be located; it was not a clutch. This feature was handy for moving the tractor in small increments. If the operator needed an emergency stop, it served that purpose too.

In brief, a variable displacement pump, directly connected to the engine, delivered high pressure oil to a hydrostatic motor that drove the final drive. Changing the output of the pump changed the speed of the motor and the tractor.

The 66.0-PTO horsepower 656 tractor was an excellent power size for introducing hydrostatic all-speed drive. The tractor was ideal for baling, chopping, and mowing where speed control at constant PTO speed is a great advantage. It was handy for plowing and tillage and certain efficiencies could be achieved, but that was not its number one application.

The spaced dual tires provided plenty of traction when draft-type implements like this IH No. 53 rear-mounted cultivator were hitched to the 90-drawbar horsepower International Farmall 856 tractor.

The "56" Series

The 1968 Buyer's Guide helped introduce the New International Farmall 756, 856, and 1256 Turbo tractors with Position Comfort Design. The Guide's list of new features included hydraulic seat suspension, five-position tilt steering wheel with hydrostatic power steering, 38-inch wide platform, 8-forward and 4-reverse speeds standard, and new "h" pattern shifting that provided neutral between HI and LO ranges. Shifting was exceptionally easy. Another comfort feature was the availability of factory-installed cabs made by Excel Industries. A new addition to the

The 826 (shown here) and 1026 were both available as hydrostatic or gear-drive models.

The original four-wheel-drive 4100 tractor became the 4156 in 1969 and drawbar horsepower increased from 116 to 125.

top of the line was the International Farmall 1456 Turbo. The six-cylinder, 407-cubic-inch displacement turbocharged engine delivered just over 131 PTO horsepower in the 1970 Nebraska test.

IH Protective Frame

University engineers and extension personnel, along with representatives of the farm machinery industry, conducted campaigns and demonstrations stressing farm safety in the 1950s. Safe operation of tractors to avoid rolling over and proper use of PTO equipment headed the list of concerns.

With the introduction of the "56" Series tractors in 1967, IH made factory-installed protective frames available for the 656, 756, 856, and 1256 tractors. The two-post frames could be equipped with an optional canopy. To provide optimum protection, the operator needed to wear the seat belt that was included with the protective frame; this required a continuing education program. Later, when the 66 Series tractors were introduced, IH made available four-post protective structures. These could be equipped with two styles of canopies that were lined with sound-deadening insulation. ISOMOUNT insulators were used on the front and rear uprights to absorb vibration and reduce noise. The structures complied with all of the then-current Federal safety regulations.

Other New Tractors for 1967

The 1967 tractor offering included the International 444 gasoline with 38 PTO horsepower and a diesel version. Industrial International 2444 and

Industrial International 2444 Lo-Boy in both gasoline and diesel were also available. The 544 Series introduced the outstanding 52-PTO horsepower, four-cylinder, D-239 diesel engine from IH Neuss Works in West Germany. The tractor also came with a C-200 four-cylinder gasoline engine. The 544 Series introduced another first for IH, the magnetic pulse, transistorized ignition system that eliminated the breaker points and condenser. The International 544 was also offered in an International 544 row-crop version plus industrial International 2544 models. The full 544 Series could be had in hydrostatic as well as gear drive with either gasoline or diesel engines.

This International Farmall 544 Hydro tractor powered an IH No. 111 rotary mower. The 544 Series offered both hydrostatic and gear-drive models. The smooth running, quiet D-239 diesel engine was designed and manufactured by IH Neuss Works, West Germany.

Two International 544 utility tractors equipped with shakers and catching frames were the basis of an experimental IH citrus harvester. Tractors worked from opposite sides of the tree.

cyclamate solution just prior to harvest would cause the fruit to uniformly detach from the branches when the limbs were shaken. Without the spray, much of the fruit would stay on the tree. The spray was considered safe because cyclamates were a widely used sugar substitute. Lake Alfred used the pre-harvest spray method. After the IH experimental citrus harvester had shown it could successfully harvest over 85% of the fruit at one time, bad news came. The Federal Government announced that cyclamates were possible carcinogens. That news was the end of the IH tree shaker project. Tree fruits, other than oranges, are harvested with shakers on a commercial basis. Small firms that make that equipment now utilize some of the IH technology.

Shake Rattle and Roll — Oranges

International Harvester began working with University of Florida researchers at the USDA Lake Alfred Experiment Station in 1959 on a project to mechanically harvest citrus. Rising labor cost and fewer workers made the project very timely. Up to that time, a number of systems had been tried, but none were totally successful. IH engineers developed a combination tree shaker catching frame method. The hydraulic-driven shaker was equipped with a specially designed, four-pod clamp for attaching to major tree limbs. The pods were a tough rubber-like material on the outside and filled with a silastic compound commonly known as "Silly Putty." The "Silly Putty" would conform to the variations of the limb without damaging it. When shaking, the pods became rigid enough to shake the limb and remove oranges from the tree.

The catching frame was equally innovative. Two International 544 tractors were equipped with heavy canvas rolled up like a window shade on the side of the tractor. When the tractors were in position, one on each side of the tree, hydraulically operated arms would unroll the canvas and form the catching frame. A conveyor at the bottom of the catching frame moved harvested fruit to storage boxes on each tractor.

The story has a sweet start but a sour ending. Research activity in shaker/catching-frame harvest of oranges increased during this period because it had been discovered that spraying orange trees with a

More Powerful Hydrostatic Tractors

The new 1026 Hydro Diesel was introduced in 1969. It delivered over 112 PTO horsepower and came in Farmall, Farmall Hi-Clear, International, International Wheatland, and industrial International 21026 versions. Like the Farmall 544, the new Farmall 826 was offered in both Hydrostatic and gear-drive models. The 826 used the six-cylinder, IH German Neuss D-358 diesel that delivered 84 PTO horsepower and the six-cylinder, C-301 gasoline with similar horsepower. The higher horsepower of the 1026 Hydro Diesel was idea for PTO forage harvester applications.

The H.A.T. Tractor

The Multi-Purpose Tractor Task Force submitted a report to Divisional Management for approval May 26, 1969. It proposed investigation of the feasibility of developing: (1) Multipurpose four-wheel-drive tractors suitable for both harvesting and tillage use (thus the acronym H.A.T. tractor); and (2) a line of harvesting equipment for the new tractor(s).

Multiple use of a basic power unit was the "in" thing in the farm equipment industry in the late '60s. U.S. Steel had proposed the multipurpose "Vantage" tractor and by 1969 sales of New Idea Uni-Systems were large enough to get the attention of both IH dealers and IH management.

The report proposed 100 PTO horsepower and a 125 PTO horsepower four-wheel-drive power units that

This proposed multi-purpose tractor was not an IH version of the New Idea Uni-System. The H.A.T. tractor (Harvesting And Tillage) was envisioned as a high-horsepower, four-wheel-drive, four-wheel-steer tillage tractor in addition to serving as the power unit for harvesting attachments.

made maximum use of existing IH components. Processing units were to include: two sizes of multi-pass combines (the engineering name for the Axial-Flow), forage harvester, and ear corn husking bed. Future attachment plans included: windrowers, balers, cotton strippers, sweet corn pickers, chemical application equipment, and front-mounted stalk shredders. It was an ambitious proposal. The plan called for the first six preproduction power units and three kinds of attachments to be introduced by 1974. By 1980 the plan envisioned sales of 1,800 small and 3,000 large power units and over 8,000 processors.

Serious layout work and costing was invested in the proposal. This included the usual industrial design artwork and a series of practical looking 1/10 scale models. The H.A.T. tractor was definitely a tillage tractor where the New Idea Uni-System was not. However, the need to own and switch two or more processors in order to have an economic advantage still remained. Careful market evaluation revealed that high-speed, high-volume farming in the 1980s would not be receptive to switching processors, even if the process was relatively easy. The rapid decline in ear corn harvest, except for hybrid seed corn and sweet corn, was an additional factor in the decision to not reduce the H.A.T. tractor to a field-going prototype.

New Engines for a New Tractor Line

The completely new line of mid-size IH diesel engines was known originally as the 300/400 Series Melrose Park Diesel Engines. The design, tooling, and automated transfer line for the new engines represented a $25-million International Harvester investment. These direct-injection diesels had an advanced-type of injection pump that improved efficiency and produced less smoke and noise. The crankcase of the two 300 Series engines had a 3.875-inch bore; the three 400 Series engines had a

4.3-inch bore. Both series had seven main bearings. Careful design resulted in 65% of the parts being common between the 300 Series and the 400 Series and 95% of the parts being common within a series. Plateau honed, centrifugal cast-iron wet-type sleeves, jet-cooled pistons, and a torsional vibration damper were but a few of the design features and sophisticated manufacturing techniques that made the new engines the standard of the industry.

The New 66 Series Introduction for 1971

Eight New 66 Series Tractor Models
International Farmall 766 gasoline —
   79.0 PTO horsepower gear drive
International Farmall 966 diesel —
   95.0 PTO horsepower gear drive
International Farmall 966 diesel —
   90.5 PTO horsepower hydrostatic
International Farmall 1066 diesel —
   115.0 PTO horsepower gear drive
International Farmall 1066 diesel —
   113.0 PTO horsepower hydrostatic
International Farmall 1466 diesel —
   133.0 PTO horsepower gear drive
International Farmall 1468 diesel —
   133.0 PTO horsepower gear drive
International 4-WD 4166 diesel —
   140.0 PTO horsepower gear drive

Three New Utility Tractors
International 354 utility diesel or gasoline —
   32 PTO horsepower
International 454 utility diesel or gasoline —
   40 PTO horsepower

International Farmall 966 Hydro and four-bottom, 700 Series plow with spring-tooth harrow attachment. The protective frame added safety and the canopy added sunny day comfort.

The new 66 Series and World Wide tractors gathered at the IH Hickory Hill Photo Center near Sheriden, Illinois, for a family portrait. They were: International 1466, 1066, 966, and 766. The totally new World Wide 454 and 574 joined the clan. Though styled like a World Wide tractor, the 354 was a different design.

It all started here 125 years ago. A part of the new 66 Series tractor introduction was staged on Pioneer Court in front of the International Harvester World Headquarters at 401 N. Michigan Avenue, Chicago, Illinois. This Chicago River location is just a short distance from the site of the original McCormick reaper factory built in 1847. IH president, Brooks McCormick, stands between the IHC Mogul 8-16 tractor introduced in 1915 and the new 133-PTO horsepower International Farmall 1466 tractor. Three small utility tractors were introduced the same day. The smallest, the agile International 354, had twice the horsepower of, and weighed 40% less than, the cumbersome Mogul.

The 32-PTO horsepower International 354 Utility tractor was the smallest of the three utility models introduced in 1971. It had 8-forward and 2-reverse speeds, a three-point hitch, draft and position control, and constant-running PTO.

International 574 utility diesel or gasoline —
    52 PTO horsepower
International 574 row-crop diesel or gasoline —
    52 PTO horsepower

Power for the new 66 Series tractors came from the six-cylinder D-360 naturally aspirated, D-414 turbocharged or naturally aspirated, and D-436 turbocharged engines that were a part of the new Melrose Park 300/400 Series diesel engine family. A list of seven new tractor features complimented the impressive new engines. One of 66 Series features was differential lock for 766, 1066, and 1466 tractors, and another was ISOMOUNT isolators that reduced cab vibration and noise. The new two-door cabs came in custom and deluxe models. The deluxe cab included a built-in protective frame and heavily upholstered interior.

The photo illustrates the black and red strip styling of the mid-1970s Farmall tractors as this International Farmall 766 tractor pulls an International No. 125 two-way plow with two-way gauge wheel.

Two Tractors with a Bold New Look

The International Farmall 1468 was, in spite of its model number, a part of the 66 Series introduction; the tractor was basically a 1466 except for the engine. For the first time, IH introduced an agricultural tractor with a V-8 engine. This power plant was a modified version of the IH 550-cubic-inch-displacement diesel used by the Truck Division. A novel feature of the engine was a system that injected fuel into only four cylinders under no load or partial load and all eight cylinders under full load. A pair of external, heat shielded, aluminized muffles with tall stacks established a bold new look for this tractor that gave it a different appearance from the classic 66 Series.

The four-wheel-drive 4166 boasted a new DT-436 engine with 140 PTO horsepower in place of the DT-429 with 111 PTO horsepower in the original 4100. The change that caught everyone's eye, however, was the red and white styling in place of the original 4100 yellow. The change established a bold new look for the four-wheel-drive 4166 tractor. Original isn't completely accurate. During design and development of the original 4100, it was always planned to be red and white. However, during field test, it was painted yellow like the industrial equipment in an effort to disguise the fact that it was an agricultural tractor. When the Tractor Product Committee saw the tractor during field test, they agreed that the 4100 looked great painted yellow. So, it was released to production as a yellow and white tractor. Styling ideas for this tractor had come full circle.

The new six-cylinder, D-436 turbocharged diesel engine in this International Farmall 1466 Turbo tractor was a part of the impressive line of recently introduced IH Melrose Park 300/400 Series diesel engines. When introduced, the tractor had a 133-PTO horsepower rating; two years later and 200 rpm faster, the rating was 145 PTO horsepower.

New 66 Series Additions

International style 966, 1066, and 1466 tractors followed the 1971 Farmall tractor introduction. The International Farmall 666 gear-drive and hydrostatic tractors in gasoline and diesel versions joined the original 66 Series in 1973. The diesel model used the new D-312 diesel from the 300 Series engines. A Farmall 666 HI-CLEAR version with 22-inches of crop clearance was also offered.

IH Tractor Engineering turned to the IH Truck Division for the 550-cubic-inch displacement, V-8 diesel used in the International Farmall 1468 tractor shown here. When introduced, it had 133 PTO horsepower which was the same output as the six-cylinder powered International Farmall 1466 Turbo. In 1973, they both were rated at 145 PTO horsepower.

This four-wheel-drive, four-wheel-steer tractor series now had a new D-436 Turbo engine with 150 PTO horsepower. The tractor series had been yellow and white since introduction in 1965. This 4166 Turbo model changed that; it was styled with the classic IH farm tractor red and white.

World Wide Tractors

International Harvester manufactured tractors and tractor modules and components in eight countries in 1971: United States, United Kingdom, Germany, France, Japan, India, Australia, and Mexico. Tractor sales were made in 125 countries by this international farm equipment company. It would seem wise to try and serve as many of these diverse markets with the fewest, basic tractor models possible. That is exactly what International Harvester did starting in 1964 with establishment of the World Wheel Tractor Committee. After years of work, and what seemed like hundreds of transatlantic jet flights later, the Committee issued a proposed release to production of the following tractors in February 1968.

International 454 tractor —
   40 horsepower farm-utility type
International 2454 tractor —
   40 horsepower industrial-utility type
International 574 tractor —
   52 horsepower farm-utility type
International 2574 tractor —
   52 horsepower industrial-utility type
International 574 tractor —
   52 horsepower row-crop type

These tractors utilized C-157, C-175, and C-200 gasoline engines produced at Louisville Works and

International Harvester was the first farm equipment manufacturer to produce 5-million tractors. An International Farmall 1066 Turbo had the honor of being the 5,000,000th tractor. To celebrate the occasion, that particular tractor had chrome wheels and muffler and special styling. After it rolled off the assembly line on February 1, 1974, it began making the rounds of farm shows and state fairs.

In 1974, the hydrostatic tractor models got new, distinctive model names. The 966 Hydro became the new International Hydro 100 Diesel Farmall with 104 PTO horsepower. This photo shows the four-post protective frame with full canopy. To complete the new hydrostatic tractor line, International Hydro 70 tractors with 69 PTO horsepower were offered in gasoline or diesel versions.

D-179, D-223, and D-239 diesel engines produced by IH Neuss Works, West Germany. Complete tractors for the overseas market and 17 kinds of skidded units (engine, transmission, and final drive) were manufactured by IH Doncaster Works in Great Britain. Tractors for the U.S. market were manufactured from skidded units by Louisville Works, Louisville, Kentucky.

The results of the World Wide Tractor Program came to the U.S. market for the first time as part of the 66 Series introduction. Some of the most impressive features of the beautifully styled 454 and 574 tractors were internal:

Synchronized, constant mesh transmission,
    8-forward, 4-reverse speeds
HI-LO-REV range lever with built in "shuttle"
Optional differential lock
Hydrostatic power steering
Live independent hydraulics
Precise feathering, hydraulic actuated, multiple
    wet-disk IPTO
Wet, band-type parking brake
Pressure lubricated power train
Inboard, planetary final drive
Hydraulic actuated wet disk brakes
Twin-shaft, 540- and 1,000-rpm IPTO
External features:
Transmission shift levers on the left side of the seat,
    hitch and hydraulic levers on the right side for a
    clear area between the operator's knees
Operator forward for easy entry

Suspended brake and clutch pedals
Saddle-type rear fuel tank
These truly modern tractors were incorporated in skidded unit form into an extensive line of integral industrial tractors. They replaced the 3414 and 3524 Series of industrial loader and loader-backhoe tractors. The smallest member of the utility tractors in the 66 Series introduction was the International 354. This 32-PTO horsepower tractor shared the worldwide styling but it was based on older Doncaster tractor components and was powered by the British BC-144 gasoline and BD-144 diesel engines.

Articulated Steering . . . Four-Wheel Drive

International Harvester acquired a financial interest in the Steiger Tractor Company of Fargo, North Dakota, in 1972. A year later, the IH 4366, articulated-steer, four-wheel-drive tractor with IH six-cylinder, DT-466 turbocharged diesel engine was introduced. International Harvester supplied components other than the engine, but the cab, frame, and driveline were the basic Steiger design. Since the Steiger Company continued to produce related, but somewhat different, tractors under the Steiger name and for OEM, IH marketing and the IH dealer organization faced some difficult sales strategy challenges.

An Historic Event

This was a subtle change; there was no news release or major company announcement; but, the change was significant to many loyal International Farmall tractor

This versatile, IH 454 "World Wide" utility tractor had a twin shaft, 540/1,000 rpm, power actuated independent PTO. It was a perfect match for the IH 9-foot, 990 mower conditioner. An optional, 1,000 rpm, right side PTO was available for special applications.

This 52-PTO horsepower 574 "World Wide" utility tractor was the larger of the two new tractors developed for sale throughout the vast IH domestic and overseas marketing network. The International 574 also came in a row-crop version.

The new IH D-466 turbocharged diesel engine, rated at 225 horsepower, powered this International 4366 Turbo tractor. The Steiger Tractor Company assembled product gave International Harvester access to the articulated-steer, four-wheel-drive tractor market.

owners and users. After 1973, no new IH tractors carried the model name Farmall. The change had been coming for some time as Farmall-style tractors acquired the name International in large letters on the side of the hood and the model name Farmall appeared only in small letters under the model number. Changing agricultural practices had virtually eliminated the need for high-clearance, tricycle tractors; the traditional Farmall-style tractor no longer had a market. The 50-year legend of the Farmall tractor now claimed its rightful place as a part of agricultural mechanization history.

The Modular Final Drive

Tractor Engineering developed a new modular configuration for IH tractor final drive design to efficiently

Search far and wide and you won't find literature for the 654 tractor pictured here in spite of an IH file full of beautiful color and black-and-white photographs. The reason, the model number was changed from 654 to 664 before production began in 1972. The two-year production filled the 60-PTO horsepower utility tractor gap until the "World Wide" International 674 utility and 674 row-crop production began in 1973.

and reliably handle the next generation of higher horsepower tractors. The planetary final drive and axle carrier were housed in one unit bolted to the side of the differential housing main rear frame. This provided an especially rugged final drive structure, easier service, and greater flexibility for other applications. The 160-PTO horsepower International 1566 and 150-PTO horsepower 1568 V-8 diesel tractors introduced the new modular final drive in 1973. These tractors also introduced the new three-speed, easy-shifting, constant-mesh transmission with Hi-Lo speed range transmission that delivered 12-forward and 6-reverse travel speeds in TA-equipped tractors. This kind of power called for a Category III, three-point hitch and 1,000 rpm only IPTO.

This International 1566 Turbo tractor with six-cylinder D-436 turbocharged engine and the International 1568 with V-8 diesel engine were basically the same tractor, except for the engine.

International Harvester Tractors

A Size for Every Need

1586 with 160 pto horsepower and 140 at the drawbar*

1486 with 145 pto horsepower and 127 at the drawbar*

1086 with 130 pto horsepower and 114 at the drawbar*

Hydro 186 with 104 pto horsepower and 82 at the draw

986 with 105 pto horsepower and 92 at the drawbar*

886 with 85 pto horsepower and 74 at the drawbar*

*Manufacturer's estimate

The pro-ag line:
Power never came with so much comfort!

Take a Series 86 test drive at your IH dealer soon.

INTERNATIONAL AGRICULTURAL EQUIPMENT

AD-31921-E...9/76 Lithographed in The United States of America

The country spent 1976 participating in the celebration commemorating 200 years of American history. International Harvester had a celebration of its own; IH introduced the International Series 86 tractors and did it with a major four-week Chicago event. Dealers assembled, two groups each week, at the Hyatt Regency, Chicago, for an evening of music by Al Hirt and entertainment at the hotel. The next day started off with an 86 Series tractor introduction and professionally produced stage show "The Age of Agrarius" in the Arie Crown Theater at Chicago's McCormick Place. After the show, dealers made the rounds of other key IH products displayed on the outdoor, upper level of McCormick Place. Each dealer went home with a Bulova Accutron watch with a tiny 86 tractor on the minute hand. It was a "really, really big show."

Everyone's an Expert

Farm equipment senior management, in all companies, have many abilities, but there are two areas where they are sure they enjoy an unusually high level of expertise — product styling and product naming. For the new 86 Series tractors, management wanted to be sure they had the right answers for this very significant new product. Styling was not a problem, there was general agreement that the product looked great. Naming the new cab and the new tractor line was another story; no consensus seemed to exist. The new IH

designed-and-built cab was so outstanding they didn't want to call it just a new cab. A professional in the field of product naming from Philadelphia, Pennsylvania, was hired to conduct a survey of current, high horsepower tractor owners to learn their reaction to a list of proposed cab names. The number one choice of survey participants was liked by all of the IH leadership involved; unfortunately, Massey Ferguson introduced the same cab name just a week before the survey results were received. Other names at the top of the list didn't seem to fit. The name for the new IH 86 Series cab became the Control Center. IH personnel were instructed never to call this safe, quiet, climate controlled operator's station by the old fashioned name — cab!

What do you call this new line of tractors? The answer to this question came from a highly successful but totally different IH activity. International Harvester was a leader in using computers in its business, especially parts inventory control, and had led the way in computer use by IH dealers. IH took computer use one step further and offered a university research-based

The mid-mount Control Center set the 86 Series tractors apart from all previous IH agricultural tractors. This quiet, comfortable, operator enclosure was an integral part of the overall tractor design and was standard on all 86 Series tractors over 70 horsepower.

computer program for analyzing the timeliness and profitability of alternative farming systems and farm equipment mix. IH named their computer management program PRO-AG.

Participants in the IH PRO-AG seminar program filled out a computer input form describing their corn and soybean operation in detail including the machinery used. Overnight this data was sent to the IH Corporate Computer Center in Hinsdale, Illinois, for analysis and the printout was in the farmer's hands the next morning. Personal computers in the farm office were over a decade away.

The International Harvester computer-based PRO-AG equipment analysis system became recognized as a valuable, unbiased management tool in every state where the seminars were offered. IH became recognized as the leader in the field and PRO-AG program success became widely known. To capitalize on the PRO-AG positive image, the new 86 Series became the PRO-AG line of tractors.

Build it Like a Car

The outstanding feature of the new 86 Series tractors was the cab Control Center. The high capacity, molded fuel tank was located over the rear axle and the "midmount" Control Center was 1 1/2 feet further forward than prior models and the location contributed to a smoother ride. A four-post protective frame was an integrated part of the structure. ISOMOUNT insulators, thick carpeting and polyurethane foam insulation reduced sound as low as 80 dB(A). Two doors, a comfortable seat, grouped controls, telescoping steering

wheel, 43 square feet of safety glass for great visibility along with standard heater and air conditioner added up to an impressive new product.

One important feature of the new Control Center was the appreciated, but seldom mentioned, fit and finish of the entire product. Because of their know-how with sheet metal, East Moline Works was selected to manufacture the new Control Center. In order to achieve an automotive quality operator enclosure, the Modern Engineering Company of Detroit, Michigan, with their automotive expertise was hired to design the tooling and install the production line. The result was an outstanding product with automotive fit and finish.

To Curve or Not to Curve

The 86 Series tractors were greatly different from prior models and the Control Center was an integral part of the total design. Because it was so new, industrial design and the Tractor Product Committee spent many long meetings together refining the details. One of the most memorable discussions, other than one door versus two doors, concerned the windshield. This was a large and expensive piece of tinted safety glass and it was designed to be flat. Key members of the committee felt very strongly that the windshield should be curved; it should not be almost circular like the major competitor because that can cause glare problems in bright, low-angle sunshine. The real problem was cost; cost control is the never-ending struggle in all product development. Fortunately, the

The comfort and convenience of the International Harvester 86 Series Control Center interior matched the style and appearance of the exterior.

The 130-PTO horsepower International 1086 diesel tractor was the most popular of the series. This tractor and the 105-PTO horsepower International 966 diesel tractor were both available in HI-CLEAR versions.

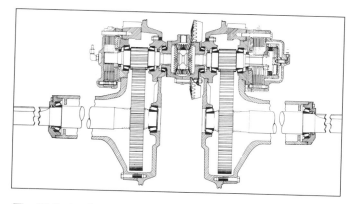

The 86 Series final drive had components sized to match increased horsepower. Wet, multiple-disk power brakes were a change from the prior line of tractors. The 1586 final drive design incorporated a planetary final reduction in place of the bull gears shown here.

final decision approved a design with a gently curved windshield that added a distinct touch of class to the new Control Center.

The Complete Tractor

Because the Control Center was an integral part of the overall tractor design and not an option, many special features could be incorporated. An example is the hydraulic-powered clutch and right and left wet multiple-disk power brake pedals; all three were suspended from the steering and instrument cluster pedestal. This arrangement helped reduce noise and kept dust out of the Control Center environment. Heater and air conditioner were standard.

The 86 Series tractors over 70 horsepower now included as standard the popular equipment previ-

ously offered as optional attachments. The new standard features included: Draft control three-point hitch with extendible lower links and Torque Amplifier (TA). Independent PTO was standard on all but the two largest models.

The 86 Series tractors with less than 70 PTO horsepower were designed to meet the needs of a market segment different from the higher horsepower segment; the Hydro 86 with 69.5 PTO horsepower and the International 686 with 66.2 horsepower served these customers. Both tractors could be equipped with either gasoline or diesel engines and both were available in HI-CLEAR versions.

86 Series 4-WD Tractors

The International 4186 with 156.6 PTO horsepower carried on the four-wheel-drive, four-wheel-steer product line started in 1965 by the International 4100. This would be the last four-wheel-drive tractor offered by International Harvester in that configuration.

A pair of Steiger Company assembled, articulated steer tractors joined the 86 Series four-wheel-drive offering in 1977. The International 4386 was powered by a DTI-466 turbocharged and intercooled diesel engine from the IH 300/400 Series Melrose Park line of engines. It developed 230 engine horsepower. The International 4586 was powered by an International Harvester 800-cubic-inch displacement turbocharged V-8 diesel engine that developed 300 engine horsepower.

In 1979, the International 4786 joined the two previously released, articulated steer, four-wheel-drive 86 Series tractors. An IH 800-cubic-inch turbocharged V-8 diesel engine rated at 350 horsepower was the power plant for this third and largest member of the 86 Series tractors. All three tractors could be equipped with optional Category III three-point hitches. With the heavy three-point implements used with these tractors, the optional quick coupler attachment was almost a necessity.

This 85-PTO horsepower International 886 diesel tractor and International 445 PTO baler with No. 15 bale thrower made hay baling a one-man operation.

This top-of-the line International 1586 tractor delivered 160 PTO horsepower. Like its high horsepower predecessor, the tractor came standard with TA for 12-forward and 6-reverse speeds. It also incorporated the planetary final drive reduction not found in the other 86 Series tractors. In this photo it pulls an International 700 trailing toggle trip, 8-bottom plow.

The tractor hydrostatic drive supplied full PTO rpm to the International No. 80 three-point hitch snow blower while travel speeds were varied from creeping to the maximum required for the job. This was accomplished by just moving the speed ratio control lever. The tight, heated, Control Center supplied the operator with a great winter environment. The 104-PTO horsepower Hydro 186, shown here with the snow blower, was also available in a HI-CLEAR version.

This International 686 tractor had the standard two-post protective frame with deluxe fenders, seat belt, exhaust pipe extension, and canopy.

The first two articulated 86 Series tractors were styled with the model number in the same band as the name International. A white panel under the model numbers extended from the grille to the engine compartment. This International 4786 has the later style with the upward rising decal for the model number.

The end of an era. The venerable offset 140 tractor and its Louisville C-123, 4-cylinder engine went out of production in 1980 and U.S. built Culti-Vision tractors came to an end. They were replaced by the IH 274 offset tractor with its 3-cylinder, 99-cubic-inch displacement diesel engine shown here.

Small Tractors from a Large Company

Komatsu International Manufacturing Co. Ltd. of Tokyo, Japan, built International Hough designed large rubber-tired equipment under an IH licensing agreement; the firm was named KIMCO. Komatsu, like many large national Japanese companies, produced a wide range of products. Product Management responsible for the IH small tractor line investigated several traditional Japanese sources for low-horsepower tractors but did not locate the right tractor and engine combination. Finally, negotiations with the long-time IH partner, Komatsu, did make available the right small tractor for the U.S. market at a competitive price.

A Japanese Product with a North Carolina Touch

KIMCO of Japan modified the imported IH 284 compact utility tractor to make it into an offset model. The senior author visited the North Carolina tobacco-producing area where the tractor was being evaluated. The basic tractor performed well, but the seat, clutch, and brake pedals were too small and not located properly for the average-size American operator who was running

the prototype tractor. The writer was impressed with how quickly the two engineers from Japan, who spoke very limited English, understood the problem. They went to the town nearby, had redesigned parts made, and kept trying different versions until a practical solution was found. Dimensioned sketches were quickly made and sent to Japan. As a result, when IH imported the 274 offset tractor, it was right for the U.S. specialty crop market.

An IH 284 offset tractor — no, this photo is the IH 274 offset tractor under development in North Carolina. The IH 284 compact utility tractor was the basis for the IH 274 offset and the IH 284 decal was used on the engineering tractor shown here during field test.

The International 844 tractor shown here was the largest of the 84 Series. The tractor had a 268-cubic-inch displacement, four-cylinder, IH-built diesel engine rated at 72 PTO horsepower. For other applications, the 884 was available in utility and low-profile models.

The 84 Series

International Harvester introduced the most complete line of small to mid-size tractors in the industry in 1980. The offering included five models from 42.4 to 72 PTO horsepower. All five models were available in both utility and low-profile models. In addition, row-crop versions were available for all but the 484, the smallest tractor in the series.

Every tractor in the 84 Series was powered by an IH diesel engine. The transmissions were constant-mesh with 8-forward and 4-reverse speeds. The International 884 had Torque Amplifier (TA) as standard; the feature was an option on the 784, 684, and 584. All models were equipped with hydraulically actuated, independent 540 rpm PTO. The two larger tractors had dual 540/1,000-rpm IPTOs. The International 584 and larger utility models could be equipped with the German-made ZF, mechanical four-wheel-drive attachment. The fuel tank located over the rear axle made possible the mid-mount design that gave the operator better visibility and a smoother ride. Controls were conveniently divided into right and left consoles.

The list of 84 Series features also included: torsion-bar draft control, exclusive IH three-lever hydraulic hitch control, planetary final drives, standard differential lock, hydraulic disk brakes, and hydrostatic power steering. A later option was an all-steel ROPS cab for all 84 Series tractors, except low profile, made by the Sims Company of Rutland, Massachusetts. It was carefully styled to look much like the 86 Series Control Center; however, it had a flat windshield.

With 62.5 PTO horsepower, this International 584 low-profile tractor and IH 122 disk harrow were the right combination for the nursery application pictured here.

The engine of the International Hydro 84 row-crop tractor was an IH-built 246-cubic-inch displacement, four-cylinder diesel that delivered 58.7 horsepower through the hydraulically actuated 540 rpm independent PTO. Utility and low-profile versions were also offered.

From left to right the 1982 International 200 Series tractors are: 254 with four-wheel-drive option, 244 with turf tires, 234 with turf tires, and the 234 with four-wheel-drive option.

The New International 234, 244, and 254 Tractors

The world's small tractor market is dominated by Japan. To supply the needs of IH dealers for modern, full-featured small tractors, International Harvester contracted with Mitsubishi for a line of under 22-horsepower tractors. The imports were styled much like other tractors in the IH line and were equipped to meet IH specifications. The 234, 244, and 254 had 15.2, 18.0, and 21.0 PTO horsepower, respectively, and each could be purchased with optional four-wheel drive. All engines were three-cylinder water-cooled diesels. The two larger models had optional live rear PTOs while the smallest model had an optional independent front PTO drive. These tractors lived up to their billing as, "The biggest little trio of diesel work-horses ever to hit the market."

International Harvester imported three models of small tractors from Mitsubishi, Japan. The Strategic Business Unitt OEM Product Special Sales manager for low horsepower tractors made a trip to Japan to be sure the new tractors were exactly as IH had contracted. This International 244 tractor photo is from a set of slides he took while at Mitsubishi.

The rear half of the 2+2 series tractors had all of the features of the 86 Series rear-wheel-drive tractors including the three-point draft control hitch system that utilized IH torsion-bar lower-link sensing.

2 + 2 = 4 — And a Whole Lot More

The 2+2 family of articulated tractors was as innovative in design as it was in appearance. The components behind the articulated joint were basically the rear half of the 86 Series conventional tractors. The front driving axle was a component of the IH world wide tractor line made in England. The engines were the proven IH six-cylinder, DT-436 and DT-466 turbocharged diesels used widely in IH farm tractors, motor trucks, construction equipment, and OEM sales. The new frame, articulation joint, and power transmission drop box tied it all together. The result was all of the comfort

and convenience of the latest in two-wheel-drive, row-crop tractors plus the traction and compaction reducing performance of a traditional equal-wheel, articulated, four-wheel-drive tractor.

During development of the 2+2 tractors, one of the questions was whether the operator should be on the rear half of the tractor or on the front half like traditional articulated tractors. To move the operator to the front half would lose one of the key advantages of the proposed design, use of the existing Control Center and final drive components with minor modification. Furthermore, with a draft load the rear half of the tractor tends to stay straight ahead when the front half moves to steer; this action is much like a standard two-wheel-drive tractor's steering mode. Operator on the rear half of the tractor became the 2+2 design.

The International 3388 with 130 PTO horsepower and International 3588 with 150 horsepower were the two 2+2 row-crop tractors introduced in 1979. In addition to all of the 86 Series tractor features, the new 2+2 tractors had a pressure and flow compensating hydraulic system that sensed the exact amount of hydraulic power required; it delivered what was required and no more . . . that saved energy. The two new-concept tractors soon found acceptance in the marketplace. In the short time between introduction and July 1980, sales of 2,974 tractors were recorded.

This International 3588 articulated steer, four-wheel-drive, 2+2 tractor pulled an International 720 semi-mounted, toggle-trip beam moldboard plow.

The International 3788 was the largest of the three 88 Series articulated steer, four-wheel-drive tractors with 170 PTO horsepower. The tractor is hitched to an International 770 offset disk harrow in this 1980 California ranch scene.

In 1980, the International 3788 tractor with 170 PTO horsepower joined the 2+2 offering. The new tractor used the six-cylinder, IH, DT-466B turbocharged diesel.

The 2+2 tractors took on a new look in 1982 with the introduction of the 60 Series. The International 6388 was the 130-PTO horsepower model and the International 6588 was the 150-PTO horsepower model. To take full advantage of the four-wheel-drive traction capability, both models came equipped with radial tires.

Plans for Three New Tractor Transmissions

International Harvester established a series of goals to achieve "M-C-A" — a Meaningful Competitive Advantage. One of the M-C-A's was a superior tractor transmission. The August 1980 Product Review covered three IH tractor transmissions:

Synchrotorque — The transmission for the engineering TR-4 (50 Series) tractors combined a speed and a range transmission module that delivered 18 forward speeds with no overlap and 6 reverse speeds. This fully synchronized, constant-mesh design was the transmission released for the 5088, 5288, and 5488 tractors introduced in 1982.

Vari-Range — The variable speed, hydromechanical module replaced the six-speed front module of the synchrotorque transmission. The result was the efficiency of a gear transmission with the variable speed benefits of a hydrostatic drive. This extensively tested and highly developed transmission with its impressive efficiency was planned for announcement in 1984.

The IH Hickory Hill Photo Center grounds provided an excellent location for photographing these 1982 International 5488, 5088, 5288, 3688, and 3288 tractors.

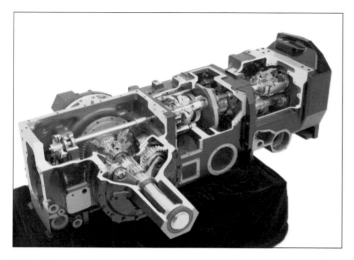

The fully synchronized, constant-mesh 50 Series transmission delivered 18 uniformly spaced forward speeds and 6 reverse speeds. The complete drive line consisted of three modules: speed transmission; range transmission; and final drive differential, planetary final reduction, and power take-off.

The smallest of the new 50 Series tractors, the International 5088 with 135 PTO horsepower, still had plenty of muscle to make good use of the mechanical all-wheel-drive attachment. The engine was an IH, six-cylinder DT-436B turbocharged diesel.

Vari-Turbine — A flywheel mounted turbine (fluid coupling) with lock-up clutch was mounted ahead of the Vari-Range transmission. The result was low speed inching control for implement hook-up and feathered load engagement for start-up of heavy draft loads. The lock-up clutch provided fully efficient, minimum slip performance. The next stage of transmission development installed this device ahead of the Vari-Range transmission. These modular transmission and final drive components were planned to be incorporated in different farm tractor configurations along with use in industrial, construction, and Hough vehicles.

The new, top-of-the-line 50 Series 5488 tractor was the "most powerful two-wheel-drive tractor International had ever marketed" with 185 PTO horsepower. The IH six-cylinder DTI-466B turbocharged and intercooled Series B diesel engine was the power source. The same engine without intercooler was used in the 5288; it delivered 160 PTO horsepower.

This studio photo helped tell the convenience story of the Control Center and its two-door design.

A choice of two luxurious interiors was offered for the new 30 and 50 Series tractors in addition to the standard interior. The Western option (pictured here) had a deluxe fabric uphol-stered seat with hydraulic, adjustable suspension and wide armrest that folded up or down. Simulated hand-tooled leather side panels had storage pockets in each door. Swivel sun visors were part of the package. A second option had the same features but the color-coordinated scheme came in cherry burgundy. Both options came with AM/FM multiplex, cassette stereo, push button radio as standard.

Electronic Control

Microprocessor control of gear selection and engine rpm for optimum fuel efficiency and productivity was under development. The electronic control system could be applied to all three transmissions.

Clean, Cool, and Quiet

The reverse air flow cooling system was introduced in a Chassis Concept for Modern Tractors engineering report in 1978. By drawing outside air in from the top of the hood, pulling it through the radiator and discharg-ing the hot air out the front grille of the tractor, many benefits were achieved. Control Center noise and heat load were reduced, less trash collected on the air inlet and discharge air did not stir up dust on the ground, and cooling was not as affected by changes in wind direction. The enclosed engine provided safety and opportunities for enhanced styling. The list of benefits was impressive; the decision was made to incorporate reverse air flow in the new 30 and 50 Series tractors.

The new 30 and 50 Series introduced the IH exclusive forward air flow cooling system. With the fan located ahead of the radiator, clean air was pulled in through the top grille and expelled out the front grille. This design blew dirt and heat away from the operator and helped control the noise level.

The forward air flow inlet grilles are clearly shown on top of the hood of this 5488 tractor equipped with duals and mechanical four-wheel drive. If any debris should build up on the inlet, the operator could easily see what was occurring.

This International 3088 tractor with 80 PTO horsepower was the smallest of the 30 Series tractor line. The middle size 3288 had 90 PTO horsepower. Both tractors had IH 6-cylinder D-358 naturally aspirated diesel engines.

Transmissions for the '80s

The final release version of the 18-speed, fully synchronized, constant-mesh transmission for the 50 Series incorporated a wet hydraulic-powered, mid-mount master clutch that required minimum pedal

The International 3688 tractor with 113 PTO horsepower was the largest of the 30 Series tractors. It had an IH 6-cylinder D-436 naturally aspirated diesel engine. The economical 30 Series tractors shared the new 50 Series forward air flow system and basic styling. In 1983, a high clear version became available and an International 3488 Hydrostatic drive model with 112 PTO horsepower was added.

effort. An exclusive computer sensor protected the power shift portion of the transmission.

The range transmission had three forward synchronized gears (low, medium, and high) and a reverse gear. The fully synchronized, six-speed transmission used two clutch packs for power shifting. This thoroughly tested transmission and already-proven IH Melrose Park 400 Series engines made it possible for the Company to offer a three-year or 2,500-hour extended warranty on the engine and drivetrain for the new series of tractors.

The transmission for the 30 Series tractors had a high, low, or reverse range transmission coupled to a four-speed transmission with power shift for a total of 16-forward speeds and 8-reverse speeds. A single control moved side to side for power shift without de-clutching or up or down through the triple "Z" pattern when clutching to shift between gears. A second control operated the range transmission; when it passed through neutral with the clutch depressed, a hydraulic brake stopped the rotating transmission members to provide easy shifting.

Big Plans for Super 70 Series Tractors

The exclusive IH 2+2 design that offered row-crop tractor flexibility in a true four-wheel-drive tractor had built a solid position for the Company in a very impor-

Here an International 3488 Hydro tractor was working with an International forage harvester with International 672-cubic-feet capacity forage box. The 30 Series tractor offered modern power, comfort, and convenience in an economical package.

The preproduction International 7288 type 2+2 tractor had 175 PTO horsepower and 50 Series synchro-torque transmission and final drive.

tant segment of the market. The Tractor Product Committee laid plans to capitalize on this position and moved forward with the International 7288 and 7488 tractors with 2+2 design. These two tractors incorporated the new fully synchronized, constant-mesh transmission and final drive design from the 50 Series two-wheel-drive tractors. The STS, Synchro Tri-Six Transmission, decal on the 70 Series tractors highlighted the impressive features of the new transmission. The next development phase would put International 7688 and 7888 four-wheel-drive, 2+2 tractors into production; the largest model would have 300-bare engine horsepower.

In January of 1985, a preproduction run included 19 175-horsepower 7288 and 16 200-horsepower 7488 tractors. These Super 70 Series 2+2 tractors were successfully retailed. Advertising took advantage of a pro-

The International 7488 tractor shown here with duals was designed for 200 PTO horsepower.

totype International 7288 tractor and photographed it along with the same tractor styled with International 7488 decals in preparation for full production of the new Super 70 Series 2+2 tractors. These two tractors were to have the same exterior. Within months of the 7288/7488 production, the IH Farm Equipment division sale to the J.I. Case Company Affiliate of Tenneco Corporation was completed. Since they had a line of four-wheel-drive tractors that included both wheel steer and articulated steer designs, they had no interest in further development of a third four-wheel-drive line of tractors. The 2+2 tractor and its unique design that provided economic utilization of two-wheel-drive tractor components in an equal-wheel, four-wheel-drive row-crop tractor would become an important part of International Harvester tractor history.

A New Life for Big Red Tractors

With Tenneco's acquisition of the major assets of International Harvester's Farm Equipment Division, tractor manufacturing at the IH Farmall Plant came to an end. On May 14, 1985, the last IH tractor came off of the assembly line. The following decade saw a total restructuring of the farm equipment industry worldwide. Under the banner of Case-IH, many loyal IH customers and future Case-IH dealers would carry on a unique tradition of BIG RED TRACTORS that had IH as part of their name.

This beautiful cutaway color art was prepared for marketing the 7288 and 7488 2+2 tractors with Synchro Tri-Six (STS) transmissions. Unfortunately, only a small preproduction run of 7288 tractors was made. These unique International 7288 tractors became valued possessions of farmers and International Harvester Collectors and restorers.

This International 5488 with mechanical all-wheel drive is representative of the last tractor produced at Farmall Works.

The banner says it all:
FARMALL PLANT
October 1, 1926
May 14, 1985
5488 ALL WHEEL DRIVE
FINAL TRACTOR BUILT AT FARMALL

223

Tillage and Seedbed Preparation
Ancient Art Becomes Modern Science

highly respected plows made by the Oliver Chilled Plow Company in South Bend, Indiana, and the Parlin and Orendorff Company in Canton, Illinois. To dramatize the power of the big new tractors, photos were made of an IHC Mogul 45-H.P. tractor pulling an 18-furrow Oliver plow complete with large signs identifying each company's product. A photo made of a 55-furrow Oliver plow pulled by three IHC Mogul 45-H.P. tractors appears to be in the same field. Large plows from these manufacturers were called "engine gang plows" rather than tractor plows.

When International Harvester entered the tractor business in 1906 with three sizes of their Milwaukee-built "Famous" engine mounted on a Morton truck, promotion said little about their 1.79- to 2.16-mph travel speed; engine power for belt work was the prime concern. By 1912, IHC 15-horsepower Type "A" and 20-horsepower Type "B" tractors had plowing speeds of 1.90 and 1.73 mph, respectively, in their specifications. The Titan Type D, 18-35-H.P. and Mogul 10-20-H.P. introduced dual horsepower ratings in that year to indicate both a drawbar and a belt pulley horsepower. The significance of tractor drawbar work was now well established. To utilize the horsepower of these large, heavy tractors with typical working speed around 2.0 mph, large plows were required. This scenario was especially true for the 45-H.P. and 30-60-H.P. tractors introduced in 1913 and 1914. However, IHC did not manufacture plows.

To assist in the sale of tractors, IHC marketed the

McCormick-Deering
TRACTOR PLOWS

Little Genius
2, 3, and 4 Furrow

Little Wonder
2 Furrow for Small Tractors

You can plow
8 to 17 Acres
a day

A plow for every farm
A Bottom for every Soil

INTERNATIONAL HARVESTER COMPANY
OF AMERICA
606 SO. MICHIGAN AVE.   INCORPORATED   CHICAGO, ILL.

Primary Tillage

McCormick-Deering Plows

In 1919, IHC purchased the Parlin and Orendorff Company and the Chattanooga Plow Company of Chattanooga, Tennessee. Because of the strong reputation held by the Parlin and Orendorff Company, IHC used the name McCormick-Deering P&O plows in order to

This Little Genius and Little Wonder plow catalog proclaimed the merits of these outstanding products. These two important IHC trade names continued in the McCormick-Deering plow line for decades to come.

This rubber-tired Farmall F-30 could deliver more drawbar horsepower at higher speeds than the steel-tired version. The 3-furrow, Little Genius No. 8 plow was just right for the job.

benefit from the well-known P&O trademark. IHC also used the Chattanooga name in conjunction with McCormick-Deering to identify products from the Tennessee plant. A 1924 plow advertisement carried the statement, "P&O and Chattanooga plows have made and kept their friends among plowmen for many years. For your plow needs this year, consult the McCormick-Deering dealer." In 1924 the tractor plow offering included the Little Genius 2-, 3-, or 4-bottom power-lift, the Little Wonder 2-bottom for small tractors, and the Mogul 4- to 8-bottom for large tractors. An eight-page, two-color brochure printed in 1941 and 1942 covered the McCormick-Deering line of horse drawn walking and riding moldboard and middlebuster plows along with riding disk plows. At this late date, McCormick-Deering P&O was printed on the side of wooden handles of walking plows. The P&O trademark appeared on moldboards of Diamond sulky and gang plows as well as the No. 1 Two-Way Success and No. 9 Success sulky plows.

This fully automatic, fully mechanical, roll-over No. 39 two-way plow came with 14- or 16-inch bottoms. A pull on the trip rope and the entire roll-over frame was inverted; the land and furrow wheels automatically adjusted themselves to the new position and the hitch swung over to the new position and locked. Another pull on the same trip rope put the plow in the ground. Both steel and pneumatic tires were available. This system was a good option for the many tractors not equipped with remote hydraulics.

An extensive line of McCormick-Deering tractor plows, both moldboard and disk, was available by 1946. Eight different kinds of plow bottoms were offered from the HSKA high-speed, general-purpose bottom made of soft-center steel and built for use behind modern, fast moving tractors with speeds up to 6 mph to the UA deep tillage bottom for use with the heavy-duty No. 10 Genius plows. Chilled cast-iron bottoms were also available and described as follows: "McCormick-Deering chilled plow bottoms are made in a factory (Chattanooga Plow had been recently sold to Herriman Manufacturing Co.) that has been turning out high-grade plows for nearly forty years. Special mixtures of iron, secret processes of casting and chilling, and our own rib design, combine to produce parts that are extremely grit-resistant, which will not break under reasonable usage, and which shed the soil with a minimum amount of draft." Literature of this period carried the statement, "Good Plows Backed by a Century of Experience." The names P&O and Chattanooga were not mentioned.

The No. 8 Genius was the most popular in the McCormick-Deering plow line. The No. 8 Genius 2- and 3-furrow plows came with 10-, 12-, 14-, or 16-inch bottoms; the 4-furrow with 12-, 14-, or 16-inch bottoms; and the 5-furrow with 12- or 14-inch bottoms. A special 18-inch bottom came on 1- and 2-furrow models. There was "A No. 8 Genius to fit your farm and your power." Literature described each feature and manufacturing process in great detail from the 22-inch under beam clearance and 21-inch fore-and-aft clearance to the land and furrow wheel spokes cast in the hub and hot-riveted into the tires. Other Genius models included the No. 10 Heavy Duty for big tractors, the No. 14 for deep tillage, the No. 11, complete with a 33-inch rolling coulter, for deep plowing in palmetto ground and heavy growth.

For small tractors, there was the McCormick-Deering No. 3 Little Wonder 1-furrow and the No. 4 Little Wonder 2-furrow plow. The No. 38 Two-Way Sulky plow and the No. 39 Roll-Over plow served the needs of hillside farming and irrigated production where it is important to eliminate dead and back furrows. Special needs could be met with the No. 459 and No. 461 Brush Breaker, single-bottom plows for plowing underbrush like hazel, blackberry, or cranberry, or the ditching plows that cut 20 inches deep.

The extensive McCormick-Deering plow line also included disk plows and harrow plows. The heavy-duty No. 99 disk plow could be equipped with 26-, 28-, 30-, or 32-inch disks and was especially well suited for the IHC TracTracTor and other crawler tractors. The lighter-duty No. 98 tractor disk plow could be equipped with 24-, 26-, or 28-inch disks. The intermediate size No. 34 tractor disk plow came in 4- or 5-furrow sizes. The No. 7 and No. 8 harrow plows were designed for smaller tractors. The No. 2 and No. 3 harrow plows were the right choice for ground preparation for wheat seeding and mulching of fallow ground. The No. 2 and No. 3 could also be equipped with a grain box seeding attachment. A new generation of one-way disks was

Hamilton Works provided IHC with manufacturing and marketing capability in Canada for products like the Hamilton 2-furrow 8-C adjustable beam plow shown here. This McCormick-Deering 10-20 tractor plowing scene was taken near Hamilton, Ontario, Canada.

This Farmall C and C-295 direct-connected plow were working on a farm at Hinsdale, Illinois. Direct-connected plows were lower cost than similar trailing-type plows. They were especially useful in small fields with narrow headlands.

introduced in 1954 with the trade name Diskall. They were composed of 3-foot disk gangs turning on white hard iron bearings for machines from 3- to 18-foot cutting width. Later, the Canadian-made trailing-type harrow plows included the No. 120 Rigid and No. 110 Flexall, flexible one way. The new No. 100 Diskall came in 12-, 15-, and 18-foot sizes made up of 4-, 5-, or 6-flexible gangs, respectively. Each gang had triple-lip, life lubricated self-aligning ball bearings like the one-way plows. Each gang was held in place with direct acting springs. The McCormick seeding attachment was available for all three sizes.

Farmall Plows

Direct connected moldboard and disk plows for Farmall A, B, H, and M tractors were promoted for "irrigated land, fields with hilly land, or for any field where short turning ability is desirable." In addition to hand lift, pneumatic Lift-All was available for the Farmall A, AV, and B and hydraulic Lift-All for the Farmall H and M. With the advent of the two-point Fast Hitch, direct-connected primary and secondary tillage promotion increased. The Farm Equipment Sales Catalog for 1962 listed 17 mounted moldboard plows and 7 mounted disk plows including the No. 201 and No. 301A two-way.

New Bottoms for IH Moldboard Plows

Super Chief Bottoms had low-cost, throw-away shares, off-center, soft-center-steel moldboards, welded-steel frogs, and replaceable shins made of the same material as the moldboard or extra-thick chilled cast iron. The off-center steel was composed of a 42%

The Farmall H with remote hydraulics made plowing a much easier job than grabbing for an allusive trip rope.

hard thick face, 33% soft center, and 25% hard back. Super Chief bottoms came in high speed, general purpose, and stubble versions. Throw-away shares came in thick-point, flat, deep-suck, and hard-surfaced deep-suck types.

Plow Chief Bottoms were all-purpose bottoms with a two-piece share that consisted of a separate blade and a spearhead point. There was a choice of heat-treated forged or chilled cast-iron spearhead points. The share blade was a high-carbon steel, throw-away type. The frog was press-forged from a single piece of steel.

The McCormick plow chief bottom flier read, "Repoint Your Plow in 5 minutes!" The forged steel or chilled cast-iron replaceable spear head point "costs no more than getting an old-style share sharpened at the blacksmith shop."

Conventional Bottoms were available in either soft-center steel or chilled cast iron. They came in the familiar eight basic moldboard types equipped with one piece, sharpenable shears in three kinds of material.

The **High-Speed Terra-Flow (TF) Bottom** was a low draft bottom designed for plowing speeds up to 6 mph (one third faster than Super Chief) to match the increased horsepower of new tractors. The high-speed plowing characteristics came from the 35% share angle compared to the 45% angle for other styles of IH plow bottoms.

Mounted and Semi-Mounted Plows

Large horsepower tractors had the draft capability to handle large mounted plows but the front-end weight required exceeded practical limits; semi-mounted plows with a share of the weight carried on the tail wheel were the answer. The No. 312, No. 412, and No. 512 were early two-point, Fast Hitch semi-mounted plows. The 1-46 and later 950 two-way disk plows also offered the advantages of semi-mounted design in the larger sizes.

The next major advance in semi-mounted plow design was the pivoting hitch that automatically steered the rear wheel for short turns in the field and maneuvering in the farm yard. The No. 510 semi-mounted, 3- through 6-bottom, steerable plow had 27-inch vertical clearance and fore-and-aft clearance of 28 inches with 16-inch bottoms and 31 1/2 inches with 18-inch bottoms. The even larger, extra-husky No. 710 semi-mounted, 4- through 8-bottom, steerable plow had 30-inch vertical clearance and the same fore-and-aft clearance as the No. 510. It was available with spring trip or automatic reset beams and either in-furrow or on-land hitch, depending on size.

The innovative International 735 semi-mounted 5- and 6-furrow plow added another dimension to IH plow design, it incorporated the ability to hydraulically adjust the cutting width from 14 to 22 inches per bottom and automatically reset the line of draft, all on-the-go.

From Shear-Pin to Sheer Joy

Plows used in most soils require some kind of protection for the plow bottoms, shares, beams, and frame when hitting a rock or other obstruction. This requirement became critical with higher horsepower tractors and faster plowing speeds.

Shear-Pin Beams: The simple, reliable — if the correct shear bolt is used — and economical system is widely used in fields with few obstructions. This is not a popular system in problem fields where frequent shear-pin replacement is required.

Spring-Trip Beams: If it trips, just back up until the beam latches, nothing could be easier. The IH spring-trip beam was extremely simple; it had just two moving parts. The trip-pin and seating notch were flame hardened for long service life; no lubrication was required. Two limitations were present: First, when the beam tripped, the point of the shear would move down and possibly hook the obstruction even harder. Second, as the beam pivoted, the entire plow would tend to raise out of the ground; this sudden action could generate huge strains. The shear-pin system had the same problem.

Automatic Beams and Toggle-Trip Beams . . . International Harvester Industry Firsts

Automatic Beams: The IH exclusive automatic beams provide two-way protection. If a bottom strikes a sloping rock it automatically rides up and over with exclusive vertical action — as high as 13 inches — and immediately returns to the preset plowing depth. If the bottom can't ride over a rock or obstruction, the beam trips. After tripping, the bottom automatically snaps back into plowing position and returns to proper plowing depth. You never stop, lift, or back the plow . . . you just keep plowing. Furthermore, when the beam trips, the share point never swings below the bottom of the furrow and tries to lift the plow. Because it's mechanical, two or more beams can ride up or trip at the same time and not affect the other bottoms. The automatic beam design was so outstanding that it was incorporated into automatic trip shanks for IH subsoil chisels; this was another IH industry first. *What a joy!*

Toggle-Trip Beams: The unique design of the toggle-trip beam allowed much greater throat clear-

ance compared to spring-trip beams. If the beam tripped, it was not necessary to back up. Just lift the plow out of the ground and the beam resets itself ready for lowering and more plowing. Because of the high pivot point, the beam did not try to raise the plow out of the ground during the tripping cycle like shear-pin or spring-trip beams.

A Full Plow Line

International Harvester moldboard plow leadership took many forms including a full product line offering. The one-bottom, Fast-Hitch International 194 in 14- or 16-inch bottom sizes matched the Farmall 140 and older tractors with one-point Fast-Hitch. The Cub L-194, 12-inch bottom fit IH Cub tractors with one-point Fast-Hitch.

The 710 semi-mounted, steerable plow could be equipped with the exclusive IH automatic beams, shown here, or the more economical spring trip beams. It was available for two-point Fast-Hitch and Category II or III, 3-point hitch for in-furrow plowing with 4-, 5-, and 6-bottom sizes. Three-point, on-land hitches were available for 5-, 6-, 7-, and 8-bottom sizes.

The International 720 plow was an extra trash clearance plow that could be equipped with 20-inch bottoms and plow up to 12 inches deep. The exclusive IH automatic beams could rise over obstacles as high as 14 inches and return to working position without tripping. If the bottom couldn't rise, it tripped and immediately returned to working position without lifting the plow out of the ground. Because the system was mechanical, two or more beams could trip at the same time without problems.

The IH 735 Vari-Width plow was the only plow on the market that automatically adjusted the line-of-draft as the plow was hydraulically changed on-the-go from the 14- to 22-inch setting. The similar 730 economy version provided the same width-of-cut range, but both adjustments were made manually.

The International No. 310 plow was a three-point hitch, single 12-inch Super Chief bottom plow for International 154 Cub Lo-Boy tractors. International 420 mounted, three-point hitch plows in 2-, 3-, 4-, and 5-bottom sizes provided reliable economy in spring-trip or shear-pin versions. International 531 and 541 mounted, three-point plows in 3- and 4-bottom sizes had three additional inches of fore-and-aft clearance with their 16-inch only bottoms than the 420 Series. A special version was offered for three-point equipped Hi-Clear tractors. The International 450 mounted, three-point hitch, 3- and 4-bottom automatic beam plow and 3-, 4-, and 5-bottom spring-trip versions brought 30-inch vertical and 26-inch fore-and-aft clearance to this "extra-strong construction" plow series.

Semi-mounted, steerable plows were available in 3- to 6-bottom sizes in the 500 Series with spring-trip or shear-pin trip beams for Category II three-point hitch

or Fast-Hitch. The 710 plows were extra-heavy construction for 5- to 8-bottom sizes with increased clearance and automatic or spring-trip beams with in-furrow and on-land hitches available, depending on plow size. One version of the 710 was a 3-bottom expandable to 4 and a 4-bottom expandable to 5 for purchase flexibility.

Growth in the mounted and semi-mounted plow market did not mean IH disregarded its trailing plow customers. The International No. 60 trailing plows were designed for plowing up to 10-inches deep and were available in 2-, 3-, and 4-bottom sizes with spring-trip or rigid beam. The more rugged, greater fore-and-aft clearance No. 70 plows were designed for plowing up to 12-inches deep and were available in 3- to 6-bottom sizes. Both series had models that could be reduced by one bottom. A tandem hitch made it possible to pull up to 10 bottoms by coupling together a combination of 700 and/or 70 Series trailing plows.

This International Harvester 3588 tractor and semi-mounted IH 735 Vari-Width, toggle trip beam plow was working behind the Iron Curtain in Hungary.

Bábolna Agricultural Combinate, Hungary's largest state farm, imported International Harvester tractors and implements that were all painted yellow. Selected IH implements manufactured in Hungary under IH license were also yellow. Bábolna packaged equipment and crop production technology under the IKR (Industrialized Production Systems) logo for State and Cooperative Farms throughout the country.

No plow line is complete without two-way plows. In the 1960s the International 314 two-way, mounted, 3-furrow plow had 27-inch vertical and 21-inch fore-and-aft clearance and a choice of 14- or 16-inch bottoms. Both were available with rigid or spring-trip beams. In 1970 the International 140 two-way mounted 3- and 4-furrow plow was introduced. It had 30-inch vertical on 28-inch fore-and-aft clearance. Hydraulic rollover was completely independent of lifting action. The 3-furrow was expandable to 4-furrow. The International 155, two-way plow, introduced the same year, came in 5-furrow 16-inch bottom and 4-furrow 18-inch bottom sizes. Both were designed for the tractor to run on land and were available with rigid or spring-trip beams. For 1976, IH offered the 4-, 5-, or 6-bottom International 165 two-way plow with on-land hitch for high horsepower three-point hitch tractors including big four-wheel-drive models. The International 145 two-way hi-clearance plow had automatic hydraulic reset in addition to rigid and spring-trip beams. The economy International 125 two-way in 3- and 4-bottom sizes completed the rollover lineup.

How Big is Too Big?

As tractors got larger and larger, especially articulated 4-WD models, industry analysts pondered the question of when does bigger no longer mean better; there seemed to be no simple answer to the question. To match the really big tractors, the size of moldboard plows also increased and the same questions arose about how large is too large. This problem had a more direct answer. When a plow is so big that is cannot maintain reasonably uniform plowing depth even in gently rolling land, it's too big.

IH plow engineers solved the problem with the 800 Series, Flex-Frame plow design. The massive 6- by 8-inch main frame had a center hinge and flotation land wheels that allowed the frame to flex. This design made possible a 16-furrow moldboard plow that worked well in a wide range of terrain. For transport, changing the dial hitch reduced the working width. For example, the 12-furrow model's 23-foot working width reduced to 14 feet for transport.

Radical new products always raise two questions: What will it look like? Will management understand the project and approve the proposal? This scale model of the proposed 800 Flex-Frame trailing plow answered the first question and helped secure a positive response to the second question.

Expo Express

Really big plows need really big tractors and the combination needs really big fields. International Harvester put all three together when introducing the 800 Flex-Frame plow. To dramatize the new product and do it in the right area, the Company scheduled a Burlington Northern Special Train, the Expo Express, to deliver the new 12-bottom, 800 Flex-Frame plow and IH 4366, 225-horsepower, four-wheel-drive tractor to Expo '74 in Spokane, Washington. While crossing the northwestern United States, the train made "whistle stops" at the Minneapolis/St. Paul Twin Cities; Fargo, Jamestown, and Bismarck, North Dakota; and Billings, Montana, before arriving in Spokane, Washington, for the official 800 Flex-Frame plow introduction. Dealers in the areas surrounding each stop brought prospective customers to the rail siding for a chance to see this "Biggest Plow in Production Today, International 800 Flex Plow from Canton, Illinois."

The biggest plow in production in 1974 would grow from the 12-bottom 800 Flex-Frame plow to an even larger 16-bottom Flex-Frame version in 1979.

The IH 12-bottom, trailing Flex Plow of 1974 grew to become the IH 16-bottom trailing Flex-Frame plow in 1979.

The Right Match

Farmers in many parts of the country struggled to match the size of the plow to the tractor size for different types of soil and changing moisture conditions. The plow size decision is usually a compromise; if it's on the conservative side, it reduces productivity. The International 735 Vari-Width 5- or 6-bottom plow introduced in 1978 was the answer to this farming challenge. On-the-go Hydraulic adjustment changed cutting width from 14 to 22 inches to match tractor power or changing conditions. The IH design automatically changed the line of draft as the cutting width changed. In 1981 a lower cost International 730 Vari-Width 4- or 5-bottom plow was introduced. It had the same 14- to 22-inch cutting width range but the hitch and width adjustments were made manually.

The Stockton Connection

To serve the special needs of West Coast farmers, IH produced a line of heavy-duty tillage tools at its plant in Stockton, California. An example of the broad range of products produced is illustrated by the West Coast Equipment section listing in the 1966 Farm Equipment Reference Catalog: carriers and tool bars, cultivators, ditchers, dozers, ground working tools, disk harrows, land levelers, pulverizers, subsoilers, and trailers. These products were designed for the West Coast market, many times for crawler tractor applications, but they were sold in limited quantity in other parts of the country because of their heavy-duty construction.

Go Plant a Pavement

Yes this project does belong in the tillage section, and yes the results might be called a very thin pavement. Let's begin at the beginning.

There are two basic types of sandy soil in the state of Michigan used for agricultural production. The first type is pure sand and it must be irrigated because natural rainfall quickly drains below the plant root zone. The second type of sandy soil is blessed with thin layers of clay, called clay lenses, that hold natural rainfall in the root zone long enough for good crop utilization without creating drainage problems. Naturally the agricultural value of the second type of soil is higher than the first.

Soil scientists and agricultural engineers at Michigan State University, East Lansing, Michigan, reasoned that perhaps a thin layer of asphalt placed 2 feet below the surface of a pure sandy soil, the first type, would give it moisture-holding capacity similar to sandy soil with the naturally occurring clay lenses. With this treatment the soil should perform like the more valuable second type. After years of experimentation in cooperation with the American Oil Company, MSU developed a machine and system for placing instant hardening asphalt emulsion in 30-inch wide, interlocking bands for establishing small test plots. Crop response and projected economics were favorable.

In order to install field-scale tests in various parts of the country, the researchers needed a cooperator from the farm machinery industry. International Harvester joined the asphalt barrier research and development team in 1966. For the first two field-scale experiments in Florida, IH furnished an International TD-15 crawler tractor equipped with a Stockton Works, combination dozer/tool bar for mounting the Michigan State built, 30-inch wide asphalt applicator sweep. A special hitch pulled the engine-equipped asphalt tank and pumping system.

A 1960s IH tillage research and development project was under the ground instead of on the surface. This IH TD-25B gear-drive crawler is equipped with an Advanced Engineering designed sweep that is capable of placing a 90-inch wide, thin band of hot asphalt 2 feet below the surface of sandy agricultural soils. A clever system joined the bands to form an artificial subsurface barrier that retained moisture and nutrients for improved crop yields. The project was a joint effort between International Harvester, the American Oil Company, and Michigan State University.

Next, the International Harvester Advanced Engineering Department developed a 90-inch wide sweep for the International TD-25B or TD-25C gear-drive crawler tractor. Mounting the asphalt tank and handling system on the front of the crawler improved performance and increased productivity to one acre per hour. Results from field-scale experiments conducted in seven states recorded that yield increases of 11 vegetable crops grown on non-irrigated barrier resulted in a fresh market increase in value of $53 to $200 per acre. Eight of the vegetables sold fresh would return the $250/acre barrier installation cost in three years. Additional benefits included reduced fertilizer and irrigation water cost.

Based on good economics, the American Oil Company established a subsidiary company, Amoco Moisture Barrier Company, AMOBAR, to license the technology to carefully selected contractors for commercial application in the United States and foreign countries. Several factors changed the optimistic outlook for asphalt barrier installation: No world food shortage developed; bankers didn't want to lend money for barrier installation without positive proof it would last 20 years — the Michigan State plots were not that old; but one factor ended commercialization indefinitely, the surplus of asphalt that existed in the mid-1960s disappeared and the Arab oil embargo of 1973 drastically increased the price of all petroleum products including asphalt.

International didn't sell large numbers of crawler tractors as a result of the Asphalt Project but they did receive wide recognition for their support of a worthwhile university research project. Furthermore, IH demonstrated how two major corporations can work together for the benefit of agriculture.

This photo of a Farmall M coupled to an M-11 four-row middlebuster represents only a small fraction of the variations possible with the IH tool bar "erector set" offered over the years. In addition to busting or listing bottoms, border, barring-off and bedding disks, rotary moldboards, chisel teeth, coil spring teeth, wide and narrow sweeps, and subsoiler beams were available. As tractor horsepower grew, so did tool bars. The International 82 Series 6- by 8-inch tool bar main frame could handle up to 8 or 9 wide rows for planting or middlebusting.

Secondary Tillage

With the advent of tractors, many farmers were hard pressed to effectively use the increased "horsepower." With slow moving tractors, hitching two or more horse-drawn implements together offered a workable solution. As the population of tractors grew, the industry began to offer tillage tools for tractors.

Tractor Disk Harrows

One IHC product developed for the new market was the McCormick-Deering leverless tractor disk harrow. Literature for 1924 describes it as the "first leverless harrow ever built exclusively for tractor use." The entire operation of setting the gangs, changing the angle, or straightening up was accomplished without

By the time this 1919 photo was taken of an International 8-16 tractor and McCormick-Deering flexible tandem tractor harrow, tillage tools designed for tractors were replacing modified horse-drawn implements used behind tractors.

requiring the driver to leave the tractor seat. To set the angle, the tractor was backed up until the front and rear sliding hitches locked each gang in full working position. To reduce the angle or straighten the disk, a

This 1937 photo of a McCormick-Deering W-30 tractor and 9-foot McCormick-Deering No. 3 harrow plow with seeding attachment pulling a McCormick-Deering land packer. was taken in Saskatchewan, Canada. It is typical of small grain seeding practice in Western Canada and the U.S. Upper Midwest. By 1962 the harrow plow grew to include the 16 1/2-foot rigid and 18-foot Flexall with disks up to 26-inches. The 100 Diskall, more like the photo, came in 12-, 15-, and 18-foot sizes with 18- or 20-inch disks and optional McCormick seeding attachment.

pull on the front and/or rear gang ropes would do the job while the disk was being pulled forward.

The actual weight of the disk was said to be only a little more than the same size horse harrow but, "the construction is such that the heavy push and pull of the tractor does not shake the harrow to pieces." No doubt this was the common fate of horse harrows behind tractors.

When rubber tires became available for tractors in the 1930s, the higher field speeds needed to achieve maximum horsepower made it necessary to develop tractor implements to match this new "breed" of tractors. Rubber-tired wheel tractor percentage increased from 14 percent in 1935 to 95 percent by 1940. Implement manufacturers responded.

A 32-page, two-color, McCormick-Deering tillage tool booklet published in 1946 still covered most of the products offered in the 1930s. The tractor photographs, however, promoted the new Farmall A, B, H, and M tractors. Billed as offering "TILLAGE TOOLS FOR EVERY FARM AND EVERY CROP," it included disk harrows, weeder-mulchers, peg-tooth harrows, spring-tooth harrows, soil pulverizers, rotary hoes, rod weeders, land packers, tractor cultivators, and field cultivators.

The McCormick-Deering No. 10-A tandem disk harrow was billed as "The World's Most Popular Tractor Disk Harrow." It could be equipped with the regular, manual angling devise, or the automatic, tractor-operated, gang-angling devise. An optional hydraulic de-angling device was available along with

an optional, independent gang-angling attachment. Sizes ranged from 5 to 8 feet and came with either 16- or 18-inch diameter disk blades. This popular tandem disk harrow was part of a family that included the heavier No. 9-A with 6 5/8-inch disk spacing, the No. 9-B with 9-inch disk spacings, and the No. 9AB with combination front to rear disk spacing. The No. 9

This Farmall MV high-clearance tractor was working beds for sugar cane in Louisiana. To complement the "V" series Farmall tractors, IH offered a complete line of tillage and cultivation tools for sugar cane production.

McCormick-Deering No. 9-A tandem tractor disk harrows were designed to handle the higher field speeds of rubber-tired Farmall tractors. Heavy springs with three adjustments held the disk gang scraper in working position near the disk hubs. A pull on an individual gang scraper rope would pivot the scraper to the outside edge of the disks. The disk harrow in the photo is equipped with hydraulic Lift-All de-angling attachment.

Series came in 5- to 10-foot sizes. The No. 7 Series had the frame below the top of the disks for orchard applications. The heavy-duty No. 11B came regularly equipped with cut-out disks. The No. 7, No. 9, and No. 10 Series disks were also available as single action disks. "Wide-type" single-action No. 18-A disk harrows were available in 11 1/2-, 15-, and 18-foot sizes. The two larger sizes had end sections that could be pivoted around behind the front gang for passing through gates or could be completely removed. Three models of disk with horse hitches were still listed. The last 14 pages of the booklet described the balance of an extensive tillage line.

Wheel-Controlled Disk Harrows

The 1950s saw the introduction of wheel-controlled disk harrows. International Harvester offered the No. 45 V-Tandem (offset) and No. 37 Tandem wheel-controlled disk harrows. The No. 37 incorporated a torsion-frame design with "built-in give" to allow each gang to follow the ground surface independent of the other gangs. The No. 37 came in 8 1/2- to 14-foot sizes with 7-inch, 9-inch, or combination disk spacings. Plain or notched-type blades came in 16-, 18-, or 20-inch sizes. In 1959 the No. 37 came standard with hard, white-iron bearings with pressure lubrication or optional triple-sealed, prelubricated ball bearings on special order; they became standard in 1962. The IH exclusive, crimp-center design disk blades with vertically ground edges, were made from breakage resistant "Tuf-Edge" material.

The IH 48 wing-type, wheel-controlled tandem disk harrow was a 21-foot machine that weighed over 240 pounds per foot of cut. Folding the spring counter-balanced wings reduced the IH 48 to just over 13 feet for transport. For deep penetration in extra hard soil, the harrow could work with the wings folded and deliver over 360 pounds per foot of cut. This weight per foot compared favorably with the IH 51 heavy-duty offset disk harrow. The largest size, 10 1/2 feet, delivered 340 pounds per foot of cut.

The IH 48 became the International 480 in 1966 and the offering was expanded to include two sizes of non-folding and four sizes of wing-type folding, wheel-controlled, tandem disk harrows. The lighter weight International 470 offered a similar design in three sizes of non-folding and five sizes of folding-type up to 19 feet 1 inch with 9-inch disk spacing. A Flexi-gang attachment was available for both the IH 48 and International 480. At the same time the IH 37 became the International 370 with sizes from 8 feet 7 inches to 14 feet 2 inches. The International 350 was an economically priced harrow of similar design with sizes from 7 feet 8 inches to 15 feet.

The extra-husky International 500 disk harrow was available with 22- or 24-inch, plain or notched blades as thick as 1/4-inch mounted on 1 1/2-inch round arbor bolts with exclusive interlocking spools. The 500 disk

The intermediate weight, wheel controlled International 370 disk harrow with its Torsion-Frame design was a good match for the International 684 tractor with ROPS and canopy.

harrow was an ideal primary tillage tool for working up to 9 inches deep. It came in three sizes from 12 feet 15 inches to 15 feet 9 inches.

In 1969 IH Stockton Works, Stockton, California, introduced the International 610 offset disk harrow. The new design offset permitted gang angling adjustment from 0 to 46 degrees to matched soil conditions. This offset family also included the International 630 and 640. The big clearance, brute strength International 660 wheel-controlled offset disk harrow had 28- or 30-inch notched blades on 1 3/4-inch round arbor bolts. This 660 pounds per foot of cut disk could till up to 12 inches deep.

Tremendous capacity and sizes from 20 1/2 to 32 3/4 feet described the new International 490 disk harrow in 1975. New features included hydraulic folding, floating wings gauged on full-size wheels, and precision-type, regreasable triple-sealed, self-aligning ball bearings in rubber mountings.

Closing of Stockton Works in 1972 brought about the introduction of a complete new 700 Series line of offset disk harrows including the 750, 760, 770, deep tillage, and 780 models. The 770 deep tillage offered 22-, 24-, or 26-inch blades and exclusive automatic wing-latch system on the two hydraulic folding wing-type models available in 20 1/2- and 24-foot sizes.

The new International 496 folding wing, tandem disk harrow in sizes up to 32 feet was introduced in 1981. The IH-patented master and slave, automatic re-phasing hydraulic cylinders teamed up with synchronized wing and center frame wheels for level disking across the width of cut as well as fore and aft. The

The International 596, hydraulic folding, tandem disk harrow weighed in at 575 pounds per foot of cut with 26-inch disk bla[?] *and sizes up to 30 feet 10 inches. It was the ideal primary tilla*[?] *tool to hitch behind a powerful four-wheel-drive tractor.*

advanced self-leveling spring-cushioned hitch prevented digging-in and shallowing out. In 1982 the 496 was available in a cushion gang version for high-speed operation in rock or root infested fields.

The tandem disk harrow line that year extended from the lightweight, Category I, 3-point hitch 122 with a 5 1/2 foot width of cut to the heavyweight 596 Folding Wing Disk Harrow that weighed 575 pounds per foot of cut and came with 26-inch diameter disk blades. Model number 350, 370, 475, 480, 485, and 501 filled out the extensive International Harvester tandem disk harrow line. Most models featured the IH Earth Metal™ disk blades that provided up to 20% more wear than regular disk blades. Hamilton Works manufactured the IH Earth Metal™ disk blades and marketed them OEM to other farm equipment companies.

Final Seedbed Preparation

The International 365 Vibra tine field cultivator was described as a soil conditioning tool in 1981 when it was introduced; a year later it was listed under seedbed tillage equipment. The action of the S-shape Vibra tines and the rotary mulching attachment made it an ideal tool for finishing seedbeds and incorporating preemergence chemicals. Because of its typical use, it is included in this family of tools in spite of the field cultivator name. Mounted versions started at 13 1/2 feet and trailing versions started at 16 1/2 feet. Maximum size was 25 1/2 feet for both versions.

The International 415 Roller-Mulcher that could be equipped with notched or crowfoot rollers was also introduced in 1981. The two ranks of hydraulically controlled teeth between the front and rear rollers could

The 770 offset risk harrows came in three versions: non-folding regular, folding regular, and folding deep-tillage. Sizes ranged from 10 feet 4 inches to 23 feet 9 inches. Equipped with 28-inch plain blades, the largest model weighed in at just under 5 ton. The one in this photo is an International 770 folding wheel-controlled, offset disk harrow and an International 4386 tractor.

This International 415 Roller-Mulcher is shown with an International 6388 tractor. The 415 was available in both rigid and flat folding wing type. It could be equipped with either looped spring ("S-shape") or Vibra tine teeth. With the teeth raised, it performed as a conventional roller-packer.

be either looped spring (the term S-shaped could no longer be used) or Vibra tine. The machine came in non-folding trailing sized from 10 feet 1 inch to 15 feet 3 inches. Flat folding, wing-type trailing machines came in 20-foot 10-inch to 30-foot sizes.

Another seedbed finishing tool was the International 468 seedbed conditioner for once-over, pre-plant tillage. It combined spiral reels up front followed by peg-tooth harrow sections and finally a rear leveling board. A special Vibra tine or Vibra Shank tooth attachment could be mounted ahead of the reels. Trailing machines came in sizes from 12 1/2 feet to 19 feet and trailing wing machines from 19 feet to 25 1/2 feet.

Not to be forgotten are the spring-tooth and peg-tooth harrows. The economical 352 trailing spring-tooth came in sizes up to 27 feet and the wings folded forward manually. The trailing spring-tooth 354 came

in sizes up to 39 feet and the 356 up to 60 feet; the wings of these two big machines folded automatically to the rear for easy transport. The trailing Number 9 peg-tooth harrow came in 6-foot sections with sizes up to 42 feet. Sections came in three types: flexible open-end, rigid open-end, and rigid closed end.

Changes in Primary and Secondary Tillage

As disk harrows got heavier and worked deeper they performed more of a primary, rather than a secondary, tillage role. Increased concern for soil conservation and soil compaction brought about reduced usage of disk harrows and moldboard plows; as a result, field cultivators and chisel plows found wider application. In fact, the products listed in the Chisel Plows and Field Cultivators section of the 1981 IH Buyers Guide were under a new Soil Conditioning section in the 1982 IH Buyers Guide. Therefore, IH products with well known trade names like Vibra Shank, Vibra Chisel, and Vibra Tiller are covered in the Cultivation and Weed Control section rather than in this section.

Spiral reels up front cut down beds and chopped stalks, peg-tooth center sections pulverized and loosened the soil, and rear leveling boards smoothed out the surface. An optional Vibra tine or Vibra Shank attachment could be mounted up front. The 468 seedbed conditioner came in trailing rigid and folding-wing models up to 25 1/2 feet.

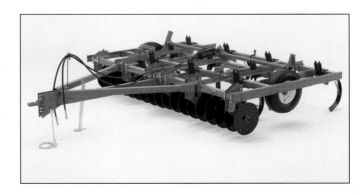

The 6000 and 6500 International Conser-Till plow eliminated a tillage operation by combining a rank of straight disks with a chisel plow.

Planters and Grain Drills
From Broadcast to Precision

In the spring of 1855 a corn planter trial was advertised to take place at Jacksonville, Illinois. George W. Brown and his planter, shown in the illustration, were the only ones to appear for the test. When this appeared in the 1922 Farm Implement News the caption read, "Do You Remember Way Back When Corn Planters Looked Like This?"

The American Seed Trade Association motto is "First the Seed." Just as seedsmen strive to develop the best genetics and produce seed of the highest quality and germination, farmers strive to provide the seed they plant with the best possible environment for optimum growth and production. Centuries of primitive agriculture passed before mechanized means of uniformly placing and covering seed in rows or hills replaced broadcasting or hand placement. Englishman Jethro Tull is credited with developing a horse-drawn implement to promote planting in uniformly spaced straight rows as early as 1701. In America the first practical, two-horse corn planter was developed by George W. Brown of western Illinois around 1850 and several years later it was offered for sale. The first true manufacturer of grain drills in the United States was Bickford and Huffman Company, Macedon, New York, starting in 1848. A significant breakthrough in grain drill development came with introduction of the double disk opener by F. R. Packham in 1893. He followed a year later with the single disk opener.

International Harvester Planters — One Company, Many Brand Names

Uniting five companies into the International Harvester Company in 1902 created a giant corporation that dominated the reaper and binder business. The new corporation did not, however, manufacture many of the important implements offered to the trade by smaller, specialized firms. In order to quickly broaden the product line sold by International Harvester dealers, IHC filled the void by purchasing companies with well-established and proven planter, drill, and other related lines. Marketing these kinds of products manufactured by others also extended the variety of machines the Company could offer. IHC

One row at a time made even small fields seem large with this single-row, horse-drawn (mule-drawn), P&O walking planter.

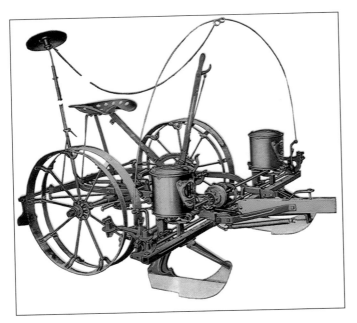

The wide frame of this IHC No. 1 corn planter provided for planting 40-, 42-, or 44-inch wide rows. The IHC No. 2 corn planter could handle rows as narrow as 28 inches. The IHC No. 3 corn planter could power hill-drop or drill but did not have check wire heads or reel. Note the economical, one-arm, single-disk, row marker that swung from one side to the other.

acquired a line of corn planters, along with grain drills and broadcast seeders, when they purchased the Keystone Company of Rock Falls, Illinois in 1904.

The well respected CB&Q planters and Hoosier and Kentucky grain drills were manufactured and sold by the American Seeding Machinery Company of Richmond, Indiana. These same products were marketed by IHC through a selling agreement beginning in 1912. The CB&Q planter line included:

- CB&Q No. 1 Regular corn belt planter, 40-, 42-, and 44-inch row checkrow
- CB&Q No. 2 Narrow-row planter, adjustable checkrow
- CB&Q No. 3 Corn drill
- CB&Q No. 4 The same as No. 1 but with 36-inch wheels in place of 30-inch wheels
- CB&Q No. 5 Wide-row planter, 42-, 44-, 46-, and 48-inch rows

Purchase of American Seeding Machinery Co. by IHC in 1920 gave the company total control of this extensive line of proven corn planters and corn drills along with other important seeding machines. International Harvester Company marketed the same line of planters under the International name and added the No. 6 drill planter and 1-row Empire corn drill.

Purchase of Parlin and Orendorff in 1918 placed the excellent P&O planters in the line for marketing under

the McCormick-Deering name. By 1925 IHC was producing planters in the Richmond, Indiana, and Canton, Illinois locations plus West Pullman (the old Plano line) in Chicago, Illinois, and Hamilton, Ontario, Canada.

The IHC Agricultural Extension Department

Agricultural research information disseminated through the State and Federal Cooperative Extension Service was sometimes augmented by industry, and IHC was a leader. They established their own Agricultural Extension Department under the leadership of P. G. Holden, former Vice Dean and professor of agronomy, Iowa Agricultural College (later became Iowa State University), Ames, Iowa. The Agricultural Extension Department included seven divisions: Short Course and Campaign, Lecture, Chart-Slide and Reel, Publicity (100 different booklets were available), Lecture, Library, and Art. Subject matter covered almost every aspect of crop production, animal husbandry, and homemaking relevant to the first three decades of the 20th century. Educating farmers in the proper use, maintenance, and repair of engines and engine powered equipment was a major part of the program. The Extension Department was a sound business investment because by making farming more profitable, IHC could build broader markets for their machines. Sound public relations was an added benefit. With rapid advances being made in agronomy during this period, tillage, seedbed preparation, and proper use of planters and drills were covered thoroughly by the department. Their publications and meetings effectively supported those product lines.

In 1917 the department published a 30-page illustrated booklet titled *Seed Corn, Do You Know That It Will Grow? Test — Don't Guess.* The emphasis on corn production was totally in keeping with the leadership of P. G. Holden. He was known as the "Corn Evangelist" and had introduced the Ten Ear Corn Show to Iowa. With the exception of a few seedsmen who offered their selections of open-pollinated corn, there was no organized seed corn industry; hybrid corn was considered an impractical university curiosity and farmers saved their own seed corn. The booklet described how to gather ears from "a hundred of the best ears planted together on the south or west side of the main field from which to select seed for next year's planting." Most of the booklet was devoted to detailed descriptions of two methods of germination testing: a sawdust filled germination box or the cheaper, simpler, rag doll test. The importance of germination testing was promoted with religious fervor, "Thou shalt test six kernels from every ear of corn intended for seed." As late as 1930 the Extension Department printed 10,000 copies of the booklet.

The best row-crop cultivators could not control all of the weeds in the row. Check-wire, hill dropping, if done accurately, made it possible to cross cultivate, and get the job done right. The photo clearly shows the check wire.

Checkrow Planters

Weed control dictated the need for the checkrow planter. A check wire unrolled from the planter reel was laid out the length of the field, staked at one end and tensioned at the other end. The check wire had buttons spaced the same distance apart as the row width being planted. Forty- to 42-inch rows were common since this was about the width of a horse's hindquarters. At the start of each row the check wire was laid in the check fork on the planter and the check head closed. Near the end of the row the check wire had to be released. After turning the planter in preparation for the return trip, the check-wire stake was moved to its new position and the process repeated. Single seeds metered by the seed plate were caught in groups of 2, 3, or 4 by the hill drop valve in the planter boot. When the check-wire button tripped the check fork, the valve opened and the hill of corn dropped to the seed furrow. If every step of the checkrow planting procedure was done carefully, the result would be beautifully aligned hills at right angles to the planter rows. Checkrow planting made it possible to cross cultivate and remove the in-row grass and weeds left from

cultivating the planter rows. Checkrow planting was time consuming, but it was the only satisfactory way of thorough weed control by cultivation alone.

The McCormick-Deering No. 8 checkrow corn planter was quite unique; the seed plates were not driven by the ground wheels. Referred to as the "wire drive" planter, the buttons on the check wire powered the seed plate drive and operated the duck-bill type, hill-drop valve mechanism.

Horse Power to Tractor Power

When tractors began to replace horses, the horse-drawn planter and other horse-drawn implements were still around and considered useful. Many new tractor owners solved the planter problem by shortening the tongue of their horse-drawn planter and installing a tractor hitch. If there was lots of help, someone rode the planter to work the markers and lift the planter at the end of the row. Jumping off the tractor twice at each turn row was an unpleasant option for one-man operation. Extended lever conversion attachments were the method of choice.

Using horse-drawn implements behind tractors didn't effectively use the power available. Horse planters, especially checkrow and hill-drop models, were not designed to operate at higher speeds. Hitching two, 2-row horse planters together was a very effective way to utilize tractor power. The first IHC tractor planters were basically horse-drawn planters,

Horses did most of the corn planting when this photo of a McCormick-Deering No. 102 checkrow planter was taken in 1935. A cut-off tongue and bolt-on hitch made for a quick conversion to tractor power; lifting the planter at the end of the row didn't have such a simple solution.

Too Much Time Off

The son of a successful Indiana corn farmer relates the following story. After several years of trying to convince dad it was time to buy a tractor, the two sons won out and that fall a bright, shiny new tractor and tractor plow arrived at the home place. The horses were kept for the important jobs of corn planting and cultivating. With the new tractor, spring plowing was completed ahead of schedule and planting started exactly as planned. To plant all of the land prepared by the tractor, the son, his team and the horse-drawn planter put in a 10-hour day. That evening after the son put up the team, he came to the house and asked dad to come to the horse barn; both horses stood shaking in their stalls and wouldn't eat. Dad realized immediately that since the team had not been gradually brought into condition through weeks of spring plowing, they were not fit for a full day of work in the warm May weather. The next day it rained and dad went to town and purchased a tractor planter. The two sons helped the dealer assemble the planter so it would be ready as soon as it was dry enough to plant. Total tractor farming was soon to follow.

The Model No. F-72, shown here, was the single seed (drill) planter. The Model No. F-73 had the combination reverse cotton and flat-drop corn hopper. Since the planter frame was rigidly attached to the Farmall drawbar, side motion was prevented and the planter would stay centered on the top of the bed. The arch over the pipe extending back to the caster wheel provided for up and down motion of the planter while further controlling side motion.

complete with driver's seat, adapted for operation from the tractor seat; they came in 2- and 4-row versions.

Advent of the Farmall tractor opened the way for a completely new family of planters: the front-mounted and rear-mounted tractor planter. This design accomplished two things: First, by eliminating part of the frame, wheels, and some other components, weight and cost could be saved. Second, mounted units were easier to keep on top of planting beds and could maneuver easier on short headlands than drawn planters. Some models used front-mounted cultivators

to carry the fertilizer attachments in combination with a rear-mounted planter. Some rear-mounted planters were chain driven from a sprocket on the tractor rear axle. Some others were chain driven from a lugged wheel forward of the planter that ran on the ground between the rows. The transmission driven, ground-related PTO of the Farmall Super A made it possible to drive the rear-mounted A-218, A-219, and A-222 planters from the tractor right angle PTO.

Planters Are a Complex Product Line

Plate planters require what seems like an infinite number of edge drop and flat drop plates to match a wide range of seed kinds and types that also exhibit changes from year to year. In spite of large inventories at the dealer and parts warehouse level, it was next to impossible to have what every customer needed, every year.

The IHC designed "A"-frame hitch for coupling two, 2-row planters together offered one major advantage over most field conversions; the operator could raise the planters from the tractor if a pair of riders were not available.

In 1934, tractor-mounted planters were still essentially horse-drawn planters with elaborate linkages for attaching them to the tractor. This planter was equipped with the combination corn and pea attachment. Peas or beans in the upper hopper could be dropped in the hill with the corn or dropped through a separate spout and drilled separately.

This Farmall F-20 was direct connected to a McCormick-Deering No.110 QA checkrow planter. QA stood for Quick Attach. It was not Fast Hitch or 3-point hitch, but progress was being made.

The rear-mounted Farmall H-110 checkrow, corn planter (shown here) was chain driven from a two-piece sprocket clamped to the tractor axle. When the planter was lifted, a clutch on the planter disconnects the planter drive.

Farmall Touch-Control raised and lowered the planter. An attachment could make a power hill drop planter from the C-220 checkrow planter (shown here with a Farmall C). The clutchless checkrow planter made possible closer control of the total population of kernels planted per acre. Literature promoted the feature by stating, "The corn grower who knows his land will probably know very closely, from past yields or soil analysis, the size of stand that will give the best yield." Infinitely variable seeding rate control and global positioning information for yield mapping and optimum production could hardly have been imagined when this innovative method of plant population adjustment was offered.

The 4-row A-435 planter shown here direct connected to a Farmall Super A tractor was also available in a 6-row A-635 version. Ground-driven Planet Jr. planter units could be located in a wide range of row spacings on the 72-inch angle-iron main frame. Hydraulic Farmall Touch-Control effortlessly raised and lowered the planter.

openers, as well as Blackland types, are required. Typical of these specialized planters was the popular Farmall M-57 and M-59 power lift, 4-row direct connected, cotton, corn, and peanut planter introduced with the M tractors. It had long planter unit drawbars that pivoted on a sturdy pipe mounted under the "belly" of the tractor. This design kept individual row units centered on top of planting beds even under difficult conditions. A bedder attachment used in place of the regular planting units made it possible to prepare beds for future planting. The No. 28 hill-drop attachment and other attachments matched this versatile planter to different regions and specific cultural practices. The platform, or walk board, at the rear of the planter allowed an additional operator to change the planting depth of individual rows when required. Also, the operator could check to see that fuzzy cotton seed was feeding properly.

However, cooperation between IHC and the industry with those in seed production kept serious problems to a minimum. In addition, totally different seed hoppers were required for peanuts and fuzzy cotton seed planting. The combination corn and pea attachment consisted of two hoppers, one above the other, which made it possible to plant two kinds of seed at the same time. Peas or beans could be dropped in the same hill as the corn seeds or drilled separately.

Planter complexity doesn't stop with seed selection systems. To serve the wide IHC marketing area it was necessary to provide checkrow, drill, and power hill-drop corn planters in tractor front-mounted, rear-mounted, and drawn versions, plus horse-drawn models.

Very specialized tractor-mounted planters are required for vegetables and tobacco. A 32-page booklet, *Vegetable Truck Farming*, described in great detail the extensive line of front- and rear-mounted planters and planters and cultivators mounted between the front and rear wheels designed specifically for planting and cultivating small seeded crops in row spacings from 10 to 68 inches apart.

Special Planters for Special Southern Needs

Corn and cotton in the South are usually planted on beds. A wide range of front- and rear-mounted tractor planters equipped with runner openers or double disk

This is an example of the forward-mounted vegetable planters offered for Farmall Cub, Super A and C tractors. Each tractor-driven planter mechanism and hopper served two rows. Front gauge wheels and rear press wheels regulated planting depth from 1/8 to 1 1/2 inches. When the Farmall Touch-Control raised the ground units, the seed drive automatically shut off.

This rear-mounted M-57 4-row, cotton and corn planter design was so well suited to planting on beds that the basic configuration continued through several models including a 6-row International No. 86, rear-mounted version produced in the 1970s.

To market the low horsepower A and B tractors, IHC offered a wide range of tools and attachments matched to their capability. This 1939 photo of a Farmall B tractor with 1-row B-14 middlebuster, taken near Canton Works, shows a pair of spaced, very narrow, dual tires that would avoid compacting directly over the row. A note on the photo says, "See Mr. Gray before using." This interesting application may never have been offered as approved.

This particular planter worked so well in the regions that plant their crops on top of beds, especially cotton, that the basic design stayed a part of the IH planter offering for over three decades. The 6-row International No. 86 rear-mounted planter introduced in 1972 provided the latest in row-unit design including the exclusive IH rotary valve; the proven long drawbar configuration remained. However, the walk board disappeared.

IHC also supplied lister planters and middlebuster planting attachments. The final combination demanded by the marketplace resulted from tradition combined with appropriate cultural practices. The result was an extensive line of planting equipment offered in a wide range of row widths and assorted specialized attachments.

Saving the Good Earth is Everybody's Business

The Company made a major effort to advance soil conservation practices. *Terracing to Save Our Farms* was an IHC motion picture made in 1935 that was followed over the next decade with three other sound and color movies made in conjunction with the Soil Conservation Service. The International Harvester Company also published three books promoting soil conservation programs with a total distribution in excess of half a million copies. Dedication to soil conservation concerns continued throughout the history of the Farm Equipment Division.

This HM-47 planter and fertilizer attachment were part of a 1948 U.S. Soil Conservation Demonstration at Albuquerque, New Mexico. The planter is driven by a center-mounted, ground-drive wheel. When the Farmall Lift-All raises the planter, the drive wheel leaves the ground and planting/fertilizing stops.

The statement, "Prepares the seedbed and plants in one operation." summarized the M-21 and 4M-21 Till Planter capability. The system reduced soil erosion by leaving a protective surface mulch. The till planter was based on agronomy research of the time and appropriate concern for soil conservation. The till planter was released in 1953 for the M tractor family and later the 400 tractor. The high horsepower requirement per row and the lack of effective grass and broad-leaf weed control kept the till planter from becoming accepted commercially. However, decades later the same objectives would be achieved by different means.

IH Equipment for Soil Conservation

International Harvester World, published for IH employees worldwide, summarized the activities of IHC in promoting soil conservation in its April 1947 issue. One article in the issue announced the appointment of Russell R. Poynor to the newly created position of Agricultural Engineer in Charge of Soil Conservation. This appointment coincided with the first public demonstration of the M-21 till planter concept he had developed while working in the engineering department at IHC's Canton Works. This machine could plant two rows of corn or soybeans directly into sod or crop residue with no prior tillage.

McCormick M-21 Till Planter

International Harvester first produced the M-21 for mounting on the Farmall M, Super M, or Super MTA tractor in 1953. The combination machine used a pair of 36-inch upper sweeps to shear roots and break up the top 2 or 3 inches of soil while leaving the mulch on top of the ground. A pair of 18-inch lower sweeps made a band-type seed bed and provided for deep placement of fertilizer from the front-mounted fertilizer units. A four-wheel rotary hoe unit drove each fertilizer unit and worked the seed bed. Trash bars on the sweep shanks kept the row area clean for planting. A rear-mounted, 2-row drill planter with split-boot fertilizer attachment placed the seed, covered it with disk covers, and firmed the soil with press wheels. A second version, the 4M-21 till planter, was adapted to the Farmall 400 tractor and benefitted from the increased horsepower; however, it was still a 2-row planter in what was becoming a 4-row world.

The M-21 till planter concept and objectives were right, but the timing was wrong. Wide sweep tillage and mechanical cultivation were required because burn

down chemicals and season-long, broad-spectrum grass and broad leaf herbicides were yet to be developed. Only a few of the 50 units produced were retailed. Several 4M-21 till planters were given to land grant universities to encourage research into alternate methods of row-crop production. One result was the incorporation of the M-21 trash bars into the Nebraska till planter that found commercial application in selected areas.

Bigger Tractors — Bigger Planters

With the more powerful tractors that came to the market after World War II, farmers doubled their planter capacity by hooking two, 2-row pull planters together. IHC and the industry did the same thing but with functional and reliable designs. The early 4-row

With the wide use of rubber-tired tractors that had adequate horsepower, 4-row planters grew in popularity. Pneumatic rubber tire press/gauge wheels eliminated the nuisance of metal mud scrappers on metal wheels.

The 40 Series planters came in three models: No. 40, 4-row beet and bean planter; No. 41, 4-row corn and bean drill; and the No. 42, 6-row beet and bean planter (shown here in a 12-row, duplex hitch version). They came with either double disk or runner opener. Row spacings from 18 to 24 inches in 2-inch increments were available. Double-disk openers could be equipped with depth bands

planters were essentially A-frame hitches with "jockey tie bars" attached at the rear corner of the planter to maintain row alignment. The IHC FA 114 and FA 115 Farmall 4-row planters and drills were typical. The same hitch arrangement continued for the No. 440, No. 441, and No. 442 tractor trailing corn planters.

These were checkrow, drill, and power hill-drop planters in that order. The same hitch arrangement held true for the No. 443 and No. 445 corn and cotton drill planters. The Richmond, Indiana plant was closed in 1957 and production moved to Canton, Illinois. The move laid the groundwork for a new planter line.

Introduction of the McCormick No. 449/450 and No. 649/650 trailing-type planter line in 1959 revealed planters that had frames designed as 4- and 6-row machines. Each frame was supported on its own set of carrying wheels that drove the planter boxes and optional fertilizer attachment. This design kept the weight off of the row units. A companion 2-row No. 249/250 had the same basic design. The "49" Series were drill planters. The "50" Series were power hill-drop planters that could be converted to checkrow planters with an attachment. Narrow-row planting in the Corn Belt was gaining acceptance; the 2- and 4-row drill and hill-drop models could be set for rows as narrow as 28 inches. Four- and 6-row models in either series required hydraulic cylinders for the lifting the planter.

New Planters for New Requirements

University research from the 1950s demonstrated the benefits of high starter fertilizer rates for corn if placed 2 1/2 inches to the side of the row and 2 1/2 inches below the seed. To press a fertilizer opener that deep in even a well prepared seed bed required a strong planter frame and adequate down pressure. The No. 49 and No. 50 Series design could not achieve that requirement. Higher fertilizer rates required larger fertilizer hoppers and a stronger frame. Higher seed population recommendations required larger seed boxes. To meet the new requirements, Product Planning, Marketing, and Engineering developed a completely new IH planter configuration.

The new IH No. 455 drill planter and the new No. 456 rotary valve hill-drop planter introduced in 1964

Most accurate, high-speed trailing corn planters

Check-row...hill-drop... drill...2, 4, 6, and 8-rows

You'll plant for top yields with the world's most accurate high-speed corn planters in two to six-row sizes. Plant eight rows with two No. 450A four-row models on a squadron hitch. Fertilize, control weeds and insects too, as you plant. Drill only with lower cost Nos. 249A, 449A, and 649A planters.

Lightweight, pressed steel valves made it possible to plant up to 211 hills per minute with the McCormick No. 450A trailing-type hill-drop, drill, and checkrow planter. This equated to hills 32-inches apart at 6 1/2 mph. With the checkrow attachment, hills 40-inches apart could be planted at 5 mph. This planter is equipped with special 170-pound plastic fertilizer hoppers and 7- x 16-inch zero pressure tires for the press wheels. Gandy dry insecticide and herbicide planter attachments were marketed by IH. Eight-row planting used two No. 450A 4-row planters and a duplex hitch.

The 1964 Buyers Guide described the introduction of the No. 455 drill and No.456 hill-drop planters as "Revolutionary new pull-type Corn Planters that are a major breakthrough in row-crop planting." The design was totally different from any planter the Company had offered before. Eight-row planting utilized a duplex hitch and two, 4-row planters. Future 58 Series planters would offer 4-row wide planters convertible to 6-row narrow and 8-row narrow models. A new A-frame duplex hitch attachment could handle two, 6-row planters for 12-row planting.

with a spring tooth harrow attachment that mounted ahead of the planter frame for combined tillage and planting with one tractor pass through the field.

Rotary Valve Planters . . . An International Harvester First

From CLICK-CLICK to WHIR-WHIR

Corn Belt farmers who used hill-drop planters from the time of horse-drawn to modern tractor models knew only the familiar click-click of hill-drop valves opening and closing in the planter boot. The exclusive International Rotary Valve changed that forever. The simple, quiet rotor with interchangeable lugs made it possible to hill-drop 2, 3, or 4 seeds per hill or power drill single seeds. The International rotary valve had the shortest free fall distance in the industry — only 3 1/2 inches. Furthermore, the rotary valve ejected seeds backwards at a velocity equal to the forward travel of the planter. As a result, seeds fell at zero velocity with vir-

were totally different from any previous IH design. A 500-pound fertilizer hopper located at the front of the planter utilized an auger to deliver material to two rows. Up front location and a rigid A-frame hitch provided all the down pressure needed for the fertilizer openers without affecting the planter units. The big 70-pound fiberglass seed hoppers combined with high fertilizer capacity kept refill time to a minimum. The new 500-pound fertilizer hoppers added capacity and convenience to the central-drive 80 Series listers that were available in 4-row wide or 6-row narrow versions.

For 1967 the new planter line grew into the 56 and 58 Series rotary valve corn planters. The 56 Series offered 2-row 28- to 40-inch, 4-row 28- to 40-inch, 4-row 28- to 40-inch with adjustable wheel frames, and 6-row 36- or 38-inch planter models. The 58 Series included a 4-row 36- to 40-inch planter with a longer frame for conversion to 6-row 28- or 30-inch spacing if desired by adding extra row units. The largest 58 Series was an 8-row 30-inch machine with end transport. This big planter could carry 2,200 pounds of dry fertilizer in translucent fiberglass auger hoppers or 200 gallons of liquid fertilizer. Optional Gandy dry insecticide/herbicide row units with "Ro-wheels" were available. The need to reduce wheel traffic in the field was recognized

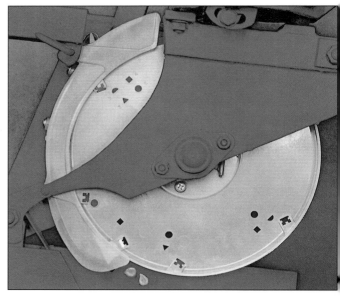

Planter literature stated, "Seeds are ejected backward at a rate that is equal to the forward speed of the planter – the seeds fall at zero velocity, have no scatter or bounce." Developed originally for cotton planters, the IH rotary valve found strong acceptance in the Corn Belt too. The snap-in drill guide quickly converted the rotary value from hill-drop to straight power drill.

tually no bounce or scatter. It represented a "quiet revolution" in hill-drop planting technology for corn and cotton farmers alike.

To complete the No. 455 and No. 456 family, two more pull-type planters were added a year later. The 66 Series rotary valve 2-row planter provided for a wide range of row spacings and modern features in a product suited to smaller farms. The 66 Series rotary valve 6-row 36- or 38-inch cotton planter was built on a main frame with "big" 8-row construction features, and dual planter and fertilizer drives. This planter was definitely geared to the needs of the large acreage operation.

Protecting the Fragile Soybean

The International Harvester Company encouraged employee participation in many national organizations in support of agriculture, including: American Society of Agricultural Engineers, American Society of Agronomy, Society of Automotive Engineers, American Seed Trade Association, 4-H, Future Farmers of America, and many more. At a National Soybean Association meeting in 1966, one of the speakers asked the question, "Why are we only getting 40% to 50% of the soybean seeds we put in the ground to produce bean plants? I am very suspicious of the design of the corn planter box used for soybeans." The IH representative at the meeting accepted the challenge.

The following year, a soybean seed meeting test was conducted at the IH Farm Equipment Research and Engineering Center at Hinsdale, Illinois. Two varieties of certified soybean seed were purchased; each variety contained a normal moisture lot and a low moisture lot. Soybeans were metered at rates equal to 5- and 7-mph field speeds through a standard IH corn hopper using three different recommended soybean plates, and through a John Deere standard corn hopper and their recommended soybean plate. Peanut seed is very fragile and requires special hoppers for metering with minimal damage; IH had just released a new rotary cone hopper for peanuts — this hopper was included in the test. The Seed Division of F. S. Services at Piper City, Illinois, conducted standard warm germination tests and the more rigorous cold germination tests on seed metered through each of the hopper and plate combinations and seed sampled from the bag.

The results indicated that variation within seed lots is likely greater than the recorded change from metering soybeans through a corn planter hopper with a properly sized plate. Plates not properly sized may cause wedging of two or more seeds and damage can result. The rotary cone hopper designed for peanuts eliminated this problem of seed plate selection when used for soybeans, but the seeding rate accuracy is not as high. Four years later, International Harvester elimi-

nated the concern over possible mechanical damage to soybean seed by the corn hopper plate and cutoff with introduction of the Cyclo Planter seed selection system.

The Stockton Connection

The International Harvester Company acquired a presence in localized and specialized California farm equipment manufacturing by purchasing the Dyrr Manufacturing Company of Huntington Park, California, in 1945. In early 1947 they purchased a small plant at Stockton, California, and moved the Dyrr operation to the new location.

Stockton Works, which primarily manufactured tillage equipment, rates inclusion in the planter section because of their unique line of planter-equipped strip tillage, incorporation, and bed forming products. The purchase of Western Bye Hoe of Gilroy, California, by IH in 1966 provided Stockton with a line of PTO-driven strip tillage machines for seed bed preparation, chemical incorporation, and rotary cultivation. By 1968 Stockton offered:

No. 700 mounted sled (for forming, working,
    or planting on beds)
No. 701 trailing sled
No. 705 mounted sled

IH Stockton Works produced specialized equipment for the West Coast like this No. 710 mounted sled incorporator with IH No. 185 planter units. This basic tool bar carrier was equipped with bed shapers followed by 9-inch wide rotary mulchers for tilling and chemical incorporation. By adding No. 185 planter units on the fourth tool bar, three operations could be accomplished with one pass. This family of tool bar carrier machines found limited application in the bedded areas of Texas and the Mississippi and Arkansas Delta. A similar No. 704 minimum-till planter (rotary strip tillage planter) for the Corn Belt was essentially the same machine without bed shapers.

No. 710 mounted sled (chemical) incorporator
No. 711 trailing sled incorporator
No. 712 furrow mulcher
No. 703 mounted incorporator
No. 704 mounted incorporator
No. 681 rear-mounted rotary cultivator (one row on a bed)
No. 682 rear-mounted rotary cultivator (two rows on a bed)

The 700 Series sleds were essentially toolbar carriers that could be equipped with bed shapers, bed rollers, and planting units like the No. 185. Equipping the No. 700 carrier with a heavy-duty, ripple-edge colter followed by a double disk opener equipped No. 185 unit planter gave IH a no-till planter for the Corn Belt.

The Sidewinder Tilther and other rotary strip tillage practices were in vogue at that time and the IH No. 704 "minimum-till" planter was the Company's entry. Today, it's hard to understand how the industry could call a machine that used even a narrow, PTO-driven rotary tiller a minimum-till planter. The IH machine was the basic No. 704 mounted incorporator (roto mulcher) for tilling a strip 9 inches wide and an extra toolbar for mounting No. 185 planter units. Most of these 3-, 4-, or 5-tool bar machines were available in 2-, 3-, 4-, 6-, and 8-row models. Since these were toolbar carriers that provided "erector set" flexibility, the possible combinations were almost endless.

For most areas, simplicity proved to be the popular answer to the needs of planting in a wide range of row spacings and cultural practice requirement. The answer was the hitch-mounted No. 326 planter carrier. International No. 296 rotary valve planter units could

Simplicity of the drive system and the versatility of clamping it in any desired location on a 1 1/2- to 2 1/4-inch square two bar made the planter unit popular for many applications; planting rows as narrow as 14-inches was one application. Availability of 14 different beet plates and 16 different planter drive combinations made it possible to plant beets in 182 different spacings from 0.8 to 70 inches in the row. The No. 185, shown here, was used to plant corn and many small seeded crops other than beets. When the No. 185 was replaced by the similar No. 295 planter unit in 1970, an optional 75-pound fiberglass seed hopper became available in addition to the standard 30-pound round hopper. The No. 296 heavy-duty rotary valve planter unit was also introduced in 1970.

The massive 5- x 7-inch tool bar of this No. 326 planter carrier provided the stiffness necessary to properly handle eight No. 296 planter units. Rotary valve No. 386 planter units for cotton, corn, peanuts, or beans could also be mounted on the No. 326 planter carrier. This wide machine came with end transport as standard.

be located as close as 20 inches apart. A special kit made it possible to mount two, No. 295 planter units as close as 8, 10, or 12 inches apart for double-row planting on 36- or 40-inch beds. The large 5- x 7-inch bar was an ideal match for the rugged No. 386 planter unit that provided rotary value performance for hill-drop, power drill, or straight drill.

Cultural Practice Turmoil

Corn and soybean production research during the late 1950s and early 1960s at land grant universities had demonstrated the yield increases associated with production in 28- or 30-inch rows. The industry responded with Corn Belt style planters for row spacings less than the traditional 36-, 38-, 40-, or 42-inch rows. A new round of research projects indicated there was a possible yield benefit from row spacings less than 28 or 30 inches. Universities and the agricultural media chal-

This 12-row planter is actually two, 6-row planters closely coupled and controlled by a new quick attach, A-frame duplex hitch. For transport, one unit trailed behind the lead unit. Providing all of the features of a traditional, centralized drive Corn Belt planter in a 20-inch row model is no simple task; there is no room for the carrying wheels and drive chains. IH engineers solved the problem by driving the planter with 4- x 16-inch drive wheels that rode on top of the planter carrying wheels. Solving the planter design challenges did not solve the marginal economics of 20-inch row corn production. In spite of extensive attention by the agricultural press and one planter manufacturer, the practice had very limited commercial application. Corn production in 28- or 30-inch rows became the predominate narrow-row spacing.

lenged the farm machinery industry to provide planters for rows more narrow than 30 inches. (A few farmers and universities experimented with corn in 15-inch rows.) Methods of significantly reducing preplant tillage gained much attention as well.

One solution to the row-width dilemma is the toolbar-mounted planter unit. Since the planter unit design is press wheel driven, it is easy to position the units at virtually any location on the toolbar. Any location is fine as long as the planter units don't physically interfere with each other, the carrying wheel location is provided — if required — and the space between units is adequate for trash flow. Seeding rates are somewhat limited and changes must be made to each unit rather than to a single, central drive transmission. Unit planters are popular with many producers because of their flexibility.

Planting corn with unit planters was a simple solution for achieving more narrow rows, but the Corn Belt farmer wanted a narrow version of the central drive, pull-type, fertilizer planter he currently used. To meet that requirement, International Harvester released the 54 Series 12-row planter for corn or soybeans in 20-inch rows for 1967. The machine utilized a duplex hitch and two 6-row planters. They could be trailed one behind the other for easy transport. Combine corn heads were released to harvest

20-inch rows. The marginal benefit for corn grown in these extra narrow rows did not justify the added equipment expense and almost total reliance on sometimes erratic chemical weed control. The Company built a small number of 20-inch row planters and corn heads; the market never developed; 28- and 30-inch rows became the accepted standard for another three decades. With new genetically engineered varieties that tolerate specific herbicides, new interest in corn grown in less than 28-inch rows is gaining attention in the last half of the decade of the 1990s.

The yield increase for soybeans grown in rows less than 28 or 30 inches wide did provide an economic benefit. As the market for extra narrow row equipment developed, IH responded with the Corn and Soybean Special Planter and grain drills designed for seeding soybeans. These products are described later in the chapter.

The decade of the 1960s witnessed the development of a broad-based concern for reduced tillage and once-over planting systems. The response to the concerns took many forms: wheel track planting, plow-plant, rotary strip tillage, and waffle coulter planting; modified systems of tillage took the form of combined, reduced, minimum, and zero tillage. International Harvester introduced equipment for some of the systems, but most of them never gained wide acceptance. John

Deere introduced five different alternative tillage and planting systems during the 1960s. Some time later one of their engineers remarked that, "these efforts are not worth 5 cents a pound today." The turmoil did raise awareness of the need to conserve soil, reduce compaction, and lower energy input per unit of production. Decades later, modified forms of some of the 1960s approaches became commercial practice.

Two Farm Families Revolutionize the Corn Planter

The two major corn planter innovations of the 20th century did not originate in the engineering departments of the two industry leaders. These inventions were the creation of the Keeton Brothers of Trenton, Kentucky, and the Loesch Brothers of Kimball, Minnesota.

The Finger Planter Makes the Rounds

Eugene Keeton, farmer and self-proclaimed tinkerer, reduced his ideas for a corn planter seed selection system that would work with a wide range of seed corn sizes and shapes to a working model. He refined his concept and filed for a patent in 1964. When he thought he was ready for a demonstration, he contacted his friend the Chief Engineer for Planters at Deere & Company. The engineer apparently thought Mr. Keeton had an improved version of a concept they had previously evaluated; his request was turned down. Next, the Keeton Brothers made contact with J. I. Case, Massey Ferguson, and Oliver.

The Oliver Chief Engineer for Planters relates how the Keetons contacted him late one Friday afternoon and asked to make a demonstration. Because of the late hour, it was not possible. They were on their way back to Kentucky after meeting with Massey in Detroit and pressed hard for a meeting. The engineer agreed to a demonstration in the basement of his home that evening. Eugene Keeton clamped the crude model made of coat hanger wire, springs, and thin metal clips to the basement work bench. Cranked by hand, the model selected single corn seeds of uneven sizes with impressive accuracy. Oliver, like Case and Massey Ferguson, were minor players in the corn planter market and did not have the financial or engineering resources to bring this simple model to the point of commercial manufacture. Oliver, like the other firms, was not properly positioned to make an offer.

The Keeton Brothers then took their model to Hinsdale, Illinois, to demonstrate it for International Harvester. Like the other firms, IH engineers and product people were impressed with the demonstra-

tion. They recognized the potential of the concept, but they also fully understood the size of the engineering development task and related high tooling cost. In spite of the challenge, IH sent a representative to Kentucky with a substantial offer for the Keeton patent. The Keetons were shrewd businessmen. They took their IH offer and secured, on the second try, a demonstration with the Chief Engineer of Deere Planter Works, sold their idea, and negotiated a very favorable contract. Deere planter engineering did an impressive job of producing a product that, in spite of its spring and cam controlled finger complexity, became a commercial product. The Keeton concept, however, could not meter soybeans; that required a separate metering system.

Plateless Seed Corn Metering, the Simple Way

Since IH was not the successful bidder for the finger-pickup patents, the search for other plateless planter concepts took on new urgency. The Winter vacuum planter developed by an Illinois farmer in cooperation with the Eureka Company, Bloomington, Illinois, was brought to Hinsdale and thoroughly evaluated. Like the vacuum planters developed in Europe, it was best suited to small seeds, tended to plant seed corn doubles, and had inherent seal and dirt intake problems.

Each year during the late fall and winter IH Product Planning Research conducted a series of "Farmer Meetings" across the United States to evaluate changing cultural practices and farming trends. One of the farmer participants in the Sleepy Eye, Minnesota "farmer meeting" in February 1967 told the senior author about a unique plateless planter developed by the Loesch Brothers located near Kimball, Minnesota. The information was shared with the IH Planter Product Committee. Sometime later the sales member of the Committee visited the Loesches and made a generally favorable report, but no other Company follow-up was made. The inventive farmers continued to develop their planting system and took it to the field in 1968. Since the Loesch Brothers heard no reply from the first IH contact, they submitted their patent to the International Harvester Corporate, Non-Employee Idea Submission Department. The submission went to the Planter Chief Product engineer for evaluation; he was impressed.

Key personnel from the Planter Committee — including engineering — visited the Loesch Brother's farm and found a well-developed seed corn selecting system that utilized a large rotating drum and positive air pressure. The demonstration in the well-equipped, well-heated shop that winter day impressed the IH

Leo and Claude Loeschs' air-powered seed metering system working model, shown here, was the Genesis of the 400 CYCLO planter. The Loesch bothers not only invented a new method of seed metering that was suited to precision planting of unsized seed, they had the mechanical ability to reduce their ideas to a working module for planting their own fields of corn.

visitors. In addition to accurate seed singulation of unsized corn seed, the concept had two outstanding features lacking in the John Deere/Keeton Brother's finger planter. First, this invention was extremely simple; it had only two moving parts and an air supply. Second, engineering recognized that this concept could be made to plant soybeans and other crops by simply changing to a drum with different hole sizes. The finger pickup could work only in corn. And, perhaps best of all, the Loesch concept utilized only one central seed hopper.

Once the patent purchase contract was finalized, the Loesch Brothers agreed to let their well-developed working model come to Hinsdale engineering with the understanding that it was to be returned for planting the next spring. Their excellent cooperation continued throughout the project; however, they never totally understood why IH wasn't interested in some of their other ideas.

Major improvements made to the Loesch model and patent by IH engineering included:

1. Development of seed drums capable of planting a variety of seed types and sizes.
2. A method for quick interchange of seed drums.
3. Seed release wheel development to achieve uniform timing of seed release.
4. Development of a seed cut-off brush to eliminate most doubles.
5. Seed manifold development to accommodate variables in seed trajectory at the time of release.

In the summer of 1969, engineering assembled their own field-going, functional, but very crude looking Loesch system planter for concept evaluation. When certain management saw this first effort, it was hard to convince them that the final machine would be both profitable and represent a marketable, modern design. The first true engineering prototype was tested at the IH Sales and Service Training School near Tifton, Georgia, in the spring of 1970. This farm land was all in the government program; so, after the crop emerged and stand counts taken, the crop was destroyed. The chief planter product engineer said, "The results seemed to confirm our excellent laboratory tests." The next test location was North Carolina where the harvested results pleased both engineering and the farmer. When planting began in the Corn Belt, 15 units were involved in the test program.

The CYCLO Planter

Most engineering managers will admit that when a development project comes from an outside source, it usually is plagued with the "not invented here" syndrome, and progress is slow. Development of the Loesch seed selection system was just the opposite. From the planter engineering group, engineering management, sales, and product management, right up to the Farm Equipment Division President Brooks McCormick, they all gave enthusiastic support to what would become the CYCLO planter. As a result, what seemed like totally unrealistic completion dates were actually achieved, and a well-tested design was released to limited production for sale in the spring of 1971.

Beauty is a Beast

The Loesch Brothers used inexpensive, dull looking, hardware store variety black plastic tubing to deliver seed from the metering drum to each individual row of their planter; IH engineering did the same as they developed the CYCLO planter from working model to finished design. When the first CYCLO planters went into production, the supplier finished smooth, black, shiny tubing that really looked great. Wisely, engineering checked the accuracy of a sample of these first production planters and found the in-row seed spacing was not good. After checking a number of possible causes, it was learned the "pretty" black delivery tubes interfered with uniform seed flow. Seven miles of shiny, black plastic tube was scrapped and the planters were fitted with dull looking tubing like that used during development. The planters with the dull looking seed delivery tubes now delivered "beautiful" performance. The beast was tamed before the first CYCLO planter went to the field.

Limited first production of the 400 CYCLO planter in 1971 included a 4-row wide model and a 6-row narrow version shown here equipped with dry fertilizer attachment. Availability of other models, seed drums for crops in addition to corn, milo, and soybeans, and an extensive list of attachments would follow in 1972.

The International 400 Series CYCLO planter brought "the farmer a long-sought-after combination of features which included accuracy, simplicity, reliability and convenience." The planter was introduced in two trailing models: a 4-row 36-, 38-, or 40-inch wide row and a 6-row 28- or 30-inch narrow row in runner or 13 1/2-inch double disk versions. The dry fertilizer attachment had two 550-pound fiberglass hoppers for the 4-row 400 CYCLO planter, and it had two 850-pound fiberglass fertilizer hoppers for the 6-row 400 CYCLO planter. Combinations of 60- and 100-gallon liquid fertilizer tanks were offered for 4-, 6-, and 8-row 400 CYCLO planters. Stainless steel seed drums with transparent fiberglass reinforced polyester ends were available in three versions: corn drum with 24 seed pockets per seed row;

This International 400 Series CYCLO planter is pictured a year after introduction. The planter is equipped with IH designed and manufactured International granular chemical applicators for insecticide and herbicide that were offered with the original CYCLO planter introduction. "Micrometer" flow rate control was dial adjusted for rates between 3 and 50 pounds per acre. Each translucent fiberglass hopper held 35 pounds of material and came with hinged, polyethylene lids. The liquid fertilizer attachment, shown here, was introduced in 1972. The seed release wheel arm has an extension so the end is visible from the tractor seat. As long as that arm was moving up and down, the operator knew the drum was turning.

soybean drum with 144 seed pockets per row; and milo drum with 72 seed pockets per row.

Introduction of the CYCLO planter was complemented by the introduction of the new International Harvester designed and manufactured "Micrometer" granular chemical applicators for insecticide and herbicide. These replaced the "McCormick Gandy" units purchased OEM in the past.

The advantages of a planter that planted unsized seed corn and could be easily switched to soybeans or milo were immediately apparent to farmer prospects. Likewise, the convenience of a single, 11-bushel seed hopper needed no explanation. However, the seed selection system was such a novel concept that it was necessary to fully explain how the CYCLO planter worked. Colored line drawings, photos, print

The Loaded Question

The International 400 Cyclo planter was introduced to representatives of the Seed Industry prior to the public introduction. At this meeting the President of the Pioneer Hi-Bred Seed Corn Company asked the IH Chief Planter Engineer, "What part on the CYCLO Planter do you expect to fail first?" After a short pause he replied, "If I could predict that, it wouldn't happen!"

"How the CYCLO Planter works . . . Seed, any size, leaves master seed hopper and enters the ground-driven revolving seed drum through delivery chute. (PTO-powered blower supplies equalizing air pressure to seed hopper and drum). Seeds are held in pockets of drum by constant air pressure. As seeds ride to top of drum, brush removes any excess seeds. Rubber cutoff wheels momentarily close drum's holes, releasing seed into discharge manifold. Air pressure then carries seed through the tubes and into the furrow."

descriptions, and dealer meetings told the story and promoted this innovative new product across the Corn Belt.

For 1972, IH introduced the 400 CYCLO planters in 6-row wide, 8-row narrow models. A new duplex hitch

with hydraulic drive for two planter blowers made possible 8-row wide and 12-row narrow CYCLO planters. Seed drums for popcorn, acid delinted cotton seed, pelleted beet and grain sorghum, and a wide range of edible bean sizes were added for a total of seven drums. A simple little seed monitoring devise was a small plastic whistle mounted near the end of each seed tube. If the end of a delivery tube became plugged with dirt the whistle sounded. A tillage hitch made it possible to pull a single planter immediately behind a tractor and hitch-mounted tillage tool.

International 500 Series Toolbar Planters

Flexibility of the Cyclo seed metering concept made it ideal for adapting to planters other than the traditional pull-type, Corn Belt style. The first application was the 500 Series tractor hitch mounted toolbar planter introduced in 1973. Models included were a 4-row wide or narrow, and 6- or 8-row wide all on a 5- x 7-inch main frame. A 7- x 7-inch main frame accommodated two hydraulically driven Cyclo modules for planting 12 narrow rows. To provide for wider 500 Series planters, a Flax-Frame feature made it possible to offer a 12-row wide 36- to 40-inch planter and a 16-row narrow 28- to 30-inch planter.

Running changes and improvements continued for the Cyclo planters year after year. One of the significant changes was the 1977 introduction of the posi-depth gauge wheel attachment that ran directly alongside the point of seed placement for precise depth control.

The year following the introduction of the revolutionary CYCLO planter, a 6-row wide and an 8-row narrow planter were added to the original 4-row wide and 6-row narrow models. These wide planters were equipped for endwise transport as standard.

A Cyclo Planter for Solid-Stand Soybeans?

University of Illinois/International Harvester joint 1974 narrow row soybean production research.

Experimental plots demonstrated that soybeans in rows more narrow than 28-inches had a higher yield response than corn in the same row width. This was especially true with the new varieties being released in the 1970s. However, there were serious questions about seeding rate accuracy and seeding depth control when grain drills were used to plant soybeans in 7- or 8-inch rows. International Harvester offered to furnish the University of Illinois equipment needed for conducting a carefully controlled 7-inch row soybean production field experiment between the CYCLO planter and a grain drill.

IH planter engineering used two hydraulically driven 8-row modules on a toolbar to build a 16-row CYCLO planter for 7-inch row soybeans. The Company also furnished an International No. 620 combination 24 x 7 press grain drill with staggered double disk openers equipped with depth bands.

Results of the two-year study demonstrated a 6-bushel per acre yield advantage for soybeans grown in 7-inch rows compared to 30-inch rows. However, the yield differential between the experimental 7-inch row CYCLO soybean planter compared to the grain drill did not justify its weight, cost, and limited width. Useful information was gained, and IH turned its attention to grain drill and CYCLO planter modifications better suited to more narrow row soybean production. Suggestion made at the conclusion of the study for a 30-inch/15-inch corn and soybean planter would later become a reality with the 1981 introduction of the International 800 Cyclo Air, Corn and Soybean Special planter.

Many areas prefer tool bar planting equipment; the CYCLO metering system was ideally suited for that application, as seen here with this International 500 Series, flex frame, 16-row CYCLO planter.

The parallel linkage of the No. 87 rear-mounted blackland planter provided for "accurate planting even on rough or soft beds." Seed hoppers and optional fertilizer attachments were driven by the carrier wheels to assure minimum slippage. The planter was available in 4- and 6-row models for 38- to 40-inch row spacing.

A New Generation of Cyclo Planters for the '80s

"Four years in the making, $25 million in development cost, 30 patent applications and 35,000 acres of field test in four countries including 20 states in the U.S. — the result:" The International 800 Early Riser Cyclo Air Planters.

"The advanced planting system that accelerates seed germination, improves seed placement and electronically monitors all critical functions" was loaded with new features:

- Staggered, double disk opener
- Exclusive, precision controlled equalizing gauge wheels
- Unique furrow firming point, a patented feature
- Twin inverted covering disks
- Wide press wheel with center rib provides a "cracking" slit
- IH exclusive Cyclo Air seed selection with new manifold
- Fifteen different seed drums expands the range of crops planted
- "Cou-till" attachment for minimum or no-till conditions
- Central seed hopper with 15 bushel capacity, a 36% increase
- Seed Flow II monitor standard. Optional, more sophisticated Cyclomitor III or "Performance Center" microprocessor monitor

Early Riser Cyclo Air planters were available in 4-row wide, 6-row narrow, 8-row wide and narrow, and 12-row narrow sizes. Mounted vertically-fold models were offered in 8-row wide and 12-row narrow sizes.

Numbered graphics were used to illustrate the superior seed environment produced by the new Early Riser row unit. One simple knob adjustment on each row unit controlled planting depth and covering pressure; indicator scales assured setting all rows alike. Not so obvious were improvements in the Cyclo metering system. The seed intake manifold was moved from the top, or 12 o'clock position, of the drum to the 9 o'clock position. This location eliminated the effect of gravity on seed trajectory at release and accuracy was improved over a wide range of planter speeds and seeding rates.

The new names, Early Riser and Cyclo Air, called attention to the fact that this 800 Series planter was significantly different from the previous models.

Vertical fold made this 800 Early Riser Cyclo Air 12-row narrow mounted planter easy to convert from working position to transport position. An 8-row wide, 36-, 38-, or 40-inch vertical fold was also available.

The Early Riser term summarized the benefits of the new row units on the 800 Series planters. The same row unit benefits were incorporated in this plate-type model as in the Cyclo Air. Seed hoppers with standardized bottom rings accommodated equipment for peanuts, acid delinted cotton seed, and beets as well as corn and soybeans.

International 800 Plate-Type, Early Riser Planters

All of the outstanding seed placement and soil environment features of the Early Riser row units were made available in a plate-type planter. Standardized hopper bottom rings provided for quick change when switching from corn or soybeans to cotton or peanuts. A Seed Count III monitor was an option for plate planters. Plate-type 800 Early Riser trailing planters were available in 4-row adjustable from 30- to 40-inch rows and 6-row narrow. Rigid frame, mounted versions were offered in 6-row wide and 8-row narrow models.

New Models for Special Markets — The Best of Both Worlds

Seedsman Special — Hybrid seed corn producers appreciated the benefits of the 800 Early Riser Cyclo Air planter, but the centralized seed hopper ruled out its use in

most seed corn production planting patterns. For planting seed fields, 8-row plate planters usually had pollinator seed in the two outside rows and parent seed in the six inner rows. This resulted in the popular six and two planting pattern for seed production. The new 800 Early Riser Cyclo Air, Seedsman Special supplied parent seed from the Cyclo centralized hopper to the center six rows and the two outer rows were equipped with plate-type Early Riser row units for planting pollinator rows. The Seedsman Special provided the best of both worlds.

To meet the unique needs of hybrid seed corn producers, IH married the 800 Cyclo Air planter and the 800 plate planter to develop the Seedsman Special. The Cyclo seed metering module supplied seed to the center six rows while the two plate-type units planted the two outside rows. This made it possible to plant male pollinator rows and female seed rows at the same time.

With the inter-units in working position, this planter is drilling 13 rows of soybeans in 15-inch rows. There are two 30-inch spaces and no inter-units in line with the rear lift-assist wheels.

This photo demonstrates the Corn and Soybean Special planter changeover. Seed drums on the ground show how the rows of unused seed pockets are blocked off with wide rubber bands. The corn drum is on the right and the soybean drum is on the left. No cut off wheels are used for the blocked off rows.

Corn and Soybean Special — Optimum production of both corn and soybeans was made possible with the 800 Early Riser Cyclo Air, Corn and Soybean Special. The planter was a basic 8-row, 30-inch, semi-mounted toolbar planter with two Cyclo seed metering modules. Additional row units were located between the two outside pairs of rows and the center pair. When all units were planting soybeans, the row spacing was 15 inches except for two 30-inch spaces where the rear lift wheels ran; this arrangement provided a 13-row, narrow row planter for soybeans. Three unused rows of soybean drum pockets were blocked off with wide rubber bands that covered the holes. For planting corn a cable winch hooked to a support rod over the main frame was used to lift the five inter-row units and lock them in the raised position. Soybean drums were replaced with corn drums that had half of the pockets blocked off with wide rubber bands; this arrangement provided an 8-row, 30-inch corn planter. Like the Seedsman Special, the owner had the best of both worlds.

For planting corn, the inter-row units on this 800 Early Riser Cyclo Air Corn and Soybean Special are lifted and locked in the raised position. The two soybean drums are switched to 8-row corn drums with half of the seed pockets blocked off with a wide rubber band. The Special is then ready for working as a conventional 8-row, 30-inch corn planter.

Big planters are purchased for planting large acreage and frequently that means transporting the planter to many locations. This multi-phase, hydraulically actuated, rear fold 16-row, narrow-row planter was the right answer for large volume farming.

Hydraulic Control Ballet

Ever larger farm equipment require even more ingenious methods of safe transport for these giant machines, and planters are no exception. A 16-row, 30-inch planter is 40-feet wide when working in the field; it's too long for end transport. The rear fold, 16-row Cyclo Air planter used hydraulics to unlatch, tilt, position, and fold the two halves of the planter from working position to transport position in a series of synchronized moves that seemed like a well choreographed dance performance. Transport position to working position was accomplished with similar ease.

The Cyclo Cycle Goes On

Within a decade, International Harvester took the basic concept of two farmers, the Loesch Brothers, and developed it into the industry's premier line of planters. Twenty-five years after the introduction of the first two models of Cyclo planters, the Loesch/International Harvester seed metering system remained the most versatile, reliable, and accurate product on the market.

IHC marketed this Light Draft Kentucky grain drill and other American Seeding Machinery Company products manufactured at Richmond, Indiana, under a licensing agreement until 1920 when they purchased the firm.

International Harvester Grain Drills — One Company, Many Brand Names

International Harvester Company got into the grain drill business the same way it entered the planter, manure spreader, wagon, and other kinds of farm equipment businesses — it purchased companies, or marketed for companies, already in the business with well-established products and brand names. As a result, IHC grain drills carried such trade names as: Keystone, Victor, Kentucky, Hoosier, and Empire Jr. These brand names were eventually replaced by McCormick-Deering, McCormick, and International. Purchase of the American Seeding Machinery Company, Richmond, Indiana, in 1920 firmly established IHC in the grain drill business with an extensive product line.

Basic components of most fluted feed grain drills on the market were similar. One area of differentiation was the opener design. The size and type of bearing, sealing method, and system of lubrication were described in great detail in Company literature. Lubrication of the Keystone and Victor single disk opener was by a hard oil compression cup "conveniently" located just above the bearing. The importance of keeping sufficient grease in the bearing was stressed over and over in an IH advertising booklet. The description ends with the amazing offer: "These bearing will be replaced free of charge if worn out." It is hard to imagine filling a grease cup for each opener and then frequently screwing it down to keep the bearing lubricated as a convenient task. Double-disk openers had an oil tube cast in the bearing standard that was closed with a stopper. The same free bearing replacement applied.

The McCormick-Deering Hoosier 12x7 fertilizer grain drill pictured here was equipped with open delivery, chilled bearing, single-disk furrow openers. Closed delivery and steel bearing opener combinations were available. Double disk and shoes were other opener options including the "Saw-Blade," double-disk opener so named because the disks were made of saw-blade steel.

Horse-Drawn Drills and Seeders

Drivers usually walked behind small end-wheel drills. If larger drills were equipped with a footboard, he could ride most of the time. Keystone drills as large as 22 disks, 6-inches apart were available in 1912 and required a four-horse hitch. Some drivers chose to ride on the front of the grain box if they were convinced a sudden lurch would not send them tumbling.

The Kentucky and Hoosier line included a wide range of products. Kentucky Hoe broadcast seeders were made in the spring-trip style only; it could be adjusted for "easy," "medium," or "hard" trip release. Spring-protected scattering spouts conducted seed from each fluted force feed outlet to below the drag bars where it was spread evenly over the ground ahead of the shovels. Another interesting seeder was the Hoosier Narrow Track. Two, 28-inch diameter steel carrying wheels spaced three or four "corn row spaces" apart were located behind the grain box. Like the Hoe seeder, metered seed fell through "Scatter Spouts" for uniform spreading on the ground. The driver's seat was centered on the frame that carried the axle bearings and supported the seed hopper. In addition to driving the team, the driver operated the metering drive clutch. The machine was designed to "sow in corn-stalk ground or other fields which were covered with low obstructions, stumpage, etc." The third member of the fluted force feed seeder family was the Hoosier 11-foot Jumbo seeder. The hopper held 5 3/4-bushels. This drill came in only one size so the capacity was fixed. Other

models came in different sizes and the capacity was different for each size. Wheels 48-inches in diameter were carried on stub axles extending from the end of the hopper. This arrangement placed the fluted force feed outlets close enough to the ground so that short scatter spouts could be located between the frame sills for protection from "injury by striking corn stalks, stubs, stones or other obstructions." The most economical wheeled machine was the Hoosier 11-foot Hornet seeder. This was a simple agitator feed hopper supported on 40-inch steel end wheels. The most common answer for economical seeding was the Hoosier No. 3 End Gate seeder. The two "scattering wheels" (gear-driven, flat spreader disks, each with

IHC Hamilton Works, Hamilton, Ontario, Canada, arranged for photographing their modern steel hopper grain drill pulled by a beautifully outfitted team in 1935. This particular model was called an Eastern Canada grain drill.

The Purdue University livestock farm was the site of this 1938 photo. Like many farms of the '30s, tractors did the plowing and tillage but faithful teams were called on for planting, seeding, and drilling. The D-2 International Harvester truck complements the McCormick-Deering grain drill.

four, half-round flingers) could spread wheat from 42 to 52 feet and timothy 20 to 24 feet. Driving 2 1/2 mph, the Hoosier No. 3 could broadcast about one acre every five minutes or about 100 acres per day.

McCormick-Deering Kentucky and Hoosier Drills

Purchase of American Seeding Machinery Company added the McCormick-Deering name to the highly regarded Kentucky and Hoosier brand names for the IHC grain drill line. Literature from 1924 covers a wide range of end wheel drill sizes that included pin or spring trip hoe drills, single or double disk, disk drills and zig-zag rank shoe drills. Seed metering systems included the "reliable flute force feed" and the internal or double run feed. One side of the double run feed wheel was used for corn, beans, peas, and other large seeds. The other side was used for wheat, rye, flax, and other small seeds. Metal flappers fastened on the bridge over the feed wheel covered the die not in use. A speed transmission with 20 settings determined the seeding rate for the double run system.

In addition to end wheel drills, the booklet also included the McCormick-Deering Kentucky press drills. This type of drill was used in the dry, wind blown area of the western United States and Canada. Few, if any, press drills were marketed in the state of Kentucky;

however, the significance of that trade name was so strong that it, along with the name Hoosier, would continue to dominate product identification of the Richmond line. The McCormick-Deering Kentucky press drill was made in 12- x 7-, 16- x 7-, and 20- x 6-inch sizes. It had staggered openers, the traditional two-wheel forecarriage, and 26-inch diameter steel press wheels. The driver's seat was positioned well behind the press wheels so his weight, as well as part of the drill weight, rested on the press wheels. This geometry provided a powerful foot lift to "assist in raising the front frame."

There was no seat on the McCormick-Deering Hoosier one-horse 5-disk drill. This narrow, walk-behind drill could successfully seed between standing corn planted in the common 40- to 42-inch rows. Like the big end wheel drills, it could be equipped with fertilizer and/or grass seed attachments. Before drilling wheat or other fall seeded crops, it was frequently necessary to walk the field and turn any lodged or broken corn stalks that were in the middle of the row to be in line with the row. One of the great selling points for hybrid seed corn when it was first introduced in the mid-1930s was its superior standing ability; that was an especially important benefit for anyone who drilled in standing corn. The plain and fertilizer 5-disk drill was still offered in the IH 1955 drill catalog. One of the specialty drills was the McCormick-Deering Kentucky

Seeding wheat or other fall seeded crops in standing corn was still an accepted practice in many areas at the time this 1952 Memphis District photo was taken of a McCormick 5-disk, one-horse, fertilizer grain drill. When grain dryers made early corn harvest practical, drilling wheat with conventional drills after corn harvest finally eliminated this slow and laborious method.

alfalfa and grass seed drill that had 20 single-disk farrow openers spaced 4-inches apart. Disk blades were 11-inches in diameter.

To match an increasing number of tractors on farms, McCormick-Deering Hoosier tractor drills were offered. In addition to the steel tractor hitch, they came with mechanical power lift as standard. Five sizes of plain drill were offered in 1923 including the 18-disk, 7-inch spacing largest plain model, a single 12-disk, 7-inch spacing fertilizer model. Many extra equipment options were offered including a foot board, seat attachment, and horse hitch.

Hamilton, Ontario, Canada

IHC grain drills made in Canada carried the McCormick-Deering name in the 1930s. This facility eventually became the sole North American source of grain drills for International Harvester. After World War II, International Harvester offered Type R

tractor and horse-drawn end-wheel drills in 15 plain and 11 fertilizer sizes. Both offered fluted or double run feed systems. Horse-drawn drills could be equipped with a tractor hitch at any time. Deep furrow drills were available in 16 x 10 and 12 x 10 sizes equipped with 14-inch disks in place of the standard 13-inch disks. Type H drills came in three larger, heavy-duty models for tractors only. Type B power-lift tractor press drills came in three sizes with either saw-blade double disk or shoe openers. Tapered hopper ends permitted hinging two drills together for end-to-end operation. Adjustable plow press drills came in 8-disk and 10-disk sizes to match 3- and 4-furrow plows.

"There is a McCormick Drill or Seeder for Every Planting Job," said a 1955 booklet. It covered everything from steel wheeled, end-wheel horse-drawn drills, 5-disk one-horse drills and end gate seeders to modern rubber tired end-wheel drills and press drills. The McCormick Model M plain drill and Model MF fertilizer drill shared the same features. These end-wheel tractor drills had pneumatic-tired wheels for smoother, faster travel in the field or on the highway. Quick-acting mechanical power lift was standard; hydraulic control with an 8-inch stroke cylinder was optional. Opener choice included single disk, double disk, shoe, or spring-hoe types in eight different models. Grain

This Canadian-made 13 x 7 single disk opener, fertilizer grain drill is hitched behind a Farmall F-14 tractor. Mechanical power lift and screw-type depth adjustment made this wooden box drill a true tractor drill.

One-pass plowing and drilling was possible when this 8-disk size, adjustable plow press drill was hitched to a 3-furrow (14 or 16-inch bottom) plow. The plow packer firmed the soil and removed air pockets to provide a proper seed bed.

hoppers were copper-bearing steel and the fertilizer hoppers were galvanized steel. The McCormick No. 6 hopper-type fertilizer spreader was also available; it came in 8-, 10-, and 12-foot sizes.

Pasture Renovation

University research had demonstrated the benefits of improving pastures with new grass and legume varieties. In order to do this without the erosion risk of major tillage, new seeding equipment was needed; the International Harvester answer was the No. 1 Pasture Renovator introduced in 1956. The 8-foot 9-inch wide machine could be equipped with seven furrow openers spaced 11 inches apart or with four furrow openers spaced 22 inches apart. A 12-inch plain or an optional 14-inch notched coulter cut a slit in the undisturbed pasture ahead of each deep fertilizer applicator. Placement down to 4 inches was possible. Seed metered from the unhulled seed hopper and small grass seeds or legumes metered from the clover seed attachment were deposited over the fertilizer band. Optional press wheels could be used to help close the furrow opening.

No. 10 Grain Drill . . . Plain or Combination

The traditional angle iron drill frame used on previous IH grain drills was replaced with sheet metal channel sections fabricated at Hamilton Works for the new McCormick No. 10 end-wheel drill introduced in 1959. The new design provided reduced weight with maximum rigidity. Available sizes included: 16- to 24-opener drills with 6-inch spacing, 12- to 18-opener drills with 7-inch spacing, and a 16-opener model with 8-inch spacing. The No. 10 had grain capacity of 1 1/2 bushels-per-foot of hopper. An exclusive feature was the optional "Easy-to-Clean Fertilizer Hopper" — the bottom of the hopper swung open for fast, easy cleaning. Legume and grass seeding options were avail-

able so a fully equipped drill could do four jobs at once. All models except the 24 x 6 came on 15-inch wheels; that model came on 20-inch wheels which were an option for the other models.

The McCormick International No. 10 combination end-wheel drill introduced in 1966 was not a replacement for, but an addition to, the No. 10 plain drill. The combination hopper provided 85 pounds of fertilizer and 1 1/4 bushels of seed capacity for every foot of width. Models available included three sizes of 7-inch spacing and one 8-inch spacing. No 6-inch spacing models were available in the combination drill. Both models of the No. 10 end-wheel drill with 7-inch or larger spacing could be equipped with exclusive IH openers for placing fertilizer 1 inch to the side and down to 2 inches below the seed. A single disk fertilizer opener was attached behind and to the side of the double disk seed opener and could be adjusted to the desired depth. "This advanced-design opener unit provides the kind of separate fertilizer placement that has long been advocated by agricultural colleges as a needed feature on grain drills," stated 1966 IH literature.

The Pick-Up-and Go Drill

For unmatched simplicity, economy, and maneuverability, the McCormick International No. 10 semi-mounted grain drill was the answer. This 13 x 7 drill with combination-style hopper directly mounted behind tractors with Category I or II or Fast Hitch systems. The rear of the drill was supported on a single caster wheel. The gauge wheels on each end of the drill had four positions. One wheel drove the grain seeding mechanism and the other wheel drove the fertilizer unit. When the drill was lifted, seeding and fertilizing stopped without the need for a throw-out clutch.

Old Technology — New Precision

Power fluted feed metering had been used on the earliest IHC grain drills and seeders. What was different about metering for the numbered series drills in 1966 was the precision and manufacturing technology employed for accuracy and long life performance. The precision feed cup features included:

1. Precision, die-cast feed cups made from smooth, corrosion-proof zinc; "it stays that way."
2. Fluted feed rolls and shutoff blocks made from sintered (powdered) metal — a high precision process that assures extreme uniformity for precision metering.
3. Rustproof, long-wearing, cadmium-plated, fluted washer for years of service life.
4. Special sintered metal insert protects the feed cup from washer abrasion.
5. Feed cup bottom adjustment to three positions without tools.

Because of the high volume of feed cups required, Hamilton Works did their own feed cup die casting.

Cultivator Drills

In the 1920s IHC offered the McCormick-Deering cultivator drill. The long frame of the drill provided for two ranks or "floats" of rigid or spring tine shanks up front to cultivate. This was followed by two smaller ranks or "floats" with boots for conducting the fertilizer and/or grain directly behind the 4-inch point equipped shanks. The two gangs of "floats" had separate depth adjustment. Precision drills eventually displaced the cultivator drill.

The needs of Australia still required a cultivator drill. The McCormick International 6-2 cultivator drill manufactured by the International Harvester Australian Company was described in 1968 sales literature as follows: "The rugged frame carries four ranks of spring tines or spring release tines, or 'floats.' Grain tubes conduct seed and fertilizer behind the appropriate spring tine."

When "zero till" wheat drilling was first under consideration, the senior author investigated importing a McCormick International 6-2 cultivator drill to the United States and modifying it for experimental "zero till" wheat production research. Further investigation revealed that the cost of ocean freight from Australia was more than the cost of the drill. Since this was not a viable option, experimental work continued with traditional North American drills.

Press Drills

The McCormick No. 100 press drill introduced in 1959 brought modern grain drill features to the IH line for western needs. Models with 6-inch spacing were offered in 5-, 6-, 7-, and 12-foot sizes. Models with 7-inch spacing were offered in 11-foot 8-inch and 14-foot sizes. Separate fertilizer attachments featured the same hinged hopper bottom that swung down for easy cleaning that was available on the No. 10 drills. Positive-firming, 20-inch steel press wheels were standard; zero-pressure, press wheel tires were an option. With large acreage the norm, the two-drill hitch attachment with bumper plates and connecting links was a popular item of special equipment.

The McCormick International No. 150 shovel-press drill offered a separate fertilizer hopper with drop bottom for easy cleaning like the other current drills. The grain hopper held 1 3/4 bushels per foot of length. Shovel types included polished share iron, polished steel, and tumbled steel in 3-, 4-, 5-, and 6-inch widths. For fields measured in sections where drills were not raised for hours at a time, a hand lift attachment was available.

Hitching three McCormick No. 100 press drills together provided the high capacity needed for large western wheat farms.

This design was ideal for deep seeding and working in heavy trash. With 24-inch spacing between the ranks of shovel-type openers, the No. 150 had 40% more fore-and-aft clearance than major competition. Large operations could couple two drills together with the two-drill hitch and cover from 24 to 32 feet.

The International Diskall flexible one-way disk with seeding and fertilizing attachments was not a grain drill in the true sense, but for some operations it was a way to prepare a seedbed and seed small grain in a high capacity, one-pass operation.

For uneven rolling ground, McCormick International No. 150 press drills were offered in a 7-foot wide 10 x 8 size plus 8-foot wide 8 x 12 and 10 x 10 sizes. Multiple hookup of two or three of these narrow drills provided big-acreage capacity with the required flexibility for uniform coverage.

The International No. 150 hillside press drill had split press wheels that left soil loose directly over the seed. The spring trip furrow openers came with exclusive "Eagle Beak" deep penetration points for seeding up to 8 inches deep. Openers were equipped with adapters and deflectors to keep excess soil out of the furrow. Because it was designed for hillside operation, the furrow openers were in a straight line directly ahead of the split press wheels. This 1970 product came in an 8 x 18 size convertible to a 10 x 14 size.

Industry's Highest Capacity

Introduction of the International 620 press drill line in 1970 brought many new features. The plain drill could hold 2.0 bushels per foot of hopper length, the biggest capacity in the industry. Combination drills had a unique reversible hopper divider that made possible either 142 pounds of dry fertilizer with 1.4 bushels of grain per foot or 85 pounds of dry fertilizer and 1.95 bushels of grain per foot. International No. 620 press drills came in seven sizes ranging from 7 to 14 feet. A 24 x 7 combination drill model was available with liquid fertilizer tanks located in the dry fertilizer hopper along with 1.5 bushels of grain capacity per foot. Five years later 620 press drill capacity increased 145% and combination drills offered 4 seed/fertilizer ratio.

The No. 10 Becomes the No. 510 End-Wheel Drill

The No. 510 brought many of the design features of the No. 620 press drill to a line of end-wheel drills. Nine sizes from the 13 x 7 to an over 13-foot wide 16 x 10 were offered in addition to the innovative semi-mounted 13 x 7 model. Plain hopper grain capacity increased from 1.5 to 2.4 bushels per foot of length for the No. 510 compared to the No. 10. Rather than an add-on attachment for fertilizer, the No. 510 offered a choice of two different grain/fertilizer capacity combinations. The grain/fertilizer ratio could be changed from 1.35-bushels grain/108-pounds fertilizer to 1.71-bushels grain/79-pounds fertilizer per foot of length. The flexibility aided in matching the growing conditions of the different areas. A complete selection of furrow openers included a double-disk opener with separate fertilizer placement. Options included seed firming wheels and depth bands for double-disk openers, gang press wheels, and 16 other attachments.

This International No. 620 press drill has double-disk openers equipped with depth bands for drilling narrow-row soybeans. The spring tooth harrow combination hitch made possible final seedbed preparation and drilling in the same operation on this Central Illinois farm in 1975.

This 24 x 7 model was equipped with a fiberglass "Liquitanker," liquid fertilizer tanks that held 14 U.S. gallons per foot and fit inside the regular metal dry fertilizer hopper. Grain capacity was 1.5 bushels per foot of length. Three ground driven squeeze pumps accurately metered the desired quantity of liquid fertilizer regardless of differences in travel speed.

Big capacity in the plain drill could be converted to a combination drill with two ratios of seed to fertilizer with this No. 510 end-wheel grain drill. This system replaced the add-on fertilizer attachment of the No. 10 end-wheel drill.

To meet the needs of large acreage producers, a pair of International No. 5100 end-wheel drills could be teamed up using the hydraulic two-drill hitch attachment available in 1981. Hydraulic power would shift the drills from transport to working position, and back to transport, without the operator leaving the tractor seat.

Grain Drills for the 1980s

Agricultural economics of the '80s required producers to do more work in less time. To meet the needs, International Harvester introduced a number of high production features in the new No. 5100 and No. 5100 Soybean Special end-wheel drills; No. 6200 press drills; No. 7100 shovel press drills; No. 7100 hillside shovel press drills; and No. 7200 stubble mulch press drills.

For fast transport from field to field, two No. 5100 end-wheel drills could be hitched behind one tractor with the two-drill, hydraulic control hitch. End transport attachments for 2, 3, or 4 press drills provided for moving multiple drills as wide as 56 feet. All parts of the transport system were carried on the drills and the transport width was reduced to 14 feet.

To speed routine servicing and extend service life, regreasable press wheel bearings and central lubrication of shafts and drive bearings enhanced these high production machines. High-speed drilling with wide machines requires more than the operator's sense of sight and sound to be alerted to potential problems. Optional monitors that constantly checked seed flow and warned of malfunction at the feed cups provided the needed information.

This International 7200 stubble mulch, 24 x 7 drill had openers on three zig-zag ranks that provided 7-inch spacing with effective 19-inch lateral and 19-inch fore-and-aft trash clearance. The design met the requirements for trouble-free drilling of spring crops in heavy trash. It was available in this size only.

Two zig-zag ranks of openers on this International 7100 shovel press drill provided 28-inch fore-and-aft clearance for excellent trash flow. Openers lifted 6 inches above ground in transport.

Cultivation and Weed Control
From Horse Power to Tractor Power

United States census data records almost 250,000 tractors in agricultural use in 1920. Five years later the number would double. These tractors were replacing horses for tillage, both primary and secondary, pulling reapers and binders, and other drawbar work. However, horses still did the row-crop cultivating. The industry, including IHC, tried to totally mechanize row-crop production by introducing motor-cultivators; this was not the answer. The ultimate answer was a totally different kind of tractor. This need was the driving force behind development of the revolutionary Farmall. That fascinating development story is told in the chapter titled "The First Farmall."

Horse-Drawn Row-Crop Cultivators

When International Harvester purchased Parlin and Orendorff and Chattanooga Plow in order to compete with Deere & Company in tillage, they also acquired a well respected line of riding and walk-behind, horse-drawn cultivators. Horse-drawn planters didn't always make straight rows. Even careful checkrow planter operators didn't always end up with cross-row hills of corn in perfect alignment. Row-crop cultivators had to be able to follow crooked rows and dodge out-of-place hills.

An International cultivator catalog from 1913 reveals a complex offering of horse-drawn cultivators and options including the following:

International No. 1 pivot pole cultivator — The pole could be made rigid by inserting a pin. This riding cultivator could be equipped with the regular bucket seat or a hammock seat like a racing sulky. An elaborate arrangement of high mast supports, bail rods, and crank push rods provided parallel movement of the gangs when the operator pushed on the foot stirrup to dodge a hill of corn or correct for a crooked row. The cultivator could be equipped with 4-, 6-, or 8-shovel gangs. Round or slotted shanks came in pin-break or spring-trip types.

International No. 2 combination cultivator — The operator could ride this cultivator or throw the seat

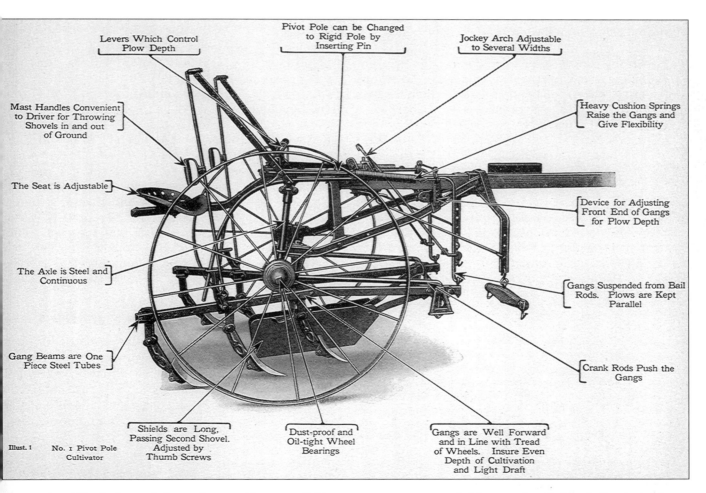

International No. 1 pivot pole horse-drawn cultivator — Cultivator gangs were suspended from, and guided by, bail rods that kept the gangs parallel while the driver pushed on foot stirrups to shift the gangs and keep them centered on the row or to dodge out-of-place hills. The pivot pole feature could be locked out by inserting a pin. Seven different models of one-row riding or combination walking and riding cultivators were offered in 1913.

forward, walk behind and guide the gangs with wooden handles. Gangs and tooling were simple and it had no linkages to keep the gangs parallel like the No. 1 cultivator.

International No. 22 leverless cultivator — This cultivator was exactly the same as the No. 2 except depth was controlled by chains in place of levers.

International No. 23 pivot pole cultivator and International No. 24 pivot pole cultivator were exactly the same as the No. 2 and leverless No. 22 except for the addition of the pivot pole.

If the ground was hard and stoney, any of the above cultivators, except the No. 1, could be equipped with heavy, parallel gang equipment.

International No. 4 pivot axle cultivator — This cultivator, called the Hillside, was quite different from the No. 1 and No. 2 Series. Instead of moving the cultivator gangs to follow crooked rows or dodge out-of-place hills, a slight push on either foot lever turned the wheels at an angle that carried the front end of the frame and the gangs sideways. To reduce "steering" effort, ball bearings were used in the axle support brackets. Advertising said, "These foot levers afford such great leverage that a boy can handle the No. 4 and do excellent work." Eight pages were devoted to a detailed description of the No. 4 and its tooling.

The basic design of the No. 4 one-row, horse-drawn, riding cultivator was so well accepted that a new No. 4, "The World's Most Popular Riding Cultivator," was promoted in a McCormick-Deering two-color booklet in 1945. A new fertilizer attachment made side dressing possible. The new model TF was a disk cultivator.

The driver used his feet to pivot the axles and shift the gangs. "A boy who can drive three horses can handle the No. 5, 2-row cultivator," said the 1913 literature. For hard ground or steep hills, a four-horse hitch could be purchased.

Included in the booklet were four pages of "One-Horse Cultivators for Every Crop That Is Planted in Rows."

Completing the original 1913 catalog were the International No. 5, 2-row cultivator with 3- or 4-horse hitch and two versions of its International No. 6 wheel supported, walking cultivator.

The McCormick-Deering horse-drawn cultivator pamphlet for 1923 introduced names in place of model numbers. In addition to the new No. 4 were "Old Reliable" Jewel Hammock, Balance Rider, Wiggletale, Victor, Combined Walker and Rider, and Volunteer "Walkers." An illustration for the McCormick-Deering lister cultivators made it clear that these machines were direct descendants of the original lister line; "the first lister ever built was built in the P&O factory."

Horse Cultivators Did It — Tractor Cultivators Must Do It!

Development of the Farmall tractor is in many ways the development of a tractor-mounted cultivator. Operator controlled, lateral movement of horse-drawn cultivator gangs was always considered a requirement in order to do close cultivation in crooked rows,

The new No. 4, 1-row, horse-drawn cultivator in this 1923 catalog is very similar to the International No. 4 pivot axle cultivator of 10 years earlier. The McCormick-Deering new No. 4 was still the featured riding cultivator in a 1944 catalog of horse-drawn cultivators.

When the driver turned the steering wheel, the front axle shifter lever moved the Farmall cultivator to correct for crooked rows or dodge an out-of-place hill of corn. The Farmall Regular tractor and Farmall 2-row front-mounted cultivator could do work like a good horse-drawn cultivator only faster, easier and cheaper. For the first time, total tractor farming was possible.

on hillsides, and especially cross-cultivation in fields planted with a checkrow planter. This requirement was incorporated in the short-lived motor cultivator project. It was an equally important requirement during development of the Farmall and its matching, mounted cultivator. The role of the cultivator in Farmall development is covered fully in the chapter titled "The First Farmall."

The Farmall Regular incorporated the distinctive cultivator shift lever keyed to the front axle shaft that extended out from the front bolster. When the end of the shift lever was linked to a shifting gang cultivator, that all important "hill dodging" ability was incorporated in a tractor-mounted cultivator. Steering the front end of the tractor resulted in twice as much

movement of the cultivator as the front of the tractor. When the Farmall Regular was replaced by the Farmall F-20 and F-30 and later when the F-12 and F-14 joined the family, the cultivator shift lever was there.

Unlike horses, this pair of Farmall Regular tractors with Farmall cultivators could work all day, regardless of the heat, and never need a rest. The year was 1926 and the Farmall revolution had begun.

By 1938, rigid-mounted cultivators like the 218H were demonstrating that they could do a quality job of cultivating in many applications. They were cheaper and less complicated than shifting cultivators.

A New Family of Cultivators

The totally new design of the Farmall H and M still provided for the cultivator shift lever. However, it was now neatly tucked away behind a radiator screen cover panel. For use with shifting gang cultivators, the panel was removed and an extension bolted in place. The HM-221 shifting gang 2-row cultivator "is a great favorite in sections where corn is planted in checked rows," said the 1945 booklet, *The Farmall System of Farming-Farmalls H and M*. A great advance for these two tractors was the cultivator power lift when the tractor was equipped with hydraulic Lift-All. It came in single, delayed, or selective lift versions. Manual lift was also available.

The HM-229 2-row shifting gang cultivator was a totally different design from the HM-221. Gangs were clamped to a square tool bar that was suspended by two swinging rods pivoted from vertical brackets supported near

the top of the radiator. Two pivoted pipes running from the cultivator tool bar to the tractor rear axle housing absorbed the thrust load. Originally designed for the F-20, as the No. 229, it was a great improvement over the shifting gang cultivator introduced with the Farmall Regular. Production ended in 1942. The HM-228, a disk cultivator, was especially suited for fields infested with morning glory, creeping jenny, or other noxious weeds.

The B-221 and BN-221 provided 2-row, shifting gang cultivation for the two models of Farmall B tractors. Cultivators for the Farmall A were the one-row, mid-mounted A-136 and A-138. For the Farmall AV, IHC offered the AV-138 for high beds or where high clearance was required.

The HM-236, 238, and 240 were 2-row cultivators mounted directly to the front of Farmall H or M tractors. The HM-236 had round tool bars for working the sides of beds and trenches. The HM-238 and 240 had rectangular tool bars. Attachments included Connecticut potato hiller, potato hoe, peanut digger, spring tooth, and fertilizer. The B-236 and B-238, along with BN-236 and BN-236, were available for the Farmall B and BN.

Texas was the driving force behind IHC producing a 4-row cultivator for the Farmall Regular shortly after it was introduced. For the new line of tractors, the M-420 cultivator met the needs of the 4-row corn and cotton farmer. With 4-row equipment it was possible to cultivate up to 70 acres per day. The M-420 could work in either level or bedded crops in rows from 36 to 42 inches. The V-rim gauge wheels or flat-rim gauge wheels with rubber over tires were popular special order attachments.

This 1929 McCormick-Deering Farmall H is equipped with a MH-229 cultivator. This model shifting gang cultivator moved the square main frame and all four gangs whenever the front axle shifter lever moved. This kept all gang movement parallel.

When Canton Works needed to test a new cultivator design and no row crop was available, they planted a crop of stakes. The combination being tested in 1940 was a Farmall B and B-221 cultivator.

This Farmall H with HM 249 cultivator was laying by a good stand of corn near Springfield, Illinois in 1946.

Attachments made tractor cultivators extremely versatile. This McCormick-Deering Farmall B Cultivision tractor was working near Mission, Texas, in 1945. The B-236 cultivator was equipped with a McCormick-Deering No. 99 planting attachment. The non-IH middlebuster attachment is making water furrows. This photo was taken by Firestone as part of their tractor tire promotion which explains the non-IH component. The tractor is equipped with the IH Pneumatic Lift-All system that operated on pressure diverted from the exhaust manifold for lifting the cultivator.

The needs of beet and bean growers were met with the 4-row HM-439 and 6-row HM 639, double tool bar cultivators. The No. 19 and No. 28 bean harvester attachment added another use to these cultivators.

The P&O leadership in lister equipment was not forgotten. The new tractors could be equipped with the 2-row No. 35 or the 4-row No. FA-40 rear-mounted lister cultivators.

The Power-Lift, 4-row M-448 cultivator mounted on the Farmall M and MD; a parts package would mount it on Regular, F-20, and F-30 Farmall tractors.

The Farmall System of Cultivation . . . ### FIRST CHOICE OF 1,500,000 USERS

This statement headlined the 1952 McCormick cultivator catalog for Farmall Cub, Super A, and Super C tractors. These small tractors could perform many operations well, but they were outstanding cultivating tractors, especially in tobacco, vegetables, and other specialty crops. THE CULTI-VISION logo helped tell that story. Another feature was economy. With the Farmall Super C and 2-row C-254 cultivator, "cultivate 35 acres a day with a tankful of gas!" proclaimed the literature. High clearance was another feature. Crop clearance on the Cub was 19 5/8 inches; the Super A, 21 5/8 inches; the Super C, 23 3/8 inches; and the Super AV, 27 1/2 inches. Beet and bean cultivators came in the 2-row Cub-252, 4-row A-452, and 6-row C-652 sizes.

Goodbye Tractor Prefixes for Cultivators

The Product Identification Committee took a bold step in 1957. Their decision stated that cultivators and other mounted implements would no longer have a prefix to indicate the tractor or tractors they would mount. Thus, began a new system of cultivator model numbering.

The 4-row No. 461 front-mounted cultivator fit the Farmall 350 and 450 tractors. The 2-row No. 261 front-mounted cultivator fit the same tractors plus the Farmall 300 and 400. Parts kits mounted these cultivators as far back as the Farmall Super H, M, and Super M. Later versions fit the Farmall 460 and 560 tractors.

In 1958 the 6-row No. 665 front-mounted cultivator for 36- to 40-inch rows was introduced for the Farmall 400 and 450 tractors. It was the same basic cultivator as the 4-row No. 465. By adding a section to each end of the frame, it became the 6-row No. 665. The attaching points were actually hinge plates that could be locked together. This feature made it possible to unlock the hinge and fold the ends forward for transport. The No. 465A and No. 665A were for mounting the Farmall 460 and 560 tractors. The 8-row No. 865 rounded out the front-mounted cultivator line.

Hydra-Touch hydraulics provided unison lift with one value, delayed or selected lift with two valves, and unison, delayed, or selected lift with three valves. Farmall 230 tractors with Hydra-Touch could be mounted with the K-254, 2-row cultivator. The 2C-254A was for Farmall 230 tractors with Touch-Control hydraulics.

Never Look Back

The wide use of 2,4-D after World War II for broad-leaf weed control changed row-crop cultivation forever. Mechanical cultivation was still needed, but careful cultivation to control weeds in the row was no longer as critical. This opened the door for wide use of rear-mounted cultivators. With half sweeps or shovels and shields moved further from the row, rear-mounted cultivators could do the job quickly and without plant damage.

The McCormick-Deering Farmall C tractor and front-mounted cultivator working at the IH Hinsdale Farm in this properly contoured field bears witness to International Harvester's long-standing commitment to soil conservation practices.

The spring-mounted rolling guide fin provided stability and resistance to side movement.

"Just Back . . . Click and Go" described the convenience of rear-mounted Fast-Hitch cultivators. If the operator got off of the tractor seat, hooking up three-point hitch versions was not too difficult if the cultivator was not too large. One thing was totally different. Operators of front-mounted cultivators knew they must keep their eyes on the sweeps to keep the tractor exactly on the row. How do you keep your eyes on the sweeps when the cultivator is behind you? You don't! You watch the guide marker on the front of the tractor and keep it exactly over the row; the cultivator will follow where it belongs. If you turn around to look at the cultivator, the tractor will usually wander off the row. The secret of good work with a rear-mounted cultivator is, never look back!

International Harvester offered rear-mounted 2-row No. 263 and 4-row No. 463 cultivators for the Farmall 300 through 450 tractors. Later they would fit Farmall 460 and 560 tractors and the 6-row No. 663 would be added. Rear-mounted cultivators introduced another change, they could be used with Fast-Hitch equipped International 340, 460, and 460 Hi-Utility tractors. The flexibility of rear-mounted, tool bar cultivator design made it much easier to adapt to narrow-row corn and soybean planting patterns. These changes in cultivator design and application along with advances in chemical weed control would have a major impact on future tractor design and model mix.

Too Hot to Handle — International Harvester seriously considered producing a line of flame cultivators in support of their strong market position in cotton growing areas. They terminated the project because of possible liability exposure. About the same time, a line of anhydrous ammonia application equipment was developed. That project was canceled for the same liability concerns.

New Series Cultivators for New Tractor Requirements

Front-Mounted Cultivators

A new series of front-mounted cultivators was developed for use on the '06 and '56 Series tractors. These new cultivators were a response to change in cultural practices and in tractor model preferences. The 68, 78, and 85 Series all would mount on either tricycle or wide front axle tractors.

The 68 Series 2- and 4-row models were for 28- to 42-inch rows. The 6-row model was for 28- or 30-inch rows. This series would also fit Farmall 504 and F-544 Hydrostatic tractors.

The International 78 Series front-mounted cultivators were located well behind the tractor's front wheels and had clearance for the big 10.00- and 11.00-16-inch tires. They came as a 6-row for 28- to 30-inch rows or as a 4-row for 36- to 40-inch rows. To assist purchasers considering a change, the 78 Series was available in a 6-row frame with 4-row tooling for later change to 6-row use by adding two rows of tooling.

Front-mounted 6- and 8-row wide and 8- and 12-row narrow cultivators in the 85 Series posed serious transport problems; forward fold was the solution. Castered carrying wheels supported the hinged frame when working in the field and carried the front of the cultivator in transport position.

The completely new International 85 Series front-mounted cultivators introduced in 1969 were mostly supported on the front of the tractor, but the tooling beams were actually mid-mounted. This design provided clearance for the big front tires on the large tractors. The 85 Series cultivators were available in 6- and 8-row, wide-row or 8 and 12-row, narrow-row models. To maintain uniform working depth with such wide cultivators, each side was hinge mounted at the tractor and supported on the end by a 13-inch carrying wheel. To transport these large cultivators, each side frame was pivoted forward while still supported on the end carrying wheel. It may have looked strange, but the transport system really worked quite well.

Large Rear-Mounted Cultivators for Large Tractors

The new high horsepower tractors created a need for 6-, 8-, and 12-row rear-mounted cultivators in the same way they did for front-mounted cultivators. The 1967 introduction for narrow rows was the International 43 Series 6- and 8-row, single-sweep, rear-mounted cultivators. Individual 4- x 12-inch zero pressure gauge wheels kept the standard 20-inch sweeps working at the set depth. IH responded two years later with a pair of traditional and a pair of non-traditional row-crop cultivators for these tractors.

New for 1969, the International 163 Series and International 153 Series rear-mounted traditional cultivators were built around massive 5- x 7- and 7- x 7-inch tubular frames depending on the size of the cultivator. The 163 Series were 6- and 8-row cultivators for 36-, 38-, and 40-inch spacing with two gangs per row. The 153 Series were 8- and 12-row cultivators for 28- to 30-inch spacing with one gang per row. An 8-row beet and bean, 28- to 30-inch row and a special 8-row, 22 to 30 inch were also in the series along with a 6-row, 28- to 40-inch row machine. The end transport wheels and tongue were carried on the machine when not in use rather than left at some easily forgotten location.

For 1970, the International 153 Vibra-Shank cultivator added a non-traditional 6- and 8-row narrow machine to the cultivator family. Mounting the famous IH Vibra-Shank tooling in a row-crop, one gang per row configuration on a tubular steel main frame resulted in a high speed cultivator that worked especially well in trashy conditions. Each gang was mounted on a heavy-duty

With two gangs per row, the International 8-row No. 163 wide-row cultivator with blade-type row shields could cultivate fast, thoroughly, and close to the row. All components were attached to the 7- x 7-inch tubular steel main frame with U-bolts; so, row spacing adjustments were easily made.

parallel linkage controlled by a 4- x 12-inch rubber tired gauge wheel. By replacing the clipped wing sweeps on each side of the row with full width sweeps and repositioning the Vibra-Shank location, these machines could be used as full coverage field cultivators.

Herbicides controlled weeds and grasses in the row; the International 153 Vibra-Shank cultivator destroyed them between the rows. With only one parallel linkage gang per row, plant damage was kept to a bare minimum.

The 183 row-crop cultivator could be equipped with either Vibra-Shank or Vibra tine tooling and came in both rigid and flat folding wing models depending on size.

The second non-traditional row-crop cultivator family introduced in 1970 was the International 353 and 363 Series rotary cultivators. Four-, 6-, and 8-row cultivators were available in wide and narrow row models, depending on width and tooling. "Spoon-shaped" modular iron tillage wheels were mounted in pairs; they were 14 1/2 inches in diameter. RoWeeder wheels, 13-inches in diameter, were like slender rotary hoe wheels that worked close to the row. The two kinds of rotary wheels were followed by a single sweep. The cultivators came with either square or round tooling. The round tooling worked especially well for bed shaping and cultivating on beds.

Is it a Tillage Tool or a Cultivator?

The No. 8 field cultivators were described in a McCormick-Deering tillage tool booklet in 1945 that covered 10 products including disk harrows. The No. 8 field cultivators for tractors came in 5 1/2- to 12-foot single section sizes and a 14-foot duplex model that came with depth regulators and power lift. Horse-drawn machines came in the same single-section sizes but were regularly equipped with hand lift and seat. Gang equipment included light or heavy spring teeth, stiff teeth, or wide spaced subsurface sweeps.

The No. 9 trailing field cultivator and No. 11 hitch-mounted field cultivators still made their home in the tillage tool section of the 1962 Farm Equipment Sales Catalog. In organizing the Farm Equipment Reference Catalog that followed, the editors listed the new International 45 Vibra-Shank field cultivator in the cultivator section. So, field cultivators then became cultivators.

The new International 45 Vibra-Shank three-rank cultivators were described as having, "Exclusive shank action and outstanding trash clearance that make them superior to any other cultivator for minimum or secondary tillage practices." Trailing models from 8 1/2 to 19 feet and duplex version from 18 to 22 feet were available in 1969. Trailing wing-type from 22 1/2 to 28 1/2 feet were also offered. In addition, the popular 45 Vibra-Shank cultivators came in hitch-mounted versions from 8 1/2 to 19 feet. The No. 5 combine tillage hitch made it possible to pull a planter directly behind a hitch-mounted 45 Vibra-Shank cultivator for once-over corn and soybean planting on previously plowed ground.

This McCormick-Deering W-30 and 11 1/2-foot No. 3 field cultivator was working near Sperling, Manitoba, Canada in 1937.

Conservation Preview

A very prophetic description of field cultivator use is contained in the No. 8 field cultivator section of a 1945 McCormick-Deering Tillage Tool booklet. It reads, "The subsurface tillage gangs enable the user to cultivate the soil thoroughly without turning it over or burying any of the crop residues. By keeping the trash on the surface, the soil is well protected against blowing and water runoff." Three decades later, concern for soil conservation would move field cultivator use from limited to extensive as producers changed their tillage practices to maintain surface residue, conserve soil, and meet government program requirements.

Exclusive shank action of the 45 Vibra-Shank cultivator and the convenient one-bolt clamping system made this machine stand above the competition. This cultivator is equipped with hinged "C" frame extensions and spring assisted folding. The IH triple rank, spring tooth mulcher attachment adds the final touch to quality seedbed preparation.

International 645 Vibra-Chisels in mounted, trailing, and trailing wing models provided a tool between the 45 Vibra-Shank and the 55 chisel plow. Shank spacings of 9 3/4 or 13 1/2 inches were available. Working width of basic machines could be increased by adding one or two shank extensions.

The International 55 chisel plows in mounted, trailing, and trailing wing models were still listed in the Reference Catalog cultivator section. "Rocking action of patented International spring-cushion clamps lets springs and alloy steel shanks flex continuously. There are no pins to wear or fittings to grease." This was how the merits of the No. 55 were described. The simple, reliable chisel plow shank was a totally different design than the Vibra-Shank or the Vibra-Chisel. Each did an outstanding job for their intended use. Trailing duplex versions up to 26 feet were available. Single-wing folding models up to 20 feet provided quick, easy transport. A rod weeder attachment was offered for regular trailing and duplex International 55 chisel plows.

This International 365 Vibra tine field cultivator and rotary mulching attachment was an excellent chemical incorporator. Trailing, folding models featured a new hydraulic depth control system for maintaining uniform working depths.

This International 55 single wing trailing chisel plow is an ideal match for the Farmall 1466 turbo tractor. The single folding wing 55 came in 16-, 18-, and 20-foot sizes. This machine filled the gap between the 17-foot trailing 55 chisel plow and the 22-foot dual-wing 55 chisel plow.

The International 4586 tractor shown here displayed the new 1979 paint and decal scheme that introduced the new Control Center with color-coordinated interior and deluxe Con-touride seat. It is pulling a 29-foot trailing, wing model International 5500 chisel plow. The model 5500 replaced the International 55 chisel plow.

IH introduced the trailing, wing model 4700 Vibra Tiller in 1981 in sizes up to 52 feet. It could be equipped with either Vibra-Shank tooling or Vibra chisel shanks. The 6000 Conser-Til plow that had a spring-loaded disk gang assembly with 20-inch coulters on the front rank was introduced the previous year. Subsoil chisel deep tillage tools with rigid or optional automatic recovery shanks rounded out the line.

This McCormick-Deering rotary hoe working on the Prospect Farm near Centerville, Iowa, in 1925 was in the field at just the right time to kill germinating weeds and not damage the small corn plants.

options built around the exclusive IH rotary hoe wheel. Wheels were formed by riveting the interlocking teeth together and to the hub. No. 3 wheels were 18 inches in diameter and had 12 teeth per wheel while the No. 4 wheels were 21 inches in diameter and had 16 teeth per wheel. Popularity of the No. 4 rotary hoe wheel resulted in the No. 3 wheel being dropped from the line. Mounted versions handled two or three sections. Sections came in 42- and 48-inch widths. The International 18 implement carrier handled four rotary hoe sections and folded for transport. The rear-mounted International 300 rotary hoe had a rigid tube frame for flexibly supporting the correct number of hoe gangs to cultivate 4, 6, or 8 rows in both wide and narrow rows versions. The International 224 flexible rotary hoe had two pivoted hoe sections per row to deliver thorough coverage when working on beds.

Get Up and Go!

Rotary hoes are useful tools for early weed control if you can get in the field at the right time. They can be a life saver if soil crusts form before seedlings emerge, especially crops like beans and cotton that emerge in the crook. McCormick-Deering rotary hoes with horse hitches were essential implements on many farms in different parts of the country.

Rubber-tired tractors increased the effectiveness of the rotary hoe because of increased field speeds. Horses and mules couldn't deliver the 10-mph speeds required for optimum performance. The second advantage of the rotary hoe is its ability to cover a large acreage in a short time. To take full advantage of critical timing, the McCormick No. 2 rotary hoe with exclusive "chisel-tip" spokes was available in 4-, 5-, and 6-section sizes.

In 1967 IH offered a wide range of No. 3 and No. 4 rotary hoe

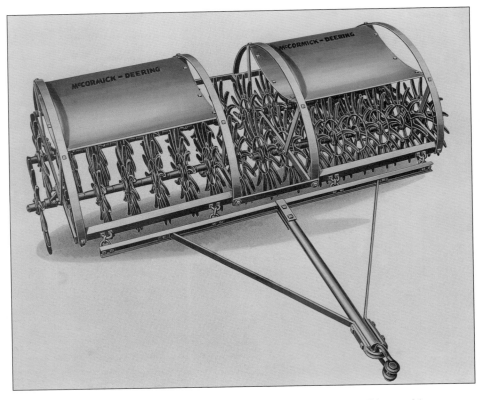

The McCormick-Deering No. 7 rotary hoe was an 84-inch wide, flexible machine designed for high-speed tractor operation. Concave pans were used to carry bags of dirt or sand to add weight for added penetration in hard soil. For transport, the units were turned over and dragged on the curved bands above the pans.

IH hitch-mounted rotary hoes got really big, up to 30 1/2 feet, with the 1981 introduction of the International 181. Exclusive IH design innovations included individually suspended hoe wheels for following contours and working beds; new Earth Metal hoe wheels of modular iron that were said to have twice the strength of ordinary wheels; and hoe wheels that turned on sealed ball bearings. Folding wing models and rigid frame models with optional endwise transport were offered.

The 4-row wide and 6-row narrow models of the hitch-mounted International 300 rotary hoe were transported on the tractor hitch as shown here. The 6-row wide and 8-row narrow were equipped with transport wheels for fast, safe endwise transport. A pair of pressure springs could add up to 250 pounds of down pressure to each gang.

Hay and Forage Harvesting
Mechanizing Ancient Drudgery

Harvest of that all-important crop of hay, plagued by weather uncertainty and untold hard physical work, is almost universally thought of as one of the nastiest jobs on the farm. Hay stored outdoors in small hay doodles or large stacks reduced the harvest time labor pressure compared to mow-cured hay but made up for it when animals stabled in a barn needed hay.

In the low rainfall areas of the West, mechanization of hay storage in loose stacks progressed from horse-powered sweep rakes and stackers to tractor-mounted sweep rakes and even old car chassis with permanently mounted sweep rakes. Eventually hydraulic powered, vertical compression stackers produced moderate size stacks for outside storage that could be power loaded on stack movers for transport. If not fed at or near the storage site, loose hay still needed to be baled if it was to be marketed as a commodity or transported great distances.

Forking hay from the windrow to the top of a moving hay wagon is a mean, physically demanding job. When the hay wagon got to the barn, a grapple-type hay fork transported large bunches into the top of the hay mow. Some unfortunate person got to "mow back" the hay from where the hay fork dropped it to where it needed to be. The loft of a barn at hay making time can seem like one of the hottest places on earth.

With the acquisition of Keystone Manufacturing Company of Rock Falls, Illinois, and the Osborne Company of Auburn, New York, IHC acquired a line of proven hay loaders. Different sizes and designs met the needs of a wide range of farming operations. Capacity was increased, pitching hay from the ground was eliminated but the one or two men on the wagon who forked the hay back from the loader discharge had a really hard, no-let-up job especially if the team hitched to the wagon were really stepping along or the tractor had a surging governor.

It takes about 800 cubic feet of space to hold one and a half tons of loose hay. That's not a very practical commodity to transport. Packaging hay, straw, or other material into denser units with a stationary baler made it practical to transport hay reasonable distances and significantly reduce storage space.

This McCormick-Deering No. 15 power baler was equipped with self-feeder and block setter attachments. The Farmall B tractor would have supplied adequate power since the standard engine attachment was the McCormick-Deering Model LB, rated at 5 horsepower.

Balers

International Harvester Company entered the stationary hay press (baler) market in 1907 with units powered with one horse; a two-horse unit followed a year later. Walking in a circle, the "horse power" from the hitch pole was transferred to a center post where the energy could be utilized by the press. The next logical step was to power the stationary hay press with one of the popular IHC single-cylinder engines mounted directly on the frame. Because of the reciprocating action of the press, large heavy flywheels were required to store energy for the plunger compression stroke. Some models provided relatively easy ways to use the engine for other jobs. As tractors with belt pulleys became more widely available, belt-powered hay presses became popular and had much greater capacity. Amazingly, the horse-powered press remained in the line for the better part of four decades.

The First Break in Hay Making Drudgery

The pickup baler changed hay making forever; no longer did the hay come to the baler — the baler could go to the hay. The IHC No. 15 pickup baler was a two wire, "low-cost baler for the smaller jobs" that made a 16- x 18-inch bale in the 40- to 85-pound class. Like its

Pickup Baler

Illust. 2.
The Pickup
Baler shown
in transport posi-
tion. For transport
the pickup attachment is
trailed behind the press and
in this manner the effective width
of the machine is reduced to 8 ft. 10 in.
Steel wheels are regular equipment.

The McCormick-Deering Type M, 3-wire pickup baler shown above was equipped with a 3-inch bore x 4-inch stroke, four-cylinder, 14 1/2-horsepower engine.

One Man Hay Baling

The automatic tie baler changed the labor requirement from three or four to only one — the tractor driver. The frustration of trying to outguess the weather, at least in the humid growing areas, was as much of a problem as ever, but the advent of one-man baling changed everything.

The McCormick-Deering No. 50-T self-feeding, self-tying automatic twine balers introduced in 1945, along with other industry twine balers, started the decline in baling wire use in most parts of the country. The day would come when Midwest farmers would buy rolls of soft iron wire to replace the piles of bailing wire that came in handy for so many little "jobs" around the farm. These were totally different machines from the No. 15 and Type "M." The new line of balers power fed hay into the bale chamber, inserted the twine between bales with long curved needles — the familiar wooden baler block was gone forever — and automatically tied a knot in the twine with much heavier knotters than the ones used on binders. Wire balers were still important where the commercial hay market required dense, heavy bales for economical shipment. The 50-W and later wire tie models met that need.

higher capacity companion the Model "M," both balers were essentially stationary balers mounted on wheels for towing through the field and equipped with a powered pickup apron. Three to four men were required to operate it: a driver for the tractor; a baler operator who stood on a platform behind the cross-deck and forked or regulated the flow of hay into the bale chamber; and one or two bale "tyers" [sic] who set the division blocks, inserted the bale wires, and did the tying. The larger Model "M" was unique in that it came in a conventional 14- x 18-inch bale chamber version and also an IHC exclusive 17- x 22-inch bale chamber, three-wire model. It was equipped with the McCormick-Deering exclusive two-section cross conveyor and gate. The conveyor eliminated the need for the operator to hand fork the hay into the bale chamber before each stroke. The manually operated gate stopped the outer section of the conveyor while the inner section continued to run and it created a break in the hay stream for inserting the block. Lots of hot, sweaty work, but not the back breaking demands of hand forking onto a hay wagon.

A Baler for the Family-Sized Farm

The low cost, PTO-driven, McCormick-Deering No. 45 baler was just right for the family-size farm. Later, an air-cooled engine drive version helped expand the market. The popular 14- x 18-inch bale chamber turned

This preproduction No. 55W was the replacement for the No. 50AW, automatic pickup, self-feeding, self-tying, wire tie hay baler.

The IH McCormick No. 45 PTO baler was perfect for the family farm.

out an easy to handle bale that typically weighed 50 to 70 pounds. Capable of baling 75 tons of hay or straw in two days, it was promoted as an effective answer to hiring the crop custom baled, "You and your tractor can do the job when the crop is ready." A wagon hitch for pulling a bale wagon directly behind the baler and a bale chute made it a two man operation from field to storage with no bales to be picked up behind the baler. Popularity of the No. 45 was attested to at Memphis Works by celebrating the 100,000th McCormick-Deering No. 45 produced.

A Baler for the Big Farmer, Market Hay Grower or Custom Operator

The big capacity engine drive, No. 55-T and No. 55-W balers had the IHC exclusive 15- x 19-inch bale chamber and could handle up to 12 tons per hour. Because of the wider bale size, ties were 5 1/2 inches from the edge of the bale. The bale size was promoted as requiring less twine or wire to bale the same amount of hay. The same "Sure-Tying" twine knotter was used on both the No. 45 and No. 55-T. The twister on the No. 55-W made firm wire twists close to the bale described as "looped, 4-wire, 3-turn twists that won't slip." Features included the power-driven pickup and McCormick hydraulic density regulator. Attachments available were a pickup gauge wheel, plunger and flywheel safety shield, dual wheels, and an automatic engine shut off when the baler was out of wire.

"A Totally New Baler"

The McCormick No. 46 baler was a significant change from the No. 45 it replaced and targeted the important 14- x 18-inch bale PTO drive twine tie market segment. By moving the flywheel and bevel-gear case to the left side of the bale chamber, the baler frame and pickup shifted to the right while maintaining a straight PTO drive line. This configuration provided greater clearance between the tractor's right tire and the windrow for more driving room. An extra-wide feed opening, three wide-sweep packer fingers, and other design changes resulted in extra capacity compared to the prior model. A rating of 10 tons per hour was claimed at introduction; later versions claimed 13 tons per hour. Advertising featured line drawings of the material path through the baler dubbed the, "Super hay-way through the No. 46." This was a fitting analogy since America was just learning to appreciate the interstate highway system.

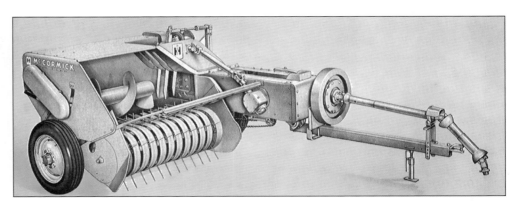

The "All-New" McCormick No. 46 twine tie baler shown here incorporated a long list of major and minor changes and improvements over the model it replaced.

IH Stockton Works at Stockton, California, designed and manufactured 17- x 22-inch bale chamber, three-wire baler for the commercial hay producing areas of the West. This field test scene of the No. 70 is from Tracy, California. The No. 60 decal was used to reduce competitor's curiosity.

Balers for the Desert

As the American farm machinery industry became aware of the special equipment needs of California, Arizona, and other areas of western irrigated agriculture, the major equipment firms established manufacturing facilities in the area. International Harvester responded by purchasing the Durr Manufacturing Company of Stockton, California, in 1937, and the facility became known as Stockton Works. The Durr Company reputation was based on a successful line of specialized, heavy-duty tillage tools and that continued under International Harvester ownership.

In the late '50s a joint program between Memphis Engineering and Stockton Engineering developed a heavy-duty baler for the irrigated hay producing areas of the West. This line of balers was based on a 17- x 22-inch bale chamber, three-wire, engine drive only design aimed at the predominate custom hay bailing market. The first model, the No. 60, was introduced in 1958. The No. 70 followed two years later. A model No. 71 that incorporated features of the Memphis-built No. 56, 15- x 19-inch, two-wire baler was introduced two years after the No. 70.

By 1964, plans were laid to develop a "West Coast" baler with a 16- x 23-inch bale chamber. This was the size the four major competitors had established as the standard. Fortunately, analysis of this very small market and the relative strength of the two major competitors resulted in a decision to end the project; this proved to be a sound business decision.

"Handle Your Hay Like Grain or Ear Corn"

Mechanization of American agriculture progressed at a rapid pace following World War II. However, following the development of the pickup baler and the bale thrower, post-harvest hay handling stubbornly refused to yield to further mechanization and labor reduction.

Research by the Agricultural Engineering Department at the University of Wisconsin demonstrated that when dry alfalfa hay was subjected to high pressure in confinement, natural bonding agents in the alfalfa would cause the leaves and stems to stick

Total hay handling and feeding mechanization was the goal of this IH experimental alfalfa hay wafer machine. The design was based on the 2 1/2-inch fiber length animal scientists said was required for optimum cattle performance. The project never went beyond the experimental stage.

together. Research with dairy cows indicated that in order for the rumen to function properly and avoid butter fat depression, some hay pieces needed to be 2 1/2-inches long. Based on that research information, International Harvester developed an experimental field-going machine for producing alfalfa hay wafers 2 1/2 inches in diameter. The wafers could be bulk stored, transported, and fed all by mechanical means. Enthusiasm for the project resulted in widely distributed photos of the experimental machine and the wafers it produced to farmers, dealers, and the press with the headline, "Push-Button Hay Handling Ahead." High horsepower requirement and low capacity associated with this reciprocating machine, along with other factors, resulted in recognition that the approach would not result in a commercial machine. In order to encourage further research on the problem of post-harvest mechanization of hay, International Harvester gave their experimental machine to the University of Wisconsin in 1960. Lundell Company manufactured and sold a small number of marginally functional "hay wafer" machines starting in 1961. The owner of Lundell attempted to interest IH in purchasing his machine on two occasions, fortunately without success.

The University of Wisconsin, other land grant universities, and other farm machinery companies continued to search for ways to solve the final hay mechanization challenge. Deere & Company developed a field-going machine for making 1 1/4-inch cubes in a continuous flow machine using a circular arrangement of square dies and an internal, roller press wheel. It was introduced in 1965. Advent of the machine opened a market for the export, primarily to Japan, of these dense, flowable, hay packages. Since hay in the windrow had to be in the 10 to 12% moisture range, the machines were only suited to the very dry, irrigated hay-producing areas of the Southwest and other scattered locations. The machines were expensive and slow with a high horsepower requirement. A stationary version was introduced three years after the field-going version, but the basic

limitations persisted. A limited number of machines were marketed over an 18-year period ending in 1983. In spite of the John Deere being the only viable machine in the marketplace, their cuber "was only a partial commercial success."

Introduction of the International Harvester No. 10 bale thrower reduced the peak harvest labor demand and made possible true one-man hay baling and storage. However, dragging randomly stacked bales out of a wagon onto an elevator or later out of a hay mow full of randomly stacked bales was not an easy task. The elusive goal of mechanized, post-harvest hay handling and feeding was yet to be achieved.

The White Demonstration Baler

Many small farms needed to bale hay; so, there was a universally recognized need for a reliable, low-cost baler. Memphis Engineering recognized that to cost reduce a current product without cost-saving design changes results in either minimum cost savings or a product that has lost performance and/or reliability. To achieve the cost target set for the McCormick International No. 27 economy baler, the auger and packer finger feeding system was replaced with a Shuttle-Glide feeding devise. This innovative system used an "aircraft quality" steel cable attached to the plunger that created an oscillating motion across the cross deck. Pivoted, plastic packer fingers suspended from the cable-powered carrier delivered hay to the

Dealers at this demonstration were given the features and benefits of the new No. 27 baler and told how to capitalize on customer interest generated by balers painted white.

bale chamber as they moved forward and folded up to glide over the incoming hay as they moved backward. Since the system was totally different from any other system on the market, farmers were naturally skeptical. The most effective way to deal with this situation was to demonstrate, demonstrate, demonstrate! To be sure the local dealer got the attention of his customer base, the first run of No. 27 balers was painted white and carried a bold demonstrator decal. Company promotion and dealer incentives completed the white No. 27 economy baler demonstration program. The white No. 27 got the attention of the customer and the new balers moved to retail.

All-Twine Knotters

The new International 400 All-Twine baler series introduced in 1970 included the model 420, 430, and 440 with the last two available in All-Twine or Loc-Twist versions. The big news was the All-Twine knotter. "Switch from sisal to plastic twine, from light duty to extra heavy twine, from small to large bales, from alfalfa to straw, from prairie hay to cane, the New All-Twine knotter will handle all of the variations without adjustment." Quite a feat!

The new All-Twine knotter had a cord holder assembly that consisted of three disks and was self-cleaning. The keeper blade assembly consisted of two spring-loaded blades. A split casting on the knotter

This International No. 440 baler was the largest in the 400 Series line that included the 430 and 420 balers. They introduced the "All-Twine" knotter that tied a bow-type, double-diameter knot and the "Lok-Twist" wire twister that made double-thick, 4-wire twists. Later this series became the No. 445, No. 435, and No. 425 rectangular bales in 1980 and 1981.

shaft permitted easy removal of the complete knotter head for service. The new knotter tied a bow-type, double-diameter knot that tested 17% stronger; that was the significant feature.

The Final Memphis Rectangular Balers

The Class I economy baler market was said to account for 45% of the total market. International Harvester participated in that important market segment with the No. 425 in 1981. It was similar to the

Two Tall Twine Tales

Tale number one. When plastic baler twine was ready to come on the market as a replacement for sisal twine, International Harvester and the IH twine mill were ready to tool up for the new product. However, there was concern that if a cow should eat some of the plastic twine — just as they eat sisal twine from time to time — there might be a serious health risk to the animal. To assure everyone about safety, samples of the International Harvester plastic twine were taken to the University of Wisconsin for evaluation. A length of plastic twine was cut into short pieces and placed in an open-mesh nylon bag. Research cows with fistulated rumens were used for the test. These cows had a surgically implanted window in their side that connected to an opening in the rumen. The nylon bag of plastic twine pieces was inserted into the rumen, with a tether so it wouldn't get away, and left for a number of days. Results: The cows showed no sign of health problems and the twine came out fine too.

Tale number two. When the International Harvester twine mill was preparing to produce plastic twine, the marketing department requested that this high quality IH twine be colored red so it could be differentiated from ordinary plastic twine. The first shipment of red plastic baler twine went to the commercial, three-tie area of California where bales are stored outdoors in large, neatly arranged stacks. Bales tied with IH red plastic twine photographed under the bright California sun were a most impressive sight . . . impressive until weeks later when the plastic twine on the outside bales began to break. A quick check of twine from the same lot proved tensile strength was not the problem. The beautiful red color was the culprit. The color soaked up the ultraviolet radiation from the California sun and caused the plastic twine to deteriorate rapidly. Plain looking plastic twine with a UV-inhibiting pigment was the answer. The result: A product long on quality but short on marketing appeal.

two high-capacity bales but had a more narrow pickup, shorter bale chamber, and top-only density control. The greatest difference was the old style Deering type knotters in place of the McCormick All-Twine knotter. The No. 435 twine and 445 twine or wire, higher-capacity balers rounded out the line in 1982.

High product cost for hay tools manufactured at Memphis was a long standing problem. Fierce price competition from hay tool firms with totally different manufacturing structure and labor cost kept profitability marginal at best. The final solution proved to be a manufacturing and marketing agreement with Avco New Idea of Coldwater, Ohio. In July 1982, Avco New Idea purchased the IH patents, designs, and tooling for mowers, mower-conditioners, and rectangular balers. Avco New Idea manufactured these products at Coldwater for IH to market through its 1,800 North American dealer organization. In addition, Avco New Idea produced IH red versions of the New Idea round balers and rakes for marketing by IH. The IH forage harvester product line stayed at Hamilton Works, Hamilton, Ontario, Canada.

Smaller Is Better/Larger Is Better

When Allis-Chalmers introduced their baler for making small round bales, it introduced a whole new way of thinking about post-harvest storage of baled hay — leave it in the field. Many farmers purchased AC balers because they thought it would reduce alfalfa leaf loss compared to conventional balers. They stored them much like rectangular bales even though they did not stack well. Missouri became the leading state for storing and feeding these small round bales in the field.

This IH experimental concept, mock-up, large round baler had the engineering code name, RB-7. The chain and bar design was not totally satisfactory; so, the program shifted to the belt system.

Introduction of the large round baler by the Vermeer Manufacturing Company of Pella, Iowa, introduced a different school of thought about round bales. Like the small AC round bale, the Vermeer bale could be stored outside; however, the large size of the bale — up to 1,600 pounds — made it an ideal package for mechanized, short range transport and even mechanized feeding (depackaging). Many hay producers were not easily convinced the large round bale was the right method for packaging and storing high quality hay. This was especially true of dairymen with high producing herds. Also, feeding was difficult in older style barns. The harvest speed and labor-saving benefits of the large round bale method, however, resulted in expanded use year after year.

Vermeer patents thoroughly covered the use of rubber belts in a variable chamber, large round baler. New Holland elected to avoid the patents by designing a large round baler that formed the bale with a system of chains and metal-tube cross slats. International Harvester engineering considered avoiding the patents by using a system of chains and curved round bars to form the bale. Careful analysis resulted in the IH decision to pay the royalty and use the more effective rubber belt system. Interestingly, New Holland went with the belt design in their replacement machine.

International Harvester introduced the 241 bigroll baler in 1974 with an impressive list of exclusive features: patented, slack belt starting; laced, full-width lower conveyor belt; individually replaceable upper belts; twine guide and position indicator; vertically adjustable hitch; rubber-mounted gear box; and a chain and sprocket driven pickup. Since the IH No. 241 made a soft center bale, it eliminated the hard core feeding problems and the hay cured better. The No. 241 made 60-inch wide bales that could be varied from 2 1/2 feet to a full 6 feet in diameter and weighing up to 1,500 pounds.

The International No. 11 bigroll bale carrier was a low-cost, two-prong, three-point hitch unit. The need to transport two or more big roll bales at one time was met with the International No. 30 and No. 50 bale movers.

Continued expansion of the large round bale market resulted in the 1979 introduction of the International No. 2400 variable chamber bigroll baler with a 72-inch wide pickup for making bales up to 6 feet in diameter.

The Big, Fragmented, Hay Equipment Market

Hay is big business and big companies like big markets. In 1977 the value of the North American hay and forage equipment business was estimated at $731 million and was expected to exceed $1 billion by

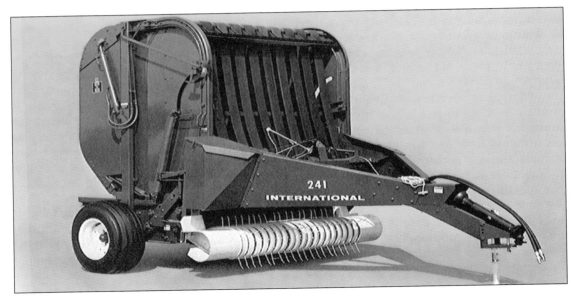

Round bales 60 inches wide and up to 6 feet in diameter could be quickly formed by this International 241 bigroll baler. Different diameters were possible because of the variable chamber design.

the mid-1980s. One third of those sales were for hay packaging equipment. The problem: The market was so fragmented and so impacted by regional requirements and preferences that reliable information for making sound business decisions was not readily available. To deal with this dilemma, Farm Equipment Division management established the 1977 Hay Packaging Task Force.

The Hay Packaging Task Force membership consisted of a Chairman and seven individuals with expertise in marketing, manufacturing engineering, finance, patent, and business research. All but the representative of the patent department was assigned full time to the task force. The eight task force members interviewed 353 individuals in 25 states in the United States and 6 Canadian provinces, including 28 major universities, and generated 24 man-weeks of travel over the four months of the study.

The task force identified 28 hay packaging innovative concepts. Eleven were related to conventional methods and 17 were non-conventional. The non-conventional methods were divided into fluent and non-fluent. Fluent concepts were those that could be bulk mechanized from field, to storage, to final use. Each of the concepts was assigned an alpha designation. Each concept was critically examined using the "Product Opportunity Evaluation"

method of systematic evaluation developed by Schrello Associates Inc.

Recommendations:
- Remain in the rectangular baler market with products currently under development.
- Remain in the large round baler market by developing positive start models in the 5- and 6-foot diameter classes.
- Conduct a concept and feasibility study of advances made in fluent packaging technology.
- Institute a concept and feasibility study of the 3- x 3- x 4 1/2-foot square baler and support products.
- Implement a research effort to determine the feasibility of Concept "S" protein extraction.

Concept "S"

When the new IH senior management team asked each of the divisions in 1978 to present their most

This International 3450 and companion No. 3650 expanded the IH large round baler line to include the fixed chamber design. These balers were manufactured for IH by White-New Idea, Coldwater, Ohio.

recent plan for innovative product development and supporting market analysis, none were prepared to respond except the Farm Equipment Division. They presented the Hay and Forage Packaging Task Force study and conclusions. Senior management was looking for a truly innovative, high technology project that had worldwide implications; Concept "S" was the answer. The prospect of harvesting alfalfa for weather independent haylage plus a high protein concentrate was intriguing and met management's criteria.

Research on leaf protein extraction conducted in England during World War II was aimed at developing a source of edible protein from green crops for human consumption in the event of a successful blockade of the island by the Axis Powers. Later, engineers and scientists in Hungary constructed a pilot plant that successfully extracted leaf protein for high quality poultry feed. In 1978 the French were in the process of building a large plant for protein extraction from alfalfa in conjunction with a dehydration plant. Research at the University of Wisconsin demonstrated that standing alfalfa could be macerated (the fiber converted to pulp and the plant cells ruptured) and the material put through a press that would express the green juice and deliver alfalfa fiber at the proper haylage moisture to go directly in the silo. High quality haylage in the silo without the field wilting risk and losses of conventional harvest offered a huge benefit. The green juice could be coagulated and protein separated for concentrated livestock feed or reprocessed into white protein for human food products. The leftover brown juice would be returned to the soil for its nutritive value.

Advanced Harvesting Systems

To achieve management's requirements, a special venture group named Advanced Harvesting Systems (AHS) was formed. They were given two objectives: First, establish a research facility separate from International Harvester operations and demonstrate how that independence can result in product development done well and done very quickly. Second, reduce the pilot plant research to a cost-effective, field-going harvester processor for IH manufacture.

The AHS operation was established in rented office facilities at Hillside and development was done under contract at Bridgeview; both locations are near Chicago suburbs. Within three months a group of five IH career managers had recruited most of the 33-member team of engineers, designers, field testers, three Ph.D. scientists, and support staff. Within 18 months, a field-going prototype demonstrated the principals of alfalfa leaf protein extraction, and animal studies demonstrated the economic benefits of the end products.

Objective one was accomplished: The AHS machine was developed and demonstrated in the field in a fraction of the time required under the traditional IH system.

Objective two, phase one, was accomplished: The AHS machine was a functional, field-going harvester processor. Phase two would have required massive capital investment in component design for IH manufacture; the financial condition of the Company at that time prohibited such a commitment. Furthermore, development of the infrastructure required to support a commercial market for leaf protein concentrate was recognized as a decade long commitment not suited to a farm equipment manufacturer.

Hay-In-A-Day . . . Well Almost

University research in important hay and dairy states demonstrated the importance of hay conditioners in reducing field drying time. International Harvester introduced the No. 1 hay conditioner in 1957 and followed with the No. 2 in 1959. Promotion of the machine was covered in a 20-page booklet titled, "How to Cut Curing Time and BOOST Feeding Value of Your Hay." The publication stressed the value of hay conditioning and the superiority of the IH design with both upper and lower rolls made of rubber with four spiral groves. The most significant design feature was power separation of the rolls when the machine was raised; this made it easy to clear the rolls if they became plugged. Alfalfa hay cut and conditioned around 11:00 AM on a typical good hay making day in the Midwest would usually be ready to bale the afternoon of the second day. Typically this saved a day of field drying time and significantly reduced the weather risk. It wasn't hay-in-a-day, but it was a great improvement.

It is extremely important to condition hay as soon as possible after cutting; for some producers this meant one tractor with a mower followed promptly by another tractor and hay conditioner. Next came semi-mounted mowers and trailing mowers with a PTO shaft on the back of the gear box so the mower and hay conditioner could be hitched together. On each round the hay cut the previous round was conditioned and it was a one man, one tractor operation. The next evolution was to combine the cutting operation and the conditioning operation into one machine. New Holland successfully accomplished this with their Haybine® which included a pickup reel; it was introduced in 1964 and established the industry term, mower-conditioner.

Mower-Conditioning the Economy Way

International Harvester Advanced Engineering had observed how the IH rubber hay conditioner rolls aggressively grabbed hay from the mowed swath and pulled it into the rolls. Based on this, they built an experimental mower-conditioner with the cutter bar positioned directly in front of the rubber to steel conditioning rolls; this eliminated the need for a reel. The machine was widely tested by both Advanced and Product Engineering; the results were favorable and the new No. 816 mower-conditioner was released to production in 7- and 9-foot versions for 1966.

In an effort to push the new mower-conditioner to the limit, it had been tested mostly in tall, high-yielding hay; it worked well. After it was in production and customers used it in both good and bad conditions, it was learned that without a reel its rolls would not grab short, sparse, or spotty material. To try and overcome this shortcoming, the regular flick-bar that pushed the top of the crop forward to aid in cutting was replaced with a power flick-bar equipped with rubber flaps or fingers. Unfortunately, this was not the solution and the lack of performance of the No. 816 mower-conditioner under varied conditions resulted in the Company buying back the machines that did not meet the customer's needs.

Mower Conditioners for the Major Markets

International Harvester entered the traditional mower conditioner market in 1970 with the No. 990 in 7- and 9-foot versions. Like the IH hay conditioners, it had conditioning rolls that separated when the header

AHS and the Malnourished Children

Developments resulting from the IH Advanced Harvesting System (AHS) leaf protein harvester project and its impact on continued research at the University of Wisconsin and other institutions have had a very encouraging outcome. Research studies in Mexico and several other countries have demonstrated that small quantities of leaf protein from green plants added directly to the protein deficient native diet of malnourished children can result in significant improvement in the children's health. To make this practical, small low-cost low-power macerator/presses have been developed that are suited to the needs of even very small, rural villages. Research projects that prove to be far ahead of their time for one application can sometimes have very useful near term results in other forms.

was raised; a great help if the rolls should plug. With the increased popularity of large round balers, there was an increased need for large windrows of hay. In the humid hay growing areas, windrow size is limited in order to speed drying; the windrow placement attachment for the 990 mower-conditioner met both requirements. Power-activated windrow shields could position the windrow to the right or to the left. The side-by-side windrows would dry properly and still be in position for raking together with very little leaf-loosing movement.

Formation of large windrows was made even easier with the introduction of the tractor front-mounted No. 8 placement rake. Teamed with the No. 990

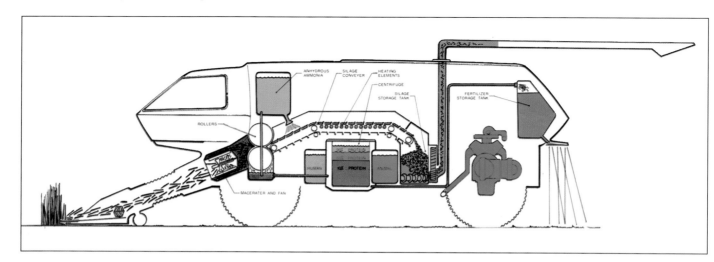

This cross-section art rendering of a self-propelled, field-going alfalfa leaf protein harvester looks like nothing more than futuristic daydreaming. Actually, the processes illustrated here were reduced to practice in a field-going prototype by the International Harvester Advanced Harvesting Systems Group in 1981. Economic restraints kept this project from advancing to the next stage.

The McCormick International 816 mower-conditioner pictured here represented a simple, economical method of mowing and conditioning hay. The No. 816 and Power Flick-Bar performed well in many, but not all, field and crop conditions. This limitation made it necessary to replace it with the traditional design No. 990 mower conditioner.

windrow placement attachment, it eliminated a separate raking operation.

In areas where larger windrows were needed, the International No. 1290 mower-conditioner was the high capacity answer with its 12-foot cut. The exclusive IH dual auger platform — proven in the IH self-propelled windrower line — gently delivered hay to the offset, 6-foot long combination steel and laminated rubber conditioning rolls. This No. 1290 exclusive kept the tractor tires off of the previously cut windrow. Transport width of this wide machine was reduced to less than 9 feet by means of the exclusive end transport hitch.

In 1979 the No. 990 mower-conditioner was replaced with a totally different No. 1190 machine in 7- and 9-foot sizes. The advanced-design frame-over configuration made possible three-point, cross-linked suspension for header lateral and vertical float that provided unmatched, uniform-cutting ability even in rolling land. The new design also made it easy to hydraulically shift the No. 1190 from working to transport position. A different hydraulic approach was used for quickly changing large grain and hay swathers from field to transport and back to field operation.

It Started with the Reaper

Cyrus Hall McCormick could not create a satisfactory reaper until he had an effective way of mechanically cutting the standing grain. Naturally,

The International 1190 mower conditioner, shown here, and the previous No. 990 both incorporated the IH patented system that automatically separated the full-width conditioning rolls when the header was raised. That feature allowed the operator to power clear slugs without leaving the tractor seat.

This International 1590 mower conditioner incorporated the center-pivot drawbar design. This feature made it possible for the operator to hydraulically move the machine from right hand cut to left hand cut to center transport position without leaving the tractor seat.

When machines became extremely large like this International swather, engineering must meet the challenge of end of field turning and appropriate transport width; this demonstration shows they succeeded.

improvements in the cutting means for reapers, and later in binders, would lead to parallel improvement in mowers.

Horse-drawn No. 9, Zerol-Gear mowers were shown in the IHC 1946 Farm Operating Equipment, General Sales Catalog. Zerol bevel and pinion gears were described as, "high-grade, precision-machined, steel gears with teeth slightly curved and arranged at a slight angle . . . the most efficient bevel gears ever used in a horse-drawn mower!"

The No. 9 was basically a horse-drawn machine, but it could be ordered with a stub tongue hitch for use behind a tractor. A special lift attachment, rope controlled from the tractor seat, was available. To be really modern, it could be equipped with special pneumatic-tired wheels. Reminders of this mower's long and varied history come from the attachment list: A reaping attachment including an extra seat over the right wheel for the operator who rakes the crop onto the platform and retains it until a gavel of the right size is secured, then dumps it on the ground; a driver-controlled buncher for very short hay or special seed crops; a tongue truck to prevent tongue "whipping;" and thrills for a one-horse hitch.

Pulling a single horse-drawn mower with the extra power of a tractor was very inefficient. The Company, along with farmers, created ways of hitching two or more horse-drawn mowers together in an effort to use the new power source more effectively. The advent of the PTO made the tractor-mounted mower a practical, convenient, and

cost-effective machine; attaching and removing these early mounted mowers was another matter.

Cutting square corners while hardly slowing was one of the major features of rear-mounted tractor mowers. This was a major feature even if the mower was equipped with a manual lift. Advent of hydraulic lift for ease of operation and rubber-tired tractors for speed and comfort represented major advancements in hay harvest mechanization.

This fully-mounted PTO sickle-bar mower and McCormick Deering Farmall F-12 tractor was parked in the McCormick Works yard in 1933.

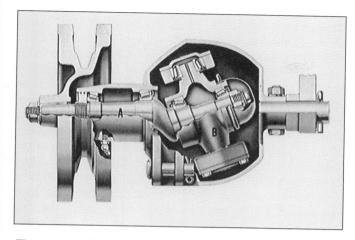

The exclusive International wrist-action drive for IH pitman-less sickle-bar machines found application in many IH products.

Pitmanless Cutterbar Drive

For over a century, mower cutterbars were pitman driven; vibration and high maintenance were accepted facts of life. Then a series of pitmanless designs appeared on the scene. Balanced-head cutterbar drives developed by International Harvester employed a wrist-action design that "converted the flywheel rotary motion to reciprocating motion without the use of a pitman, connecting bars, or gears." This smooth, quiet-running drive remained parallel with the knife regardless of the cutterbar position. This feature was a significant plus when mowing banks along roadsides. The wrist-action, balanced-head drive had only three moving parts that employed six precision tapered bearings. This excellent cutterbar drive had only one drawback — manufacturing cost.

Balanced-head cutterbar drive advantages resulted in their incorporation in a family of International balanced-head mowers that included these models: No. 1000 semi-mounted; No. 1100 trailing; No. 1200 fast-hitch; and No. 1300, 3-point. All were available with 7- or 9-foot cutterbar lengths and optional drive parts for use with hay conditioners. The International No. 1110 side-mounted, balanced-head mower offered PTO or hydraulic drive in a mid-mounted tractor mower ideally suited to highway mowing applications. Any of the 5-, 6-, 7-, or 9-foot cutterbars would operate from vertical to 45 degrees below horizontal. These outstanding mowers would, with minimal change, stay in the product line for decades. Only the rotary disk mower and its outstanding performance in adverse field and crop conditions would challenge the leadership of the balanced-head family of mowers.

This International 484 tractor and category I, three-point hitch were well matched to the International 1300 rear-mounted mower. The IH-built, 3-cylinder, diesel engine rated at 42.4 PTO horsepower could easily handle either the 7- or 9-foot cutter bar.

The International 1100, trailing-type, sickle-bar mower is shown with an International 584, 52.5-PTO horsepower tractor. This series included the No. 1300 rear-mounted and the 1000 semi-mounted mowers in 7- and 9-foot sizes. All models had IH wrist-action, balanced head drives.

A Problem Turned into a Benefit

Pitman drive mowers have lots of vibration; that's bad. Balanced-head mowers have minimal vibration; that's good — well, almost.

The "revolutionary" International No. 200 mower achieved the best of both worlds with a cost-effective design. The IH-patented pendulum (a free-swinging, rubber-mounted, modular iron block) put the vibration to work in the knife and the slab, while taking it out of the mower frame. Promotion materials stated that, "because of cutter bar motion, even the heaviest grasses and legumes fall away quickly and cleanly to assure non-plug moving." Multiple exposure action photos illustrated how the design isolated pitman vibration from the No. 200 semi-mounted mower. Lower cost was an additional advantage.

A Rake for Every Application

Dump rakes date from the earliest efforts to improve the arduous task of harvesting hay. This very simple basic tool, the McCormick International No. 2 dump rake, still rated a page in the 1964 Farm Equipment Reference Catalog. However, only the tractor version was available and included a rope-controlled trip mechanism for dumping from the tractor seat. Ruggedness was attested to with the statement, "Rake has mountain-type steel wheels on roller bearings."

The Keystone, wood frame, parallel bar (2-bar) rake was introduced in 1893. Raking continuously around the field or from one end to the other was a great improvement over the dump rake method and popularity of side-delivery rakes progressed steadily. Side-delivery rakes that could also be used as tedders to lift and fluff hay and speed drying, or hopefully reduce problems caused by an unexpected rain, delivered an extra benefit. Initially, rakes marketed by IHC were produced by firms they had acquired and for some time carried the name of the manufacturer. Machines that worked much like the hand operations they replaced were considered by some to be preferred by farmers. The International Harvester Company produced a gearless side-delivery rake that used four oscillating, pitch fork like elements to move the hay swath into a windrow; it definitely fit the description. Another product that fit the description was the single purpose hay tedders that used crank-operated, miniature, two-tine pitch forks to ted the hay. McCormick tedders with six or eight forks were available as early as 1894.

Speed and gentle action are both critical elements in turning a standing crop into quality hay. The 4-bar side-delivery rake did a good job of building windrows with minimal leaf loss if the timing was right. Equipping the rake with rubber tires and pulling it with a tractor could significantly reduce the raking time. The tractor side-delivery rake rated two full pages in the 1946 General Sales Catalog. Interestingly, a horse-hitch attachment with seat and spring was still available under Special Equipment along with steel wheel extension rims, supplemental caster wheels, and pneumatic-tired wheels. A cut-away graphic of the ball-bearing eccentric promoted that feature.

Pictured here is the McCormick-Deering tractor side-delivery rake pulled by a McCormick Farmall A tractor working on the Cleary Farm near Hinsdale, Illinois. "This machine is not a modified horse-drawn side rake. It is especially designed and built for use with tractors," stated the 1946 literature. The enclosed gear drive, 4-bar reel rake is shown equipped with optional pneumatic-tired 44-inch diameter main drive wheels and 17-inch diameter rear caster wheels. The second caster wheel was an option.

IH Exclusive "Minimum Raking Angle" (MRA) Rake

The International No. 14 and No. 16 ground drive MRA rakes were a complete departure from the design of the traditional side-delivery rakes. The 20-degree angle of the basket built windrows with less hay movement. These were tractor rakes; seat and horse-hitch attachments were no longer available.

By 1965, IH made available the McCormick International No. 9 side-delivery rake for coupling directly to three-point hitch tractors. A simple belt drive from the PTO contributed to a lightweight, economy priced rake. For many owners, the raise-the-hitch-and-go feature for transport was one of its greatest benefits.

The basic elements of the parallel bar, tractor side-delivery rake of the early '60s changed little in the following decades; however, many useful improvements were incorporated: offset wheels, optional fifth bar, rubber-mounted teeth and higher tooth counts, along with a hydraulic drive option in place of ground drive. The need for large windrows resulted in right and left hand rakes working in pairs to produce double windrows in a single pass.

A novel innovation in hay rakes was the wheel rake developed and patented by Farmhand. The design was well suited to the light stands of grass and prairie hay typically grown in their key market area. A seven-wheel

Large round balers require large windrows of hay. International No. 96 and No. 97 right hand and left hand rakes with dual hitch shown in the photo with an International Hydro 84 tractor were a high capacity answer to the requirement.

machine covered 11 feet, and since the machine performed well at high speeds, large acreages could be raked quickly. Teeth on the independently-mounted, 48-inch diameter wheels turned them at ground speed; no driving elements were needed.

Corn Silage Makes More Profit . . . Corn Silage Makes More Work

No one disputed the benefits of feeding corn silage. Likewise, no one looked forward to the days of the extremely hard work it took to fill even a modest size silo using a ground-drive or power-drive corn binder in the field and an ensilage cutter blower at the silo. Machines like the International Harvester No. 2 ensilage harvester changed all of that.

Gone was the drudgery of lifting and handling heavy green corn bundles (usually around 10 to 15 tons per acre). Gone was the expense of twine for the bundles and the job of keeping the knotter doing its job. Gone was the slow filling process that frequently reduced the feed value. Development of reliable, high capacity ensilage harvesters (forage harvesters), along with trouble free self-unloading wagons and high capacity blowers, brought about a major increase in silage use in livestock rations.

The losses associated with field curing of hay led to serious interest in grass and legume silage. A 1939 *Harvester World* article proclaimed "A Revolution in the Hayfield," and discussed in detail the steps required in the operation. McCormick-Deering green-crop loaders designed to handle the heavy, green material were the featured piece of equipment. Silo filling with hay chopper-blowers designed for high moisture grass and legume crops was recommended. The importance of adding molasses or other preservatives was stressed. Unfortunately, even with careful management, ensiling at these high moisture contents did not always result in quality feed from the silo.

The International 30 basic 7-wheel rake shown here could be converted to an 8- or 9-wheel rake by adding front and/or rear wheel extensions. In a like manner, the basic 5-wheel rake could be converted to a 6- or 7-wheel rake.

The original McCormick-Deering No. 2 ensilage harvester was designed to keep the horsepower requirement low to match the popular 2- and 3-plow tractors. To accomplish this objective, material was moved from the 14 1/4-inch wide, four spiral knife cutter head to the pulled wagon by a totally enclosed chain and half-round flight conveyor. A small thrower was located at the top of the elevator. The later version shown here used a small blower for moving chopped material to the truck or wagon.

The revolution did not stop here; three important events brought about major expansion in grass and legume silage. First, research demonstrated that legumes field wilted to between 40% and 60% moisture range would produce high quality feed if fine chopped and stored in a tight silo capped with a layer of wet, heavy crop to exclude air. With careful attention, no preservative was required. Second, forage harvester and handling equipment improvements made high capacity harvest of wilted grass and legume silage (now universally called "haylage") into a smooth, flowing system. Third, the A. O. Smith Company introduced a glass-lined, bottom unloading, oxygen-free storage structure — the Harvestore. This "Blue Bottle" was widely marketed for haylage, high moisture shelled corn, and other crops. The new Harvestore silos were expensive, but they made it easier to make high quality haylage; they offered push button feeding.

The bottom unloading feature of the Harvestore required that haylage be cut very short and be free of long material. To meet this criteria, one less-than-full-line farm equipment manufacturer released a forage harvester with a screen underneath the cutter head that held back material and reduced particle size by recutting. The design met the requirements of the Harvestore but required a large increase in horsepower.

International Harvester had two sizes of cylinder-type forage harvesters that relied on the energy from the cylinder to blow the cut material to the wagon. These machines did an excellent job in corn and when set for the 7/64-inch fine cut would put out a good haylage product for well managed conventional silos. However, the Harvestore unloading problems and the perception that a screen was required for haylage persisted. Incorporating a screen into the IH forage harvester required a major redesign of the basic forage harvester. As other companies responded to the call for machines with recutter screens, IH initiated a development program that resulted in the No. 650, pull-type forage harvester with recutter screen in 1972. Introduction of the IH No. 780 and 880 forage harvesters with 12-knife cutter heads provided machines that produced uniform short cutting without the need for capacity robbing recutter screens.

Blowers That Go with the Flow

Ensilage cutter/blowers had tables that delivered the crop at right angles to the blower disk. When single purpose blowers were developed, they had the crop enter at right angles to the blower disk. As silos got larger and taller the blower got larger and used more horsepower, but the material still entered at right angles to the blower disk.

A very astute engineer at the Hinsdale Engineering Center observed that the current designs applied energy for moving material from the hopper to the blower disk, but when that material made a 90% turn into the blower, all of that energy was lost. As a result, he developed the International No. 56 blower to incorporate an exclusive 45% auger feeding system that

This Hinsdale photo of a preproduction green hay chopper is another example of the continued effort to design machines to match low horsepower tractors. The direct-cut machine used an elevator to deliver chopped material to the wagon rather than use a power consuming blower.

This illustration from a 1957 sales bulletin shows the flywheel-type cutter head No. 36 field harvester. The wheel was regularly equipped with six knives for cutting and three wings for blowing; three extra wings could be added for abnormal conditions. It could be equipped with cutter bar, row-crop, or pickup units.

The International 881 forage harvester in the photo had a 1,000 rpm PTO for tractors up to 190 horsepower. The 12-knife cutter head delivered uniform cutting without using screens. Electric remote controls changed spout direction, angle of discharge, or controlled the feed elements. Two-row wide or narrow or 3-row narrow Quick-Attach crop units were available. The forage box is an IH No. 130.

added some of the feeding energy to the capacity of the blower. The unmatched capacity, efficiency and convenience of the new blower set the industry standard. Demand for even more capacity resulted in the 60-inch diameter No. 600 blower with a 12-inch, 30% entry feed auger and rotating back sheet. The new blower had capacity of 180-tons per hour into 100-foot high silos; that level of performance set the standard for 1982.

IH replaced the flywheel design forage harvesters with 16- and 20-inch wide, 9-knife cut and throw cutter head No. 15, No. 16, and No. 50 forage harvesters. The No. 650 was the first IH forage harvester that could be equipped with a recutter screen. The No. 550 was a cut and throw version of the No. 650.

The International 56 forage blower, shown here, introduced the IH exclusive 45% angle feed auger that significantly increased the capacity of the 56-inch diameter rotor. The even higher capacity International 600 forage blower was introduced in 1982. It had a 60-inch diameter rotor with rotating backsheet and 12-inch, 30% angle feed auger.

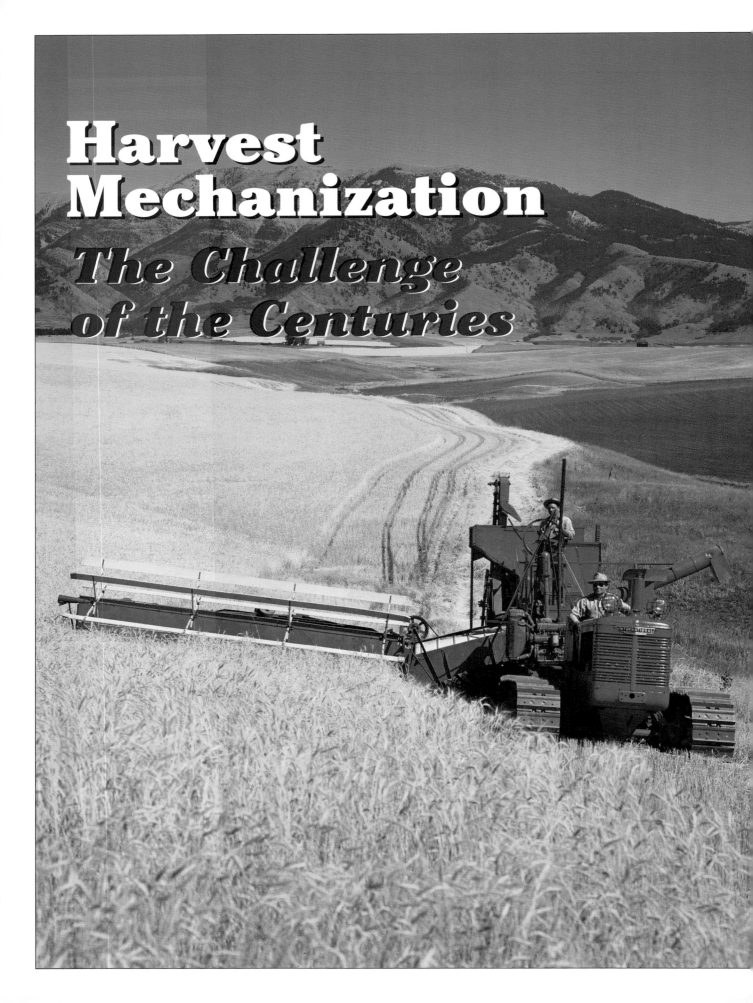

Harvest Mechanization
The Challenge of the Centuries

The drudgery of grain harvest plagued civilization from the dawn of agriculture. Improved hand tools and the eventual utilization of animal power eased the demand for manual labor. Significant mechanization was not achieved, however, until reapers and thresher/cleaners were developed into practical machines suited to farms and farmers of the 19th century. Early chapters in this book address the role Cyrus Hall McCormick and his company played in grain reaping mechanization. This chapter covers the International Harvester Company's entry into the stationary thresher business and evolution into the manufacture and sale of harvester threshers which were later called combines.

Development and marketing of the innovative Axial-Flow combine is a subject that deserves thorough coverage. That fascinating story is covered in the next chapter titled "IH Axial-Flow Combines — The Long Road to Success."

Stationary Threshers

IHC Marketing Arrangements for Stationary Threshers

All of the firms that joined to form the International Harvester Company manufactured various designs of reapers, but none of them produced stationary or portable threshing machines. It became obvious that reapers and threshing machines should be marketed together. Rather than purchase a threshing machine company or design and build their own product, IHC decided to sell proven threshers from established manufacturers.

The first threshing machine line acquired for marketing was Belle City; these products were manufactured in Racine, Wisconsin. Starting in 1907, the Belle City thresher was produced in 24- x 24-, 32- x 32-, and 40- x 40-inch sizes. During the next two years, 24- x 32-, 32- x 40-, and 16- x 24-inch sizes were added and the 40- x 40-inch model was discontinued. The first number is the cylinder width and the second number is the separator and cleaner width.

In 1910, Belle City manufactured, and IHC marketed, the New Racine thresher. Over the next three years, five models of New Racine threshers were introduced including the 36- x 56-inch model, the largest machine in the line.

The New Racine Jr., 20- x 32-inch model, introduced in 1914, had a wood frame and galvanized iron sides. An IHC sales booklet rated the New Racine Jr. at 30 to 60 bushels of wheat or 70 to 120 bushels of oats per hour, depending on conditions. This smaller thresher could be mounted on its own wheels, or truck, or a special long truck, and powered by an IHC 8 H.P. Titan oil engine.

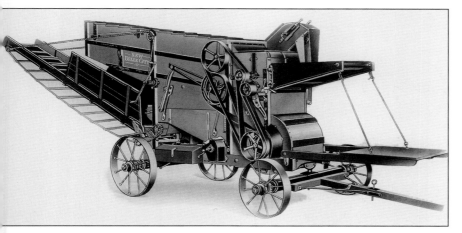

International Harvester marketed the New Belle City thresher . This model was available in three sizes: 16 x 24, 24 x 24, and 24 x 32 inch. The first number is the cylinder width and the second number is the cleaner width. This model is equipped with a hand feeder and a plain stacker. The low head of the tailings return elevator and the folding top at the rear of the separator made the machine low enough to be "Conveniently Operated in Any Ordinary Barn."

Purchase of a new threshing machine and a new traction engine was always a major event and many times rated a photograph. Photographs were uncommon enough to make getting yourself included in the photo rather important and a really grown-up event for a youngster. This scene, possibly a delivery, was included in an IHC sales booklet for New Racine Threshers. We have no way of knowing, maybe the photo records that special day when the threshing machine arrived and soon the friends and neighbors would gather to provide labor for the big event.

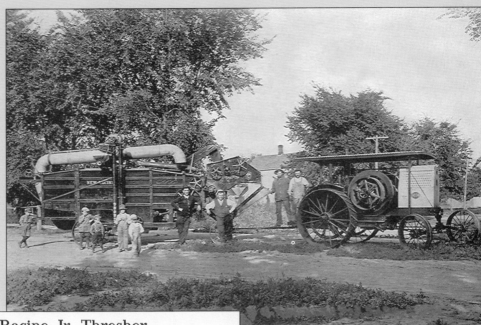

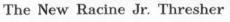

The New Racine Jr. Thresher

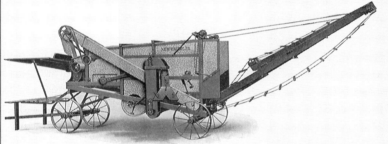

To meet the needs of the smaller farmer, IHC marketed the New Racine Jr. thresher manufactured by Belle City of Racine, Wisconsin. The hand-fed little 20- x 32-inch thresher is equipped here with a short clean grain elevator for bagging grain at ground level. A long clean grain elevator with swing spout was available for bulk loading wagons. The very long, plain rake stacker is folded for transport.

Clearly lettered on the sides of this New Racine thresher are the words, "Manufactured for International Harvester Co. of America." This 24- x 40-inch thresher was the smallest machine in the standard, full feature line. Shown here with the power feeder folded and the wind stacker pipe in its cradle, the machine was ready for transport.

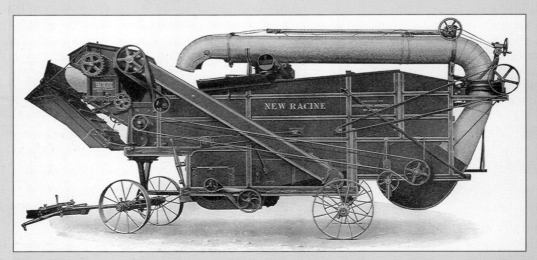

In the hands of a skilled operator, the wind stacker controls and power oscillator made it easy to build a uniform, well-shaped straw stack that would stand up to both wind and rain. If the stack later turned green with sprouted grain, the farmer and the neighborhood knew the thresherman had done a poor job.

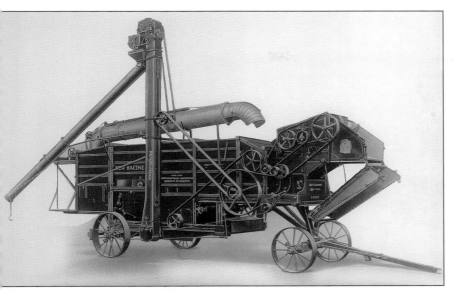

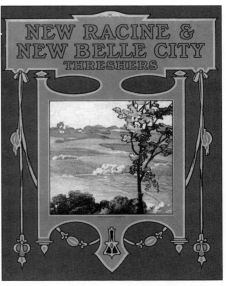

This graphic from a 1915 sales booklet shows one of three big models of New Racine threshers equipped with power feeder with knives for cutting the twine on the sheaves of grain before they entered the cylinder. The Perfection bucket elevator and weigher discharged grain high enough to load wagons on either side. Weighers not only told the farmer how much grain he had but provided the thresherman with accurate information for charging for his work or for accurately charging each members of the threshing ring.

IHC gained prompt entry into the threshing machine business by marketing the New Racine and New Belle City threshers as well as machines from other manufacturers. These machines were sold under the manufacturer's brand names.

Addition of the Sterling Model 21, 21 1/2, 26, and 30 in 1909 gave IHC four smaller, lighter weight threshers with cylinder and separator widths, respectively, of 21 x 28, 21 x 33, 26 x 33, and 30 x 37 inches. Since the cylinder width was used to denote the model number, the 21- x 33-inch machine had to be named the Model 21 1/2 to distinguish it from the smaller Model 21. A major feature for IHC was the long truck combination version that mounted the thresher and an IHC engine on the same chassis equipped with a fifth-wheel steer truck, or running gear, for easy transport. Engines like the Titan 4-, 6-, or 8-H.P. hopper-cooled oil engines were the power sources. Advertising promoted the system as, "A Combination Outfit of Great Practical Value — With the Thresher dismounted, the engine can be hauled around on the truck to various jobs whenever the occasion arises. It is an easy matter to adjust the truck so that a feed grinder, corn sheller, or sawing outfit can be mounted or belted to the engine in place of the thresher."

These compact, economical, light running machines were ideal barn threshers, especially in the skidded version. The 30- x 37-inch model Number 30 was the largest of four Sterling models, but it was available in a very basic, skidded version that was ideal for barn threshing. Clean grain from the half-round grain spout had to be caught in a bucket or scooped from the barn floor; tailings had to be caught in a bucket under a small, square spout and hand fed to the cylinder; economical simplicity made the Sterling ideal for small farms. More affluent purchasers could add a floor height bagger and/or a tailings return elevator.

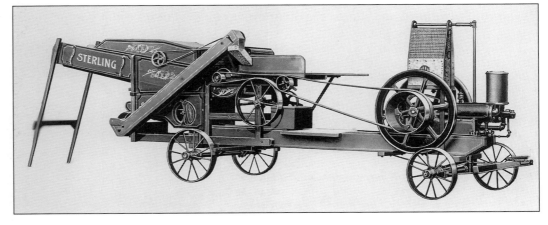

This Sterling thresher and IHC gasoline engine is shown on a combination transport truck.

Selling the Buffalo Pitts thresher made in Buffalo, New York, gave IHC a second line of high-capacity threshers and an ideal source the eastern market. Advertising booklets said, "sold by International Harvester Company of America" but, graphics of the full size machines carried no IHC identification. The Pitts Company manufactured their own weigher and cross conveyor which is in the fol position on the back side of the machine. They also produced their own steel feeder which is shown here in the transport position.

The next addition to the IHC line of threshers was the Buffalo Pitts manufactured in Buffalo, New York. These steel frame, wood sided threshers came in sizes as large as 41-inch cylinders with 62-inch rear separators. Now the International Harvester Company could offer the latest in high-capacity threshers suited to the plains states and areas where large threshing rings were popular. Threshing rings were associations where a number of farmers would work together cooperatively to share the work of binding and shocking the grain and also the threshing. In some threshing rings, one man would own the threshing machine and steam engine or stationary traction engine or tractor with belt pulley and charge each member for the amount of grain threshed. In other threshing rings, the group purchased the equipment and shared the other expenses.

In 1926 the Company introduced an all-steel thresher manufactured at its own facility. During the 1934 to 1940 period, IHC built 22- x 38-inch and 28- x 46-inch size threshers at East Moline Works. A 35 1/2-inch cylinder thresher was introduced in 1942. Low demand for threshing machines resulted in production ending in 1946. The rapid growth in self-propelled and small pull-type combine sales after the end of World War I had signaled the coming end of thresher production. Many areas of the country kept the thresher inventory in use long after new machine production ended. Today we can go to a thresheree and see and hear these fascinating big machines chew up sheaves of grain, spit out straw in beautiful golden stacks, perhaps get some chaff down our neck and listen to the click of a weigher bucket count out the bushels of shining grain.

This interior view of Buffalo Pitts Niagara second steel frame thresher clearly shows how threshers of the period were designed with cylinder widths substantially less than the separator. The two sets of straw racks do not seem aggressive enough by today's standards. It is interesting to note that the front rack moved at 70 feet per minute while the rear rack moved at 90 feet per minute. Advertising copy stressed, "that all bearings are attached to the steel frame and none of the working mechanism is attached to the wooden sides." The company manufactured a full line with five sizes from 30-inch cylinder and 50-inch rear to an impressive 41-inch cylinder and 62-inch rear in the Niagara II steel frame line and three sizes each of rice threshers and hard wheat special threshers.

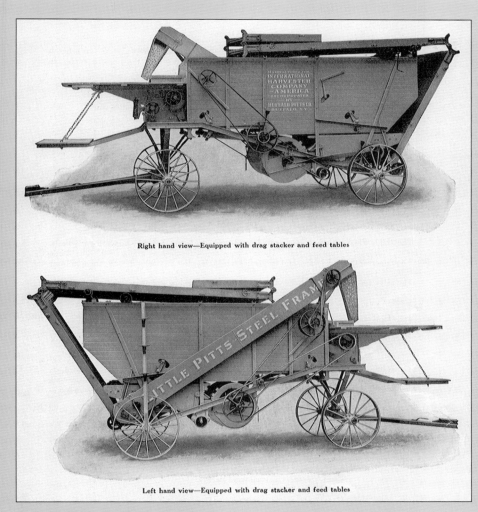

The bold lettering on the "Little Pitts" steel frame thresher made it clear who made the product and who sold it. For 1914 this little machine was available only in the 28-inch cylinder and 48-inch rear size. This simple machine with drag stacker for the straw and plain feed table for feeding sheaves to the cylinder was a totally different design than the other threshers in the Pitts line.

Right hand view—Equipped with drag stacker and feed tables

Left hand view—Equipped with drag stacker and feed tables

This is an example of threshing on the Chas. Schmidt Farm, Crown Point, Indiana, in August 1923. After years of selling threshers made by other companies, IHC entered the market with the McCormick-Deering thresher built in their own facilities. Fifteen years after this photo was taken, you could add the senior author to a scene like this at a location in Eastern Indiana carrying cool spring water to a thirsty threshing ring crew.

Farmall H and M tractors powered many kinds of farm machines including the rubber tire equipped McCormick-Deering all-steel thresher in this 1940 scene. This photo was used on the cover of a 32-page advertising booklet covering the McCormick-Deering thresher line.

Harvester-Threshers to Combines

The First Successful Machine

Credit for development of the first workable harvester-thresher for cutting the standing grain, threshing the grain from the straw, and separating and cleaning the grain in a single operation as it passed through the field belongs to Hiram Moore of Kalamazoo, Michigan. He built the first machine in 1834 and it was patented in 1836; this places his development in the same decade as the Cyrus Hall McCormick reaper. John Hascall's name appeared on the patents, but Hiram Moore was the inventor who reduced the idea to practice. Moore's machine was large and expensive and the ground drive required 14 to 16 horses to pull the machine. In addition, the harvest weather in Michigan was usually too wet to allow standing grain to dry down to safe moisture levels for storage. When a Moore Hascall machine was shipped to California for the 1854 harvest, it performed well in the large fields and dry harvest conditions. The machine laid the basis on which several California innovators developed large harvester-threshers suited to the dry western climate. Utilization of steam traction engines and later

gasoline engines led to expanded use of harvester-threshers in the West, but they continued to be large, expensive machines.

The Prairie-Type Harvester-Threshers

The needs of farmers on smaller acreage prairie farms were met with the advent of lighter, simpler, less expensive harvester-threshers; they were collectively called "prairie-type." The International Harvester Company developed experimental pull-type and push-type harvester-threshers of the prairie-type at McCormick Works as early as 1913. Neither of these ground driven machines went into production. Experimental work at Deering Works at the same time led to the Deering No. 1, ground drive, harvester-thresher built in 1915. This 9-foot cut machine "employed a side shake to the riddles" that was not used in the models that followed. The Deering No. 2

This aging 1913 photo is a record of one of the first experimental ground driven, pull-type harvester-threshers developed at McCormick Works. The machine never went into production.

Equipped with a 4-cylinder International Harvester type F engine, the Deering No. 2 harvester-thresher of 1919 could deliver performance far superior to strictly ground drive machines.

and No. 3 as well as the McCormick No. 2 and No. 6 were similar designs.

The McCormick-Deering No. 4 produced from 1924 to 1926 and the McCormick-Deering No. 5 produced only in 1925 were transition machines that introduced design features that would be incorporated in the Company's future harvester-threshers. Expanded use of engine drive in place of ground drive significantly improved performance whether pulled by horses or tractors.

The McCormick-Deering No. 7 hillside harvester-thresher provided a leveling system for uniform cleaning and separating when working in the hills of the Pacific Northwest and North Africa. The standard 12-foot floating platform could be increased to 16 feet

The McCormick-Deering No. 3 harvester-thresher shown in the factory yard went into production in 1924. This and all future harvester-threshers intended for domestic sale carried the McCormick-Deering trade name. In addition to engine drive and a 12-foot cutting platform, this machine was equipped with an auger tube, wagon loader. Like its predecessors, the No. 3 could be pulled with a tractor or with horses. This same photo, with the background removed, was used for a 17- x 22-inch poster.

A lot of "horse power" was required to operate this early McCormick ground drive harvester-thresher. It was not necessary for the horses to pull large quantities of harvested grain through the field because clean grain was immediately bagged and the full bags dropped to the ground singularly or in groups of two or three. Bagged grain was later loaded on wagons, or occasionally a truck, to be hauled to a farm storage bin or to market.

This McCormick-Deering No. 7 harvester-thresher has a promotion slogan on the rear panel that aptly describes this new harvesting method, "Once Over and its All Over." Note the frame for a sun shade and the high front and center location of the bagging platform.

To provide flexibility for owners of McCormick-Deering harvester-threshers, feeder and straw stacking conveyor attachments were available so the machine could be used as a stationary thresher. The McCormick-Deering No. 8 harvester-thresher in this 1927 photo is equipped with a straw stacking conveyor.

with an optional extension. Other features included a counterbalanced cleaning shoe, recleaner sieves, straw raddles, and a recleaner. The machine had two cleaning fans, one for the shoe and one for the recleaner. This successful product was built from 1925 to 1930.

The PTO "Power Drive" Harvesters

The McCormick-Deering No. 8 harvester-thresher was originally designed to use power from the tractor power take-off. It eliminated an engine to drive the harvester-thresher, provided controls within easy reach of the tractor operator, and included a self-unloading grain tank with leveling auger. The No. 8 harvester-

thresher was a true, one-man machine that suited the smaller farms of the central, eastern, and southeastern states.

The later engine drive version of the No. 8 located the engine parallel to the center line of the machine rather than crosswise. This arrangement utilized the right angle gear box drive from the PTO-drive version. Another version of the No. 8 had the single outlet, gravity unloaded grain tank mounted low enough to accommodate ground level bagging; it was known as the Australian-type grain tank, because the same system was used on the Australian stripper harvesters. The popular 10- and 12-foot cut McCormick-Deering No. 8 harvester-thresher was built from 1926 to 1935.

This McCormick-Deering No. 8 is boldly labeled a "POWER DRIVE HARVESTER-THRESHER." Shocked grain to the left of this 1926 field scene makes it very clear that the switch to harvester-threshers, especially in the Midwest, was only beginning.

One version of the McCormick-Deering No. 8 was the McCormick Type "C" harvester-thresher. These machines were built for Azar Cross and Company and had changes intended to differentiate them from the McCormick-Deering No. 8. Since the horse-drawn, engine-drive harvester-thresher in this photo has oval grain elevators and a design in the place where the McCormick-Deering logo and model number would normally appear on the side sheet, it is reasonable to assume this is a Type C. The rotary weed screen above the two-way bagger still carries the IHC logo.

Introduced at the same time as the No. 8, the McCormick-Deering No. 11 harvester-thresher was a similar design, but the recleaner and individual recleaner fan were built into the basic machine. It came with 9- or 12-foot headers and could cut 16 feet with a header extension.

The McCormick-Deering No. 20 had a sharply angled canvas conveyor that discharged cut grain from the cutting platform into a large hood with a curved top located ahead of the cylinder. The No. 20 could be equipped with the high, gravity unloading grain tank or a low grain tank with two outlets for unloading at ground level. The No. 20 and No. 21, along with the No. 22, each had 22 3/4-inch wide cylinders. These were the smallest cylinder width harvester-thresher IHC ever produced. The No. 20 accommodated an 8-foot header and could be expanded to 10 feet with an extension. The No. 21 came with 5- or 7-foot headers. These two machines were produced during difficult financial times from 1930 to 1937.

The McCormick-Deering No. 22 harvester-thresher was literally an engine-driven threshing machine with a header attachment for going to the field; in fact, it carried the same No. 22 model numbers as the IHC stationary thresher. It came standard with a 16 1/2-horse-power engine, 22 3/4-inch wide x 18-inch diameter spike tooth cylinder, 8-foot platform, straw spreader, and direct-connected tractor hitch. The machine could be ordered with either a grain tank or bagging attachment. An optional 2-foot platform extension was available.

A fleet of 12 engine-driven McCormick-Deering No. 8 harvester-threshers pulled by 12 McCormick-Deering 15-30 tractors is an impressive sight on this Okley, Kansas wheat farm in 1930. The operator's platform was first introduced in 1929 and became a standard feature on all McCormick-Deering No. 8 and No. 11 harvester-threshers. The Okley wheat farm needed 24 men on the equipment and another fleet of trucks or wagons and men to haul the grain away from such a high capacity operation. Another 1930 photo in the archives shows a fleet of six McCormick-Deering No. 11 harvester-threshers with McCormick-Deering tractors near Colby, Kansas. Fleet scenes like these were frequently used in IHC harvester-thresher promotion.

McCormick-Deering
No. 11 Harvester-Thresher

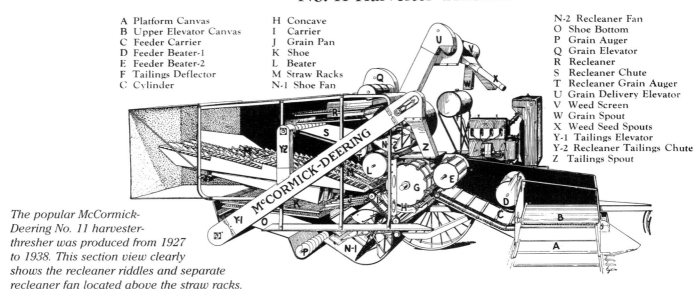

A Platform Canvas
B Upper Elevator Canvas
C Feeder Carrier
D Feeder Beater-1
E Feeder Beater-2
F Tailings Deflector
G Cylinder

H Concave
I Carrier
J Grain Pan
K Shoe
L Beater
M Straw Racks
N-1 Shoe Fan

N-2 Recleaner Fan
O Shoe Bottom
P Grain Auger
Q Grain Elevator
R Recleaner
S Recleaner Chute
T Recleaner Grain Auger
U Grain Delivery Elevator
V Weed Screen
W Grain Spout
X Weed Seed Spouts
Y-1 Tailings Elevator
Y-2 Recleaner Tailings Chute
Z Tailings Spout

The popular McCormick-Deering No. 11 harvester-thresher was produced from 1927 to 1938. This section view clearly shows the recleaner riddles and separate recleaner fan located above the straw racks.

One extra equipment option was a power platform control (power lift) for adjusting cutting height; it was rope controlled from the tractor seat or by lever if the optional operator control platform was used. In keeping with the trend, the No. 22 could be ordered with optional pneumatic tires; or, if the purchaser was conservative, it could be ordered with a four-horse hitch. Sales of this very popular harvester exceeded 13,000 units during the 1935 to 1945 production years.

The McCormick-Deering No. 31 harvester-thresher of 1935 came in three models:

The No. 31T was built with a traditional spike-tooth cylinder. Regular equipment included a 12-foot header, expandable to 15 feet, fanning-mill type recleaner, 35-bushel grain tank, 6-cylinder 30-horsepower International Model HD engine, fore-carriage with tractor hitch, straw spreader, and operator's platform with tiller wheel control. Extra equipment included

This McCormick-Deering 10-20 tractor supplied the PTO power for the McCormick-Deering No. 20 harvester-thresher. It was promoted as, "A Light-Weight, Medium-Capacity Harvester-Thresher, Within the Reach of Every Grain Farmer." This photo of soybean harvest was taken in 1930 near Bagley, Iowa.

This version of the McCormick No. 21 harvester-thresher was intended for export to Europe. It was equipped with torpedo divider, grain-type reel, low-grain tank with two ground-level bagging outlets, and operator's platform. A version for the U.S. market had the traditional, high-mounted grain tank. The underside of the rectangular cross section clean grain elevator had a long section of fine screen for removing weed seed; this system was less costly than the rotary screen.

The McCormick-Deering No. 22 harvester-thresher was described as a "light-weight prairie-type." It came with the engine as standard equipment.

The McCormick-Deering No. 40 harvester-thresher, International A-4 truck, and McCormick-Deering 15-30 tractor make this an all IHC scene. Since the No. 40 does not appear on the machine production list, it may have been a preproduction run that never went into full production. The photo was taken in 1930, the same year the No. 20 went into production and five years ahead of the first No. 41 production.

power platform control with parts for tractor seat operation, driver's seat with main wheel brake attachment, and parts for an 8- or 12-horse hitch. The extra equipment option list for all three models included pneumatic tires by 1938.

The No. 31RD was very similar to the No. 31T with a major exception: it came with what literature described as, "the improved rub-bar cylinder and combination concave and grate of special design thoroughly thresh the toughest heads without chopping up the straw." In addition, the cylinder shaft was supported on eccentrics that provided quick, easy cylinder/concave clearance adjustment.

The No. 31 series harvester-threshers (shown here with a Farmall F-20) were available in three models: the No. 31T with spike-tooth cylinder, the No. 31RD with rub-bar cylinder, and the No. 31RW with rub-bar cylinder and special features for the West Coast market.

The No. 31RW was designed especially for West Coast growers. The major differences between the RW and the RD was an 8-inch deep platform, a "laid down" type elevator, a single canvas continuous throughout the entire length of the platform, and a combination bagging and operator's platform with long chute.

The rub-bar machines had a combination concave and grate with 15 cross beams and closely spaced steel rods running lengthwise underneath the bars to constitute the grate. This general configuration that started as an option later became standard for all IHC conventional rub-bar/rasp-bar combines.

The 42-inch wide separator of the McCormick-Deering No. 41 harvester-thresher was the same as the separator width of the No. 11. By increasing the cylinder width to 28 inches compared to the 24-inch cylinder of the No. 11, the separator was only 50% wider than the cylinder. The No. 31 and No. 51 harvester-threshers had separators only 22% wider than the cylinder and the No. 22 harvester-thresher separator was essentially the same width as the 22 3/4-inch wide cylinder. Comments accompanying a 1933 photo indicated the No. 41 would go into full production as soon as the inventory of No. 11 harvester-threshers was sold. Economics of the time — this was the great American depression — and perhaps cost or performance problems resulted in full production being delayed until 1935. The No. 41 harvester-thresher incorporated an improved system for pivoting the grain

The McCormick-Deering No. 41 harvester-thresher in this 1932 photo is one of four produced that year, one machine was exported; inventory problems delayed full production until 1935. Two ropes for operating the power platform control are clearly shown running from the tractor's right fender to the control arms on the harvester-thresher.

wheel — the wheel that supported the platform — and folding the platform back alongside the separator for transporting. It was claimed the job could be done in a few minutes by one man. The optional, curved metal straw walker discharge hood with IHC logo in place of the all canvas hood provided a finished look to the machine.

The 1935 production version of the McCormick-Deering No. 51 harvester-thresher came with a standard 14-foot platform; a 2-foot extension was available. The "laid down" platform elevator could float to accommodate sloping terrain while the separator was kept level side-to-side by a power leveling system controlled by the operator. Two other features made the No. 51 a West Coast and intermountain hillside harvester: First, the self-contained fan and cleaning unit were pivotally mounted so the action of a heavily weighted pendulum could level the system fore and aft. Second, the conventional straw walker separating system was replaced with a raddle-type straw carrier that combined grain separation with material transport. A standard equipment, square canvas box attached to the rear of the separator was a straw collector for leaving straw in bunches. An optional, metal straw hood and straw spreader were available as extra equipment. The operator's control platform was combined with the grain bagging station and provided a seat for both the operator and sack sewer. A long sack chute with coil spring shock absorbers lowered

This rear view photo of a 1932 experimental McCormick-Deering No. 51 harvester-thresher demonstrates the product to be a true hillside machine. The operator standing on top of the separator was responsible for keeping the machine level side-to-side. The large, black IHC letters on the back of the platform in the photo are much like the bold lettering in the same location on the West Coast, Holt machines. This identification was ruled out, and the photo carries instructions, "Do not show with IHC." The platform could be detached and mounted on a two-wheeled truck for transport behind the machine.

Smaller farmers, like this McCormick-Deering Farmall owner, found an answer to their grain harvest needs in the McCormick-Deering No. 60 harvester-thresher. IHC was not bashful in promoting their new 6-foot cut, power-driven (PTO), one-man combine: "It fits all territories, handles all threshable crops, and brings the advantages of low-cost efficient combining within practical reach of farmers everywhere." A simple to adjust rubbar cylinder coupled with an auger-type platform offered operating ease and reduced maintenance.

1. Slatted chain feed carrier.
2. Spike beater.
3. Tailings return spout.
4. Spike-tooth cylinder.
5. Concave.
6. Finger grate.
7. Hinged plate giving access to concave.
8. Main beater.
9. Shelled grain return spout.
10. Beater flap.
11. Slatted grain conveyor.
12. Toothed beaters.
13. Picker rolls.
14. Raddle type straw carrier.
15. Self-leveling cleaning unit.
15A Cleaning fan.
15B Chaffer fingers.
15C Adjustable chaffer.
15D Adjustable chaffer extension.
15E Adjustable cleaning sieve.
16. Tailings auger.
17. Clean grain auger.
18. Clean grain elevator.
19. Weed screen compartment.
20. Weed screen spout.
21. Power leveling device.
22. 6-cylinder engine.
23. Seat for bag sewer.
24. Operator's control seat.
25. Sack chute.

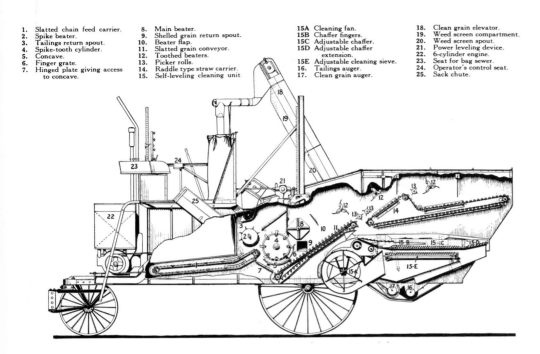

This cutaway line drawing shows the raddle-type straw carrier that made the McCormick-Deering No. 51 hillside harvester-thresher significantly different from machines with straw walkers. This was the IHC version of the "cell belt" straw and grain separating system used on the Holt-Caterpillar No. 36 West Coast, hillside combines.

the sacked grain from the platform to the ground. A 45-bushel grain tank with unloading auger was available as extra equipment in place of the grain bagging system. Just under 2,500 No. 51 hillside machines were manufactured during the 1935 to 1950 production years. No model of harvester-thresher or combine before or since has enjoyed a 16-year life cycle; it served this small niche market very well.

First production of the McCormick-Deering No. 60 was in 1937; it was still offered in a bagging equipment

version as well as a grain tank version. By this time, however, it did come with 7.00- x 16-inch pneumatic tires as regular equipment. Since not all tractors in the field were equipped with a PTO, a 4-cylinder engine attachment was available. The No. 60 was not a "straight through" auger unloading combine, but many of the basic features of high volume combines like the No. 52 and No. 62 to follow in 1943

The McCormick-Deering No. 42 rub-bar harvester-thresher was a war baby produced from 1940 to 1944. In spite of government restrictions, the need for one-man combines to harvest the nation's crops resulted in material allotments to produce over 23,000 No. 42 harvester-threshers in the five-year period. The 4-foot header and light weight of the No. 42 made it an ideal match for the large number of small tractors on farms during the first half of the decade of the 1940s.

This McCormick-Deering No. 52R, rub-bar harvester-thresher with 5-foot cut was called a straight through design; the platform conveyor was the same width as the separator. A clever design of the right angle gear box made it possible to shift the separator out of gear and engage the unloading auger drive on the back of the gear box with a single lever. These and other economy features made the No. 52R with its 18-bushel grain tank an ideal companion machine to the larger No. 62 produced during the 1943 to 1950 period. Total No. 52R output exceeded 36,000 machines and was second in volume only to the No. 62 that generated sales from 1940 to 1951 of almost 43,000 machines and set the record for the largest number of combines ever produced of a single IHC model.

The Term Combine!

The term "combine" had been used to describe the once-over harvesting operation, but now advertising copy writers in 1937 called the No. 60 machine a 6-foot combine. Grain harvest machines were called harvester-threshers and/or combines by the International Harvester Company for many more years before the term "combine" became the exclusive, descriptive term.

were introduced in this machine. The No. 60 and No. 61 were produced from 1937 to 1940 and combined production exceeded 20,000 units.

The McCormick-Deering No. 62 harvester-thresher was a totally different machine than the prior No. 60 and No. 61 models even though it had the same 28-inch wide cylinder and a 6-foot platform. The galvanized metal was gone and it became a rounded, highly styled and painted machine like the smaller 4-foot No. 42 introduced the year before. The grain platform was equipped with an interesting top extension for reduced crop loss from grain carried over by the reel. An auger unloaded grain tank was placed low on the machine in contrast to the high placed, gravity unload grain tanks used on prior machines. A bagging platform version was offered.

Self-Propelled Harvester-Threshers, A New Era

Development of a self-propelled harvester-thresher was a major turning point for IHC grain harvest products. The first self-propelled unit introduced by the Company was the McCormick-Deering No. 123-SP harvester-thresher, or was it a combine? Even at this late date, it appears no firm policy had been set regarding the use of these terms. Dual drive-wheel tires were on the left side and a single drive tire on the right. The 12-foot, hydraulic controlled platform was equipped with a power driven reel. A unique feature was the closely spaced pair of guide wheels at the rear that tracked the left-side drive wheels. This arrangement made it possible to make the sharp, square-cornered turns considered essential at that time because pull-type machines could perform the maneuver.

Recognition of the need for clean air for the engine is clearly illustrated by the large air inlet duct extending from the radiator to above the top of the separator. Many systems were tried before the rotary screen in front of the radiator became the standard.

Just as the first harvester-threshers were much like a field-going version of a stationary thresher with a crop gathering platform added, the first self-propelled combines were much like a pull combine with added propelling and steering means. Production during World War II had many restraints and improvements were severely limited. With the war's end in August 1945, things changed rapidly. Records of the 1947 Farm Implement Division Engineering Review states that a platform without canvas for the No. 123-SP harvester-thresher had been released to production. The change "constitutes a major improvement of this machine and also effects a considerable saving. Sales of this machine, especially in the western territories, will be effected (sic) favorably by the improved feeding."

The McCormick-Deering No. 125-SP self-propelled harvester-thresher had a pair of closely spaced guide wheels similar to the No. 123-SP. However, photo renderings of the No. 125-SP dated 1949 show a conventional axle with wide-spaced guide wheels. One of the other 1949 illustrations shows the No. 125SP with dual drive wheels like the No. 123-SP while another illustration shows only single drive wheels. Platform widths of 10-, 12-, and 14-foot were available. Market demand fol-

The year 1942 saw the introduction of IHC's first self-propelled combine, the McCormick-Deering No. 123-SP harvester-thresher.

A rice version of the new McCormick-Deering No. 123-SP self-propelled harvester-thresher had wide-spaced guide wheels in place of closely-spaced guide wheels and high-lug rice tires on the drive axle. With large tires, only a single drive wheel was required on the left side. For the rice area, a novel, optional feeding attachment replaced the header and feeder house. Rather than bring shocked rice to a stationary thresher, the No. 123-SP could go from shock to shock and workers would hand feed sheaves into each side of the feeder attachment. Circular knives on each side of the attachment would cut off the wet straw on the bottom of the sheaves and feed only the dry part to the cylinder. The attachment and No. 123-SP were claimed to require only one third as many workers as the traditional stationary threshing system.

lowing the close of World War II no doubt encouraged rapid changes as better designs evolved and the needs of particular applications were identified. The No. 125-SP was produced in 1948 and 1949, the 125-SPV was produced in 1950 and 1951, and the final version, the 125-SPVC, was produced in 1951 and 1952.

Most agricultural mechanization progress is evolutionary rather than revolutionary. International Harvester, like the rest of the industry, can be credited with a few of the latter along with many of the former.

The McCormick No. 127 harvester-thresher unloading oats into an International truck helps promote both divisions in this 1954 photo. The high, central location of the engine provided good weight distribution, easy access for service and kept it out of the dirt. Grain tank and bagger versions were available. The combine could be equipped with 10-, 12-, or 14-foot platforms. During the three years, 1952 to 1954, that the No. 127 represented IHC in the self-propelled combine market, well over 9,000 units were produced.

Pull-Type Combines

The straight through No. 76 pull-type, PTO harvester-thresher replaced the similar straight through No. 64. Both machines had cylinders nominally as wide as the 64 1/2-inch feeder canvas. Promoted as a 7-foot machine, the No. 76 could be equipped with a 6-foot feeder when conditions warranted. BUILT IN BALANCE was the theme of the 1955 literature which claimed, "New grain saving performance, extra capacity, unequalled versatility and sure dependability." Major competition had closed concave machines; so, 3-point separation was featured with statements like, "On the concave. Over the cylinder beater grate. Across the straw rack." Separating the No. 76 from the competition continued with, "NO GRAIN WASTING TURNS. As grain leaves the cutter bar, it travels straight back over the

The McCormick-Deering No. 160 pull-type, hillside harvester-thresher with 16-foot platform was manufactured from 1951 to 1953 and replaced the highly successful No. 51 pull-type hillside harvester-thresher. Production of only 388 units is clear evidence that the self-propelled machines were soon to dominate the hillside market. The TD-14A crawler and No. 160 in the photo were working near Wasco, Washington. Material coming over the sieve and chaffer was being caught in a canvas collector while the straw was directed to the ground.

canvas conveyor, through the cylinder and onto the straw racks for fast, complete separation." This, and similar literature statements, made it clear the No. 76 was different from the machine whose separator was at right angles to the closed concave cylinder.

The No. 76 had two interesting design features. First, air flow to the cleaning fan was regulated by a pair of open-center "cone-shaped gates" rather than the typical fanning mill shutters. Second, the unloading auger was supported on a large, hinged, circular

Multi-Purpose Super "M" Farmall Tractor

Annual review minutes for the IHC Farm Implement Division for 1947 have a very fascinating paragraph describing the No. 93 mounted harvester-thresher. There were two separate divisions and coordination was not always optimum; however, this sounds like a true joint effort. The review report follows:

"The No. 93 Mounted Harvester-Thresher, which uses a rearward moving "M" Farmall Tractor as a chassis, has been subjected to extensive field test. This design anticipates the development of the Super "M" Farmall. Reduction in weight is essential for mounted units and aluminum has been utilized wherever feasible. The experience gained in its use on this project will be valuable also in development of reciprocating parts and in general where reduction in weight is desired." Following World War II, it is reasonable to assume a large supply of competitively priced aluminum was available, and the farm equipment designers were interested in taking advantage of the situation.

Rearward-moving "M" Farmall tractors of this period were used successfully as the chassis for the new IHC self-propelled cotton pickers and could be converted to forward-moving operation for tractor drawbar work. Tractor mounting a harvester-thresher was a logical project in this period of major emphasis on mechanizing small farms. The No. 93 must have been assigned just to this project because there never was a harvester-thresher released with that model number until the McCormick No. 93 combine from Canada 15 years later.

International Harvester management wisely planned to have a proven line of combines ready for full production following the end of World War II. To achieve this objective, a caravan of several sizes and types of harvester-threshers, test engineers, tractors, and support vehicles followed the grain harvest during 1943 and 1944.
Test engineers load a 12-foot reel on top of the separator of this preproduction McCormick-Deering No. 122 pull-type harvester-thresher in this 1943 caravan photo. A pair of steel pockets on each side of the separator received metal stakes that supported the reel. With the reel and knife removed, the header folded up and the rig was ready for road transport. Other machines in the caravan are in the background behind the Farmall M tractor.

There were 275,000 harvester-threshers on U.S. farms in 1942 and by 1945 the number climbed to 375,000. During 1946 the harvester-thresher population grew 40,000 units for a total of 415,000 machines on farms. The post World War II mechanization of grain harvest was under way.

A full page advertisement for this new machine in the 1950 issue of Tractor Farming *calls this a 6-foot McCormick straight through "combine" in the text and a McCormick No. 64 "Harvester-Thresher" in the headline. The features of the new pull-type combine were:*

- *Full-width, straight-through design*
- *Ancillary engine or tractor PTO driven*
- *Grain tank or bagger*
- *One-piece, all-steel straw rack*

The 64 1/4-inch wide cylinder, widest in the industry, and the one-piece straw rack set this 6-bar, rasp-type (no longer called rub-bar) cylinder combine apart as different from the previous models. It was even called a McCormick combine and not a McCormick-Deering harvester-thresher.

pivot so it could be stored flat against the side of the grain tank for transport. Folding was "easy" after the auger transition had been unbolted from the grain tank and the drive disconnected.

Small, pull-type combines sold in large numbers during World War II and the decade that followed. International Harvester models No. 61, No. 62, and No. 64 pull-type harvester-threshers recorded combined sales approaching 9,000 units during the 1939 to 1954 period. The No. 76 followed these machines with almost 20,000 machines produced from 1955 to 1958.

The McCormick No. 80 combine had a full-width auger platform with retractable fingers; hydraulic platform control; undershot, slatted feed conveyor; power drive reel; 42-inch wide separator, 41 1/4-inch wide x 15 9/32-inch diameter rasp-bar cylinder and a bar and wire grate concave. The unloading auger on the 26-bushel grain tank could be easily and quickly folded back against the rear of the separator for transport; this design was a great improvement over the No. 76 auger transport design. During the 1959-1965 production years, East Moline Works manufactured 8,795 of these handy, small farm, PTO pull-type combines.

IHC's entry in the medium-size, pull-type combine market was the McCormick No. 140 which offered 9- and 12-foot platforms. The header had a full-width auger tube with retractable fingers at the feeder house. A three-chain undershot conveyor uniformly and positively delivered the crop to the cylinder. A leveling auger on the top of the grain tank increased capacity while holding down overall height. The sturdy tube and channel "A" frame provided a good mounting for the engine-drive version. The engine radiator was fitted with a tall air screen. Production of the No. 140 ran from 1954 to 1962; a total 5,626 units were built during the nine-year period.

After a successful nine-year production run from 1954 to 1962, the well-received No. 140 pull-type combine was replaced by the No. 150. The new "Windrow Special" had the same 32-inch wide cylinder of its predecessor. Literature stressed fin-and-wire type walkers that provided 3,394 square inches of separating area, a 50-bushel grain tank, and 540- or 1,000-rpm PTO drive. Either a 9-foot 8-inch or a 12-foot 2-inch platform with drum pickup could be selected. Important features for the states and provinces where windrow harvest was the method of choice were a feeder beater ahead of the cylinder that, "combs bunchy windrows and feed them in a smooth, even flow to the cylinder . . . and an extra-deep separator hood (that) protects against high winds, with ample room for heaviest straw."

The McCormick International No. 82 PTO pull-type combine that replaced the McCormick No. 80 was available in an Edible Bean Special and could be equipped with a special spring-tooth cylinder. Production of just over 3,700 machines ran for nine years beginning in 1966. As the number of small farms declined, so did the market for small, pull-type combines; production of this class of combine ended at IH in 1974.

Pictured is a McCormick International No. 82 pull-type, PTO combine with 7-foot auger-type platform and a Farmall 706 tractor. The No. 82 was an improved version of the McCormick No. 80. Advertising promoted this last of the small pull-type, PTO combines from IH as, "Big Combine Features in a 7-Foot Size." The decision to discontinue the McCormick No. 82 in 1974 marked the end of an era.

A New Product and A New Name

With introduction of the McCormick No. 80 pull-type, PTO combine, the transition was complete; literature and operator's manuals both called the machine a combine, not a harvester-thresher. Furthermore, it was not just an improved version of the No. 76 it replaced; it was quite a different machine. The Harvester-Thresher committee Report No. 23 — they hadn't changed their name or their terminology — "authorized an experimental program at East Moline Works for four (4) No. 80 'Harvester-Threshers' as an eventual replacement for the No. 76 Harvester-Thresher which has an unsatisfactory profit position and has encountered a decline in customer acceptance as a result of a trade demand for an auger type platform." The most interesting statement in the report is as follows, "The No. 80 Harvester-Thresher is a 7-foot pull-type version of the 8 1/2-foot No. 91 Self-Propelled Harvester-Thresher, which has been developed by the Canadian Organization."

Corn Heads for the McCormick No. 141 Harvester-Thresher

An experimental corn head for the McCormick No. 141-SP harvester-thresher was developed at East Moline in the early 1950s. This head design adapted two row units from a tractor-mounted No. 24 ear corn snapper and combined them to form a two-row corn head. No doubt the No. 141-SP couldn't handle the material other than ears delivered by a snapper unit,

Over 11,000 McCormick No. 141 self-propelled harvester-threshers were built between 1954 and 1957. Like the McCormick No. 127 self-propelled it replaced, the No. 141 offered 10-, 12-, and 14-foot platforms. The two machines had many other similarities; however, the engine shroud, radiator air screen, and operator's station were greatly improved on the No. 141. Near the end of production a major event occurred: In 1956 a No. 2-141, 2-row corn head was released for this machine. The No. 141 was not designed to handle the demands of shelling and cleaning corn, but a major revolution in IH corn harvest technology had begun.

The first IH experimental corn head was a snapper design. It was intended for use with the No. 141 self-propelled harvester-thresher. The No. 141 couldn't handle the large amount of trash from the snapper rolls and that design was not put into production.

so this machine did not go into production. The No. 2-141 corn head that went into production in 1956 consisted of the exposed roll, deep pocket design from the 2-PR, two-row pull corn picker; this design required less combine separating and cleaning capacity than

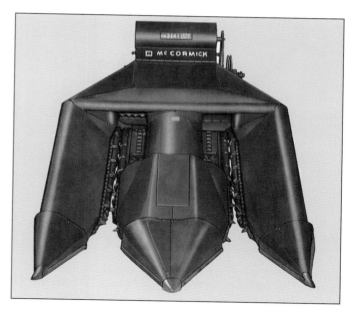

In 1956, IHC entered the corn head market for harvester-threshers with the McCormick No. 2-141. Literature proclaimed, "A New Way of Harvesting Corn. Now! Pick and shell with the McCormick No. 141 corn unit and No. 141-SP harvester-thresher. Capacity far exceeds cylinder shellers on 'picker shellers.' "

was required by the snapper system. When combine ruggedness, horsepower, and capacity caught up with the requirements of corn harvest, corn head design returned to the snapper system and the shelled corn loss reduction it provided.

A Fully Self-Leveling Harvester-Thresher

Self-leveling harvesters were not new, but the No. 141 HS-SP was the first to add fore-and-aft to a side to side leveling system. A 100-pound rigid-rod pendulum activated valves for automatic hydraulic control. The four-way leveling machine could climb hills and still keep grain loss to a minimum.

A New Line of Self-Propelled Harvester-Thresher

Release of the McCormick No. 101 self-propelled harvester-thresher for 1956 introduced a radically different kind of crop harvesting product to the IH dealer organization; this machine had been developed with corn head requirements as one of the design criteria. Production of the No. 101 approached 14,000 units during 1956 to 1961. This was the right machine for this period of increased conversion from corn pickers to combine harvest of corn. It could be equipped with the McCormick No. 21, two-row corn head and/or 10-, 12-, or 14-foot platforms. The No. 101 had a 40-bushel grain

This McCormick self-propelled No 141 HS hillside combine was the first combine with four-way automatic leveling. It could adjust 16° side to side, 18° when climbing, and 6° when going down hill. Manual override provided even greater leveling. It was produced from 1955 to 1958.

tank. The similar but larger No. 151 followed a year later in standard and hillside versions. The largest of the series, the No. 181, was introduced in 1958. The No. 101, No. 151, and No. 181 gained their increased capacity by virtue of the following specifications:

Model	Cylinder Width (in.)	Horsepower	Rack No.
No. 101	27 1/4	58	3
No. 151	37 3/16	70	4
No. 181	46 3/8	80	5

An East Moline Plant photo of a McCormick No. 101 harvester-thresher shows the machine equipped with the McCormick No. 21-101 corn head that was introduced in 1956. This corn head along with the McCormick No. 2-141 were the first ones offered by IHC. With slight modification, the head shown here became the No. 22-101 in 1958 and the No. 22, 23, and 25 in 1959. The practice of including the combine model number in the corn head model number was dropped after 1958.

This McCormick International No. 303 combine is equipped with a 10-foot grain platform and windrow pickup.

The East Moline Implement Committee Report No. 117 dated March 1961 gave authority to release to production a new line of self-propelled combines in 1962. They were identified as No. 303 (replacing No. 101); No. 403 (replacing No. 151); and No. 503 (replacing No. 181). A drawing was part of the report and used callouts on the proposed No. 403 rendering to describe the key features of the new line:

Proposed No. 403 Combine

1. "Flip-up" type upholstered seat-fully adjustable.
2. Operator's platform raised.
3. Farmall tractor type steering wheel position for operator comfort.
4. All controls redesigned for improved operator comfort.
5. Low grain tank permits viewing from seated position.
6. 65-bushel grain tank.
7. 90-horsepower engine.
8. Positive clutch in engine separator drive.
9. Rear access ladder to engine placed on left side for operator's convenience.
10. Lowered overall height for ease of truck transport.
11. Separator lengthened 14 inches and hood sides made deeper.
12. Main sill of strong angle construction eliminates need for unwieldy truss rod construction.

Edible bean, windrow, and rice special versions were offered. Major attachments included: automatic header height control, two versions of hydraulic reel drive, straw spreader, bagger and ground ear corn attachment. In addition to the standard transmission, low speed gears and a 2-speed gear box were offered.

The design of the new line of combines for 1962 stressed easy serviceability. Grain platforms came in 13-, 14-, 16-, and 18-foot widths for any of the three combines. A 10-foot grain platform was available for the

A rice special version of the McCormick International No. 503 combine met the needs of a small but important market segment. This 1964 East Moline Plant photo shows the crawler track option and draper-type platform. The high-mounted grain tank distributing auger reduced mechanical damage by dropping the rice into the grain tank rather than pushing it up from a lower position. By the time this new family of combines went into production, the bold McCormick identification seen in other photos and illustrations had been reduced to a small byline above the bold white and black International logo.

No. 303. The No. 503 had capacity to handle a 20-foot size. With the popularity of 6-row, 30-inch planters for soybeans, a 15 1/2-foot platform was released for 1967 to match that planting pattern. All three combines in the new line had 22-inch diameter cylinders, but they came in different widths to match each machine: 30-inch for the No. 303, 39 3/16-inch for the No. 403, and 46 3/8-inch for the No. 503. The separator had 3-, 4-, or 5-section rotary straw racks to match the cylinder width. The tailings delivery trough was designed to meter the tailings across the width of the cylinder to improve threshing and cleaning efficiency; this feature was an International Harvester exclusive. In addition, a conveniently located tailings access door gave the operator an easy way to check the tailings return and monitor combine performance; this was another IH exclusive. Hydraulic power steering came standard on the No. 403 and No. 503 but was an option on the No. 303. Gasoline engines were standard, but diesel

and liquefied petroleum engines were options on all three machines. During the nine years of No. 403 combine manufacture, almost 20,000 machines were produced. The very popular, smaller, No. 303 recorded production approaching 12,000 units during the same period. Production of the largest model, the No. 503, totaled just over 6,900 units during seven years. The basic components of the self-propelled No. 403 were incorporated in a No. 402 pull-type combine.

Hydrostatic Combine Drive . . . An Industry First

International Harvester introduced hydrostatic propulsion drive on No. 403 and No. 503 combines in 1965. This industry first provided one-lever, infinitely-variable combine speed control over a wide range at constant torque. Hydrostatic drive eliminated the high maintenance, variable-speed V-belt drive used on standard models and by the balance of the combine industry. The International Harvester No. 303, No. 403, and No. 503 combines led the way in a series of industry firsts in the application of hydrostatic power transmission technology.

IH first introduced hydrostatic power transmission in the HT-340 turbine tractor in 1961. Details of this fascinating technology demonstration tractor are covered in the tractor section. During World War II, a small hydrostatic drive was developed for the military to rotate turrets and raise and lower anti-aircraft guns. After the war, developments in high volume, precision manufacturing made larger, high-pressure hydrostatic components available at competitive prices. An East Moline engineer with Air Force training in hydraulics

Prior to the introduction of the No. 402, large IH pull-type combines were basically older designs that traced their 31 1/8-inch wide cylinder linage all the way back to the auxiliary engine drive 122 introduced in 1946. Pull-type models No. 140, No. 150, and the hillside No. 160 were all part of that family. The No. 402 was different. Introduced in 1962, the McCormick International No. 403 self-propelled had gone on to establish itself as a reliable, productive combine that represented real value and became the most successful of the "3" Series self-propelled combines. By developing the No. 402 around the No. 403-SP components, similar performance was achieved in a large, PTO pull-type combine that was well sized for the typical operation and tractors available in the windrow harvest area.

along with Hinsdale Engineering Center hydraulics expertise, also with a military experience component, made IH hydrostatic propulsion drive technology a key combine innovation. As a result, IH had additional industry firsts with hydrostatic propulsion for lawn and garden tractors in 1966, agricultural tractors and cotton pickers by 1967, and self-propelled windrowers in 1968.

Factory Installed IH Combine Cabs

For years western harvester-threshers and combines had canvas sun shades. IHC dealers could furnish International Harvester wind beakers useable as a sun shade or as a complete enclosure for No. 101, No. 151, and No. 181 combines. Short line companies offered will-fit cabs. By 1966 IH offered factory installed combine cabs for No. 203, No. 303, No. 403, and No. 503 combines. Cabs would not become standard until 1969 with the introduction of the No. 815/915. Advertising copy said, "Now you can raise your standard of living on an IH Combine . . . put yourself in a 'controlled environment' that rivals living-room comfort. Tinted safety glass provides horizon-wide visibility while the pressurizer fan provides filtered fresh air free of dust, pollen and fumes. The new cab environment can be equipped with air conditioning and or hot water heating that turns blustery days into pleasant Indian Summer!"

IH Combine Corn Heads

The first IHC 4-row corn heads were the McCormick No. 40 and No. 41 produced in 1960, and they featured a full-width cross auger. The 4-row market was just developing and only 545 units were manufactured during the three-year production run. These heads evolved into the McCormick International No. 429 and No. 430 4-row heads introduced in 1963 to match the new No. 403 and No. 503 combines. A year later the narrow-row No. 328N, No. 329N, No. 429N, and No. 430N versions were introduced. By 1966/1967 the wide/narrow No. 327WN and No. 328WN were added, No. 329WN, No. 429WN, and No. 430WN

corn heads provided coverage for the needs of No. 303 and No. 403 combine owners for all of the popular corn row width planting patterns.

Popularity of the 6-row narrow planter made 3-row corn heads important so matched rows could be harvested, but the harvest capacity was limited; a 6-row narrow head was needed. The size and productivity of the McCormick International No. 503 provided a perfect match for the 6-row, narrow-row No. 630N corn head offered in 1966 for this largest model in the IH combine line.

How Many Combines did the Industry Sell? . . . What was our Market Share?

The Farm Equipment Institute (FEI), which would later become the Farm and Industrial Equipment Institute (FIEI), and now the Equipment Manufacturers Institute (EMI), provides a manufacturers reporting program that generates industry retail sales numbers and the ability for each firm to determine their true market share. Each company reports their sales by size or horsepower class, depending on the product. The smallest size combines are reported in Class I followed by the larger Class II, Class III, and Class IV. As combine size and capacity grew, Class V and Class VI were added. Success of the FEI retail sales reporting program, spearheaded by International Harvester

The McCormick-International No. 429 4-row corn head was specifically designed for the McCormick-International No. 403 combine shown here. The full-width beater worked over an open throat to assure "No Plug" corn harvest.

The 1964 Buyers Guide *describes the new IHC 200/400 Series corn head stalk roll system as follows:*

> *"Exclusive scalloped stalk rolls are timed to meet, rather than mesh. Stalks are gripped firmly between notch of one roll and straight edge of the opposite roll . . . are pulled straight down through the stripper plates without kinking. Stalks are not whipped or beaten. Ears stay on until snapped and there's less trash and stalk breakage."*

These were truly, "Revolutionary new 3- and 4-row corn heads."

IH Corn Heads — Three Exclusive Features:

- *New universal corn head frame provides versatility for both wide and narrow row harvesting with the same head.*
- *Only corn head with patented IH scalloped snapping rolls.*
- *Only corn head with patented IH stripper plates that adjust equally and simultaneously over the center of the rolls, on-the-go.*

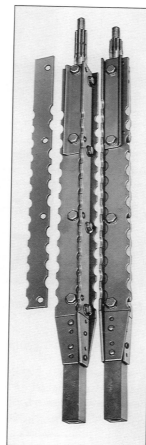

Market Research Department, resulted in the addition of an inventory reporting program that proved to be equally valuable.

The UNI Question

During the decade of the 1960s when the small combine Class I and II accounted for a major share of industry production, another combine and corn harvest story was unfolding. New Idea Farm Equipment Division of Avco Corporation acquired the UNI-Harvester System from Minneapolis-Moline and built a small number of power units in 1964. The UNI-System consisted of various harvesting modules: combine, sheller, forage harvester, and ear corn husker that could mount on a common power unit chassis. If more than one module was needed in a farming operation, dual use of the power unit made the system more economical than owning two single-purpose machines.

New Idea significantly improved the design and performance of the Minneapolis-Moline design and sales increased rapidly. New Idea manufactured 1,750 power

units in 1966 plus 1,250 combine, 550 sheller, and 500 forage harvester modules. During 1967 New Idea built almost 2,500 power units along with 1,800 combines and shellers plus 1,000 forage harvesters. Ear corn husker-harvester production quadrupled to 1,500 units. This kind of market activity could no longer be ignored; IH senior product management directed the East Moline Product Committee to come up with a proposal for a power unit/modular system and gave Product Planning Research the assignment of evaluating the UNI-System and its current and future market.

The Product Planning Research report made several conclusions: One of the major uses of the modular concept was harvest of ear corn; ear corn harvest was a declining market. The UNI-System had the ability to harvest narrow-row ear corn and to harvest more than two rows at a time. Hybrid-seed corn producers needed that capability and they accounted for a large part of the rapid growth in UNI-System sales. Changing modules on the power unit was not a quick or easy task. The modular system was not well suited to accommodate the larger combines that were projected as the future market. Product Planning Research summary recommendations were, "There are a combination of niche markets for the modular power unit approach that will support one manufacturer for a decade or so. If IH enters the market, neither firm will make a profit." Fortunately, senior management was finally convinced to abandon the proposal.

The Chief Engineer for East Moline products has summarized the importance of the decision this way, "If IH had invested the money and manpower necessary to develop a full line of modular power unit products to compete with the UNI-System, it would have so completely diluted the combine and corn head development program that IH would have become a minor player in the grain harvest market."

A UNI-System Sidelight

The senior author did the field investigation and wrote the IH Product Planning Research report that recommended the Company not enter the modular power unit market. Following his IH career, and by a strange quirk of fate, he became the New Idea (White-New Idea) Senior Product Manager for the UNI-System and guided marketing and product development to serve the same, but now much smaller, niche markets described almost 20 years earlier. By the 1990s, almost no one switched UNI-System modules during the harvest season; the concept had gone full circle and specialized, single-purpose machines were serving the needs of the major niche markets.

Small Self-Propelled Combines

The McCormick 91 combine from IH Canada introduced the 41 1/2-inch wide, 15 1/4-inch diameter cylinder that would be the basis of a family of future, small, self-propelled combines. The most unusual feature of this combine was the planetary steering system that made it the "most maneuverable combine ever built." Two control levers replaced the usual steering wheel. Each lever controlled power flow to the respective drive wheel, so the wheels could be slowed, stopped, or reversed, individually or together. The rear wheels were fully castored. An advertising logo promoted the novel steering system as, "MAGIC CIRCLE, Planetary Steering" with diagrams of the operator's right and left hand on the appropriate control handle. Arrows around a circle stressed the combines ability to turn 180% and come back almost in its tracks. The No. 91's threshing, separating, and cleaning configuration coupled with the planetary steering system resulted in an 8 1/2-foot platform combine with lots of capacity and a very attractive price. The age of the corn head had arrived and the No. 25, 2-row corn head became available for the No. 91 combine. It was similar to the No. 22 and No. 23 corn heads for the No. 101/303-151/403 combines. Over 6,000 No. 91 combines were produced from 1959-1962.

The McCormick International No. 93 replaced the similar No. 91 in 1962. The greatest difference was a 3-speed transmission with variable-speed V-belt drive and automotive-type steering in place of the planetary system. Specifications included a 37-bushel grain tank, 50-horsepower engine, and a 9-foot or 10 1/2-foot centered or offset grain platform. Like the No. 91, it could be equipped with the No. 25, 2-row corn head. In 1964 the basic machine sold for $5,742. Hamilton Works

The McCormick International No. 93 combine, the replacement for the No. 91 combine, had automotive-type steering and 3-speed transmission with variable-speed, V-belt drive. It is shown here with a 9-foot grain platform.

Export Catalog listed the No. 93 as available in a rice version with spike-tooth cylinder and optional tracks.

In 1967 IH upgraded the Canadian-built, Class I No. 93 self-propelled combine to the No. 105. The "L"-shaped, 47- or 54-bushel grain tank replaced the single side tank design of the No. 93 just as fin-and-wire rotary straw racks replaced the unit-type straw rack. Cleaning and separating area were larger and the engine had three more horsepower, but corn head size was still limited to two rows.

This Canadian-built McCormick No. 91 combine had a 41 1/2-inch wide by 15 1/4-inch diameter cylinder. Since Canada designed the IH line of planetary steer windrowers, they incorporated the same steering system in their No. 91 combine.

Grain Elevator — Grain Tank Unloader

Reel

Platform Auger

Divider Rod

Divider

"Saddle Tanks"

A major combine competitor introduced a new model in 1962 that featured twin grain tanks, one on each side of the separator. The "saddle tank" design lowered the center of gravity and also lowered the overall height. Popularity of the competitors machine was no doubt a factor in IH management approving East Moline development of the No. 203 self-propelled combine with saddle tanks for "A Sleek New Look." It had the 41 1/4-inch wide, 15 1/4-inch diameter cylinder like the Canadian-built No. 93 self-propelled combine. The No. 203 was the first wide-cylinder, twin-tank, self-propelled combine manufactured at East Moline Plant. During its five years of production, 5,135 McCormick International 203 combines came off the line.

At the same time the Canadian No. 93 was being replaced by the No. 105, the East Moline No. 203 was upgraded to the McCormick International No. 205. Cleaning and separating area remained the same size; however, addition of 6 more horsepower and 7 more bushels to the twin grain tank capacity, and other changes, made it possible for the new No. 205 to handle a 3-row corn head. The plant manufactured 2,050 McCormick International 205 combines from 1967 to 1971.

The No. 93 and No. 105, along with the No. 105 and 205 that replaced them, were all in FEI combine Class I, the smallest class. In 1964 the industry sold 12,657 Class I combines and by 1966 this class accounted for 11,286 machines and almost 30% of all combines sold. The year 1967 recorded the first significant drop in Class I industry retail and marked the start of a rapid decline in the sale of small combines. Farm size, organization, and equipment was changing and by 1970 the

Class I market dropped to 2,296 combines. By 1971 Class I industry retail was under 2,000 combines, and IH wisely got out of the small combine market and ended production of the No. 205. Production of the No. 105 had ended a year earlier.

Replacement or New?

When is a machine a replacement and when is it a new product? Product Committee records suggest that what started out as a program to update the Class I McCormick International No. 203 combine grew into the higher capacity and more costly No. 315. That made it necessary to replace the No. 203 with the No. 205 and to keep the features and price down so the machine could compete with other Class I combines.

The No. 315 shared the 41 1/4-inch wide cylinder and side-mounted, twin grain tank concept of the No. 203 and No. 205. However, with a 20-inch rather than 15 1/4-inch diameter cylinder, concave clearance adjustable from the operator's deck, 70-bushel grain tank capacity, 72-horsepower engine, shrouded steering column, a 6- x 8-inch clean grain elevator, and optional hydrostatic propulsion drive, it was a replacement for the No. 303 and belonged in Class II.

The International 315 combine was introduced in 1967 as a "new dimension in multi-crop capacity." It was available in rice special and edible bean versions and could be equipped with the options required to harvest a wide variety of other crops. With the increased capacity it could handle up to a 3-row wide corn head or a 14-foot grain platform. Major options included insulated operator cab, hydraulic reel lift, and automatic header height control.

The Product Committee report requesting release to production of the new No. 315 and authority to discontinue manufacture of the No. 303 includes no mention of the twin-tank or "saddle-tank" design. The No. 315 would be the first "full-size" IH combine with twin-tank configuration.

The McCormick International No. 205 combine shown here with a 3-row corn head replaced the No. 203 in 1967. All previous combines in this series were limited to 2-row corn heads.

There is a high capacity fire extinguisher mounted on the grain tank behind the operator of this McCormick International No. 315 self-propelled combine; this would indicate the combine was an engineering test machine. Also, the large cylinder shape on the feeder house is likely an experimental fan to pull dust away from the header and discharge it to the ground.

Critical Decisions for a Critical Product

With the successful launch of the McCormick International No. 303, No. 403, and No. 503 in 1962, combine long-range planning turned to charting the course for their replacement. Preliminary layouts were executed in cardboard and it was obvious a significantly different product was planned; replacements for the No. 403 and No. 503 would have twin grain tanks, "saddle tanks," similar to the No. 315 scheduled for 1967 introduction. This design made it possible to locate the engine on top of the frame like the No. 403 and No. 503 but now moved forward and to the right, slightly behind the operator. In addition, these new combines would have a "power swivel" unloading auger that could be hydraulically moved from transport position to discharge position and controlled from the operator's seat. This handy system could also swing the auger during unloading for topping out a load without moving the truck or combine.

Engineering assigned experimental designations of CX-2 and CX-5 to these new machines. Since they were obvious replacements for the No. 403 and No. 503, proposed model numbers of No. 405 and No. 505 were also used.

A new Chief Engineer for Grain Harvesting was put in charge of East Moline Combine Engineering in the summer of 1966. He found the No. 315 had been released for production in 1967, and the larger experimental CX-2 and CX-5 were well on the way toward a 1968 production date. Even though the development was well advanced, the new leader became seriously concerned about the design concepts incorporated in the new line of larger combines. He found he was not alone; the Product Committee, Engineering Management, and most product engineers agreed, "the whole design had to be changed." Changing these well advanced prototypes to machines with top grain tanks and rear engines was a major project. Fortunately, this decision had broad support and the redesign project moved into high gear. By spring of 1967, a top tank version of the CX-5/505, next known as the No. 515, was ready to show to management. In final form, these efforts would result in the highly successful International No. 815 and No. 915 combines.

This experimental combine designated by engineering as the CX-5 was intended as the replacement for the No. 503. The prototype represented a whole new design approach for the larger IH combines. It had twin grain tanks, "saddle tanks," a power swivel unloading auger and the engine was placed to the right, just slightly behind the operator. There was a strong family resemblance to the previously introduced No. 315.

Photographed on an East Moline golf course, this International No. 515 combine looks ready for production, but it's not. This combine is the first version of the experimental CX-5 replacement for the No. 503 that incorporated a centered, top grain tank and engine to the rear. This was a major change from the original model CX-5 concept, but the attractively styled, well-balanced machine pictured here justified the effort.

The new International No. 815 and No. 915 combines produced in 1969 came standard with hydrostatic all-speed drive, heated comfort-control cab, and solid-state monitor control along with many other new features. These combines had been designed with corn harvest as a major objective. The result was a rugged pair of machines with high capacity grain tanks and lots of power: up to 140 bushel and up to 144 horsepower for the No. 815; up to 150 bushel and up to

162 horsepower for the No. 915. Top-driven, roller-chain elevators with 8- x 8-inch rubber flights increased clean grain capacity. The high-speed unloading auger delivered 1.1 bushel per second.

The Story Behind the Poster

"Power & Comfort Plus . . . better weight distribution empty or loaded"

In 1969 the major competitive combine had the engine up front and to the right of the operator. This configuration put extra weight on the drive tires when the combine was empty and contributed even more unbalance when the grain tank was full. IH marketing promoted the benefits of the No. 815 and No. 915 balanced design in a 17- x 22-inch poster/mailer. An International No. 915 Corn and Soybean Special with No. 744, 4-row wide corn head was photographed in the large turntable studio at the IH Hickory Hill facility. Each wheel was placed on a portable "fly" scale of the kind used by state highway patrol officers when checking truck axle weights at remote locations. The combine and each scale face was photographed with the combine tank empty and full. Only 25.8% of the grain weight was added to the IH 915 rear guide wheels when the grain tank was full while the competition claimed a weight increase of 46%. When this competitor came with their next generation of combines, the configuration was like the IH 815/915 . . . the engine was in the rear behind the grain tank.

Rip VanWinkle Wakes up the World!

Combines are complex products that are required to harvest a large number of different crops. (One combine engineering study listed 131 crops typically harvested by combines.) They must do an efficient job threshing, separating, and cleaning these different crops under widely varied conditions. Laboratory test and engineering design analysis are both extremely important, but nothing can replace extensive field test conducted under typical user conditions.

During the final field test phase of the CX-2 experimental combine that would become the No. 815, one of the engineering units was placed with an experienced and knowledgeable custom cutter for use during his wheat harvest campaign. This frequently used arrangement assured the machine would harvest the large number of acres in one season needed to assure structural design and component reliability. The owner, "Rip" Van Winkle, normally ran a fleet of four International No. 403

combines. He hired an additional operator and purchased a new truck and combine transport trailer to accommodate the additional test machine supplied by International Harvester.

The CX-2/815 test combine was larger and had more capacity than his IH No. 403's; furthermore, it had a cab. In typical "Rip" fashion, he named the new addition to his fleet "Dude," complete with a "Dude" decal. When the Van Winkle custom fleet got to Argonia, Kansas, the Wichita Eagle ran an article on his operation together with a page of pictures. The pictures revealed that "DUDE" was not just another IH No. 403 combine. One picture caption declared, "Van Winkle's fleet normally consists of four combines, but this year he's carrying an extra — a hush-hush preproduction model being field tested."

Well, so much for product field test security!

This photo was used to announce the "NEW . . . International Harvester solid-state monitor control system No. 815 and No. 915 combines."

New Corn Heads for the New Combines

No. 700 Series corn heads were introduced in 1969 to complement the introduction of the No. 815 and No. 915 combines. Sizes ranged from the No. 724, 2-row wide for the No. 815, to the No. 763, 6-row narrow for the No. 815, to the No. 763, 6-row narrow for the No. 815 and No. 915. Also available were the No. 762, 6-row and the No. 782, 8-row for harvest in 20-inch rows. These new 700 Series corn heads incorporated a new lower profile; the snapping rolls were on a 30° angle. Other features included multi-lubrication as standard, stalk rolls with long-life, reversible straight plates, live points, hydraulic roll positioning from the operator's deck on the No. 815 and No. 915, and crank-adjusted stripper plates.

During the decade of the 1960s, university research had demonstrated significant yield increases for corn grown in narrow rows (28 or 30 inches) compared to

The IH 815/915 combines incorporated many innovative features. This image of an IH 915 clearly illustrates one of the most distinctive . . . the air supply for the cleaning system fan. Traditional combine fans were located underneath the main structure of the combine behind the drive tires. In this dirty, trashy location, fan screens plugged easily and reduced the grain cleaning performance. Rotating inlet

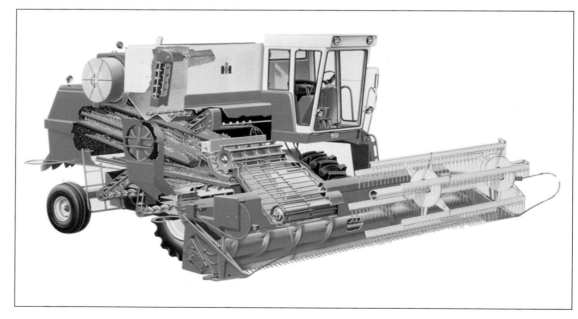

screens, rotating rubber fingers, and other attempts were made to solve the problem but none were totally successful, especially in corn harvest.

The "Even Flow" cleaning system drew clean air in from a location high on the side of the separator. The fan was a disk with eight curved radial blades on each side. The fan was a radical change from the long, straight-blade traditional design that traced its history all the way back to early fanning mills. Air from the "Even Flow" fan flowed through a rectangular duct to a two-chambered plenum where a set of carefully designed vanes directed the air to the front of cleaning sieves. Extensive design and development was invested in perfecting this totally new and different air supply for the IH 815/915 cleaning system.

with a pilot run of 16 machines. Production of 35 additional machines was scheduled for 1968. IH planters and cultivators for 20-inch rows were also available.

A 6-row, 20-inch corn head is only 10-feet wide and that makes harvest painfully slow. Introduction of the No. 762 and No. 782, 6- and 8-row, 20-inch corn heads as part of the 700 Series in 1969 kept the option alive. The 8-row, 20-inch No. 782 was 13-feet, 4-inches wide but still was narrower than a 6-row, 30-inch head.

Finally, the more than 50% excess cost to purchase 20-inch row planters, cultivators, and corn heads compared to 30-inch row equipment of similar width was recognized as not justified by the modest corn yield increases. This and other factors contributed to the disappearance of demand for 20-inch row corn heads, and IH production ended in 1971.

The Saddle Tank Legacy

This International No. 815 combine is equipped with a No. 744 4-row wide corn head. Larger corn heads included the No. 763 6-row narrow and the limited production No. 762 6-row special for 20-inch rows. The No. 782 8-row, 20-inch row corn head was only for the No. 915.

During the development of the IH 815/915 a decision was made to change the configuration from a twin grain tank, "saddle tank," design to a centered, top-mounted grain tank design; this was a major change and the production date needed to be held. Across the board support and cooperation from all involved made it possible to achieve the objective. In the process, however, the high separator profile and high cab location of the original concept remained unchanged. Farmers and dealers were enthusiastic about the comfort, convenience, and performance of the new IH 815/915 combines and they achieved a market share of almost 20%. Like all new machines, when thousands of

wide rows (36 to 42 inches). Yield increases for narrow-row soybeans were even more impressive. IH and the industry responded with combine corn heads, planters, and cultivators for 28- and 30-inch rows. Similar research suggested there were modest yield increases to be had by narrowing corn rows from 30 inches to 20 inches. Soybean yields showed an even greater benefit for the same reduction in row width.

One of the full-line farm equipment manufacturers developed a line of equipment for 20-inch row corn and soybean production and made it a lead feature in their sales and marketing program. Because of high equipment cost and the modest corn yield increase in very narrow rows, IH and the other major farm equipment firms took a more cautious approach and waited for more data and farmer reaction. The agricultural press found 20-row corn production a subject of great interest and promoted it aggressively. In response to competitive pressure, IH introduced the No. 620N, 6-row, 20-inch corn head in 1967

This graphic of an experimental 8-row, 20-inch row corn head and experimental CX-11 corn harvester is included for the significance of 20-inch row spacing corn head. The corn harvester is a great story and is covered fully in the development of the Axial-Flow combine in the next chapter.

a new products are in the hands of users, suggestions for making a good product better make themselves known. The request to lower the overall height of the No. 815 and No. 915 was recognized as valid because the overall height was considerably more than the No. 403 and No. 503 they replaced. Dealers, owners, and IH marketing all stated a need to clear the popular 12-foot storage building door; that dimension became the target for the "low profile" 815/915 program.

The 1974 low-profile No. 815 and No. 915 combines were not just reduced in overall height to clear a 12-foot door, they had an impressive list of features and specifications:

- A 12-inch diameter unloading tube delivered grain at 1.9 bushels per second (a 72% increase over the original 1.1 bushels per second). The unloading tube could be equipped with an optional 3-foot extension.
- Catwalks on both sides of the engine.
- Improved cylinder and concave design.
- New stone retarder that could be cleaned out from the top, or through a hinged door below the feeder house.
- Straw-rack throw increased to 6 inches.
- Improved even-flow cleaning system.
- Quick-attach feeder house for quick interchange of matching grain platforms and corn heads. Over-center lock system eliminated the need for wrenches.
- Comfort-control cab with open-center type, tilting steering wheel that eliminated the conventional, view obstructing pedestal.
- Optional, electronic digital read-out monitored six combine functions.
- Optional, spring-assisted, pivoted operator's ladder.
- Four special versions: grain and maize, corn and soybean, rice and edible bean.

Unfortunately, because the model numbers did not change, many items on this impressive list of improvements went unnoticed.

Patent Departments and Patent Problems

The New International 800 Series corn heads were introduced in 1974 along with the new low-profile No. 815/915 combines. The heads were described as

This new International 873 corn head was one of a family of corn heads that extended from a 3-row narrow to a 20-foot wide, 8-row narrow and included a 5-row wide or narrow and a 7-row wide or narrow.

having tool-bar type frames that permitted simple repositioning of row units to meet different row spacing requirements. Also, they had an enclosed helical-gear, gear case drive that assured quiet, long-life operation. Prior to introduction of the 800 Series corn heads, John Deere had introduced their 40 Series corn heads. The IH patent department and engineering had carefully reviewed the IH 800 Series design compared to the John Deere 40 Series. Since the 800 Series had a segmented drive shaft, one length for each row spacing in place of the John Deere continuous drive shaft, the patent department determined infringement was not a problem. However, Deere and Company filed a patent suit against International Harvester on April 28, 1976 claiming the 800 Series corn head design infringed their John Deere No. 40 corn head patents. The judge rendered a devastating decision against IH in October 1978 including an order to stop production. The appeal process lessened the judgement, and terms for continued production of 800 Series corn heads were negotiated. By 1982 the 900 Series corn heads were introduced and this frustrating chapter in International Harvester grain harvesting development was finally laid to rest.

Loss of the law suit with Deere and Company over the IH 800 Series corn heads meant the Company had to replace them quickly, replace them with a design free of patent problems, and replace them with something better. The product engineer for corn heads had been looking ahead and had a proposal for a design with greater operating speed and capacity, 20% less weight, and lower cost than the 800 Series. No patent problems were expected with the John Deere patents, and on October 10, 1979, the judge on the 800 Series case agreed. There was only one limitation to the 900 design, it would not accommodate 28-inch or narrower rows. The excitement over 20-inch or narrower rows was gone and 30-inch rows dominated the narrow-row market. So, the Strategic Business Unit (the new name for the Product Committee) quickly agreed to the proposal; the project was full speed ahead. Interestingly, the final version was even able to accommodate 28-inch rows.

Large Pull-Type Combines

International No. 403 combines enjoyed an excellent reputation for performance and reliability in the popular FIEI Class III market. The basic components of the No. 403 had been incorporated in the No. 402 pull-type windrow special, and its reputation in the windrow harvest areas of the Upper Midwest and Western Canadian Provinces was equally as good as the No. 403 self-propelled model.

In a like manner in 1970, the proven basic components of the IH 915 were incorporated in the new International 914 pull-type combine for the windrow harvest market. This approach made the No. 914 the "biggest capacity pull-type combine built." It came complete with a 150-bushel grain tank with frame and tires to support the load. By 1974, the No. 914 pull-type combines incorporated features from the new low-profile No. 915 self-propelled combines that included an 8- x 8-inch clean grain elevator, and 12-inch diameter unloading tube capable of unloading 1.9 bushels per second. Because of pull-type configuration, cleaning system air was supplied by a No. 403 style, 6-bladed rotary-type fan.

On-the-go controls from the tractor seat made it possible to electrically engage or disengage the unloading auger and operate the feeder house throw-out clutch. A third switch controlled the combine lights. Header height was controlled by the tractor remote hydraulic valve. Teamed with an IH 1026D Hydro tractor with cab, the combination rivaled similar size self-propelled combines for comfort, convenience, and performance.

Completing the IH "15" Series Combine Family

The International 403 combine had a 30% market share of the popular FIEI Class III in 1965 but began to loose share in the years that followed. Introduction of the No. 815 and No. 915 in 1969 positioned IH well in the large combine segment of the market, but new representation was needed in the smaller segment. The No. 403 combine class represented 36% of total industry sales; so, a strong replacement offering was needed. Management decided to modernize the No. 403, keep its reputation for performance and reliability, but be very careful not to increase cost in a very price sensitive segment of the market; that was not an easy task, and it needed to be done quickly. The International 715 self-propelled combine introduced in 1971 met the project objectives: It was a modern, not deluxe, combine that was reliable and delivered good performance . . . it represented one of the best values in the marketplace. IH market share with the No. 715 increased every year following introduction until it peaked in 1976 with an impressive 34.5%.

Why an IH 615 Combine ?

The International 315 combine introduced in 1967 was quite different from the No. 303 it replaced. It had side-mounted twin grain tanks — "saddle tanks" — that made servicing the drives next to impossible unless the one grain tank was empty. Also, the twin-tank design and 42-inch wide separator made a machine that was too wide to match up properly with corn heads. The No. 315 was a low profit machine that did poorly in the marketplace; a change was needed. Result: A decision was made to replace

This International 914 pull-type combine is harvesting windrowed grass seed near Junction City, Oregon.

International 715 combines and grain platforms on railroad flat cars roll past the East Moline Plant. The automated material storage building is shown under construction in the background.

the No. 315 with a modernized, cost-competitive version of the No. 303 in a program similar to the one to modernize the No. 403 to the No. 715. An aggressive program resulted in the International 615 introduction in 1971. The new small combine delivered improved profit, good performance, and a better market share than the No. 315 it replaced.

Four-Way Leveling for Hillside Combines

The International 453 self-propelled hillside combine had the exclusive four-way leveling system that saved more grain when going up or down hill. In addition, when the No. 453 was working up hill, the 4-way system put more weight on the front drive wheels which gave it more traction and better climbing ability than the two competitors with only

Photographed harvesting oats near Orion, Illinois, this engineering test International 615 version is a combine many IH 615 owners would have liked to own; it was equipped with an IH 815/915 style cab. This cab was never released to production for the No. 615 because it would have increased the cost beyond what was acceptable in this smallest and extremely price sensitive segment of the combine market.

The Brooks McCormick Factor

In the fall of 1970 the product program to modernize the No. 303 into the International 615 as a replacement for the No. 315 was moving along but not with a hard push from engineering senior management. The Chief Engineer for Grain Harvesting Engineering relates a story that occurred that same fall:

"Sometime in late 1970 I had a revealing experience with Mr. Brooks McCormick, Chief Operating Officer of the Company and then soon to be Chief Executive Officer. He had spent the day in meetings with Farmall and East Moline operations and late in the afternoon, after the regular work day was over, he excused himself from the meeting and came over to our Engineering Department all alone, which was unusual. He engaged me and wanted to know what the trouble was with the No. 315 combine. It was the first time I had been face to face with him since his review of Stockton Works in 1959. He seemed to be the same easy going, understanding gentleman we had seen back then. Of course I was dumfounded and had to gather my senses to properly answer him. I explained that the No. 315 was an excellent combine in small grain but just was not working out with corn heads, and in my opinion the best thing we could do was accelerate the program to update the No. 303 and get on with it. I had the impression he already knew about the lack of profit.

"Brooks McCormick returned to World Headquarters in Chicago and shared what he had learned at East Moline about the No. 315 and its planned replacement. It didn't take long for the No. 615 program to receive the high priority it needed."

This International 453 hillside combine was the only four-way leveling combine on the market. It had the ability not only to level side-to-side but fore-and-aft as well; that was an IH exclusive. International Harvester had been a factor in the western area hillside combine market ever since the introduction of the No. 51 hillside pull-type harvester-thresher in 1935. That product was followed by the No. 141 self-propelled hillside in 1955 and the No. 151 self-propelled hillside in 1959. The four-way leveling No. 403 self-propelled hillside was introduced in 1962. A two-way leveling version of the No. 403-HS was also available, but it was never a popular model.

two-way leveling. Smooth leveling action was controlled by a sensitive, oil-cushioned, 100-pound pendulum. Two independent hydraulic pumps powered the side-to-side and fore-and-aft leveling cylinders. The total system was hydraulic; there were no high-maintenance switches or solenoids that tend to overcorrect and cause a jerky response. The IH design made it possible to level up to a 36% side slope, up to a 34 1/2% uphill grade, and up to a 12% downhill grade.

The World Market

The *International Harvester World Wide Farm Equipment Buyer's Guide* for 1968 lists IH combines manufactured in five countries: Australia, Canada, France, South America, and the United States. Australia produced combines primarily targeted for their unique market. Canada made small combines for their eastern market, the United States, and export. France made a family of medium to large combines designed for the European market and for export to many countries with similar conditions.

The International 531 combine was designed and manufactured at Croix, France, a suburb of Lille. The covered grain tank, small section bats on the pickup reel, and distinctive platform grain dividers, identify this combine as definitely a European machine. This attractive scene was on a 1973 piece of IH French Company literature.

Combines from East Moline, Illinois, were designed for and primarily marketed to, the United States and Canada; however, a modest number were exported to countries other than Canada. The front cover of the 1971 *International Harvester World Wide Farm Equipment Buyer's Guide* pictured a U.S.-built No. 815 combine equipped with No. 744 corn head unloading into a flat-bed wagon pulled by a small, IH utility tractor manufactured by IH Europe.

This McCormick International 8-61 combine was manufactured by the IH French Company at Croix, France. This 1969 photo shows a typical conventional combine properly designed and configured for the European market. A larger model 8-91 was also offered.

A Different Harvesting System for Different Harvesting Conditions

The dry Australian grain harvest conditions makes it possible to use harvesters equipped with comb-type headers that use small diameter beater reels to strip grain from the stalk. The idea of comb and stripper harvest of grain in Australia was first introduced in 1843 when John Wrathall exhibited a model of the first head-stripper harvester to meet the requirements of Australian grain harvest.

A U.S. Patent issued to J.H. Adamson of South Australia in 1873 described a stripper combine grain harvester with a tapered cone axial cylinder for separating and cleaning. This early example is one of many axial concepts introduced in the years prior to the highly successful IH Axial Flow threshing and separating development.

In 1910 IHC introduced the No. 1 stripper-harvester for this market. By 1932 IHC contracted with the Gaston Brothers in Australia to build pull-type header harvesters under the IH name. After World War II, IH manufactured their own pull-type in the land down under. The IH No. A8-2 self-propelled was introduced in 1959.

For 1978, IH Australia offered the No. 711 header machine that could be equipped with 10-, 18-, or 20-foot combine front or 14- or 16-foot open front with standard hydraulic reel drive. A model No. 710 pull-type version was also available.

This 1918 photo shows an 8-foot Deering stripper-harvester designed for the Australian market. It was powered by a large diameter bull wheel under the grain box. When the box was full, harvesting stopped while the threshed grain was bagged at ground level through the single-outlet slide door.

The International No. 8-6 pull-type PTO header shown here could be equipped with 14- or 16-foot combine front and offered a choice of rasp-bar or peg-tooth cylinder. A rotary screen cleaner delivered clean grain to a 135-bushel grain tank and screenings to a 5-bushel second tank.

The Next Step in IH Combine Development

The strength of the IH East Moline combine line during the decade that followed introduction of the No. 815 and No. 915 made it possible for the Company to maintain its strong position in the marketplace while investing time, people resources, and money in a major combine development that was yet to come, the Axial-Flow. As stated at the beginning of this chapter, this development deserves a chapter of its own; "IH Axial-Flow Combines — The Long Road to Success," immediately follows this chapter.

Ear Corn Harvest

From the Beginning

When Columbus arrived in the new world, the Indians of North and South America had been cultivating corn, or maize, for centuries. Corn was the basis of the Inca, Mayan, Aztec, and other advanced civilizations of the New World. Corn, as we know it, does not survive in the wild. The Indians had not only preserved the production of corn but they had selected and improved five different types: popcorn, sweet corn, flour, flint, and dent corn. When Indian corn was introduced to the Old World, it rapidly became a significant agronomic crop.

Corn is North America's, and much of the world's, most important crop. It remained, however, the last to yield to mechanized harvest. Long after harvester threshers were successfully mechanizing the harvest of small grain and a wide range of other crops, corn was still harvested by hand. Eventually, the corn picker would bring mechanized harvest capability to the corn field.

The First IHC Corn Pickers

In 1904 the International Harvester Company introduced the pull-type Deering corn picker and husker and the McCormick corn picker and husker; both machines were ground driven. The Deering machine used snapping rolls to remove the ears from the stalk while the McCormick machine used a system of picking chains. In spite of glowing performance reports about these two corn pickers in the November 1904 issue of

This 1927 shop photo shows the "first all-steel corn picker manufactured at Deering Works." Advent of PTO drive for corn pickers greatly improved their performance compared to the original ground drive machines.

Farm Implement News, their performance was far short of the results of hand-picked corn and sales were limited. These somewhat similar corn pickers were improved and evolved into the Deering No. 2 in 1907, the Deering No. 3 in 1910, the McCormick No. 2 in 1909, and the McCormick No. 3 in 1914. Eventually the two lines were combined into the McCormick-Deering No. 3 corn picker in 1922. They were all 1-row, pull-type machines with side elevators.

 ## A Tractor Mounted Corn Picker . . . An International Harvester First

The design of the Farmall tractor that made it the ideal cultivating tractor also made it ideal as the basis for a self-propelled corn picker. Documentation from the Patent Department records conversations about a Farmall corn picker attachment with Bert Benjamin who was the generally accepted

One of the early Deering corn pickers and an IHC Titan tractor work at harvesting a badly lodged field of corn. The ground drive picker elevated husked ears to the horse-drawn wagon. The picker operator also had charge of the reigns.

This McCormick-Deering Farmall F-14 tractor and 1-row mounted 1-M corn picker had the "lead" in an IHC corn picker movie made at Crete, Illinois, in 1938. Stiff-stalked hybrid corn added to the practicality and performance of corn pickers in the following decade.

at the top of each first elevato
Production of the 2-M picker conti
ued until it was replaced by th
McCormick-Deering 2-ME in 1952. Th
1-row tractor-mounted picker line ha
a one-year transition with the update
model No. 11 and evolved into th
McCormick-Deering No. 1-M in 193
This 1-row version of the No. 2-M wa
produced until 1943; that was the en
of 1-row tractor-mounted pickers fo
large tractors. The McCormic
Deering No. 14-M and No. 2C-10 wer
1-row mounted pickers for Farma
230, 200, and Super C tractor
mounted pickers for this tractor si
ended in 1956. The No. 2C-11 was
snapper version.

leader of the program that resulted in the Farmall Regular. These conversations took place in 1925 and Mr. Benjamin indicated that the concept of a Farmall mounted picker had been considered prior to that date. The result was the McCormick-Deering Farmall 2-row mounted corn picker in 1929 and the 1-row mounted corn picker in 1930. The two corn pickers were produced in the new IHC East Moline Works that came on line in 1929. The new plant made the last run of McCormick-Deering No. 3 pull-type corn pickers in 1929. The Farmall corn pickers became the No. 10, 1-row and No. 20, 2-row mounted pickers in 1931. They could be equipped with an elevator that delivered ear corn to a hopper mounted well above the tractor hood. With a wagon pulled along side, a chute the full length of the hopper dropped down and ears gravity unloaded into the wagon.

After a two-year transition that included the updated model No. 22 and No. 22B, the 2-row tractor-mounted picker line evolved into the McCormick-Deering No. 2-M in 1939 for the new Farmall M as well as the F-20 and F-30. This solid design incorporated a trash roll beater at the top of the live-point snapping rolls and a 4-roll husking bed with shelled corn saver

Straight-Through Picker Design

The McCormick-Deering No. 24, 2-row, tracto mounted corn picker combined snapping rolls an husking rolls on a single pair of shafts, one pair for eac row. This design was lighter and more economical tha the Model 2-M picker with its independent, 4-ro husking bed for each row. The snapping rolls of th No. 24 were an aggressive, close-pitch spiral design wit snapping lugs in the upper half; they were intended t remove a substantial amount of husk in order to reduc the load on the husking rolls that followed. The straigh through design resulted in a low center of gravity an excellent visibility. Row units could be set for 36- t 42-inch rows on the H tractor and 36- to 44-inch rows o the M tractor. The center divider pivoted with th tractor's front wheels. The No. 24 picker was also avai able in snapper and sweet corn versions.

The No. 24 was followed by the McCormick No. 34 HM-20, 2-row mounted, the No. 34 HM-21, 2-row mounted snapper, and the No. 34 HM-22, 2-row mounted sweet corn picker.

This IHC No. mounted corn picker cutaway illustra the combination snapping and huskin done by a single pair o rolls. The design saved bo weight and cost compared to the M Series pickers that had a separate husking bed system.

The McCormick-Deering No.14-P 1-row, pull-type corn picker used the same snapping and husking system as the No. 24 tractor-mounted picker. It is shown here with a Farmall H.

Pull-Type Pickers

The McCormick-Deering No. 100 and No. 200, 1- and 2-row pull-type corn pickers were introduced in 1931, the same year as the similar No. 10 and No. 20 tractor-mounted pickers. The pull-type pickers had high-mount, gravity unloaded, ear corn hoppers similar to the tractor-mounted machines.

For 1938, the McCormick-Deering No. 1P and No. 2P 1- and 2-row pull-type corn pickers were introduced. The No. 1P had a 6-roll husking bed and the No. 2-P had a 10-roll husking bed; both machines had side delivery elevators. Each machine came standard with an adjustable hitch for pulling a wagon to the side of the picker and under the elevator discharge.

The two pull-type picker models became the McCormick-Deering No. 1-PR and No. 2-PR in 1951 and 1953, respectively. They were very similar to the previous model but the "R" suffix indicated the new machines had rear discharge elevators. These two venerable pull-type pickers stayed in the IH product line until all corn picker production ended in 1974.

The same straight-through, combination snapping and husking roll design of the No. 24, 2-row mounted picker was incorporated in the McCormick-Deering No. 14-P, 1-row pull-type picker. The result was a lightweight, approximately 1,500 pound, economical, light draft picker for operation by any 2-plow tractor.

This McCormick International 2-PR 2-row, pull-type corn picker design used the same snapping and husking system as the 2-M mounted picker. The No. 1-PR and No. 2-PR pickers both pulled the wagon to the rear; earlier models pulled the wagon to the side.

This 2-row, 2-MH corn picker mounted on a McCormick International Farmall 450 had the power and capacity to harvest the tough stalks, tight husks, and high yields that characterize hybrid corn.

Heavy-Duty Corn Pickers for Heavy-Duty Yields

The superior standing ability and stalk quality of hybrid corn contributed to improved corn picker performance and helped speed the transition to mechanized ear corn harvest. As improved hybrid seed corn, low-cost nitrogen fertilizer, chemical weed control and a host of new cultural practices combined to make corn yields of 200 bushels per acre not too uncommon by the late 1950s, corn pickers had to change. International Harvester's first response to increased corn yields was the McCormick-Deering No. 2-ME 2-row, tractor-mounted corn picker in 1952. The next model was the McCormick No. 2-MH described as the "Rugged, heavy-duty two-row mounted picker (that) is ideal for large-acreage growers and custom operators." It was introduced in 1957. Continued yield increases called for still higher capacity and reliability. To meet that need, the McCormick No. 2M-HD extra heavy-duty, 2-row mounted picker was introduced in 1960 in addition to the No. 2-MH. A 9 1/4-inch first elevator, compared to the 6 1/4-inch No. 2-MH

first elevator, and a 6-roll husking bed in place of the 4-roll husking bed on the No. 2-MH contributed to a 50% increase in capacity. An extra heavy-duty main drive gear case and other changes added extra reliability.

A Threat and a Limitation

With the introduction of corn heads for combines in the mid-1950s, the corn picker was challenged for the first time. In response to the threat, IH introduced the McCormick-Deering No. 10 shelling attachment for the No. 2-ME 2-row, tractor-mounted picker in 1958. This was followed by the McCormick No. 15 sheller attachment for the No. 2-MH and the McCormick No. 2 sheller attachment for the No. 2M-HD picker, both in 1960. The shelling attachments for corn pickers made possible the labor-saving convenience of totally mechanized material handling of the harvested produce similar to the combine and corn head.

The tractor-mounted corn picker had a pair of limitations that could not be solved with an attachment like the sheller: The picker could not harvest rows more narrow than 36-inches and harvest of more than two rows at a time was not practical. To answer these limitations, an IH experimental 4-row self-propelled corn picker was reduced to a field-going prototype in the fall of 1959. The East Moline ear corn harvester used the current IH 4-row combine corn head for snapping the ears. Clean ear corn was delivered to a large hydraulic dump box that extended the full width of the machine. The unloading system would have made this a very popular machine with seed corn, popcorn and sweet corn producers. The 4-row, self-propelled corn picker was not released for production.

This 1959 East Moline experimental 4-row, self-propelled corn picker would have overcome the 2-row limitation of the tractor-mounted picker. However, it never went into production.

Ear Corn Pickers, Where Will the Market Go?

International Harvester shipped 21,643 of the popular No. 2-M and No. 24, 2-row tractor mounted pickers plus No. 1-P, No. 1-PR, and No. 14-P 1-row pull pickers in 1951. Within three years, shipments would be cut in half and remain at just under 1,000 unit level for the next six years. The exception was 1957; IH shipped an additional 2,000 units as part of the McCormick 2-MH introduction and achieved a 30.9% market share. After 1957 the U.S. corn picker market steadily declined to under 16,000 units shipped in 1964. Shipments of IH corn pickers also declined and at a slightly higher rate.

A Revolutionary New Corn Harvester

In spite of the consistent decline in industry sales of corn pickers, IH introduced the McCormick 234 in 1965; this was a totally new corn picker design. In fact, it was rightly called the McCormick International 234, 2-row mounted CORN HARVESTER.

The No. 234 was based on a universal frame that provided for mounting on John Deere, Oliver, Allis-Chalmers, Case, and Ford, as well as IH tractors. The design provided for quickly mounting or dismounting, in five minutes or less, any of the rear processing units that included: 8- or 12-roll husking bed, snapper hopper, sheller or multi-purpose sheller-cracker that converted to a sheller-grinder. As the processing unit was raised from the storage position with the tractor hydraulics, the drive couplers on each side and the PTO main drive coupling mated automatically. The snapping roll unit design incorporated scalloped stripper rolls similar to those used in IH combine corn heads. These combined with rotary stripper plates that adjusted on-the-go and virtually eliminated butt shelling. Conventional deep-pocket snapping rolls could be interchanged with the scalloped rolls if desired.

The versatility and quick mounting system of the No. 234 set it apart from all prior models and established a new standard for tractor-mounted corn picker design. However, the No. 234 could harvest only two rows at a time and handle no row-spacing more narrow than 36 inches. By the early 1970s, combines equipped with corn heads became the predominate corn harvest method. Production of the No. 234 2-row, tractor-mounted corn harvester ended in 1974. The 23-year production run of 1-row, No. 1-PR pull pickers and a 21-year production run of 2-row, No. 2-PR pull pickers ended the same year.

The McCormick International 234 2-row, tractor-mounted corn harvester was far more than a corn picker. With a quick change of rear processing units it became a corn picker husker, a corn picker sheller, a corn snapper, a sweet corn harvester, a corn grinder, or a corn sheller cracker. The curved, adjustable stripper plates made it the premier popcorn harvester.

The Embargo

When the Arab oil embargo hit the United States in 1973, long lines formed at gasoline service stations and Interstate Highway speed limits dropped to 55 miles per hour. Agriculture was not exempt from the embargo's impact. Frantic efforts by land grant universities attempted to calculate the minimum energy requirements of productive agriculture and to promote energy conservation. Agricultural organizations prepared to lobby Washington for energy allocations for agriculture. One study indicated that 68% of the diesel fuel and LP gas energy used to produce and dry a 100 bushels per acre corn crop was used for drying. The high energy use for corn drying led to the question, why not go back to ear corn harvest and let nature do the corn drying? An IH Product Planning Research study of the question informed management that as long as energy for corn drying was available — not rationed — even at significantly higher prices, there would be no long-term shift back to ear corn harvest and open crib drying. Industry corn picker sales did increase 12.6% in 1973 compared to 1972; however, they dropped 25.6% the following year. The long lines at the gasoline pump disappeared, serious public concern about energy went away, and interest in ear corn harvest ended. The question of America's future energy needs and our reliance on foreign oil imports did not go away.

IH Axial-Flow
Combines
The Long Road to Success

This experimental No. 10 combine was the result of research that demonstrated the superiority of a cylinder and concave for separating grain compared to straw walkers. The 10-foot platform machine had a conventional cylinder and concave, rotary separating cylinder, and rotary drum cleaning system all located in the feeder house. Straw, chaff, etc. from the cleaning system discharged out the right side of the machine.

Straw walkers are the most efficient method of separating grain from stalks and straw, right? Wrong! During the mid-'50s IH engineers at East Moline Combine Works did extensive laboratory research on conventional combine performance. Results made it clear that the open concave and beater were far more efficient in separating grain than straw walkers. As a result of these findings, a conventional combine was equipped with a second cylinder directly behind the first and tested in small grain during 1956. The following year two more multi-cylinder combines were tested.

One of the experimental, multi-cylinder combines was the No. 10 rotary. This compact, little 10-foot platform machine was truly innovative. A conventional cylinder and concave and a second cylinder for separating were located in the feeder house, and not in the body of the combine. Furthermore, the rotary-drum cleaning system was also in the feeder house directly behind the threshing and separating cylinders; the cleaning system fan discharged chaff etc. directly out of the right side of the machine above the drive wheel. This compact configuration with all of the functional components in the feeder house resulted in the body of the combine serving basically as a carrier for the engine, drive line, and grain tank. Oh yes, there was an operator's platform too.

Since the body of the No. 10 was not loaded down with shafts, bearings, belts, and chains like a conventional combine, it was possible to create a sleek, styled combine body totally different from conventional combines. In addition to regular patents, the No. 10 styling was so unique that a U.S. Design Patent was issued for the "Ornamental Design for a Combined Harvester and Thresher." After three years of No. 10 field test and very limited "remodeling" effort, the Chief Engineer of Advanced Engineering determined the concept had no future and the project was canceled.

However, the ground work had been laid for innovative combine development utilizing rotary separation.

During the mid-1950s, a California firm, Harvestaire Inc., also developed a system of centrifugal fans and cyclones for threshing and separating grain. International Harvester engineers evaluated the system, but they determined it was not worth acquiring. Engineering and Product Planning Research continued to carefully monitor rotary threshing and separating projects instituted by universities throughout the Midwest.

Two Parts of IH—One Common Quest

During the late 1950s and early 1960s, engineers at the manufacturing plant in Croix, France, where IH produced combines, issued a series of test reports on a "horizontal rotary cleaning system from East Moline

Vertical Cyclo-Rotary

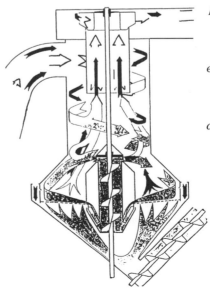

Engineering at the IH combine plant in Croix, France, investigated and experimented with various novel means of threshing, separating, and cleaning grain including the Vertical Cyclo-Rotary system.

343

Drawings." The results were discouraging and evolved into a vertical, "Cyclo-Rotary" cleaning system. IH France tested their vertical "Cyclo-Rotary" cleaning system in the laboratory, and they also evaluated a combine with a high-speed brush gathering and threshing system in the header that coupled with the "Cyclo-Rotary" cleaning system. In 1962, Croix Engineering proposed several methods of threshing and preliminary separation; one anticipated the Axial-Flow concept. During the same time, East Moline Engineering researched new threshing and separation methods and built and field tested the experimental, multi-cylinder No. 10 combine.

A First Hint of Axial-Flow Technology

There is good reason to believe that East Moline Engineering first recognized the potential for combined rotary threshing and separating not from the No. 10 rotary combine or the development work done by IH France but from development of cage-type corn shellers. With the advent of on-farm crop drying and corn heads on combines, a demand developed for sheller attachments for corn pickers. These attachments were single-rotor, cage-type shellers mounted cross-wise over the tractor hitch. IH enjoyed a strong market position with the 2-M, 2-ME, and 2M-HD tractor-mounted corn pickers and sought to maintain that position by offering sheller attachments for these tractor-mounted corn pickers.

In response to the demand for more capacity, an experimental 2-row, twin-rotor tractor mounted picker-sheller code named the 2MX was developed. The solid rotor had a spiral that fed snapped ears to a tapered cone at the front of a solid rotor. Traditional corn sheller square lugs on the rotor were coupled with angled forwarding vanes in the cage. Flat, radial paddles discharged the husk and cobs at the rear of the rotor. The 2MX corn sheller configuration exhibited virtually all of the elements that would eventually comprise the Axial-Flow cylinder design. The 2MX was field tested in 1962 and estimated manufacturing cost was

completed, but the machine was never released to production.

The two engineers from East Moline Advanced Engineering who developed the 2MX twin-rotor, tractor-mounted corn sheller saw an even greater opportunity for the principles demonstrated in that machine. They envisioned one large rotor installed in a No. 141 combine in place of the cylinder and straw walkers; the cleaning system would be conventional.

Axial Threshing and Separating Go to the Field in Disguise

Laboratory studies of a full-size rotary threshing and separating system began in 1962. Encouraging results led to installation of a 24-inch diameter rotor in a No. 403 combine chassis for threshing and separating; the cleaning system was not changed. By 1964 the new experimental harvester, known as the CX-1, was ready for secure field test in Arizona. The radical new machine had its share of disappointments, but these early CX-1 tests did reveal that the concept had merit. The journey down the long road to final development of the IH Axial-Flow combine for harvest of all traditional combine-harvested crops had begun.

U.S. Patents assigned to International Harvester between 1969 and 1971 make it clear the Company was serious about developing an axial-flow system for threshing and separating. Two patents of note described a caged, open center rotor with a short spiral or auger feed the same diameter as the rotor. The earlier patent had the rotor parallel with the

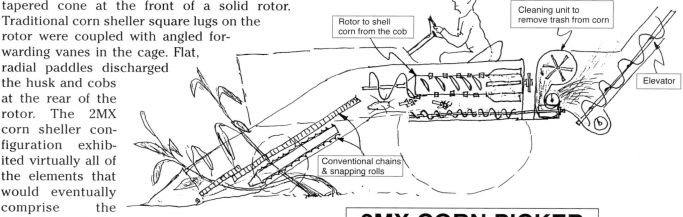

2MX CORN PICKER

An engineering sketch of the 2MX tractor-mounted, 2-row, twin-cylinder corn picker/sheller exhibits most of the elements incorporated in the eventual Axial-Flow rotor: up-front feed spiral, tapered cone cylinder transition, solid cylinder rotor, angled forwarding vanes and flat, radial discharge paddles at the rear of the rotor. This sketch was made from an assembly blue print believed to be the only remaining documentation of the 2MX.

☞ *This carefully made cardboard model of the CX-1 was styled after the twin tank, "saddle tank," design in vogue at the time. It was no doubt used to convince senior management that the crude, field test rotary experiments could be incorporated in a properly styled, production combine.*

Rotary threshing and separating development was field tested with the highly secret CX-1 (Combine Experimental No. 1) in a conventional model No. 403 combine frame. As shown in the photo below, a careful observer could spot the long feeder house that pivoted high above the normal cylinder location and straw discharged from the rectangular box on the right rear of the separator; it was not an IH 403 combine.

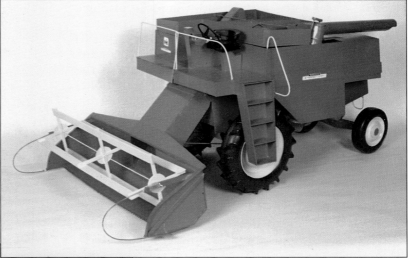

A Twin-Rotor Sheller

Concurrent with the single rotor CX-1, there was a development project code-named CX-11. This self-propelled machine had two cage-type corn shellers of the type used in the No. 234 tractor-mounted corn picker, sheller mounted side by side. A corn grinder version was also considered. Limited field test in 1966 demonstrated the need to reduce the height and identified other needed changes. Rather than update the high profile test machine, a new CX-11 version-2 was built that incorporated the changes. Late fabrication resulted in only limited test for 1967. By now the CX-1 axial-flow project had demonstrated its ability to perform as a high-capacity corn harvester and the decision was made to phase out the CX-11 twin-rotor sheller project.

ground and a conventional cleaning system mounted above. (When New Idea developed an experimental axial-flow combine module for the UNI Power Unit, it had this same configuration; it was never released for production.) The later IH patent had the rear of the rotor sharply elevated and described a different design for the threshing and separating section of the rotor. The conventional cleaning system was in the traditional location.

The experimental CX-11 twin-rotor corn harvester, version-2, shown here, was a high capacity, self-propelled, twin rotor sheller that incorporated two sets of cage-type sheller units from the successful tractor-mounted International 234 corn harvester. A larger model was planned to handle a 6- or 8-row combine corn head, be equipped with a 200-bushel grain tank, and be powered with a 150-horsepower engine. Since combine corn heads delivered larger quantities of stalks and trash than corn pickers, removing the trash and cleaning the sample were major obstacles to perfecting the harvester. The three rectangular openings on each side of the machine were outlets for fan, trash, and cleaning auger discharge. The version-2 improved the cleaning compared to version-1, but not to a satisfactory level.

Some years later a different twin-rotor machine would get IH's attention. One of the three engineers named on one of the basic Axial-Flow patents left IH shortly after the application was filed. He became the lead engineer for New Holland's development of the twin-rotor TR-70 axial combine. International Harvester sued New Holland over this engineer's role and an out-of-court settlement delayed New Holland's introduction date for the TR-70 and resulted in a modest cash settlement in favor of IH.

"MULTI-PASS"

What do you call this super secret project: Roto Combine, Axial-Thresh, Rotary-Harvester? Engineering came up with the unique and descriptive name, MULTI-PASS. The term described the axial-flow concept as presenting material being threshed and separated multiple times to the concaves and grates. The name seemed to fit and everyone associated with the project used the term in general conversation as well as in official documents. Sales and marketing weren't so sure about the name; they thought MULTI-PASS sounded like doing the job over and over. The Grain Harvesting Product Committee Chairman settled the issue; he said the new development will be called an Axial-Flow combine. The generic term became official and MULTI-PASS gradually faded away.

As recorded in this photo, senior IH management had a chance to see what a MULTI-PASS/Axial-Flow combine might look like at the Engineering Center Product Review in February of 1969. The 24-inch rotor machine had a high feeder house pivot and overshot feeding of the open rotor. It was code named CX-18. In the fully folded position, the swinging unloading auger was nested behind the sheet metal side.

The Big Machine

The two experimental engineering machines code named CX-18 and CX-18A, were both 24-inch diameter rotor combines. In addition, there was a larger 30-inch diameter rotor machine named the CX-14. In 1968 the CX-14 was an open rotor design with a long feeder house depositing material into a high inlet. Straw was discharged out the side of the machine directly from the end of the rotor. Threshed and separated material was conveyed to the cleaning system by multiple augers. To match the threshing and separating capacity of this big rotor, two No. 403 combine sieves were mounted side by side. This arrangement resulted in a 74-inch wide cleaning system that didn't match the width of the balance of the machine. Hart Carter was the only source of adjustable sieves at that time; so, an improved design had to wait until they could supply a larger, one-piece sieve.

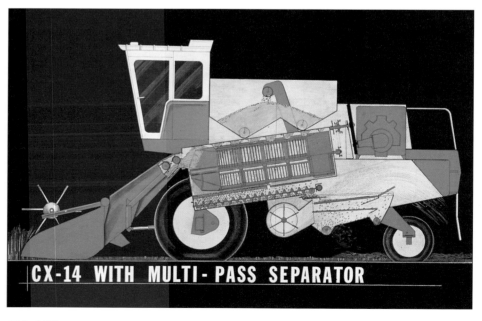

This 1968 cross-section art illustrates the experimental CX-14 MULTI-PASS combine. The 30-inch diameter, open-style rotor was fed at the top from a long feeder house. Straw was discharged out the side of the machine directly from the end of the rotor. No straw spreader was needed

Make it Look Like a Real Combine

Marketing was enthused with the prospect of a superior new harvester to sell, but they wanted it to look like a "regular" combine; straw discharged out the side did not fit that description. Engineering's first attempt at rear straw discharge used an oscillating pan; it didn't work well. Satisfactory rear discharge was achieved with a rugged, efficient rotary beater.

Other Challenges

At this stage of development, rotary threshing and separating tended to deposit more material to one side than the other. Therefore, auger conveyor delivery to the cleaning system lacked uniformity. An oscillating grain pan was tried, but that method couldn't handle the volume of material or improve the distribution. In search of a solution, a wide-belt conveyor was tried as a way to move material from under the rotor to the sieves; a belt conveyor was not the right answer either. Finally, the design returned to the positive, reliable auger conveyor system and uniform distribution was achieved by changes in the rotor and related components. Material from the augers was fluffed up on a short grain pan ahead of the sieves. One more challenge had a reliable, functional solution.

One Problem Solved — Two Problems Eliminated

Problem: During field tests, the cleaning system would be performing beautifully when suddenly the performance dropped markedly; why? Engineering continued to struggle with this problem until it was suggested that the solution was to "see" what was

The Experimental CX-18A Axial-Flow combine had the engineering "Dog House" for observing cleaning-system air-flow patterns in the field.

actually causing the problem. To do this, a rigid plexi-glass window was installed in the side of a CX-18A combine and a bench provided so an observer(s) could watch the material flow to and over the cleaning system while operating in the field. In order to see, it was necessary to construct a canvas "dog house" enclosure around the observation bench and plexi-glass window to keep out natural light. Lights inside the combine made it possible to see continuous-state flow patterns. These observations confirmed that the aggressive impellers at the front of the solid rotor acted like a large fan. From time to time the excess air flow they generated would interfere with the carefully regulated air flow through the cleaning sieves. Understanding gained from "dog house" observations coupled with extensive lab test resulted in baffles and modifications that solved the air-flow problem.

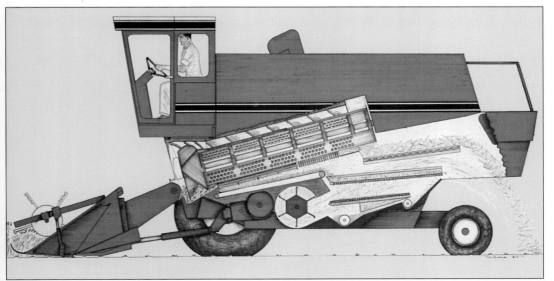

One step forward and two steps back — a low pivot location for the short feeder house and undershot feeding of the rotor, as shown in this cross-section drawing, represented a major step forward in the final design of the IH Axial-Flow combine. The oscillating pan for rear straw discharge and the wide-belt conveyor under the rotor were steps backward and were replaced.

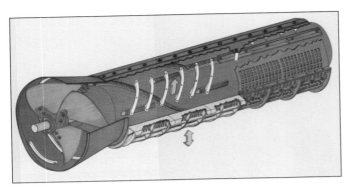

This Axial-Flow rotor and cage rendering displays all of the elements of a production Axial-Flow combine: conefront impeller with undershot feeder, closed drum-type rotor with spiral rasp bars, material forwarding vanes, and quick removable concave segments with removable wires. This 1973-74 graphic helped inform senior IH management that the final push to production was ready to begin.

Getting Our Act Together

A straight-to-the-point progress summary from the Chief Engineer of Grain Harvesting said, "In the winter of 1973-74 we began to get it all together, the cone front impeller, undershot feeder, closed drum type rotor with spiral rasp bars, auger bed under the rotor, and rear discharge with beater. At this point it all looked so logical and simple we wondered why it took so long to arrive. That's one of the wonders of hindsight vs. foresight in the complex machine development process." (The senior author would add that short test seasons coupled with the natural variations of biological material and growing seasons make the development of agricultural harvesting machines especially challenging and time consuming.)

Air flow from the rotor impellers produced an unplanned benefit. Back flow of air from conventional combine cylinders has always created dust problems that billowed out from the header and feeder house. In some crops and conditions the dust made it quite difficult for the operator to see. Air flow through the Axial-Flow impellers completely eliminated up-front dust and solved a long standing conventional combine problem.

The Corn Belt Special

In 1974, after long years of development, marketing and corporate management wanted an Axial-Flow product to sell. Machines in field test were delivering impressive performance in corn and soybeans but less than ideal performance in small grain. In response, the Product Committee proposed a 24-inch rotor "Corn Belt Special" for corn and soybeans that would at least do an acceptable job in harvesting the limited acreage of small grain typical of the central Corn Belt. This machine could be ready for limited production as early as 1976. Development of a general purpose machine should be ready by 1978. Continued development of a larger 30-inch rotor machine, a less costly 24-inch rotor machine, and an evaluation of a machine with a smaller rotor was to be considered. Typically, management had the planning and research departments survey and evaluate how marketable a "Corn Belt Special" might be. Fortunately, their cool response coupled with significant progress with the general purpose machine made it possible to end the divided effort and concentrate on just one version.

The Final Road to Limited Production and Marketing

Produce and Market Report No. 301 signed by all responsible management from President Brooks McCormick on down the line authorized production of 300 Axial-Flow combines in two sizes in 1977 and full

The first Axial-Flow combine off the line at the start of full production started out with a real "breakthrough." A gigantic paper banner at the end of the assembly line read:

. . . PRODUCING TOMORROW'S HARVESTING
TECHNOLOGY TODAY!
IH
EAST MOLINE PLANT
FIRST FULL PRODUCTION
AXIAL-FLOW COMBINE

The East Moline plant manager drove the first combine through the banner to cheers of an enthusiastic throng of employees who gathered for the special event.

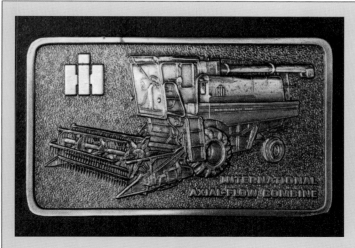

Belt buckles, belt buckles, belt buckles! No major, new, farm equipment introduction would be complete without belt buckles to commemorate the occasion; the Axial-Flow combine was no exception. The feeling of accomplishment ran so high that IH Marketing, Manufacturing and Grain Harvesting Engineering at East Moline each had special belt buckles produced to celebrate the Axial-Flow and their pride.

production the following year. To meet these objectives and be assured of a proven product, engineering placed 12 Axial-Flow combines in the 1976 field test fleet. Five more combines were to be produced from engineering drawings by manufacturing; however, East Moline Manufacturing said they couldn't handle the load. The sister division, IH Motor Truck at Fort Wayne, Indiana, came through with space and people to fabricate and assemble the needed "factory built" preproduction machines. To assure maximum benefit from 17 machines in the field, district sales and service personnel were brought into the program, and they helped

follow the fleet. Everyone benefitted, and by the season's end 43,000 acres had been harvested. Excellent machine performance in the field demonstrated that the Axial-Flow combine was finally ready.

Marketing a Radical Change

Developing an innovative new product is exciting, challenging, and loaded with risk; will the customer buy it? Launching the Axial-Flow combine had two requirements: The product had to be right and the marketplace had to believe it was right. An outstanding

Controversy and the Russian Connection

International Harvester has a long history of manufacturing farm equipment in Russia. Serious discussions were under way with IH representatives in Russia in the late '70s to build increased capacity 1480 Axial-Flow combines there. Suddenly the negotiations became tense on the Russian side, they said IH was planning to produce old models for them; they wanted only the latest IH had to offer. Russian negotiators raised the question to IH management in Chicago as well as in Russia. They were told they were getting the latest combine technology IH had to offer; the Russians wouldn't accept that answer; everyone was totally confused. The puzzle finally unfolded:

In 1976 IH was asked to participate in the USDA Bicentennial at the Kennedy Space Flight Center, Cape Canaveral, Florida. The IH assignment was to describe the combine (grain harvesting system) of the future and provide an industrial design, photo mural of the concept for the show. The Product Planning Research Group responded with detailed performance specifications for a futuristic combine comprised of a gathering, threshing and separating unit teamed with a robot controlled grain hauler. Some Axial-Flow benefits were alluded to but the name was never mentioned. The whole project was an exercise in futuristic daydreaming with the IH name attached. Somewhere in the translation, the Russians took it for real. After much to do about nothing, the issue was resolved, and discussions continued regarding production of Axial-Flow combines in Russia.

International Harvester Company participated in the USDA exhibit at the Kennedy Space Flight Center at Cape Canaveral, Florida, in the summer of 1976 as part of the U.S. Bicentennial Exposition on Science and Technology. Industrial Design created an impressive rendering of what a future crop harvesting machine might look like. The artwork was made into a 42- x 70-inch color photo mural for the exhibit. Company news releases hinted at benefits that would come with the next generation combine; everything else was next century daydreaming. The press loved it.

USDA described the IH Future Crop Harvesting Machine mural at the Bicentennial Exhibit with the following text:

"In the future, this may be what a grain harvesting machine will look like. The operator will sit comfortably in a climate controlled cab which has been designed for near perfect visibility. He will monitor adjustments made automatically by the machine as it is guided at 5 mph on the row being harvested.

"The crop will be threshed, separated, and cleaned by the harvesting unit. Cleaned grain will move directly to the transport unit, a fully automated robot vehicle. On command of the operator, the transport unit will detach itself, proceed to the grain storage site, unload, and then return to the harvesting area to await its next turn behind the harvesting unit."

program was formulated to achieve these objectives. The preproduction run of 200 No. 1460 and 100 No. 1440 Axial-Flow combines was retailed to carefully selected, loyal IH customers representing a wide range of geographic locations, crops, and conditions. Purchasers were told their machines would be updated with any changes incorporated in the 1978 full production combines. Each owner received a belt buckle inscribed, "First 300 Axial-Flow Combines." A three-step monitoring program was instituted to follow each new Axial-Flow combine: Every customer was contacted by Company personnel at the time of delivery or shortly thereafter. These customers and machines were visited again at least once during the season of use. At the end of the season, owners were contacted or surveyed to learn about their experiences. By carefully following the first 300 machines, engineering, manufacturing, and marketing gained significant, useful information about the product, customer satisfaction, and market reaction. Careful monitoring had other benefits. Small differences between hand-made engineering shop machines and production-built machines can sometimes result in problems. That difference caused one of the preproduction machines to develop a fire around the seal on the drive end of the rotor shaft. The field was alerted, changes in manufacturing were made, and a potentially serious problem was averted.

Market Positioning and Product Introduction

In order for marketing to properly position the Axial-Flow, an extensive mail survey was conducted among combine owners in April 1977 to learn what dollar value, if any, they would place on reduced grain loss and grain damage from a "new concept combine" that also incorporated an impressive list of other improvements. Survey results and input from the 300 Axial-Flow users formed the basis for an aggressive dealer introduction in the fall prior to full production.

The entire Product Committee plus the Vice-President and General Manager of IH North American Operations joined in explaining and educating the dealers. They told how IH had invested $56 million in a program that began in 1963. They explained in detail how rotary threshing and separating works and why it is superior to conventional methods. And, they stressed how these truly new combines incorporated a myriad of other features and benefits; Axial-Flow combines were new from the ground up. Driving them at the introduction and later working with customers in the field was what sold the dealer organization on the IH Axial-Flow combine.

At the end of the 1978 harvest season, each new IH Axial-Flow combine owner received a mail survey to learn why they made the purchase, how the machine performed, their level of satisfaction, and what size

The new IH 1440/1460/1480 combines looked like a modern, conventional combine on the outside; that's the way it was planned. The real Axial-Flow story was on the inside. This beautiful, color rendering was the perfect tool to communicate the nature of the rugged, simple, and radically different threshing and separating system. This image was featured over and over in the course of introducing the IH Axial-Flow concept.

These were the IH Axial-Flow survey incentives for 1978 purchases.

and capacity would be needed in the future. Each owner received a survey return incentive of a leather strapped watch fob inscribed, "FIRST FULL RUN AXIAL-FLOW COMBINE — 1978." The number of returned surveys was an order of magnitude greater than would be expected from a random market survey. Overall satisfaction was quite high. Several useful suggestions for product improvements were described.

The Axial-Flow project manager during most of the development and introduction of the Axial-Flow combine is now retired. He recently looked back over those years with the Axial-Flow project and summarized the launch as, "one of the best, if not the best, marketing jobs I saw during my IH career."

International Harvester engineered and manufactured combines at Croix, France. U.S. engineering management sent an engineering CX18-A prototype Axial-Flow (the future 1440) to France in 1973 for side by side comparison with the new conventional combine being developed at Croix. The CX-18A was far from fully developed and the Axial-Flow did not meet expectations. With proven, production machines coming off the line in 1978, an Axial-Flow 1480 was sent to France for evaluation under European conditions. This second test demonstrated solid performance of the Axial-Flow combine under the high moisture corn and long, damp straw harvest conditions typical of Europe. In 1980 IH acquired a 535,000-square-foot combine plant at Angers, France, for conversion to the production of IH Axial-Flow combines; however, the project was terminated before any combines were manufactured.

One Step at a Time

"If engineering had been able to stipulate all of the ultimate objectives of the Axial-Flow program at the very beginning, the task would have seemed overwhelming, and we never would have started," so stated the Chief Engineer for Grain Harvesting who presided over the program from 1966 forward. He goes on to say, "If we had known the real magnitude of our undertaking and the time and money it would consume, IH management would never had condoned it. By gradually stretching out the project until real objectives could be achieved, the program succeeded. No doubt, underlying management's willingness to support such a long term project was the recognition that IH needed something spectacular!" They got it.

The engineering test group at the IH plant in Croix, France placed a French experimental 953X decal on the No. 1480 test combine.

Named the "value leader of its class," the No. 1440 had a 145-bushel capacity grain tank and was powered by a 135-horsepower, 436-cubic-inch diesel engine. It could handle up to a 24-foot grain head and up to a 6-row narrow corn head. Like the No. 1460, it had a 24-inch diameter rotor.

Completing the Axial-Flow Family

By the time full production began in 1978, the Axial-Flow line included two 24-inch diameter rotor machines: the No. 1440 with 145-bushel grain tank and 135-horsepower diesel power and the No. 1460 with 180-bushel grain tank and 170-horsepower turbocharged diesel power. A larger, heavier constructed 30-inch diameter rotor machine, the No. 1480, with a 208-bushel grain tank and 190-horsepower turbocharged diesel topped out the line with adequate capacity to handle 24-foot grain headers and 8-row wide corn heads. Pull-type, hillside, rice, and edible bean models along with a small 20-inch rotor machine would follow.

The FIEI Class V No. 1460 was the most popular Axial-Flow model. Specifications included a 180-bushel capacity grain tank and a 170-horsepower, 436-cubic-inch turbo diesel engine. It could handle up to a 24-foot grain head. It is pictured with an 800 Series corn head that was available up to an 8-row narrow or a 6-row wide.

Performance in fields like this IH 1460 Axial-Flow combine with 820 flexible cutterbar header demonstrated the Axial-Flow's ability to greatly reduce soybean splits and damage compared to conventional machines. This is an extremely important benefit for soybean seed producers.

"High power and tremendous productivity put the No. 1480 in a class by itself." This combine, which was the largest of the Axial-Flow family, had a 30-inch diameter rotor, 208-bushel grain tank capacity and 190-horsepower, 436-cubic-inch turbo diesel. This is the only IH Axial-Flow combine with capacity and weight carrying ability sufficient to handle the 800 Series 8-row wide corn head.

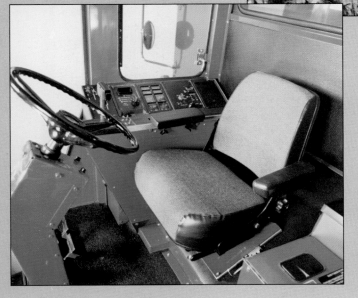

The heated, air-conditioned, control center that floated on vibration-dampening Iso-mounts offered combine operators the ideal environment and convenience so greatly appreciated during long harvest days. The quiet isolation made the benefits of monitor control absolutely essential.

IH 1420 and 1480 Axial-Flow combines team up to make short work of this farmer's corn harvest operation.

The 820 flexible cutterbar headers had cutterbars that could flex to maintain a 1 1/2-inch cutting height across the width of the head by flexing within a 6-inch range. Higher knife speed of 600 cycles per second and no hump between the cutterbar and the auger combined to provide significant reduction in soybean harvest losses. The No. 820 header came in 13-, 15-, 16 1/2-, 17 1/2-, 20-, and 22 1/2-foot sizes to match the popular row spacings and individual machine capacity.

The 810 rigid cutterbar headers were available in nine sizes from 10 to 30 feet. Hydraulic reel drive and hydraulic reel lift were standard equipment. The three smallest sizes were available without reel and cutting equipment to accommodate the 110- or 132-inch belt pickup for windrow harvest.

900 Series Corn Heads and 800 Series Grain Heads

The quick-attachable, 800 Series corn heads were the product available at the time the Axial-Flow combine was introduced. In response to losing the patent infringement law suit with Deere and Company over the 800 Series corn head design, IH developed the 900 Series corn heads. The 1981 Buyer's Guide introduced the new 900 Series corn heads as, "designed from front to back to save every possible ear from every acre." Features included: low-angle row units, slow-speed 14-inch cross auger, simple design with fewer gears and bearings, and less overall weight. The purchaser could choose from 4-, 6-, or 8-row models in wide or narrow rows and a 5-row wide version to match his combine capacity.

Power and capacity plus outstanding threshing and separating efficiency under difficult crop and harvest conditions made the No. 1480 Axial-Flow the combine of choice among many large farmers and custom operators (shown here with a No. 810 header). University research documented that the Axial-Flow could put more grain in the tank from a given area than similar size conventional combines.

Awards for the IH Axial-Flow Combine

The 50th International Salon of Agricultural Machines (SIMA) awarded the International Axial-Flow combine the No. 1 gold medal for technical achievement in Paris, France, in 1979. Other awards and recognition were to follow. The Axial-Flow combine received one of the silver medals at the Royal Agricultural Society Show at Warwickshire, England. The silver medal is the highest award a foreign manufacturer can win at that show. However, the Axial-Flow went on to be awarded the Burk Trophy, the "Oscar" of machinery awards. The Rt. Hon. Mrs. Margaret Thatcher presented the trophy to the managing director of the IH British Company. In New Zealand, the Axial-Flow received the National Field Day "Award of Merit." On a more practical note, the highly respected Prairie Agricultural Machinery Institute in Western Canada conducted extensive laboratory and field tests on the Axial-Flow No. 1460 and No. 1480 and rated their performance "very good" and issued a positive report.

Pull-Type Axial-Flow

The Upper Midwest and Canadian prairie provinces were good markets for the successful, conventional IH 914 pull combine which was the largest of its type on the market. A pull-type Axial-Flow was needed to take its place; what size should it be? John Deere's pull combine was one size smaller than their largest self-propelled combine. A pull version of the No. 1460 would equal or slightly exceed the capacity of what was expected to be the new pull-type combine from John Deere.

East Moline engineering commissioned this color cross section rendering of an IH 1482 Axial-Flow pull-type combine as a way to show the ruggedness and simplicity of this largest pull-type combine on the market.

Equipped with a 245-bushel grain tank and the 30-inch diameter rotor, the IH 1482 Axial-Flow pull-type combine required at least a 130-PTO horsepower tractor with 1,000 rpm PTO. The drive line could handle up to 200 PTO horsepower. A 132-inch wide belt-type pickup could be installed on the 12 1/2-foot header for windrow applications. In some areas and crop conditions, the 17 1/2-foot direct cut header added versatility.

The Product Engineer in charge of pull-type combines knew the windrow harvest area well and aggressively supported developing a No. 1480 size pull combine. Product Planning Research conducted face-to-face interviews with growers and determined that the market was ready for a No. 1480 size machine even though it would require a large tractor and be more expensive than a smaller machine. Sales and marketing were not totally convinced the big machine was the

"A Studio Shot" — Even though it was taken out of doors, the IH Hickory Hill Photo Center called static product photography, like the No. 1420 Axial-Flow shown above, a studio shot. The large green area of the Photo Center was used extensively as a photo location when appropriate fields or crops were not available.

hillside. However, building a low volume machine at East Moline and then doing major disassembly in order to ship it to the West Coast raised serious concerns. The final answer was to ship a special version of the No. 1460 to the Raymond A. Hanson Co. (RAHCO) Spokane, Washington, for conversion to a two-way leveling, Axial-Flow 1470 hillside. RAHCO did contract work for the military, they had a quality engineering department and were an established business; but, they had no experience in "mass" production of agricultural equipment. The learning curve was long and sometimes frustrating for both sides. Eventually the problems were solved and five preproduction machines were completed. The resulting Axial-Flow 1470 hillside combine put in production in 1980 was a quality product with all of the capacity and performance of the Axial-Flow concept. It incorporated an industry exclusive hydrostatic 4-wheel-drive system with both manual and automatic mode. The two-way leveling could accommodate up to 48% slopes. The $121,688 list price shocked the dealers when it was first introduced, but the Axial-Flow 1470 hillside combine performance soon demonstrated it was a good investment.

right answer, but in the end they agreed. The No. 1482 pull-type Axial-Flow combine was introduced in 1980. Teamed with a 130-PTO horsepower IH 1086 tractor, the combination was a high-capacity, economical package. Equipped with electronic monitoring, electro-hydraulic controls, and designed for up to 200-horsepower tractors, it was the largest, most advanced pull-type on the market. The Axial-Flow 1482 put IH in the combine technology forefront once again.

Axial-Flow 1420

To meet the need for a smaller Axial-Flow combine, a 20-inch diameter rotor machine was developed. Since the basic design had been thoroughly proven in the three larger self-propelled machines, completion of the smallest member of the family, the Axial-Flow 1420, proceeded on schedule and was introduced in 1981. This FIEI Class III Axial-Flow combine had a 125-bushel capacity grain tank and a 112-horsepower, 358-cubic-inch diesel engine. Header sizes from 10 through 20 feet were available, and it could handle 4-row wide or narrow corn heads.

Axial-Flow 1470 Hillside

IH was the leader in hillside combine technology with the four-way leveling No. 453 conventional combine sold in the Pacific Northwest. The 1460 size Axial-Flow was the logical replacement for the No. 453

Totally hydraulic, two-speed, two-way leveling and industry exclusive hydrostatic 4-wheel drive with manual and automatic mode made International Harvester's 1470 Axial-Flow hillside combines the market leader.

The IH 1480 Rice Special Axial-Flow combine was available with IH designed and manufactured tracks.

Rice and Edible Bean Specials

To complete the Axial-Flow family, one challenge remained: A machine was needed for rice and edible beans. With minor adjustments, the standard Axial-Flow rotor could harvest a wide range of crops under vastly different conditions. However, the standard rotor did not consistently deliver expected performance in rice and edible bean harvest, especially when rice straw was wet. The answer was a modified rotor which would handle rice and most other crops as well. Development of the new rotor made possible the No. 1460 and No. 1480 rice specials. In addition to the special rotor, rice specials came standard with a raised grain tank leveling auger, long unloading auger, swing-up operator's deck ladder, and rice-field tires. The No. 1460 rice special could be equipped with a 5-roller track and the No. 1480 rice special with a 6-roller track. Since the IH track attachments could be installed directly in place of regular tire equipment, they found application on combines working in

The IH Axial-Flow family is complete!
- *IH 1480 with 30-foot No. 810 header*
- *IH 1460 with 6-row corn head*
- *IH 1440 with 22 1/2-foot No. 810 header*
- *IH 1420 with 13-foot No. 820 header*
- *IH 1460 Rice Special with 20-foot No. 810 header*
- *IH 1470 hillside with 22 1/2-foot No. 810 header*
- *IH 1482 pull with windrow pickup header and IH 1486 tractor*

The Axial-Flow combine concept demonstrated its superior performance in the field and in the marketplace. The foundation was laid for a great combine line to someday be even better.

wet conditions harvesting crops other than rice. In 1981 the small No. 1420 was available in a rice special version. These successful machines accounted for 10% of IH shipments of the three larger, level land, self-propelled Axial-Flow combines.

Advanced Design Concepts Common to all Axial-Flow Combines

- Single longitudinal rotor threshes and separates — just one big moving part.
- Two speed gearcase and torque-sensing rotor drive.
- Three section, easily removable concave and separating segments.
- Auger-type grain pan.
- Opposed-action adjustable-sieve cleaning system.
- Advanced-design, variable-speed cleaning fan with digital readout.
- No straw walkers.
- Positive discharge beater propels straw rearward.
- Wide spread twin-rotor straw spreaders remove in seconds.
- Control Center is a roomy 58 inches wide and mounted on IH Iso-mounts.
- "Deep pocket" windshield provides extra-close-in view down front.
- Infinitely variable, hydrostatic ground drive with three speed ranges.
- Drive wheels and steering axle offer high and low positions.

Mechanical Cotton Harvest
International Harvester Makes it a Reality

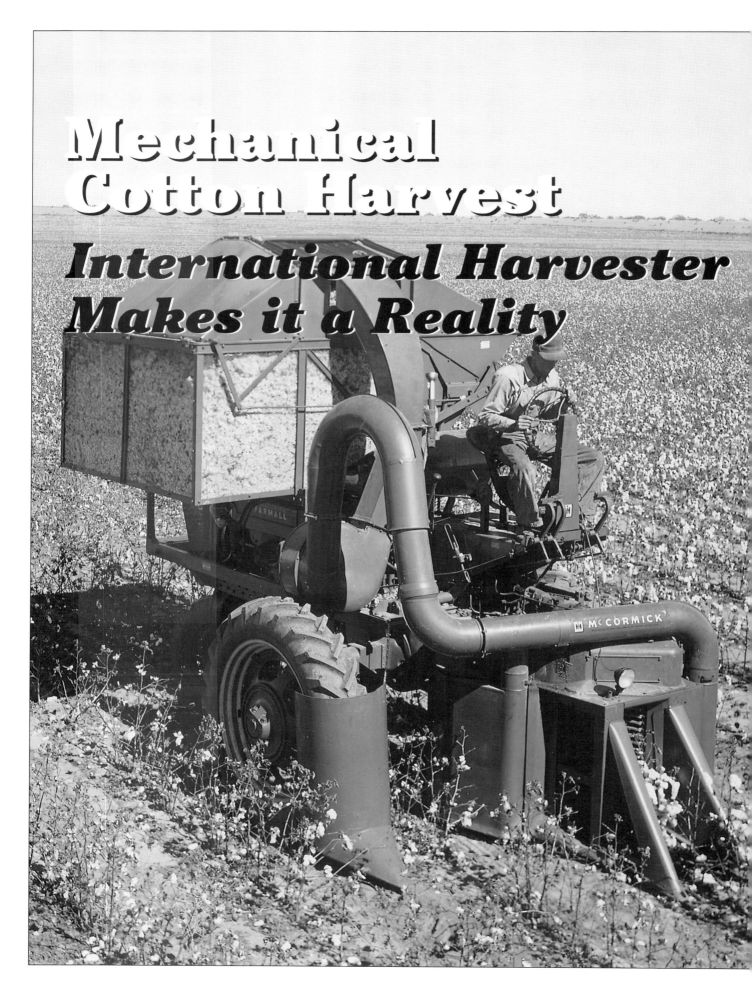

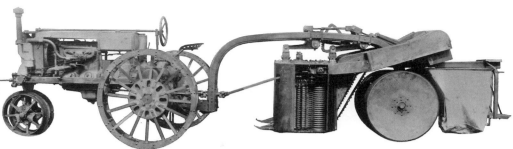

evelopment of a functional, mechanical cotton picker has a long and colorful history. Texas Experiment Station bulletin No. 452 states that, as nearly as can be determined, the first attempt to develop a mechanical cotton picker was made by S. S. Rembert and Jebediah Prescott of Memphis, Tennessee, who received a patent issued September 10, 1850. Angus Campbell, a Chicago pattern maker, put his mechanical harvester in the field in 1889. Later, as a part of the Deering Company experimental department, he worked on spindle picker concepts and evolved many features that were further developed as part of the Price Campbell Cotton Picker Corporation development program. John F. Appleby, inventor of the Appleby twine knotter and an associate of William Deering, built several spindle-type cotton harvesters. Hundreds of cotton harvester patents issued since 1850 covered concepts as widely divergent as thrashing, electrical and pneumatic harvesting, as well as the picker and stripper concepts in use today.

International Harvester showed renewed interest in mechanical cotton harvest when a vacuum cotton picker proposed by E. A. Johnston was built and tested in the fall of 1922. Two other versions of vacuum harvesters were tried before 1924 fall tests made it obvious the concept was not viable. Stripper harvest of uniform maturing, short cotton varieties had achieved moderate success by the 1920s in specific growing areas. International Harvester experimented with and developed a pull-type stripper, but spindle-type pickers dominated their effort.

This 1926 offset, trail-type cotton picker was a great improvement over the ground-driven unit built the previous year. The Farmall Regular with its high rear axle clearance and standard PTO made an excellent power source for this experimental picker.

The Company purchased the patents, drawings, and prototypes for the Price-Campbell, self-propelled, spindle-type picker in January 1924. By fall, a "radically" different four-drum version of the Price-Campbell machine was constructed and ready for testing. The next spindle-type harvester was a ground-driven, pull-type with only two drums. Much useful information was gathered from these experiments and an improved 1925 version was built and tested. Field experience with the third version revealed two serious problems: First, the machine required three men to operate — one to drive the tractor, one to steer the picker, and one to supervise cotton collection in the rear-mounted cotton sacks. Second, in tall rank cotton the tractor wheels knocked too many open cotton boles from the stalks. An engine-driven, pull-type machine with offset hitch eliminated one operator, solved problem number two and eliminated the ground drive difficulty as well. By 1927, a PTO version of the pull-type cotton harvester evolved, and that configuration continued through 1929 when plans were made to build 20 machines. The financial crash of 1929 ended production plans and made it impractical to consider introducing labor-replacing machines until economic conditions improved. Fortunately, cotton picker development work continued.

This is International Harvester's first experimental self-propelled, spindle-type cotton picker in 1924. It is similar to the self-propelled machine acquired by IHC with the purchase of the Price-Campbell patents but with a number of improvements.

This Farmall-mounted, 2-row, spindle-type picker with cleaner is a 1931 version. Efforts to develop side-mounted picker units for the Farmall tractor were carried on between 1928 and 1933.

For the first time, cotton picker engineering made serious efforts to develop spindle designs that were superior to the long, straight, or very slightly tapered Price-Campbell spindle design. Projects to develop the ideal spindle design continued for decades. A further series of International Harvester developments during the 1930s produced: a lower-cost picker mounted on the side of a Farmall F-12 tractor; a staggered drum arrangement with one drum on each side of the row and mounted on a Farmall F-20 tractor; and an air-conveying and belt-conveying system for cotton. Field tests of cotton cleaning devices, bagging systems, and self-unloading baskets added to the knowledge base.

Introduction of the impressive new line of Farmall A, B, H, and M tractors created problems for tractor-mounted pickers. The straight through axle design that replaced the

Mounting a 1-row cotton picking attachment on a reverse-operating Farmall H tractor as shown here in 1940 was a major breakthrough and established the basic configuration for all future IH spindle-type, tractor-mounted, cotton picker development. The arrangement permitted cotton plants to enter the drum area before making contact with any other part of the machine. In addition, the operator had an excellent view of the cotton row for accurate driving. The geometry provided good balance between the heavy drums carried ahead of the tractor drive axle and a full cotton basket mounted behind the axle.

drop axle design of the prior Farmall F-20 and Farmall F-30 reduced the under axle clearance. This "problem" may have been a positive event in the evolution of the cotton picker. The need for a new approach may have been a key factor in development of the reverse-operated tractor with picking drums ahead of the axle that was produced for 1940 test. Rank, high-yielding cotton harvested that year demonstrated the need for higher drums and more tractor clearance. As a result, the 10 test machines built for 1941 incorporated 10-inch taller picking drums and were mounted on reverse-operating H tractors equipped with interchangeable drop axles for improved crop clearance. This drive wheel forward configuration would come to dominate all future self-propelled picker designs.

A Commercially Produced, Spindle-Type Cotton Picker . . . An International Harvester First

Fowler McCormick, president of the International Harvester Company, publicly announced in December 1942, "The Company has been experimenting with mechanical cotton pickers for approximately 40 years. It has proved to be the most difficult designing and engineering job in the modern history of agricultural machinery. Up to now we have never said we had a successful cotton picker." He continued with, "We are now ready to state that our picker has been tested exhaustively and we know it will pick cotton profitably under conditions prevailing in the principal cotton growing

The International Harvester Company President, Fowler McCormick, drove one of the Farmall H mounted, 1-row, spindle-type cotton pickers during a public demonstration on the Hopson Planting Company's plantation near Clarksdale, Mississippi, in 1942. He announced that because of the war, only a few of these labor-saving machines would be available the following year. That was because with no prior production history, the Company had no government allocation of materials for the new pickers.

When International Harvester introduced their cotton picker to the public in 1942, they did so with both enthusiasm and reservation. Enthusiasm for the machine's performance and capability, but reservation — at least publicly — about how rapidly cotton harvest mechanization would, or should, take place. When John Rust, the self-taught "back-yard inventer," demonstrated his less-than-commercial cotton picker in the early '30s, "prophets predicted that the Rust picker would displace from two million to nine million workers." Newspapers and politicians spread the word that cotton harvest mechanization would have dire social and economic consequences. That message was not lost on International Harvester management. Public statements always affirmed the IH position that the switch to mechanical cotton harvest would come very slowly and that Negro unemployment in the Cotton Belt would not be a problem. This would be true, they said, because a large portion of field hands had already left for factory work in the North during the war and changes would not come suddenly.

areas of the country." He went on to comment that because of the war and no prior production history for this new product, they would not receive a government material allocation for pickers; therefore, the company could only plan to build a dozen or so pickers for 1943, "unless the government should feel that greater quantities are needed." The government did not!

A System Approach

President McCormick's most significant statement about cotton harvest mechanization made during the introduction was that satisfactory staple quality was obtainable when "machine picked cotton was *processed in modern gins*." (Italics are the authors.) His remark was based on extensive IH engineering development and field test experience. Cleaners on pickers had not been successful except under special conditions. As a result, a large experimental drier and cleaner had been installed in 1937 at the cotton gin building on the Hopson Plantation, Clarksdale, Mississippi. This facility produced machine-picked cotton sample grades one to three grades higher than machine-picked cotton ginned at traditional gins and processing rates. Another experimental cleaner and dryer had been built at the Ohlendorf Plantation gin, Osceola, Arkansas. These were two plantations where

HOW IT PICKS

DIRECTION OF TRAVEL

PLANT COMPRESSOR

PICKING ZONE   PICKING ZONE

PICKER BAR
CAM ARM

PLANT COMPRESSOR

SPINDLE
MOISTURE
APPLICATOR

PICKER
SPINDLE

SPINDLE
MOISTURE APPLICATOR
TUBES

CAM

DOFFER

The International Harvester cotton picker was such a new concept to most cotton producers that sales literature and advertising went into great detail to show and explain "how it works." This top view of the picker drum helped tell the story.

extensive IH field test and development had been, and would continue to be, conducted. Also, a portable version of the cleaner-dryer had followed the cotton picker test group. This experience made it clear that gins must have dryers and proper cleaning equipment for handling cotton from mechanical pickers. Engineering field results demonstrated that machine harvest of cotton required a system approach. Management knew the importance of conveying that message to future picker purchasers.

Renewed efforts to develop a low-cost picker for harvesting short growing cotton were made during 1942 to 1944. One example was the basket-equipped experimental harvester with 10-spindles-per-bar picker drums mounted on one side of a Farmall B tractor. The drums were arranged in tandem and picked only from one side. Performance was only satisfactory under the right conditions; so, the product was never introduced.

H-10-H, The First Commercial Machine

A large rectangular box was to the right of the operator's seat of the H-10-H cotton picker driven by Fowler McCormick in the photo of the official introduction. This structure has a separator box that contained a cleaning grate on the suction side of the cotton conveying system and a rotary air lock that dropped the cotton into an air blast for transport to the basket. This easy-to-recognize separator box and two-fan system was used on the 30 machines built by the engineering department from 1941 through 1943 and the 75 machines built by McCormick Works in 1944. A simple, cost-effective single-fan cotton conveying system replaced the separator box in 1945.

The age of mechanically harvested cotton arrived in 1942; but, improved cotton varieties and different cultural practices were needed to support the new pickers. Dryer-equipped modern gins were required to process machine harvested cotton into the quality staple needed by the mills. Cotton growers and ginners recognized the significance of mechanical cotton harvest and began, immediately after the war, to invest in the needed equipment and to adopt the cotton production methods required for mechanical harvest. There was no turning back; the mechanical cotton picker would profoundly change the entire cotton industry.

The Bold New Product Needed a New Home

Post World War II demand for IH products produced in the Chicago facilities made it impossible to add significant quantities of cotton pickers to their schedules. In spite of public reservation, management recognized the potential for machine harvest of cotton. They had the lead and they were prepared to invest for the future; a new plant was needed. It should be strategically located to serve the major cotton producing areas. Memphis, Tennessee, was a logical choice.

In 1948 the Memphis Works came on line with the industry's first mass-produced cotton picker. Experience with the machines built at McCormick Works, Chicago, had demonstrated that the Farmall H tractor chassis for the cotton picker lacked power under some conditions; so, the first Memphis Works production was the Farmall M based M-12-H cotton picker. About 1,300 of these 1-row, high drum, spindle-type machines were produced the first year. Each drum was equipped with 15 vertically-mounted picker bars, each containing 20 horizontally-mounted, chromium plated spindles. The picking unit contained two picking drums, one behind the other on opposite sides of the row. A total of 600 tapered, barbed spindles were used in each machine.

A 10-page, 1948 publication, *International Harvester's Great New Cotton Picker Now In Quantity Production* described every detail of the M-12-H machine and how it

This 1946 cutaway shows the new single fan air system for conveying cotton from the picking drums to the basket. The first IH commercial pickers had a two-fan system and a separator box with rotating air lock.

Lady Luck Smiled on Memphis

A story related by the chairman of the Memphis, Tennessee Area Chamber of Commerce tells of an IH representative who came to Memphis searching for a site to build a new manufacturing plant. He searched for suitable locations but without success. He gave up and was flying back to the home office when he looked out of the plane window and saw an ideal Memphis site. He got off of the plane in St. Louis and came back to Memphis for a closer look. The location he saw from the plane became the site of IH Memphis Works. The Chamber of Commerce Chairman went on to ask, what would have happened if the IH representative had sat on the other side of the plane, or if it had been an overcast day? Would Memphis have lost the $400 million IH has pumped into the local economy in the last 22 years? Would the region have lost the current 3,000 jobs and $30 million payroll? Interesting questions to ponder.

worked; this was a totally new concept to most growers and lots of education was required. The positive economics of ownership was promoted through grower testimonials. An optional, special equipment conversion package made it possible to remove the M-12-H attachment and convert the M tractor chassis for general farm use.

The Economy Answer

From the early days of cotton picker development, efforts had been made to develop a lower cost spindle-type machine for smaller acreage growers in lower yielding areas. The answer was the 14 Series Cotton Picker introduced in 1950. This new low drum machine had only 14 spindles per bar which eliminated 180 spindles and related parts compared to the M-12-H. The biggest saving came from the ability to mount the attachment on H or M tractors then in service because the special final drive drop axle and special front wheel were not needed on this lower clearance machine. Since the 14 Series used the regular 2 1/2-mph low gear of the tractor for its picking speed in place of the 2-mph picking speed of the M-12-H with its two-speed transmission, the spindles had to operate at 2,669 rpm rather than 2,000 rpm. In some conditions the higher speed actually increased the capacity of the 14 Series compared to the M-12-H.

Cotton Cavalcade

O. S. Stapley Company, IH dealer in Phoenix, Arizona, liked to do things in a big way. To dramatize their International Harvester cotton picker sales, they purchased 75 machines in 1950 and had them shipped directly from Memphis Works in a single, 25 flat car train. The event also highlighted the significance of Arizona as a cotton producing area. Stapleys arranged a celebration at the Shrine Temple for 500 prominent Arizonians, including the governor and the mayor of Phoenix. In addition, they staged a big public event complete with novelty dancers, jugglers, mimics, and musicians at the Southern Pacific siding where the pickers arrived. The cotton picker was a major factor in developing large, successful IH dealerships, like O. S. Stapley, throughout the cotton producing area.

This McCormick-Deering M-12-H is the first cotton picker model produced by the totally new Memphis, Tennessee manufacturing facility. The M-12-H cotton picker production began at Memphis in 1948. Prior model pickers were mounted on reverse-going Farmall H tractors. Experience had shown that the H tractor lacked power under difficult conditions; so, the Farmall M tractor became the chassis for the new Memphis Works produced pickers.

The Broader Line

Introduction of the 1-row McCormick M-120 and MD-120 high-drum, high-clearance cotton pickers in 1953 offered improvements over the M-12-H. These pickers were available as complete units with modified Farmall Super M or Super MD tractors or as attachments for the owners present Farmall Super M, M, Super MD, or MD tractor. The most significant improvement was the dual fan conveying system that provided one fan for each drum.

The 14 Series, single-row pickers were offered as attachments for the Farmall Super H, Super M, and Super MD tractors and they became the model HM-14 low drum pickers. Added to the line was the C-14 low drum, single-row picker attachment for mounting on the Farmall Super C tractor. The C-14 was similar to the HM-14 but with fewer 90 degree bends in the air systems conveyor pipes; it was a single fan system. Both of the low-drum machines were available as attachments only.

The most significant addition to the picker model offering in 1953 was the new 2-row McCormick M-220 high drum picker. The picking units were similar to the M-120 units except that the rear drums had 12 bars instead of 15 bars. Since the front drum does 75 percent of the picking, the reduced bar number for the rear drum did not reduce picking efficiency. The four-fan conveying system, one for each drum, located the fans in a higher position than earlier systems so sharp turns in the conveyor pipes were eliminated. The 2-row machine had a 1,200-pound (seed cotton) basket capacity compared to the 750-pound basket for the 1-row picker. The McCormick M-220 was the only 2-row picker on the market that could be removed so the tractor was available for other farming operations.

Dedicated, Self-Propelled, Two-Row Cotton Picker

The McCormick No. 220 high drum and McCormick No. 214 low drum cotton pickers introduced in 1956 were totally different products from the previous 2-row models. These were not attachments for Farmall tractors but were dedicated self-propelled cotton pickers with their own single purpose chassis. A modified International truck transmission, modified International S-180 truck axle assembly, and IH Silver

From the early days of experimental spindle-type cotton picker development, efforts were made to create lower cost pickers for the smaller cotton producer in lower yield areas. The solution proved to be reducing the height of the drum so only 14 spindles were required per bar compared to 20 spindles per bar for the original high clearance pickers. This McCormick No. 114A cotton picker was one of a long line of low drum pickers dating back to the first 14 Series in 1950.

The first IH 2-row picker introduced in 1953 was mounted on an M tractor and had the M-220 model number. This No. 220 high drum was the first of a long line of true self-propelled cotton pickers that would have their own chassis, engine, transmission, and final drive. A similar No. 214 low drum machine of the same basic design was available.

Diamond 68-horsepower engine were incorporated in these single-purpose, self-propelled cotton pickers. The No. 220 and No. 214 were essentially the same except for the number of spindles on each picker bar. The new models were equipped with new Dof-flex doffers and new IH Protec-O-Matic drum drive protection system. Hydraulic brakes and the short wheel base of the dedicated chassis made possible a turning radius of only 10 feet. They incorporated the proven IH picker drum design.

Tractor-Mounted Pickers — Three Options

Cotton growers had a choice of two IH 1-row, tractor-mounted, high drum pickers in 1961. The first was the McCormick No. 120A high clear model for Farmall 560 and older tractors equipped with axle drop housings. The second was the more economical McCormick No. 120AL that had the same high drum; it could be mounted on either the 460 or 560 tractor and older tractors without the axle drop housings for areas where under axle clearance was not a problem. Another choice was the McCormick No. 114A low-drum model for Farmall 460 and 560 and older tractors for harvesting low to medium height cotton.

These pickers incorporated the IH Tri-Clean System that safeguarded cotton cleanliness. The system included: (1) clean air intakes, (2) full-height trash outlets, and (3) basket cleaning tunnel.

The Three Hundred and Four Hundred Series Cotton Pickers

Four models of 1-row, tractor-mounted pickers made it possible to mount a picking attachment on a tractor as small as a 2-plow 240 tractor or as powerful as the Farmall 560 tractor. The 314 Low Drum version came in single-fan and dual-fan models. The 320 High Drum version came in standard and high clearance models. The latter could be factory installed only on the Farmall 560.

In 1962 the Four Hundred Series of 2-row, self-propelled cotton pickers included the McCormick International 420 High Drum and McCormick International 414 Low Drum models. They were exactly alike except for 20 spindles per bar on the high drum and 14 spindles per bar on the low drum. A new feature for this 1962 series was the contoured compressor sheet that, "guides plants close to all spindles in picking zone for full penetration of plants by all spindles for thorough picking." These pickers came with three picking speeds, dual fans, and a standard basket that held 1,650 pounds of seed cotton. Basket capacity could be increased to 2,000 pounds with an optional extension. These models were replaced with the 422 and 416 2-row self-propelled pickers that incorporated an impressive list of improved reliability and reduced maintenance features. These models could be equipped with two new attachments: one, a cotton compactor that increased basket capacity 25 percent and two, automatic hydraulic drum height control with exclusive "forward-sensing."

New Tractors Provided Easy Picker Changeover

The new 706 and 806 tractors introduced in 1963 had transmissions with four built-in reverse speeds that could be used for pickers; this was a time saving plus when mounting and dismounting a cotton picker attachment. Depending on the particular picker model, picking speeds of 2.0, 2.69, or 3.0 mph were available without making any change to the transmission. A similar benefit had been offered earlier for the 404-504 tractor with the factory-installed forward/reverse attachment.

Many picker attachments were never removed from older tractors because of the time and/or expense of reversing the bevel drive gear in the final drive to achieve the proper picking speeds. With no need for this transmission changeover, these newer tractors easily filled the dual role of general farm tractor and cotton picker chassis. This was especially true of the low drum pickers because no change of the tractor front wheel or rear axles was required.

Open Center Steering for the 500 Series

Since the operator of a cotton picker sits high above and almost directly over the picker drum, the traditional steering wheel pedestal interfered with seeing the cotton plants enter the picker. The exclusive IH "open-center steering" system offered on the 500 Series eliminated the center pedestal and provided easy on-the-row visibility straight through or under the

---

Lots of Market Potential

Twelve years after International Harvester began volume production of mechanical cotton pickers at Memphis Works, half of the cotton crop was still hand picked. The percentage ranged from 6% harvested mechanically in the Eastern Cotton Belt to 86% harvested mechanically in California. Labor shortages could bring on rapid change. For example: From 1958 to 1959, mechanical picker population increased four times in the lower Rio Grande Valley.

"OLD RED" — Honors and Questions

There is really no question that International Harvester introduced the first, successful, commercially produced cotton picker. So, it was quite appropriate that one of the original production IH pickers —affectionately referred to by early cotton producers as "Old Red" — should end up in the Smithsonian Institution in tribute to cotton harvest mechanization.

Producers Cotton Oil Company of Fresno, California, restored the IH "Old Red" picker they purchased in 1943. The picking attachment was still mounted on the original Farmall H tractor — and they donated it to the Smithsonian in 1970.

Engineering reports for the cotton harvest season of 1943 record that 12 of the high drum harvesters mounted on Farmall H tractors with high clearance attachments were built. Ten were sold outright to cotton growers in the Mississippi Delta; Phoenix, Arizona; and Fresno, California territories. Engineering test ran the remaining two machines.

The public relations department made sure there was extensive media coverage when "Old Red" left Fresno, stopped at Memphis Works, and arrived in Washington, D.C. It was a great event. Sometime later, a phone call to the Memphis District from the son-in-law of H. H. Hopson Sr. described how the H. H. Hopson Plantations of Clarksdale, Mississippi, had played an important and cooperative role in the testing and early development of

Full recognition of the International Harvester role in developing the first commercial cotton picker was achieved when the Smithsonian Institution in Washington, D.C., added a restored McCormick-Deering cotton harvester, "Old Red," from the McCormick Works first production to their collection. To highlight the progress made since IH introduced their first cotton picker in 1942, Memphis Works positioned a new McCormick-International No. 622 cotton picker along side "Old Red" during its stop in Memphis on the trip from California to the Smithsonian. The National Cotton Council President, Memphis Mayor and two IH representatives are pictured in the foreground.

After the trip from Fresno, California to Washington, D.C. — by way of Memphis, Tennessee — "Old Red" rests in its new home in the Smithsonian Institution. In 1979, the American Society of Agricultural Engineers designated the Smithsonian's "Old Red" an ASAE Historic Landmark.

the IH picker. Furthermore, they purchased pickers No. 1, No. 2, and No. 3 from the 1943 production. When their pickers were retired, No. 1 was given to Memphis Works — where sometime later it was cut up for scrap — and No. 2 was given to the Mississippi Delta Branch Experiment Station at Stoneville, Mississippi. He and his wife were very upset that they did not receive recognition for the big part the family operation had played in making "Old Red" a reality and that their "Old Red" at Stoneville had not gone to the Smithsonian. In response to the family's concerns, a special issue of the *IH Farm* magazine had a cover photo of Mrs. Mary Hopson Nance and her husband in front of "Old Red" No. 2 at the Stoneville Experiment Station and devoted an article to the development of the IH cotton picker and the Hopson contribution. The question why the Hopson "Big Red" picker didn't go to the Smithsonian may never be answered. Maybe it's best that way.

steering wheel. Basket capacity of 1,300 pounds of seed cotton was an additional feature of the new 500 Series.

The International Harvester 1-row, tractor-mounted cotton pickers offered for the 1965 season included the 501 low-drum single-fan model and a low drum dual-fan model along with the 502 high drum dual-fan standard-clearance model and a high drum dual-fan high-clearance model. Only IH offered a high-clearance 1-row cotton picker, and that machine was the only tractor-mounted, 1-row machine with two picking speeds.

New 600 Series, Super-Line Pickers

A dozen new features made the McCormick International 2-row, self-propelled 616 Low Drum and 622 High Drum cotton pickers the industry standard of comparison. In addition to IH firsts, such as offset-fan design, precision-broached spindles, oil-flush lubrication, Protec-O-Matic drum protection, and Dof-Flex doffers, the 600 Series introduced:

The all-welded drum frame, 15 bar front, 13 bar rear design, and eight other new or IH exclusive features rated a detailed cutaway to tell the story of the new 600 Series drum that delivered, "the closest thing yet to pickin' perfection."

- Low-profile high-stability design
- All-welded drums
- Drums with 15-bar front and 13-bar rear
- New moistening system
- New spring-loaded compressor sheets
- Slat bars with "dip-back" design
- Dual tunnels in basket cover
- Full-width operator deck
- New 93-horsepower engines: gasoline, LP gas, or diesel
- Hydrostatic power steering with tilt steering wheel
- Variable speed propulsion drive
- Independent shifting of drums and fans on the go.

The new pickers had a standard basket capacity of 3,000 pounds of seed cotton. With the exclusive, optional cotton distributor attachment, basket capacity was increased 25 percent.

Hydrostatic Drive Cotton Picker . . . An International Harvester First

When first introduced, the 600 pickers had a hydraulically actuated, variable speed belt drive for travel speed control. The next significant improvement for the 600 Series cotton pickers was an industry first. IH introduced hydrostatic drive that delivered infinitely variable, full torque, picking speeds from 0 to 3.3 mph. In the event of an emergency, the hydrostatic "foot-N'-inch" pedal provided for an immediate stop.

The new 600 Series super-line pickers introduced in 1967 added an impressive list of new features to the other advancements in picker technology IH had pioneered over the years. The most significant new feature on this McCormick International 622 was hydrostatic drive. The new line also offered a 616 low drum model.

The new 1978 International 782 Series II cotton picker featured a combine-like "control-center" cab and a totally new air system for conveying cotton from the drums to the basket.

International 782 Cotton Picker . . . The Most Advanced Cotton Picker You Can Buy

The Control Center cab brought modern combine comfort and convenience to the International cotton picker line. Owners of large, self-propelled cotton pickers seldom are the operators, but good managers learned that comfortable operators who were provided with convenient controls did better work; it's a sound investment.

The new picker came equipped with all-chrome, clean-line spindles. The bars ran in an advanced design cam track that increased endurance and reduced maintenance. The front rotor had 14 bars and the rear rotor had 12 bars.

The 782 introduced a completely new cotton conveying system. In place of a two-stage air system that sucked cotton from the drums and then blew it to the basket with four fans, the new air system used a single, high-capacity fan to supply air pressure at the base of each drum to blow cotton all the way to the basket. The new IH air system provided more uniform delivery, reduced embedded trash and simplified maintenance.

Mechanical Cotton Harvest

Economical, Once-Over Harvest

Cotton grown in the Texas high plains and other similar areas has a short growing period and the cotton does not mature until late in the season. Sometimes frost kills the plants before the bolls are mature. Under these conditions, many times it was too cold to pick the seed cotton from the bur with bare hands; gloves wouldn't work. Therefore, snapping the bolls from the plant — sometimes called "pulled cotton" — was the accepted method of late harvest in these areas. To speed harvest, sections of picket fence were used to strip bolls from cotton plants in west Texas as early as 1914. Later, sharpened picket teeth were attached to the front of a sled for collecting the harvested cotton and the term "sledding cotton" was coined. Storm-proof varieties developed for these areas tended to mature uniformly and aided in the development of mechanical strippers. These methods harvested the open cotton and unopened cotton bolls along with the burs, leaves, and plant stems all at one time. Cotton harvested in this manner required gins that had special equipment for removing the large quantity of foreign material usually not found in hand-picked cotton.

The McCormick-Deering Stripper

IHC entered the cotton stripper market in 1927 with a 1-row, ground-driven, chain-type stripper. A pair of dividers, similar to a corn binder, guided cotton plants into the machine. As cotton passed between the two stripping chains, stripping fingers detached and delivered the bolls to a self-dumping box. A helper rode on a platform behind the drive wheel and next to the collection box. His job was to remove any large trash or stalks and pack the cotton in the box to increase

Two men operating this ground-driven cotton stripper were able to gather from two to five bales of cotton per day. That was "equivalent to what 15 to 30 persons could pick in the same length of time." On this basis, "the stripper could save $30 to $60 per day" based on 1927 economics.

capacity. The stripper was available with either a horse or tractor hitch.

Recognizing that many gins did not have equipment to properly clean stripped cotton, IHC sold the McCormick-Deering cotton cleaner for use, as a general rule, at the plantation headquarters. It had capacity to handle cotton from several strippers.

Tractor-Mounted Strippers

The cotton areas that were suited for growing storm-proof or stripper varieties of cotton did not represent a large share of the cotton producing area, but it did represent a potential market for improved machines. However, during the 1920s and '30s, International Harvester devoted most of its cotton mechanization effort on spindle picker development for the much larger U.S. and world market.

Archive records contain photos of a Farmall M mounted 2-row cotton stripper. The machine was labeled an experimental ground-driven cotton stripper. It appeared to be leaving very little cotton in the field. The machine was apparently chain driven from the tractor axle. This would eliminate the need to synchronize the harvester with the forward speed of the tractor.

The McCormick HM-20 Cotton Stripper was a 2-row, mounted machine for Farmall H, M, and MD tractors, with PTO and hydraulic system. It incorporated a 42-inch long, smooth, six-sided stripper roll that worked against a spring-loaded, smooth stripper bar. Cotton bolls that didn't fall into the conveyor auger at the front part of the roll were knocked off the plant by tire carcass beaters at the rear part of the roll. Kicker-beaters and cross augers moved the material to the undershot, cleaning-type flight elevator. Each step was designed to remove as much trash and dirt

as possible without loss of bolls. With the advent of the Farmall C tractor, an HMC-20 cotton stripper model was released for that tractor.

The next model was the McCormick No. 21 cotton stripper. The stripping system was the same as the No. 20, but the kicker beaters were replaced with open-end auger conveyors working over slotted auger troughs for trash and dirt removal. A new belt-type elevator with rubber flights conveyed cotton on the slotted underside of the elevator for additional cleaning. A high capacity fan on the underside of the elevator provided a cleaning air blast that blew open cotton to the rear of the wagon while green bolls fell into the front of the wagon. Progress was being made toward a true green boll separator system. Mounting attachments would mount tractors from the Farmall H to the Farmall 450. Literature from 1958 pictures a No. 21 cotton stripper mounted on a Farmall 450 LP gas tractor. In view of the extensive use of LP gas in the storm-proof cotton growing areas, that was very appropriate.

Brush and Metal Roll Models

The McCormick International No. 30 cotton harvester brought the new brush roll technology with alternate rubber flaps and nylon brushes to the IH stripper product line in 1964. With lifter gathers 20 1/2 inches wide, throat openings 11 inches wide and

This HMC-20, 2-row cotton stripper is mounted on a Farmall Super M tractor harvesting near Amarillo, Texas. This Texas High Plains scene is located in the heart of the traditional cotton stripper harvest area.

38 inches high, this two-brush roll, two-conveyor auger per row unit had "outstanding harvest capacity . . . up to 3 bale per acre at 4 mph . . . in shoulder-high irrigated yields." This meant that the brush roll equipped No. 30 could satisfactorily harvest open-boll "picker" cotton varieties in some special conditions. This new capability justified changing the name from cotton stripper to cotton harvester. This would open the door to consideration of alternate harvest strategies in many cotton producing areas. The "revolutionary" auger elevator improved trash and dirt removal for increased gin turn-out of up to 2 percent. A useful design innovation eliminated the need for a remote hydraulic cylinder if the No. 30 was mounted on an IH 504, 706, or 806 tractor.

In 1966, an IH tractor-mounted, hydraulic-dump, cotton basket became available for the No. 30 cotton harvester as well as the No. 21 and No. 22 tractor-mounted strippers. The design incorporated the ability to deliver cotton to the tractor-mounted basket, use the air system to deliver cotton to a trailer, or use the conventional elevator to deliver cotton to a trailer.

Cotton Picker Challenge?

The International No. 85 cotton harvester was introduced in 1969. Its capacity and cleaning ability, especially if equipped with a basket, made it an alternative to picker harvest for "semi-open boll, semi-storm resistant and other varieties of cotton," in some areas. Many cotton producers considered brush-roll stripper harvest for the first time because of the performance of the No. 85 cotton harvester. For some, it proved to be a high-capacity, economical method of cotton harvest. For others, the spindle-type picker and multiple harvest was the only satisfactory system.

The 46-inch long, line point, brush rolls delivered cotton to two 5 1/2-inch diameter augers, one on each side of the row. The slotted housings under the augers could be opened and closed from the tractor seat for on-the-go cleanout. Further cleaning was achieved with two 9-inch vertical elevator augers with slotted housings and two cleaning fans, one for each row. Green bolls fell through the air blast and dropped into a 10-cubic-foot collection box for dumping on the turn row. A totally new mounting system made it possible to dismount the unit in about 30 minutes and remount it

Increased capacity, dual-brush roll efficiency, and greatly improved cleaning capability justified naming this International No. 85 a cotton harvester rather than a cotton stripper. It had the ability to harvest a much wider range of cotton types grown in some non-traditional stripper areas compared to the single, metal roll type strippers it replaced.

in about 45 minutes after it had been installed on the tractor the first time. Attaching parts were available for the John Deere 3010 and 4010 tractors (as they were the only other major picker/stripper manufacture).

Released for the 1973 harvest, the International No. 90 cotton harvester offered 520 cubic feet of overhead basket capacity with 12 feet 7 inches dumping height in addition to the outstanding features of the No. 85 it replaced. Automatic row unit height control was a new productivity boosting feature. International Farmall 66 Series tractor and many older Farmall tractors were on the mounting list plus the John Deere 4010 and 4020. Two years later the International No. 91 cotton harvester was designed so it would mount on Farmall 66 Series tractors with cabs. This was accomplished with only a 20 cubic foot reduction in basket capacity and no change in dumping height.

If It's Good for Corn, It Must be Good for Cotton!

University research and farmer experience had demonstrated the yield increasing benefits of growing corn in narrow rows in the central and northern Corn Belt. Why wouldn't cotton grown in narrow rows show a yield increase? Space taken up by spindle picker drums ruled out significantly reduced row spacing for this harvest method. Therefore, research and farmer experimentation was directed toward narrow row production for stripper harvest.

IH Equipment for University Research

IH Product Planning coordinated a cooperative research program between International Harvester and the University of California at Davis during the 1970s. IH supplied an International No. 85 cotton harvester and three standard stripper row units. The University Agricultural Engineering Department modified the heads to create a 3-row, 30-inch stripper header for the No. 85 cotton harvester. Cotton Extension Agents in various San Joaquin Valley counties established narrow row cotton plots for harvest by the IH/U.C. Davis harrow row harvester. The results yielded useful information about varieties, planting dates, and cultural practices. Years later, narrow row cotton production for stripper harvest found application in particular areas of California as well as other parts of the country.

The Picket Fence Revisited

The first effort to stripper harvest cotton is said to have been done with a section of picket fence. In the 1960s interest developed in a modern, mechanized

This basket-equipped stripper was mounted on a Farmall 856 tractor. The two-row units have been replaced by a finger-stripper header. This economical method had the added advantage of harvesting cotton in different row spacings — including narrow rows — without adjustment.

version called a finger stripper. Narrow steel fingers formed a comb for stripping bolls from the cotton stalk. Kicker fingers and/or augers moved the cotton to the next stage. This method of harvest was best suited to traditional stripper growing areas where weather or defoliation removed most of the leaves before harvest. In addition to being simple and economical, the stripper could harvest cotton planted in various row spacings including narrow rows without any adjustments. In the rain grown area of the southern plains of West Texas where the very short, "Coke Bottle Cotton" frequently produced only two or three bolls per plant, the stripper header was especially well suited.

Stripper Harvest Comes of Age

The International No. 95 self-propelled cotton harvester introduced in 1974 brought the comfort and convenience of spindle pickers to the owners of stripper harvesters. The 655-cubic-foot basket — the biggest in the business — coupled with features like all-

Roomy cab, hydrostatic power steering, hydrostatic drive, adjustable guide wheel axle, and vertical auger air separation all came standard in this International 95 diesel-powered, self-propelled stripper. It could be equipped with two brush-roll row units or the broadcast finger-stripper header shown here.

speed hydrostatic drive, adjustable guide wheel axle, row spacing adjustable from 30 to 40 inches, and all of the high-capacity, crop saving features of the IH tractor-mounted stripper row units, made the No. 95 an outstanding performer.

Four-row stripper harvest of wide-row, narrow-row, or skip-row planting patterns, the International 1400 self-propelled cotton harvester could do it all. This unique harvester could be purchased equipped for 2-, 3-, or 4-row harvest to match the planting pattern in use. If production practices changed, the harvester could be easily changed. With the addition of an extension, skip-row planting patterns could be harvested. The row-spacing flexibility of the header could accommodate 25 different row spacings and row patterns. An 8-channel monitor came as standard on the 1400. It "watched" the row units, cross auger, boll-box augers, and air system to alert the operator to any possible problem. Indeed, stripper harvest equipment had truly come of age.

Four-row harvest capability came to the IH cotton harvester line with the new International 1400 cotton harvester. With an attachment, 4-row skip-row planting patterns could be harvested.

More than Planting and Harvest

Producing a high yielding, high quality cotton crop requires proper equipment and careful management from soil preparation to final harvest. One of the critical steps is weed and insect control. To apply the right product at the right time in tall growing cotton, high clearance equipment is needed. International Harvester met that requirement in 1966 with introduction of the McCormick International No. 660 high clearance carrier. Equipped with IH, C146-cubic-inch displacement engine, transmission, and differential that all came from field-proven tractor products, the new high clearance carrier offered the reliability required for these time sensitive operations. A 215-gallon spray tank and self-priming centrifugal pump provided essential spraying and agitation capacity. Two years later two new models, the 770 and 780, were released. The new models offered increased clearance and spray tank capacity. The 770 could accommodate row spacing from 30 to 40 inches. The 1969 release for the new products called for production of 125 model 770s and 75 model 780s. Suggested list prices were $5,213 and $5,229, respectively.

Chemical weed and insect control are critical operations in cotton production. The 780 was built for 38- to 42-inch rows and the companion International 770 was for 30- to 40-inch rows. The 770/780 hi-clear machines were built from proven, IH tractor components for outstanding reliability and performance in a "tractor" with 68-inch clearance. These versatile products found application in crops other than cotton.

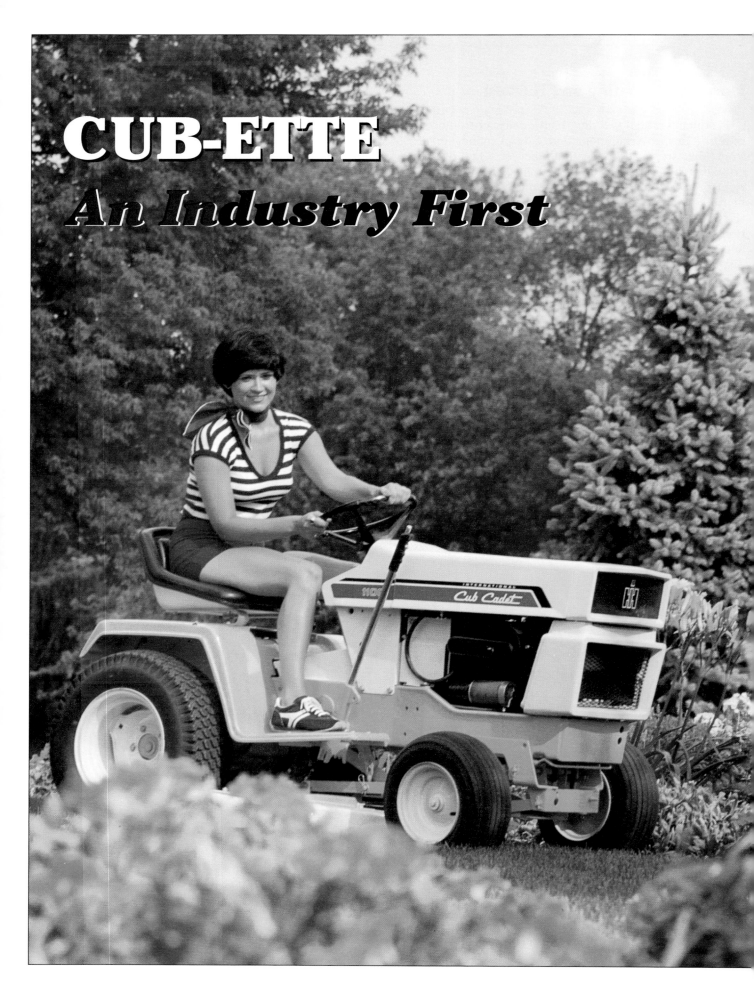

CUB-ETTE
An Industry First

The IH Farmall Cub tractor sold well in 1959 and good used Cub tractors were in high demand. However, the Cub was a rugged, relatively expensive small farm tractor that didn't fit the growing market for lawn and garden tractors. In July of 1959, a Committee on Concept of New Vehicle Study was established to review the Farm Equipment Product Planning recommendations for developing a garden and lawn-type tractor and a new farm and farmstead materials handling utility vehicle or "Trucktor." The first meeting published three conclusions: (1) Institute a study to cost reduce the current Farmall Cub tractor. (2) Design a different type of small tractor, preferably with rear mounting of the engine for better application to forward-mounted equipment to provide an acceptable compromise in both price and capability between the Farmall Cub and the present variety of garden-type riding mowers. (3) Design a farmstead-type utility vehicle or "Trucktor." Recommendation three evolved into the Hamilton Works developed truck/tractor discussed in the "The Second Generation Farmall Family — Four New Farmalls Lead the Way" chapter.

The second meeting of the committee was held in December of 1959. They concluded that the Farmall Cub could not be cost reduced enough to be price competitive with lawn and garden tractors. They requested Farm Equipment Product Planning to develop specifications for a "low-cost riding lawn tractor and a higher priced riding garden tractor." Farm Equipment Product Planning responded with the following tentative specifications:

I. A small riding lawn and garden tractor of about 4.5 horsepower, priced under $100/horsepower, and conventional V-belt type clutch.

II. A utility-type riding tractor of about 8 to 9 horsepower, priced under $100/horsepower, dry-type clutch, and with optional hydraulics for one-way lift.

The groundwork was laid for what would become a major new product line for the Farm Equipment Division.

Tractor Committee Report No. 31 spelled out the details of a garden-type tractor incorporating an air-cooled engine of approximately 7 horsepower and utilizing as many parts of the Farmall Cub tractor as possible including the Cub transmission, Cub styling, and the hood. The decision was made to develop the garden-type tractor, and the design was started in February 1960. The Cub hood and styling was not right for a small garden-type tractor, so it received its own distinctive look. Proposed names included: Cub-ette, Cub-Urban, and Ranch-All. Dealer surveys had determined the importance of "eye appeal, including the most appealing and appropriate color combination." By consensus it was decided, "the red and white of our

current line should be adopted for the basic tractor." When the new tractor was released for production in November 1960, the report identified the new product as the "7-HP CUB-ETTE Tractor."

Before the introduction, CUB-ETTE became Cub Cadet; red and white became yellow and white. When the initial 100 tractors were shipped from Louisville Works in early 1960, International Harvester became the first full-line farm equipment company to manufacture and market their own garden-type tractor. Sales estimated demand to be between 5,000 and 10,000 units per year. Before the first year ended, the original conservative production plans were increased five fold. Market opportunity for a more complete product line was readily apparent.

Make it a Real Tractor

Success of the original Cub Cadet tractor opened the door for improved and expanded products. For the first time it was possible to determine who the customer was for an IH riding tractor and what the customer wanted in this new product. Surveys made it clear that most of the customers were suburbanites in the middle income group. Farm and commercial operators were important, but the individual residential home owner was of extreme importance. This customer wanted the appearance, performance, and durability of a full-size utility tractor in a small, easy to service unit at an estate tractor price.

The original Cub Cadet had a single, high speed, highly reliable V-belt drive from the engine to the transmission input shaft. "Real" tractors don't have V-belts

It all started here in 1961. The 7-horsepower, 4-cycle, air-cooled engine powered Cub Cadet was the beginning of what would become an extensive new IH lawn and garden product line. The mid-mounted IH-built mower and a dozen other attachments or drawn pieces of equipment were offered with the original introduction.

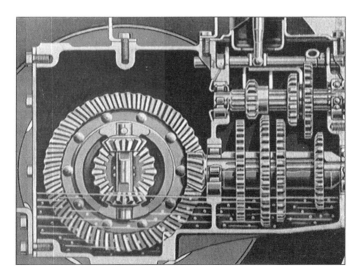

The Cub Cadet was unique because it used the proven, reliable, Farmall Cub transmission and final drive. This feature, as well as others, made the Cub Cadet look and perform like a scaled down Cub tractor.

When this Cub Cadet 70/100 prototype tractor was shown to management at the Farm Equipment Research and Engineering Center, they liked what they saw. When the service, function, and reliability improvements were reviewed, they liked what they heard. Except for the front implement mounting system and decals, the tractor in the photo became the Cub Cadet 70 and 100 lawn and garden tractor introduced in 1963.

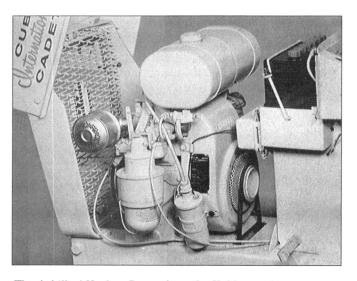

The Achilles' Heel — Power from the Kohler engine was transferred to the input drive by a high speed V-belt. Engineering tests had verified the reliability of the design. Customers and many dealers, on the other hand, associated V-belts with automatic washers and furnace fan drives that required service and maintenance. "Real" tractors don't have V-belts in the drive line. The V-belt had to go!

in the drive line, so the typical suburbanite customer considered this drive a potential trouble spot. The new 70 and 100 Cub Cadets were 7- and 10-horsepower models that replaced the original 7-horsepower Cub Cadet in 1963. They had a direct drive from the engine to the transmission; no belts! Extensive coordination with the Kohler Engine Company resulted in 7- and 10-horsepower engines that were directly interchange-

able in the new frame design and met the requirements of direct-drive geometry. In fact, The basic frame design would ultimately accommodate an interchangeable 16-horsepower engine. The new 70 and 100 Cub Cadet tractors added improved reliability, increased frame strength for heavier attachments, increased under frame clearance, two-wheel wet oil brakes, and reduced service requirements to the direct-drive feature. Options included a disk-type implement drive clutch mounted on the front of the engine, a pair of lights mounted in the grille, and a planetary creeper drive. These were "real" tractors designed for the discriminating suburban customer.

Hydrostatic Drive Lawn and Garden Tractors . . . An International Harvester First

For 1966, IH expanded the Cub Cadet line to include a Model 71 with 7-horsepower; a Model 102 with 10-horsepower; and a Model 122 with 12-horsepower. The following year, 1967, IH introduced another lawn and garden industry first, the Model 123, 12-horsepower Cub Cadet with hydrostatic drive. The hydrostatic line was broadened to include both 10- and 12-horsepower hydrostatic models for 1968. These two sizes plus a 7-horsepower size were available as gear-drive versions.

This yellow and white Cub Cadet 129 hydrostatic was just as much at home on the farm as in suburbia. This new series represented the fifth model change since the 70/100 introduction in 1963. The 1972 line included a new 8-horsepower Model 86 gear-drive as the smallest tractor; 10- and 12-horsepower models in either hydro or gear drive; and a 14-horsepower, hydrostatic-only Cub Cadet 149 that replaced the prior model Cub Cadet 147.

Two years later, in 1970, a 14-horsepower Cub Cadet 147 was introduced along with 10- and 12-horsepower models in either hydro or gear drive and a 7-horsepower gear-drive only Cub Cadet 73. The new product offering for 1972 included the 8 and 9 series gear-drive and Hydro models in 10-, 12-, and 14-horsepower models. The new 8-horsepower Cub Cadet 86 replaced the 7-horsepower models that had been the smallest size since the original Cub Cadet was introduced in 1961. A totally new tractor for 1972 was the Cadet 76 lawn tractor. This unit had the general family appearance of the Cub Cadet line, but it was powered by a 7-horsepower vertical shaft engine. This economy-priced lawn tractor included a 36-inch rotary mower for 1 1/2- to 4 1/2-inch cutting height. Accessories included the ability to haul, grade, sweep, seed, spray, or fertilize. Typical 1972 F.O.B. factory retail prices were: Cadet 75 riding mower, $584.63; Cadet 76 lawn tractor, $798.59; and Cub Cadet 149 Hydro, $1,629.33.

"Trapping a New Market"

Golf courses purchase specially designed tractors for tending the rough and mowing fairways. Management saw the possibility of selling Cub Cadets to golf courses for tending sand traps if the right tool was available. A 1969 Farm Equipment Division Committee report described the International No. 1 sand trap rake for the Cub Cadet tractor. The front gang had three articulated sections with 54 replaceable

long spikes to break up crust and stir up weeds. The rear gang had five overlapping sections to smooth out the sand. It optimistically forecast sales of 1,000 sand trap rakes and a minimum of 500 additional No. 125 Hydrostatic Cub Cadet tractors. The good news was, no appropriations or funds approval was required. The No. 1 sand trap rake was in the line for several years as an aide in marketing to the golf course market segment, but a demand for mechanized sand trap maintenance never developed.

Other Lawn & Garden Opportunities

When the market potential for IH in lawn and garden power equipment was first discussed, the need for a low horsepower, economical riding mower was proposed. Success of the Cub Cadet and the need to expand the line overshadowed riding mower development. This changed with 1968 production of the Model 60 Cadet riding mower. Later, the line would include the Model 55 and 75 Cadet riding mowers as replacements for the Model 60 Cadet riding mower. These machines had steel frames, one-piece fiberglass decks, and rear-mounted, vertical shaft engines. This configuration made it possible for IH to manufacture and market a reliable, attractive riding mower and compete in this very price competitive segment of the market. The Cadet 85 and Cadet 85 Bagger Special were added to the riding mower line in 1975.

Another opportunity to expand the Lawn and Garden offering was by marketing walk-behind rotary lawn mowers. IH entered into an agreement to market yellow and white versions of the highly regarded Lawn-

Not everyone needs, or can justify the cost of, a Cub Cadet tractor when used primarily for mowing. Most everyone likes to ride if there's much grass to mow. Model 60, 55, and 75 (shown here) Cadet riding mowers with one-piece fiberglass decks provided an attractive, reliable, economical answer.

Boy products with International Harvester decals and product support. This seven-model line of solid-state ignition, two-cycle, side-discharge push and self-propelled lawn mowers complimented the quality Cub Cadet line of lawn and garden products. This line of walk-behind lawn mowers was extremely popular for discounted IH employee purchase. These mowers were later replaced with a line of 4-cycle engine power mowers from another source.

The Quiet Revolution

In the early 1970s, the City of Chicago and an agency of the Federal Government proposed regulations that would set maximum permissible noise levels for lawn mowers and lawn tractors; International Harvester took the prospect of such an ordinance seriously. To thoroughly understand the sources of Cub Cadet noise, International Harvester funded a research project at the Herrick Laboratory, Purdue University, West Lafayette, Indiana. Hinsdale Engineering worked closely with this nationally recognized sound/noise research laboratory and developed a system of engine enclosure and other improvements that markedly lowered the drive-by sound level. Now that they had a quiet tractor, operators suddenly became aware of noise from the mower. Further research on mower design reduced the sound level slightly. It was not until the tip speed of the rotary mower blade was reduced that mower noise was significantly lowered. There was only one problem; the reduced speed mower didn't cut

This International Cadet 85 special riding mower had an 8-horsepower, Briggs and Stratton, syncro-balanced engine. It was equipped with a single-blade, 28-inch mower deck that was ideal for the optional, 5-bushel grass catcher/bagger shown here. The bagger could collect clippings directly in a standard plastic refuse bag. The regular Cadet 85 riding mower had a 32-inch mower deck with side discharge or rear discharge that was ideal for the Model 1A lawn sweeper.

"Free of noise, fumes and pollution, the International 95 Electric Rider is virtually maintenance free," stated the news release. Nothing could have been more timely in meeting the social concerns of the decade of the 1970s. The 95 electric rider had three 12-volt electric motors. One was for forward and reverse and two were used to drive the blades on the 32-inch mower. One charge was sufficient for 1 1/2 hours of operation.

"Purrs Like a Kitten, While it Works Like a Tiger." Sophisticated University research combined with IH engineering know-how resulted in the new line of Quiet Cub Cadet tractors for 1975. Instead of mounting the engine directly to the frame, the design used iso-mounts to absorb engine vibration and reduce noise and operator fatigue. Specially designed engine enclosures further reduced the noise level. The 14-horsepower Cub Cadet 1450, shown here, as well as the 16-horsepower Cub Cadet 1650, came with hydraulic lift as standard.

grass very well. Fortunately, the City of Chicago and the agency abandoned the idea of a noise control standard for lawn and garden tractors.

Based on the knowledge gained at the Herrick Laboratory, IH introduced the "Quiet Line" of Cub

Cadet lawn and garden tractors in 1975; this was another IH lawn and garden industry first. For the first time a 16-horsepower size Model 1650 Hydro was offered. In addition, 12- and 14-horsepower 1250 and 1450 Hydro models along with 8-, 10-, and 12-horsepower standard shift models filled out the line.

A Half Million Cub Cadet Tractors

When IH was formulating the original 7-horsepower Cub Cadet concept in 1959, it enjoyed good company support, but the market share available to a farm equipment manufacturer was considered somewhat limited. However, customer acceptance the first year exceeded the most optimistic expectations, and major changes in production schedules were necessary to meet the demand. With the knowledge gained about the actual retail customer this first year, the improved No. 70 and No. 100 Cub Cadets were developed. During the succeeding years, new models were introduced and improvements made to meet the needs of this new market. Success of the program was celebrated on May 1, 1974, with the production of the 500,000th Cub Cadet tractor.

The little Cub Cadet tractors were big business for the IH plant at Louisville, Kentucky, with 500,000 Cub Cadet tractors produced. The foundry produced these 6-inch high, cast-iron Cub Cadet figures to celebrate reaching production of half a million units in 1974.

More Than Tractors and Lawn Mowers

Success of the Cub Cadet tractor revealed a market in urban and suburban areas far removed from the traditional IH Farm Equipment Dealer. Also, growth was taking place in the Industrial Equipment line of IH products. To serve these markets, a separate Lawn and Garden contract was made available. To meet the needs of a broader market, a wide range of Cub Cadet attachments and related products were offered. Cub Cadet mounted snow blowers and blades were

No company could let 1976 go by without at least one product that helped celebrate the country's 200 year anniversary. International Harvester was no exception; they introduced the Bicentennial "Spirit of '76" Cadet 76 lawn tractor.

The 12-horsepower Cub Cadet 1200 ge[...] drive tractor and the 12-horsepower Cu[...] Cadet 1250 hydrostatic tractor were bo[...] so versatile they worked the year arou[...] from winter snow removal, to spring a[...] summer mowing, to fall chores.

complimented by walk-behind snow throwers and snow blowers for winter work. Cub Cadet powered rotary tillers were complimented by walk-behind rotary tillers for spring and fall. Other useful products included shredder-grinders and power washers. Two-wheel trailers and lawn sweepers matched to the capacity of Cub Cadet tractors helped fill out the line. To meet limited volume needs, specialized products from various manufacturers were tested and approved for use with Cab Cadet tractors. Through the parts department, a wide range of lawn and garden accessories from gloves to gas cans were also available.

This deluxe, 21-inch rear bagging, self-propelled, walk-behind mower readily converted to a mulching mower. The 4-horsepower Briggs and Stratton, 4-cycle engine easily handled bagging or mulching. A 21-inch side-discharge, self-propelled and a 19-inch economy push mower completed the walk-behind mower offering.

Déjà vu

When the Tractor Committee described the new IH garden-type tractor in 1959, their specifications called for a red tractor with white wheels and trim like the full-size agricultural tractors. When the first Cub Cadet tractors were introduced, they were Federal yellow with white wheels and trim like the industrial tractor line. Two decades later the new 82 Series of eight models of Cub Cadet tractors would be introduced in official International Harvester red with white wheels and black-and-white trim, just like the full-size agricultural tractors. Even the venerable Lo-Boy tractor shed its yellow and white colors for red, white, and black — just like the compact tractor line. The members of the first Cub Cadet Tractor Committee who reached a con-

sensus agreement on red garden-type tractors must have been amazed when they first saw the new red 82 Series Cub Cadets. The circle was complete.

"The Smallest General Purpose Tractor Ever Built"

The July/August 1947 issue of *IH World* introduced the new Farmall Cub as the "answer to the small farmer's problem of mechanization" and "The Smallest General Purpose Tractor Ever built." This small, rugged, offset version of the larger Farmall tractors

If they work like "real" tractors, make them red like the best "real" tractors — After two decades of lawn and garden tractor leadership in the yellow and white colors of the Industrial tractor line, the new line of International Cub tractors arrived in IH red with white wheels and black-and-white trim just like the full-size agricultural tractors. This 982 Cub Cadet, largest of the Cadet family, was equipped with a 19.9-horsepower twin-cylinder engine, hydrostatic transmission, hydraulic lift, and high flotation tires as standard. The full line included eight models. The smallest were the 8-horsepower International Cub Cadet gear drive 182 or the hydrostatic drive 282.

Most tractors manufactured around the world, regardless of size, have diesel engines. Though fuel prices are not high in the United States, addition of the International Cub Cadet 782D diesel lawn and garden tractor to the new line filled the needs of some customers.

found applications far beyond what was originally expected. Equipped with a mid-mounted rotary mower, it became the ideal answer for large, more difficult mowing jobs.

By 1964 this versatile little tractor was available in International Cub and International Cub Lo-Boy versions; both were yellow and white. These two yellow and white International tractors were then marketed as part of the total lawn and garden line. The International Cub 154 Lo-Boy, introduced in 1968, was a different design than prior International Cub tractors. This tractor used the Cub C-60 engine in a 15-horsepower version and the Cub final drive; but, it was a center-line design, rather than offset, and incorporated a steel channel frame.

"The Cub Tractor, a Real Workhorse for 25 years," said the 1977 literature that displayed a photo of this Cub tractor and Model C-3, center-mounted, 60-inch cut, rotary mower. The IH C-60, 4-cylinder, water-cooled engine that was an improved version of the engine that powered the original Cub was still the power plant. However, the horsepower output had almost doubled to 15 horsepower.

Right at home on the farm, this Cub tractor and No. 144 one-row cultivator are ready to go to the field. The offset engine design and high ground clearance made it an ideal cultivating tractor. Independent rear wheel braking, "Touch Control" hydraulic lift system, and one-point Fast-Hitch made the Cub the ideal answer for small or specialty crop farms. Attachments included Cub Fast-Hitch implements like the L-38 disk harrow in 48- or 61-inch sizes and the L-194 one-bottom moldboard plow. For heavy mowing jobs, the No. 22 sickle bar, side-mounted, 5-foot cut mower was the ideal answer. The Cub tractor and its attachments provided everything needed to serve its special markets.

The Cub Cadet Line Goes On

During the early 1980s, International Harvester management faced many challenges that required difficult but essential decisions. One such decision was the sale of the total Cub Cadet/Lawn and Garden product line to the MTD Corporation, Cleveland, Ohio. The purchaser had a successful line of lawn and garden power products sold primarily through mass marketers. They recognized the value of the Cub Cadet quality reputation and the different market segments it served. Therefore, they created a separate Cub Cadet Corporation. As a result, Cub Cadet products are widely available in the marketplace today, and the proud Cub Cadet tradition of quality products goes on.

The International Cub 185 Lo-Boy Tractor measured in at only 49-inches tall. The low-to-the-ground profile Lo-Boy was considered one of the most stable tractors available in its class. It combined the efficiency of a fabricated steel frame design with the reliability of the legendary IH C-60, 4-cylinder, water-cooled engine now engineered for 18.5 bare engine horsepower.

International ®

Industrial Equipment
The Other Yellow

This International 300 Utility tractor was the first IH product to have features that made it fit the needs of the rapidly developing industrial equipment market. International Harvester tested and approved products like this Pippin backhoe for use on recommended IH tractors.

When International Harvester began selling tractors and equipment for the Industrial Equipment market, the products weren't yellow; in fact, the products were not even part of a separate IH equipment group. The concept of serving the emerging non-farm industrial market began by offering limited heavy-duty tractor options and by developing a list of Special Duty Equipment suppliers whose products were approved by engineering for mounting, or use with, IH Farmall or International tractors. Use of products from the Special Duty Equipment list would not affect the warranty of the IH tractor. Performance and warranty of the equipment were the responsibility of the individual manufacturers. The first tractor model aimed at the industrial market was the 1949 Super A with heavy-duty front axle, Henry backhoe, and Twin-Draulic loader.

The July 1956 Special Duty Equipment list approved equipment for mounting, or use with, International Cub Lo-Boy, International 100, International 300 Utility, and International W400. The Farmall 100, 200, 300, and 400 plus the Farmall Cub were also on the tractor list.

The compact, low-profile International 300 Utility tractor was introduced in 1955. It was a good match for the important front-end loader and rear-mounted backhoe applications. The 196-cubic-inch displacement IH gasoline engine developed over 41 belt horsepower which matched the needs of most industrial tractor users at that time. It came standard with Fast-Hitch, single valve Hydra-Touch hydraulics and heavy-duty, tubular, telescoping adjustable front axle. Optional special equipment included Torque Amplifier (TA) and a choice of completely independent or transmission driven PTO.

The New International 300 Utility enjoyed some extra introduction publicity, it became the 300,000th tractor built by International Harvester since the Company starting tractor manufacturing in 1909. This utility tractor equipped with Fast-Hitch, tachometer, and one-valve Hydra-Touch sold for $1957.00 F.O.B. factory in 1955. It wasn't yellow, but it was the beginning of a long line of IH tractors that would become the basis of the Industrial Equipment product line. Thirty-three different kinds of Special Duty Equipment products were approved for use on the International 300 Utility.

From Approved to Marketed

A major step toward serving the needs of the industrial market came with direct marketing, servicing, and factory installing loaders and backhoes manufactured by others. Literature printed in 1958 featured the new 35-belt horsepower International 330 Utility tractor equipped with International Pippin No. 250 backhoe and International Pippin No. 225 front-end loader. With both International and Pippin on the same decal it was clear the backhoe and loader were more than just approved products. The four-page literature also pictured an International 330 Utility tractor equipped with an International Wagner No. 130 front-end loader. Thirty-two pieces of Special Duty Equipment were

This photo shows an International 330 Utility tractor with Pippin No. 250 backhoe and Pippin No. 125-250 loader. These Pippin products were approved by IH engineering and were listed as Special Duty Equipment suited for use on this tractor without affecting the tractor warranty.

listed and eight were pictured. The International 330 Utility was a more economical unit than the International 350 Utility tractor. Optional special equipment included power steering for tractors equipped with live Hydra-Touch hydraulics. Power steering was a "must feature" for tractors equipped with front-end loaders and a feature lacking on the International 300 Utility.

For more power, the International 350 Utility with over 44 horsepower in either gasoline or diesel versions did the job. With standard one-valve Hydra-Touch, optional power steering, and extra heavy-duty fixed front axle, the tractor was ready to be equipped with International 325 Pippin front-end loader and International 350 Pippin backhoe, the total package made an ideal industrial backhoe/loader tractor.

In 1960 another red utility would join the IH tractors intended for the industrial market, and this addition would come from overseas. The British McCormick International B-275 low profile diesel tractor delivered 34 PTO horsepower. Standard features included differential lock, eight forward and two reverse speeds, straight-through axle-to-hitch clearance, and live hydraulic power. A plus for this tractor was the 3-point hitch with mechanical weight transfer. A minus, was the constant running PTO rather than independent PTO. The 1960 Farm Equipment Sales Catalog listed matched industrial equipment that included backhoes, loaders, post-hole diggers, blades, fork lifts, and many others totaling over 40 items. Within a year, the B-275 was replaced by the British International B-414 low profile tractor that came in either gasoline or diesel versions. The B-414 was similar to the B-275 except the 3-point hitch had hydraulic draft control. The impact of the B-414 would not be as a complete imported tractor but as an imported skid (engine, transmission, and final drive only) for incorporation in the soon to be released line of Unit-Frame industrial loader tractors.

Yellow IH Industrial Tractors and Equipment

Publication of the 98-page, *1963 International Industrial Tractors and Equipment Buyers Guide*, brought all of the Farm Equipment Division's yellow Industrial Equipment Group products together in one document. IH Industrial Equipment dealers would have access to a very long line of products stretching from the newly introduced Cub Cadet lawn & garden tractor, already

This International 330 Utility tractor replaced the International 300 Utility and was featured on a literature cover. It is equipped with International Pippin No. 250 backhoe and International Pippin No. 225 loader that were mounted on a sub frame to protect the tractor from shock loads. These were not IH approved Special Duty Equipment; the Pippin backhoe and loader carried the IH International Pippin logo decal and were marketed and supported by International Harvester.

This International I-404 Utility tractor is equipped with the 3-point hitch International Harvester No. 50 yard scraper designed and manufactured by the IH Stockton Works, Stockton, California. The yellow No. 50 in this 1961 photo is an indication of the full line of "other yellow" Industrial Equipment products that were soon to follow.

yellow and white, to a yellow International T-340 A Series crawler. Major product groups included: loaders and backhoes, blades, scrapers, scarifiers, mowers, rotary cutters, fork lifts, and trailers all manufactured by International Harvester. Included in the catalog were products marketed and supported by, but not manufactured by, IH. These included: International Harlo tractor fork lifts, International Danco rotary mowers, International Johnson No. 83 elevating scraper for semi-mounting on a modified I-660 diesel tractor, and the International Drott 4-in-1 skid shovel for the T-340 A crawler tractor. The catalog also carried four pages of photos and descriptions of Special Duty Equipment approved for use with IH tractors but not supported or marketed by the Company. International Harvester now demonstrated that they were committed to meeting the needs of the industrial equipment purchaser and supporting the IH dealers who served that market. International joined with other members of the industry as part of the Industrial Equipment Manufacturers Council (IEMC).

The IH Industrial Equipment Buyers Guide covered tractors that were yellow, had special features needed for industrial applications, and carried their own unique model number. The I-404 with its U.S.-made 3-point, single-acting, draft controlled hitch that was introduced in 1961 was available in three industrial yellow versions. The International 404 industrial tractor was essentially the same as the agricultural tractor. The International 404 Lo-Boy high stability tractor was the same as the I-404 but came on dual 8.3-24, 4-ply (R-3 tread) rear tires for operation on inclines up to 40 degrees. The new series was represented by the International 2404 industrial tractor that had a 52-inch tread, non-adjustable front axle, and standard power steering. The I-504 and I-606 came in similar International 2504 and International 2606 industrial tractor versions.

The Unit-Frame Loader Tractor

The year 1961 represented a significant benchmark in developing the industrial equipment product line; IH introduced the International 3414 loader tractor with Unit-Frame construction. The new frame design was described as, "One-price frame unit is an all-welded, formed steel plate structure which absorbs the front-end stresses of loader operation, completely insulating engine and power train from all direct shocks." To complete the rugged package, the fixed 54-inch tread front axle was made of solid cast steel rated at 8,500-pound working capacity. The loader had a

This rugged, innovative unit-frame International 3414 loader tractor with its 43.5 maximum horsepower engine would become the foundation for the new IH Industrial Equipment product line.

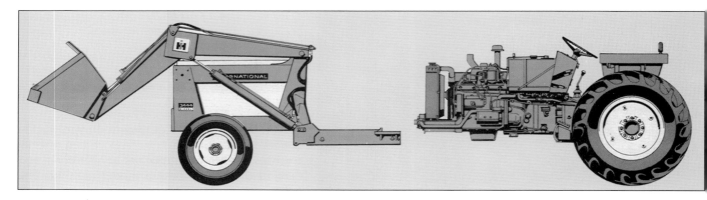

The term Unit-Frame was changed to Integral with introduction of the International 3616, 3514, and 3444 Integral loader tractors.
- *The 1-yard International 3616 had a 6-cylinder gasoline or diesel engine rated at 70 horsepower with Hydrostatic Transmission or 66 horsepower with the standard forward and reverse drive.*
- *The 1-yard International 3514 had a 4-cylinder gasoline engine rated at 58 horsepower or a 4-cylinder diesel engine rated at 61 horsepower. Both were available with Hydrostatic Transmission or standard forward and reverse drive.*
- *The 7/8-yard International 3444 had a 4-cylinder gasoline or diesel engine both rated at 43.5 horsepower. It was available with Hydra-Shuttle and Torque Converter or a choice of two mechanical transmissions.*

2,500-pound lift capacity. This impressive new loader tractor utilized the British B-414 tractor skid for the engine, transmission, and final drive. Designed for loader operation, the forward and reverse drive option reversed the tractor without shifting gears and provided 26 percent (later models 22%) faster reverse speed than comparable forward speed in any gear; this was a great time-saver in loader operation. By 1966, IH loader tractors utilizing the important Unit-Frame concept would be renamed International Integral loader tractors. This significant development in loader tractor design would be incorporated in a new family of rugged IH integral loader tractors that included the 54-PTO horsepower 3616, 46-PTO horsepower 3514, and 36-PTO horsepower 3414. They had 11,000-, 10,000-, and 8,500-pound front axle ratings, respectively. Power steering and automatic hydraulic bucket leveling were standard. Later units were equipped with a patented IH system that prevented the automatic leveling feature from rolling back the bucket and spilling dirt on the tractor and operator. All three integral loader tractors were available in models with Hydra-Shuttle and torque converter drive.

The Hydra-Shuttle feature had two pedals to the left of the operator. Pressing on the forward accelerator pedal determined the forward speed and direction. Shifting the foot to the reverse accelerator pedal reversed the direction of travel and determined the reverse speed. This convenient arrangement could shorten loader cycle time and provided for ease of operation.

Not every industrial equipment purchase needed the heavy duty features of the Unit-Frame or Integral design family of loaders. To meet that demand, yellow farm-tractor loaders were available for the industrial

The International 3000 loader was designed to quickly and easily mount tractors like the International 2504, 2544, 2606, and 2656.

market. The 450-pound lift capacity single arm model 1000 loader mounted on International Cub, Cub Lo-Boy, and International 140 tractors. The 2,000-pound lift capacity model 2000 loader mounted on the B-414, International 404/2404, 504/2504, 606/2606 plus the 240, 340, and 460 older model tractors. The 3,000-pound lift capacity model 3000 loader mounted the same larger tractors as the model 2000 loader, but not the smaller B-414, International 404/2404, and 240.

IH Designed and Manufactured Backhoes

The IH 3414 loader tractor was the leader in its size and price class. To complete the package, an outstanding backhoe to match the features of the tractor was

This International 2500A tractor was part of the IH worldwide tractor program. Equipped with heavy-duty front axle, vertical muffler, and four-post ROPS, it made an excellent base for this industrial loader/backhoe tractor.

needed; the IH designed and manufactured 3120 backhoe was the answer. The rack-and-pinion swing system set it apart from other backhoes on the market. The design provided fast, positive, "no-lag" swing action for outstanding operator control and short cycle times. Automatic cushioning eased the swing action to a stop. Maximum digging depth was 12 feet 6 inches; swing was 180 degrees. The 3120 backhoe had a 17-gpm hydraulic pump to power the crowd, lift and bucket cylinders while a completely independent 7-gpm hydraulic pump powered the swing and stabilizer cylinders. The output of the two pumps automatically combined to supply 24 gpm for maximum crowd. The system flow became independent for powering lift and swing cylinders for fast dump and return cycles. The controls were split so the operator had an unobstructed view of all digging operations and his hands and arms were in a natural, non-fatiguing position. The 3120 backhoe would also mount on 504, 2504, 606, and 2606 tractors.

The IH backhoe line was expanded to include the 3130 with 13-foot 6-inch digging depth and 3140 with 14-foot 6-inches digging depth. With introduction of the 3514 and 3616 Integral Loader Tractors, the new 3121, 3131, and 3141 backhoes were released with the same digging depths as the models they

The 3820A backhoe/loader had a loader-chassis-backhoe integral frame, twin turbine torque converter and an IH D310 diesel engine with seven more bare engine horsepower than the prior model 3800. This product and other heavy-duty units in the International Equipment line were considered competition by the IH Construction Equipment Division, the "original" yellow line.

replaced. Later the 3121 would have a digging depth of 13 feet. With introduction of the 2400A, 2300A, 3400A, 3500A, and 3600A integral loader tractors, the 3122, 3142, and 3152 backhoes with digging depths from 12 feet 4 inches to 17 feet 5 inches with hydraulically extendible dipperstick option were released.

The Industrial Equipment Group offered a pair of totally different loader and loader backhoe products in 1968. Both units shared many basic design features including 90-horsepower gasoline or 94-horsepower diesel engines, 2-stage torque converter, dual-range single-lever power shift transmission, and four-wheel, steerable-axle drive with standard 14.0-24 tires front and rear. The 3850 loader had the engine in the rear of the operator for optimum visibility. The 3800 backhoe/loader located the engine to the rear of the 15-foot digging depth backhoe; the loader was in the traditional location in front of the engine. The hydraulic system used a 24-gpm main pump and a 10-gpm secondary pump for a total capacity of 34 gpm.

Centralized Sales Training

In 1960 IH opened the Industrial Equipment Training Center at the Hickory Hill Farm near Sheridan, Illinois. The five-day, intensive classroom and field operation course provided dealers and dealer salesmen with the knowledge and experience needed to demonstrate and sell the IH Industrial Equipment line effectively against any competition. The Company assembled almost half a million dollars worth of IH and competitive equipment for hands-on operation by students. The nearby Prairie Lake Hunt Club provided lodging and meals; a Scout and several Travelalls provided transportation to and from the Training Center. A similar training program was located at Tifton, Georgia, for farm equipment products.

The Hickory Hill location was originally acquired to serve as a location for the IH Photo Center. This impressive facility included a photo studio large enough to accommodate the largest IH combine and corn head and rotate it 360 degrees on the floor-level turntable. Black and white as well as color processing was done on site. Motion picture and video production was a part of the Photo Center's capability. The Hickory Hill location would later also house the IH Farm and Industrial Equipment Service Training Program.

Show and Tell

With a full line of Industrial Equipment products to market, International Harvester put on its first presentation conducted specifically for Company Industrial Dealers and District Personnel. The big April 1970 presentation was at Freedom Hall on the Fairgrounds, Louisville, Kentucky. The manager of Industrial Tractor and Equipment Sales challenged the dealers to, "Put Yourself in the Industrial Profit Picture." The show covered everything from Cub and Cub Cadet tractors through crawlers, fork lifts, skid-steer loaders, rubber-tired skidders, loaders, and loader/backhoes.

With the new 3400, 3500, and 3600 integral loader and loader/backhoe tractors, and other new products to introduce, the big Industrial Equipment Show moved to the International Hilton hotel in Las Vegas for a February 1972 presentation. Almost 1,000 industrial dealers heard the manager of industrial dealer development say, we're here "to demonstrate to our dealers that we are deadly serious about being number one in the industrial field." The finale included a Las Vegas-style show featuring Elvis Presley.

Fork Lifts

The IH Industrial Product Group offered fork lifts for IH tractors on the 1956 Special Duty Equipment list for International 300 Utility tractors. Approved manufacturers included Blackwelder Corporation, Edwards Equipment Company, and the Kirkhoff Manufacturing Co. (Harlo). International Harvester also sold basic tractor units to Kirkhoff for incorporating in the Harlo line of fork lift trucks. By 1963 IH marketed a broad line of International Harlo fork lifts for rear mounting on IH 340, 460, 560, and 660 tractors and front mounting on IH 340 and T-340/TD-340 crawler tractors. In addition, IH offered three models of Harlo SP-40 fork lift trucks that incorporated specially modified IH 340 tractors and carried the International name in place of Harlo.

It was not practical for IH to try and compete directly with the low-cost, limited future high-lift fork lift that was the market leader. The four-wheel-drive, four-wheel-steer International 9000 High-Lift fork lift with IH gasoline or IH diesel engine and Allison 2-speed power shift, 2-stage torque converter transmission was a high quality, heavy-duty product. The 9000 was positioned to meet the needs of a different market segment than the market leader.

By 1965 IH offered their own line of tractor fork lifts. The International 4000 Series and 5000 Series fork lifts provided 4,000- and 5,000-pound lift capacity with lift heights ranging from 10 1/2 to 21 1/2 feet. The 7000 Series with integral design and hydro-shuttle torque converter was introduced in 1969; it included a side-shift option. The 8000 Series joined the IH fork lift family in 1970 with capacity to 6,000 pounds and lift height to 28 feet. In 1973 the 4500A fork lift series with 4,000- and 5,000-pound lift capacities and lift heights up to 28 feet represented the traditional fork lifts in the IH industrial line and replaced the prior models.

With increased popularity of multistory building construction, a market developed for high-lift fork lifts. International Harvester responded with the International 9000 Series fork lift in 1973. This high-lift fork lift had a four-wheel drive that incorporated Hough planetary steerable axles for two-wheel and four-wheel steering. The full lift height of 40 1/2 feet could accommodate up to 3,500 pounds. The 48-inch horizontal carriage forward movement was hydraulically actuated with positive gear drive on the carriage rollers. This made it possible to insert a load carefully through doors or windows without tilting the mast.

Elevating Scrapers

In 1963, trailing model Johnson Elevating Scrapers were in the Special Duty Equipment section for use with IH 560 and 660 tractors. The International Johnson

No. 83 elevating scraper was semi-mounted on a modified 660 tractor that became the prime mover. The 9 1/2-cubic-yard scraper had a 94-inch width of cut.

The International Johnson elevating scraper took on a totally different form in the International E-200 Pay Scraper introduced in 1969. This unit was a 9-cubic-yard version of the very large machines used by major contractors for road building and other large projects. The E-200 was ideal for the general contractor market for use in residential development sites and other small-scale earth moving jobs. The 135-horsepower prime mover had only two drive wheels; it was supported by the massive hinge that connected it to the Johnson-built elevating scraper bowl section. It steered by 2-stage hydrostatic power steering. This was a useful addition to the Industrial Equipment line and was sold by specially selected dealers who held that contract. The similarity of this product to the large machines in the Construction Equipment Division resulted in management eventually turning it over to that Division.

This 9-yard, 135-horsepower elevating scraper was aimed directly at the Industrial Equipment market where this affordable, small machine filled a market niche. However, with the name E-200 pay scraper, it soon became a Pay Line Division Product.

Crawler Tractors and Log Skidders

International Harvester's Farm Equipment Division entered the small crawler tractor market with a track version of the 340 wheel tractor in 1959; it was called the

T-340. The 47 engine horsepower T-340/TD-340 Series "A" were the only crawler tractors in the 1963 Industrial Equipment Buyers Guide. By 1965, crawler tractors included the T-6/TD-6 bulldozers and bullgraders as well as T-6/TD-6 loaders. The T-340/TD-340 Series "A" came in hydraulic bullgrader, 600 straight dozer, 700 angle dozer, and 4,200-pound lift capacity loader versions. The 47-horsepower gasoline or 43.5-horsepower diesel engine International 500 crawler tractor manufactured by IH Canada became part of the Industrial Equipment crawler tractor offering in 1966. Equipment for use with the 500 crawler included: 3/4-yard loader, three models of backhoes, dozers, scarifier, winch, side boom, firelane plow, 3-point hitch, drawbar, log grapple, and factory-

The Industrial Equipment family of crawler tractors included an impressive group of products in 1971. Machines in the photo are from left to right: 56-net horsepower International TD-7C crawler; 69-net horsepower International TD-8C crawler; 69-net horsepower International 1 1/4-yard 125C loader with multi-purpose bucket; 56-net horsepower International 1-yard 100C loader with multi-purpose bucket; and 44-net horsepower International 500C crawler with No. 75 loader and general purpose bucket.

The International articulated steer S11 pay logger shown here was the largest of the three models available from IH in 1969. It was powered by an IH DT407 engine rated at 135 flywheel horsepower at 2,500 rpm. The Carco winch had a maximum line pull of 20,000 pounds.

installed canopies. By 1972 the IH "Track Team" included: 500C-75, 100C, and 125C crawler loaders and TD-7C, TD-8C, and 500C bullgraders.

Articulated log skidders were offered to specially selected IH Industrial Equipment dealers in 1969. The 85-horsepower S7 pay logger had a Warner synchromesh transmission and Rockwell-Standard transfer case. The 100-horsepower S9 pay logger and 135-horsepower S11 pay logger both had Hough full power-shift transmissions.

The Timber Harvest Dilemma

As part of International Harvester's strategic planning for achieving a larger share of the timber harvest market in the Pacific Northwest and the South East, they hired the consulting firm of Woods Gordon of Vancouver, British Columbia, Canada to assess the market and make recommendations for IH action. The report of their in-depth study was not what the Industrial Equipment Group wanted to hear. The Woods Gordon study revealed that customers for timber harvest equipment said IH sold some equipment through the large Construction Equipment Distributors and some equipment through Industrial Equipment Dealers and they found that to be a problem; they wanted sales and service all in one location. Woods Gordon made a number of recommendations, the most significant was, market all of your timber harvest products through one organization. That was no doubt a significant factor in management's decision to merge Industrial Equipment — "The Other Yellow" — into the International Pay Line Division.

Skid-Steer Loaders

International Harvester entered a totally new kind of market through O.E.M. purchase and introduction of the hydrostatic drive, International 3200 A (Skid-Steer) loader tractor. This product was so well suited to the farm market that it was marketed painted red and white through IH Farm Equipment Dealers and yellow and white through Industrial Equipment Dealers where there was also a good market. The 30-brake horsepower, air-cooled, Wisconsin VH4D, 4-cylinder, 4-cycle engine powered the dual path hydrostatic drive that consisted of two pumps and two motors (one set on each side of the loader). Eleven styles and sizes of loader buckets ranged from a 6.8-cubic-foot dirt bucket to a 17 1/2-cubic-foot snow bucket.

Right and left control levers for the respective right and left variable-volume, piston-type hydrostatic pumps determined direction and skid-steer operation. With both control levers in neutral; the unit stopped. Attachments included: 8 1/2-foot backhoe, fork lift, field grapple, manure fork, crane lift, five-position angle blade, and 48-inch snow blower.

The 3200 A was replaced by the 3200 B in 1975 and the higher horsepower 3300 B was added. Backhoe attachments were available for both of these skid-steer loader tractors. International Harvester manufactured the "B" Series skid-steer loaders until production ended about one year later. The Pay Line Division dropped the skid-steer loaders in 1976. Because of the importance of skid-steer loaders for the agricultural market, IH

This scene of an International 3200 Series A hydrostatic, skid-steer loader is a classic farm application; it was painted red and white and sold through IH Farm Equipment Dealers. A substantial market existed for the International 3200 Series A in the industrial market; IH Industrial Equipment Dealers sold the yellow and white version.

acquired a different O.E.M. line that included four skid-steer loaders. They ranged from the 16-horsepower, engine in front, operator in the rear, 4120 "baby" loader for light-duty work in cramped places to the 58-horsepower conventional 4150 top-of-the line. The three larger models had enclosed in oil, all gear drive from the hydrostatic motors to each pair of drive wheels. One T-bar control handle controlled forward-reverse ground speed and steering. A second T-bar control handle controlled loader operation.

Hydraulic Excavator

A totally new product joined the Industrial Equipment line in 1972, the hydraulic excavator. International Harvester imported the Yumbo hydraulic excavator from France in two versions. The International 3960 crawler model was equipped with heavy-duty tracks that matched crawler tractor quality. The International 3960R rubber-tired, four-wheel-drive, self-transporting model was equipped with three-position hydraulic stabilizers. Both models could be equipped with the short S-boom or long L-boom. The booms could mount either the short or the long dipperstick. The two dippersticks for the S-boom were adjustable. Assorted buckets, clamshells, and a crane boom made these extremely versatile machines. The Pay Line Division replaced the 3960 and 3960R with the 3964 and 3984 Hydraulic Excavator models in 1975. As part of the program to serve the timber harvest market, the 3966 feller buncher, tree shear was added in 1976.

How Do You Successfully Market Industrial Equipment?

The slightly modified tractors and Special Duty Equipment that comprised the start of the Industrial Equipment product line fit very easily in the traditional IH Farm Equipment Dealer's way of doing business in the decade of the 1950s. The 1960s saw the start of a decline in the number of farm equipment dealers, especially in the northeastern United States and around rapidly expanding suburbia. Small, urban contractors, developers, and land improvement contractors needed equipment smaller than was available from large Construction Equipment Distributors. Furthermore, these distributors served very large territories, had high service shop rates, and generally were not interested in

International Harvester entered the Hydraulic Excavator market with a quality, proven product in 1972 by importing the Yumbo Hydraulic Excavator from France. It was available in both a crawler track and a rubber-tired version. The International 3960 hydraulic excavator with S-boom and adjustable dipperstick is shown here.

serving the small contractor. Developing Industrial Equipment dealers and Company Stores in selected market areas served these specific markets well.

Schools of business generally support competition between divisions within a corporation if properly structured. When the Industrial Equipment Group was formed within the Farm Equipment Division, the Construction Equipment Division paid very little attention to the "Other Yellow" organization that painted agricultural tractors federal yellow and marketed a few "light-duty" pieces of earth moving equipment.

The decade of the 1970s brought larger, more specialized equipment into the Industrial Equipment product mix, few of these products were related to similar farm equipment products. The Construction Equipment product line and the Industrial Equipment product line began to overlap at the lower and higher end, respectively. The entire industry struggled with what might be the most cost-effective way to serve these diverse but related markets. By 1975, International Harvester chose to combine the two efforts. The "Other Yellow" line of Industrial Equipment products was absorbed into the International Pay Line Division. Other events that resulted in the sale of Pay Line to Dresser Industries and the Farm Equipment Division to Case/Tenneco precludes determining what would have been the best way for International Harvester to market Industrial Equipment products in the long term.

Appendix

Production Dates and Serial Numbers

Model	Production In	Production Out	Serial No. Start	Serial No. Finish	Model	Production In	Production Out	Serial No. Start	Serial No. Finish
Farmall A Series					**British Imports**				
Farmall A	1939	1947	501	220829	B-275D	1959	1964	501	48173
Farmall AV	1941	1947	41500	220829	B-414	1961	1966	501	6526
Farmall Super A	1947	1954	250001	355679	B-414D	1961	1966	501	53258
Farmall Super AV	1947	1954	250001	355679	B-414HC	1961	1966	501	6526
Farmall Super A-1	1954	1955	356001	357502	B-414D HC	1961	1966	501	53258
Farmall Super AV-1	1954	1955	356001	357502					
International A	1941	1947	41500	220829	**International 424/444 Series**				
International Super A	1947	1948	250001	264693	International 424	1964	1967	501	17223
Farmall 100	1955	1956	501	18940	International 424D	1964	1967	514	17223
Farmall 100HC	1955	1956	501	18940	International 2424	1964	1968	501	5093
International 100	1955	1956	501	18940	International 2424D	1964	1968	501	5093
Farmall 130	1956	1958	501	10209	International 2424 Lo-Boy	1964	1968	501	5093
Farmall 130 HC	1956	1958	501	10209	International 2424D Lo-Boy	1964	1968	501	5093
International 130	1956	1958	501	10209	International 444	1967	1971	501	13407
Farmall 140	1958		501		International 444D	1967	1971	501	13407
Farmall 140 HC	1958		501		International 2444	1967	1971	501	6260
International 140	1958		501		International 2444D	1967	1971	501	6260
					International 2444 Lo-Boy	1967	1971	501	6260
Farmall B Series					International 2444D Lo-Boy	1967	1971	501	6260
Farmall B	1939	1947	501	220829					
Farmall BN	1940	1947	6744	220829	**World Wide**				
Farmall C	1948	1951	501	80432	U.S.A. Models				
Farmall Super C	1951	1954	100001	198310	International 454	1971	1973	501	8313
Farmall 200 Series	1954	1956	501	15698	International 454D	1971	1973	501	8313
Farmall 230 Series	1956	1958	501	7671	International 454HS	—		Never built	
Farmall 240	1958	1962	501	4124	International 454D HS	—		Never built	
International 240 Utility	1958	1962	501	10789	International 2400 Series A	1971		501	
Farmall 404	1960	1967	501	3075	International 2400D Series A	1971		501	
International 404	1960	1967	501	11077	International 2400 Series A HS	1973		501	
Farmall 404 LPG	1960	1967	501	3075	International 2400D Series A HS	1973		501	
International 404 LPG	1960	1967	501	11077	International 2400 Lo-Boy Series A	1971		501	
International 2404	1960	1967	501	11077	International 2400D Lo-Boy Series A	1971		501	
International 2404 LPG	1960	1967	501	11077	International 2400 Lo-Boy Series A	1973		501	
International 2404 Lo-Boy	1960	1967	501	11077	International 2400D Lo-Boy Series A HS	1973		501	
International 2404 LPG Lo-Boy	1960	1967	501	11077	International 464	1973		100001	
					International 464D	1973		100001	

392

Model	Production In	Out	Serial No. Start	Finish
Farmall H Series				
Farmall H	1939	1953	501	391730
Farmall HV	1942	1953	93237	391730
Farmall Super H	1953	1954	501	29285
Farmall Super HV	1953	1954	501	29285
Farmall 300	1955	1956	501	30508
Farmall 300HC	1955	1956	501	30508
International 300 Utility	1955	1956	501	33664
Farmall 350	1956	1958	501	17215
Farmall 350HC	1956	1958	533	17150
Farmall 350D	1956	1958	581	17149
Farmall 350D HC	1956	1958	581	17149
International 350 Utility	1956	1958	501	18346
International 350D Utility	1956	1958	739	18274
International 330 Utility	1956	1958	501	4763
Farmall 460	1958	1963	501	33028
Farmall 460HC	1958	1963	2916	33028
Farmall 460D	1958	1963	663	33028
Farmall 460D HC	1958	1963	1863	33028
International 460 Utility	1958	1963	501	11911
International 460D Utility	1958	1963	579	11911
International 606 Series	1961	1967	501	7939
International 2606 Series	1961	1967	501	7939
Farmall 656 Series	1965	1972	8501	49904
Farmall 656 Series Hi-Clear	1965	1972	8501	49904
Farmall 656 Series Western Special	1965	1972	8501	49904
International 656	1966	1973	7501	16241
International 656D	1966	1973	7501	16241
International 656HS	1967	1973	9621	16241
International 656D HS	1967	1973	9621	16241
International 656 Row Crop	1966	1973	7501	16241
International 656 HS Row Crop	1967	1973	9621	16241
International 2656	1966	1973	7501	16241
International 2656D	1966	1973	7501	16241
International 2656 HS	1967	1973	9621	16241
International 2656D HS	1967	1973	9621	16241
Farmall 656 HS	1967	1972	29156	49904
International 656 HS	1967	1973	9621	16241
Farmall 666 - GD	1972		7500	
Farmall 666D - GD	1972		7500	
Farmall 666 - HS	1972		7500	
Farmall 666D - HS	1972		7500	
International 664D	1972	1973	2501	3399
Hydro 70				
Hydro 70D				

Model	Production In	Out	Serial No. Start	Finish
Farmall M Series				
Farmall M	1939	1952	501	298218
Farmall MD	1941	1952	25371	298218
Farmall Super M	1952	1954	F501 L500001	F52627 L512541
Farmall Super MD	1952	1954	F501 L500001	F51976 *F512541
Farmall MV	1942	1952	50988	298218
Farmall MDV	1945	1952	88085	298218
Farmall Super MV	1952	1954	F501 L500001	F51976 L512541
Farmall Super MDV	1952	1954	F501 L500001	F51976 L512541
Farmall Super M-TA	1954	1955	60001	81847
Farmall Super MD-TA	1954	1955	60004	81848
Farmall Super MV-TA	1954	1955	61726	81467
Farmall 400	1955	1956	501	41484
Farmall 400HC	1955	1956	2517	41422
Farmall 400D	1955	1956	505	41485
Farmall 400D HC	1955	1956	505	41081
Farmall 450	1956	1958	501	26066
Farmall 450HC	1956	1958	596	26025
Farmall 450D	1956	1958	585	26067
Farmall 450D HC	1957	1958	2607	25832
Farmall 560	1958	1963	501	66032
Farmall 560HC	1958	1963	1422	66032
Farmall 560D	1958	1963	725	66032
Farmall 560D HC	1958	1963	3740	66032
Farmall 706 Series	1963	1967	501	46647
Farmall 706 Series HC	1963	1967	501	46647
Farmall 756 Series	1967	1971	7501	18477
Farmall 756D (Mexico)	1967	1971		
Farmall 756D Custom	1969	1971	7501	18477
Farmall 756HC Series	1967	1971	7501	18477
Farmall 826 Series HS	1969	1971	7501	17089
Farmall 826 Series HC HS	1969	1971	7501	17089
Farmall 826 D	1969	1971	7501	17089
Farmall 766	1971		7101	
Farmall 966D HS	1971		7101	
Farmall 966D	1971		7101	
Farmall 966D HC HS	1971		7101	
Farmall 966D HC	1971		7101	
W-4/W-6 and International Series				
O-4	1940	1953	501	34043
OS-4	1944	1953	11170	33753
W-4	1940	1953	758	34176
Super W-4	1953	1954	501	3292

*Suspected source list typo: "F" should be "L"

Model	Production In	Out	Serial No. Start	Finish	Model	Production In	Out	Serial No. Start	Finish
W-4/W-6 and International Series (con't)					Farmall 806 Series HI-Clear	1963	1967	501	43458
O-6	1940	1952	501	45782	International 806 Series	1963	1967	501	8553
OS-6	1944	1952	6313	45843	International 2806	1963	1967	501	8553
ODS-6	1947	1952	17792	45280	Farmall 856 Series	1967	1971	7505	34394
W-6	1940	1952	501	46011	International 856 Series	1967	1971	7502	9716
WD-6	1940	1952	501	46011	Farmall 856D Custom	1969	1971	21116	34394
Super W-6	1952	1954	501	9084	Farmall 856 Series Hi-Clear	1967	1971	7501	34394
Super WD-6	1952	1954	2277	9084	International 856D Wheatland	1967	1971	7501	9716
Super W-6-TA Series	1954	1954	10001	13006	International 2856 Series	1967	1971	7501	9716
International W-400	1955	1956	501	3858	Farmall 1026D HS	1969	1971	7501	9915
International W-400D	1955	1956	501	3858	Farmall 1026D HI-Clear HS	1969	1971	7501	9915
International 450	1956	1958	501	2295	International 1026D HS	1969	1971	7501	7559
International 450D	1956	1958	529	2294	International 1026D				
International 560	1958	1963	501	6049	Wheatland HS	1969	1971	7501	7559
International 560D	1958	1963	525	6049	International 21026D HS	1969	1971	7501	7559
International 706 Series	1963	1967	501	5988	Farmall 1066D	1971		7101	
International 2706 Series	1963	1967	501	5988	Farmall 1066D HS	1971		7101	
International 706D					Farmall 1066D HC	1971		7101	
(For export)	1967	1968			Farmall 1066D HC HS	1971		7101	
International 756 Series	1967	1971	7501	8426					
International 756D Wheatland	1967	1971	7501	8426	**Farmall 1200/1400 Series**				
International 2756 Series	1969	1971	7501	8426	Farmall 1206D	1965	1967	7501	15903
International 686D (Australia)	1969	1971			International 1206D	1965	1967	7501	9090
International 756D (Australia)	1969	1971			International 21206D Turbo	1965	1967	7501	9090
International 826 Series HS	1969	1971	7501	7827	Farmall 1256D Turbo	1967	1969	7504	14646
International 2826	1969	1971	7501	7827	International 1256D Turbo	1967	1969	7503	8732
International 826D Wheatland	1969	1971	7501	7827	International 1256D				
International 826D	1969	1971	7501	7827	Wheatland	1967	1969	7504	8732
					International 21256D Turbo	1967	1969	7503	8732
International Four-Wheel Drive — Four-Wheel Steer					Farmall 1456D Turbo	1969	1971	10001	15583
International 4100D	1965	1968	8001	9218	International 1456D Turbo	1969	1971	10001	10295
International 4156D	1969		9219		International 21456D Turbo	1969	1971	10001	10295
International 4166D	1972		10001		Farmall 1466D	1971		7101	
					Farmall 1468D	1971		7201	
W-9/Farmall and International Series									
W-9	1941	1953	578	66870	**Farmall and International 340/504 and 544 Series**				
WD-9	1940	1953	501	67898	Farmall 340	1958	1963	501	7711
WDR-9	1945	1953	11459	67506	Farmall 340D	1958	1963	501	7711
WR-9	1945	1953	11459	67919	International 340	1958	1963	501	12338
WR-9S	1953	1956	501	779	International 340 Grove	1958	1963	501	12338
Super WD-9	1953	1956	501	7253	International 340D	1958	1963	501	12338
Super WDR-9	1953	1956	501	7249	International 340D Grove	1958	1963	501	12338
International 600	1956	1956	501	1985	Farmall 504 Series	1960	1968	501	16175
International 600D	1956	1956	501	1985	International 504 Series	1960	1968	501	20438
International 650	1956	1958	1044	5040	International 2504 Series	1960	1968	501	20438
International 650D	1956	1958	501	5324	International				
International 650LPG	1957	1958	1275	5433	"Constructall" 2500	1960	1968	501	20438
International 660	1959	1963	617	7445	Farmall 504 Series Hi-Clear	1960	1968	501	16175
International 660D	1959	1963	501	7445	Farmall 544 Series	1968	1973	10253	16049
Farmall 806 Series	1963	1967	501	43458	Farmall 544 Series HS	1968	1973	12442	16049

Farmall and International 340/504 & 544 Series (con't)

Model	Production In	Out	Serial No. Start	Finish
International 544	1968	1973	10253	16049
International 544D	1968	1973	10253	17428
International 544HS	1968	1973	12598	17428
International 544D HS	1968	1973	12598	17428
International 544 Row Crop	1968	1973	10253	17428
International 544D Row Crop	1968	1973	10253	17428
International 544 Row Crop HS	1968	1973	12598	17428
International 544D Row Crop HS	1968	1973	12598	17428
International 2544	1968	1973	10253	17428
International 2544D	1968	1973	10253	17428
International 2544 HS	1968	1973	12598	17428
International 2544D HS	1968	1973	12598	17428

World Wide
U.S.A. Models

Model	Production In	Out	Serial No. Start	Finish
International 574	1971		501	
International 574D	1971		501	
International 574HS				
International 574D HS				
International 574 Row Crop	1971		501	
International 574D Row Crop	1971		501	
International 574HS Row Crop				
International 574D HS Row Crop				
International 2500 Series	1971		501	
International 2500D Series	1971		501	
International 2500 Series A	1973		501	
International 2500D Series A	1973		501	
International 2500 Lo-Boy Series	1971		501	
International 2500D Lo-Boy Series	1971		501	
International 2500 Lo-Boy Series A HS	1973		501	
International 2500D Lo-Boy Series A HS	1973		501	
International 674	1973		100001	
International 674D	1973		100001	
International 674 Row Crop	1973		100001	
International 674D Row Crop	1973		100001	

10-20/15-30/W and Farmall Series

Model	Production In	Out	Serial No. Start	Finish
WA-40	1935	1940	501	10559
W-40 and WK-40	1935	1940	501	10559
WD-40	1935	1940	501	10559
F-12	1932	1938	501	123942
W-12	1934	1938	501	4133

Model	Production In	Out	Serial No. Start	Finish
O-12	1934	1939	501	4286
Fairway 12	1934	1939	501	4286
F-14	1938	1940	124000	155401
W-14	1938	1940	4134	5296
O-14	1938	1940	501	4286
Fairway 14	1938	1940	501	4286
F-20 (Reg.)	1932	1940	501	148810
F-20 (N.T.)	1932	1940	501	148810
F-20 Fairway	1938	1940	501	148810
F-20 Cane	1938	1940	501	148810
W-30	1932	1940	501	33041
W-30 Orchard (Reg.)	1932	1940	501	33041
W-30 Orchard (CFA.)	1932	1940	501	33041
F-30 (Reg.)	1931	1940	501	30221
F-30 (N.T.)	1932	1940	501	30221
F-30 Cane	1935	1940	501	30221
F-30 Cane Reg. 1938	1938	1940	501	30221
F-30 Cane H.S. 1938	1938	1940	501	30221
Farmall (Reg.)	1924	1932	501	134954
Farmall (N.T.)	1924	1932	501	134954
Farmall Fairway	1924	1932	501	134954
15-30 (4-3/4")	1929	1934	99926	157477
15-30 (4-3/4") Orchard (Reg.)	1929	1934	99926	157477
15-30 (4-3/4") Orchard (CFA.)	1929	1934	99926	157477
15-30 (4-3/4") Orchard (Low Wheel)	1929	1934	99926	157477
15-30 (4-1/2")	1921	1929	112	99925
15-30 (4-1/2") Orchard (Reg.)	1921	1929	112	99925
15-30 (4-1/2") Orchard (CFA.	1921	1929	112	99925
15-30 (4-1/2") Orchard (Low Wheel)	1921	1929	112	99925
10-20 (Reg.)	1923	1939	501	215973
10-20 (N.T.)	1926	1939	501	215973
10-20 Orchard (Reg.)	1926	1939	501	215973
10-20 Orchard (CFA.)	1926	1939	501	215973
10-20 Mod. Orchard (Reg. 3 Speed)	1926	1939	501	215973
10-20 Mod. Orchard (N.T. 3 Speed)	1926	1939	501	215973
10-20 Mod. Orchard (N.T. 4 Speed)	1926	1939	501	215973
10-20 Orchard (Low Seat)	1926	1939	501	215973
10-20 Rice Field	1926	1939	501	215973

Cub Cadet — Cadet Lawn Tractor — Cadet Riding Mower

Model	Production In	Out	Serial No. Start	Finish
International Cub Cadet	1960	1963	501	65457
International Cub Cadet 70	1963	1965	65458	127160
International Cub Cadet 71	1965	1967	127161	218009
International Cub Cadet 100	1963	1965	65458	127160

Model	Production In	Out	Serial No. Start	Finish
Cub Cadet — Cadet Lawn Tractor —				
Cadet Riding Mower (con't)				
International Cub Cadet 102	1965	1967	127161	218009
International Cub Cadet 122	1965	1967	127161	218009
International Cub Cadet 123	1966	1967	157490	218009
International Cub Cadet 72	1967	1969	218010	306085
International Cub Cadet 104	1967	1969	218010	306085
International Cub Cadet 105	1967	1969	218010	306085
International Cub Cadet 124	1967	1969	218010	306085
International Cub Cadet 125	1967	1969	218010	306085
International Cub Cadet 73	1969	1971	307000	400000
International Cub Cadet 106	1969	1971	307000	400000
International Cub Cadet 107	1969	1971	307000	400000
International Cub Cadet 126	1969	1971	307000	400000
International Cub Cadet 127	1969	1971	307000	400000
International Cub Cadet 147	1969	1971	316816	400000
International Cub Cadet 86	1971		400001	
International Cub Cadet 108	1971		400001	
International Cub Cadet 109	1971		400001	
International Cub Cadet 128	1971		400001	
International Cub Cadet 129	1971		400001	
International Cub Cadet 149	1971		400001	
International Cadet 76 Lawn Tractor	1971			
Cadet 60 Riding Mower	1968		7501	
Cadet 55 Riding Mower				
Cadet 75 Riding Mower				
Farmall Cub — International Cub Lo-Boy —				
International Cub 154 Lo-Boy				
Farmall Cub	1947	1958	501	205808
Farmall Cub	1958	1964	210001	224703
International Cub Lo-Boy	1958	1968	10001	26007
International Cub	1964		224704	
International Cub 154 Lo-Boy	1968		7501	
Industrial Tractors 1923 to 1953				
Industrial 20	1923	1925	KC501	32604
Industrial 20	1925	1926	IND32605	45075
Industrial 20	1926	1940	IN1053	18896
Industrial 30	1930	1932	HD501	1032
I-30	1931	1940	IB501	5468
I-12	1934	1938	512	2703
I-14	1938	1939	2704	3598
I-40 and ID-40	1936	1940	501	849
I-4	1940	1951	501	31839
I6 and ID6	1940	1953	501	45274
I9 and ID9	1940	1953	501	67968

Model	Production In	Out	Serial No. Start	Finish
Industrial Equipment				
International 3414 Loader	1961	1967	501	8274
International 3414D Loader	1961	1967	501	8274
International 3414 Dozer	1961	1967	501	8274
International 3414D Dozer	1961	1967	501	8274
International 3444 Loader	1967	1971	501	5483
International 3444D Loader	1967	1971	501	5485
International 3514 Loader	1965	1972	501	3869
International 3514 HS Loader	1965	1972	501	3869
International 3514D Loader	1965	1972	501	3846
International 3514D HS Loader	1965	1972	501	3846
International 3616 Loader	1965	1971	501	2715
International 3616 HS Loader	1965	1971	501	2708
International 3616D Loader	1965	1971	501	2722
International 3616D HS Loader	1965	1971	501	2720
International 3600 Series A Loader Backhoe	1971		501	
International 3600D Series A Loader Backhoe	1971		501	
International 3800 Loader Backhoe	1967	1971	751	1553
International 3800D Loader Backhoe	1967	1971	751	1561
International 3850 Loader	1967	1971	751	
International 3850D Loader	1967	1971	751	
International 3820D Series A Loader Backhoe	1971		600	
International 3200 Series A Loader Tractor	1971		501	
World Wide Industrial Equipment				
U.S.A. Models				
International 3400 Series A Loader	1972		501	
International 3400D Series A Loader	1972		501	
International 3400 Series A Loader	1972		501	
International 3400D Series A Loader HS	1972		501	
International 3500 Series A Loader	1972		501	
International 3500D Series A Loader	1972		501	
International 3500 Series A Loader HS	1972		501	
International 3500D Series A Loader HS	1972		501	

International Harvester Company
Tractor Production 1918-1929
(Milwaukee Works, Tractor Works, and Farmall Works)

1918 — 25,269 Tractors Manufactured

	Milwaukee	Tractor
Titan 10-20 H.P. 2-cylinder	17,675	
International 15-30 H.P.	420	
International 15-30 H.P.		865
Mogul 12-25 H.P.		1
Mogul 10-20 H.P. 2-speed		3,146
International 8-16 H.P. 4-cylinder vertical		3,162
Total	**18,095**	**7,174**

1919 — 26,933 Tractors Manufactured

	Milwaukee	Tractor
Titan 10-20 H.P. 2-cylinder	17,234	
International 15-30 H.P.		1,652
Mogul 10-20 H.P. 2-speed		476
International 8-16 H.P. 4-cylinder		7,571
Total	**17,234**	**9,699**

1920 — 28,419 Tractors Manufactured

	Milwaukee	Tractor
Titan 10-20 H.P. 2-cylinder	21,503	
International 8-16 H.P. 4-cylinder vertical		5,848
International 15-30 H.P.		1,068
Total	**21,503**	**6,916**

1921 — 17,762 Tractors Manufactured

	Milwaukee	Tractor
Titan 10-20 H.P. 2-cylinder	7,729	
New International 15-30 H.P. 4-cylinder, gear drive	199	
International 8-16 H.P. 4-cylinder vertical		9,013
International 15-30 H.P.		821
Total	**7,928**	**9,834**

1922 — 11,781 Tractors Manufactured

	Milwaukee	Tractor
Titan 10-20 H.P. 2-cylinder	2,925	
New International 15-30 H.P. 4-cylinder, gear drive	1,350	
International 8-16 H.P. 4-cylinder vertical		7,506
International 15-30 H.P.		
Total	**4,275**	**7,506**

1923 — 12,026 Tractors Manufactured

	Milwaukee	Tractor
McCormick-Deering 15-30 H.P.	4,886	
McCormick-Deering 10-20 H.P.		7,117
McCormick-Deering Industrial 10-20 H.P.		23
Total	**4,886**	**7,140**

1924 — 18,749 Tractors Manufactured

	Milwaukee	Tractor
McCormick-Deering 15-30 H.P.	7,321	
McCormick-Deering 10-20 H.P.		11,197
McCormick-Deering Industrial 10-20 H.P.		31
McCormick-Deering Farmall		200
Total	**7,321**	**11,428**

1925 — 32,588 Tractors Manufactured

	Milwaukee	Tractor
McCormick-Deering 15-30 H.P.	12,978	
McCormick-Deering 10-20 H.P.		18,436
McCormick-Deering Industrial 10-20 H.P.		328
McCormick-Deering Farmall		838
McCormick-Deering 10-20 H.P. Narrow Tread		8
Total	**12,978**	**19,610**

1926 — 50,900 Tractors Manufactured

	Milwaukee	Tractor
McCormick-Deering 15-30 H.P.	20,001	
McCormick-Deering 10-20 H.P.		25,021
McCormick-Deering Industrial, 10-20 H.P.		1,300
McCormick-Deering Farmall		4,430
McCormick-Deering 10-20 H.P. Narrow Tread		148
Total	**20,001**	**30,899**

1927 — 55,727 Tractors Manufactured

	Milwaukee	Tractor	Farmall
McCormick-Deering 15-30 H.P.	17,554		
McCormick-Deering 10-20 H.P.		26,646	
McCormick-Deering Industrial 10-20 H.P.		1,842	
McCormick-Deering 10-20 H.P. Narrow Tread		183	
McCormick-Deering Farmall			9,502
Total	**17,554**	**28,671**	**9,502**

1928 — 94,148 Tractors Manufactured

	Milwaukee	Tractor	Farmall
McCormick-Deering 15-30 H.P.	35,525		
McCormick-Deering 10-20 H.P.		30,353	
McCormick-Deering Industrial 10-20 H.P.		3,048	
McCormick-Deering 10-20 H.P. Narrow Tread		323	
McCormick-Deering Farmall			24,899
Total	**35,525**	**33,724**	**24,899**

1929 — 108,728 Tractors Manufactured

	Milwaukee	Tractor	Farmall
McCormick-Deering 15-30 H.P.	28,311		
McCormick-Deering 10-20 H.P.		39,433	
McCormick-Deering Industrial Model 20		4,607	
McCormick-Deering 10-20 H.P. Narrow Tread		388	
McCormick-Deering TracTracTor, 10-20 H.P.		472	
McCormick-Deering Farmall			35,517
Total	**28,311**	**44,900**	**35,517**

First 200 Farmalls, 1924
(Location Shipped and Serial Number)

	Location	Serial Number		Location	Serial Number
1.	Amarillo, Texas	QC-516	52.	Grand Rapids, Michigan	QC-522
2.	Amarillo, Texas	QC-521	53.	Indianapolis, Indiana	QC-555
3.	Houston, Texas	QC-501	54.	Indianapolis, Indiana	QC-560
4.	Dallas, Texas	QC-517	55.	Indianapolis, Indiana	QC-561
5.	Davenport, Iowa	QC-503	56.	Indianapolis, Indiana	QC-564
6.	City Sales, Chicago	QC-506	57.	Indianapolis, Indiana	QC-565
7.	Little Rock, Arkansas	QC-535	58.	Indianapolis, Indiana	QC-571
8.	Little Rock, Arkansas	QC-537	59.	Des Moines, Iowa	QC-557
9.	Memphis, Tennessee	QC-504	60.	Davenport, Iowa	QC-511
10.	Memphis, Tennessee	QC-525	61.	Davenport, Iowa	QC-576
11.	Evansville, Indiana	QC-507	62.	Davenport, Iowa	QC-573
12.	Evansville, Indiana	QC-514	63.	Davenport, Iowa	QC-569
13.	Evansville, Indiana	QC-526	64.	Sioux, City, Iowa	QC-552
14.	Evansville, Indiana	QC-540	65.	Sioux, City, Iowa	QC-577
15.	Evansville, Indiana	QC-541	66.	Sioux, City, Iowa	QC-578
16.	Evansville, Indiana	QC-546	67.	Denver, Colorado	QC-548
17.	Cincinnati, Ohio	QC-536	68.	Denver, Colorado	QC-581
18.	Cincinnati, Ohio	QC-542	69.	St. Joseph, Missouri	QC-562
19.	Cincinnati, Ohio	QC-543	70.	St. Joseph, Missouri	QC-570
20.	Cincinnati, Ohio	QC-545	71.	Kankakee, Illinois	QC-505
21.	Cincinnati, Ohio	QC-551	72.	Milwaukee, Wisconsin	QC-556
22.	Louisville, Kentucky	QC-510	73.	Mason City, Iowa	QC-583
23.	Louisville, Kentucky	QC-519	74.	Mason City, Iowa	QC-589
24.	Louisville, Kentucky	QC-524	75.	Eau Claire, Wisconsin	QC-586
25.	Louisville, Kentucky	QC-539	76.	Eau Claire, Wisconsin	QC-554
26.	Louisville, Kentucky	QC-553	77.	Evansville, Indiana	QC-587
27.	Terre Haute, Indiana	QC-509	78.	Mankato, Minnesota	QC-592
28.	Terre Haute, Indiana	QC-523	79.	Mankato, Minnesota	QC-602
29.	Terre Haute, Indiana	QC-534	80.	Fort Wayne, Indiana	QC-603
30.	Terre Haute, Indiana	QC-547	81.	Minneapolis, Minnesota	QC-549
31.	Terre Haute, Indiana	QC-563	82.	Minneapolis, Minnesota	QC-588
32.	Rockford, Illinois	QC-508	83.	Aurora, Illinois	QC-572
33.	Rockford, Illinois	QC-512	84.	Aurora, Illinois	QC-580
34.	Rockford, Illinois	QC-566	85.	Aurora, Illinois	QC-582
35.	Rockford, Illinois	QC-567	86.	Aurora, Illinois	QC-590
36.	Rockford, Illinois	QC-568	87.	Aurora, Illinois	QC-597
37.	Columbus, Ohio	QC-527	88.	Aurora, Illinois	QC-599
38.	Columbus, Ohio	QC-528	89.	Aurora, Illinois	QC-579
39.	Columbus, Ohio	QC-529	90.	Fort Dodge, Iowa	QC-584
40.	Columbus, Ohio	QC-532	91.	Fort Dodge, Iowa	QC-593
41.	Columbus, Ohio	QC-550	92.	Fort Dodge, Iowa	QC-598
42.	Madison, Wisconsin	QC-513	93.	South Bend, Indiana	QC-585
43.	Madison, Wisconsin	QC-518	94.	Aberdeen, South Dakota	QC-574
44.	Madison, Wisconsin	QC-531	95.	Aberdeen, South Dakota	QC-575
45.	Richmond, Indiana	QC-530	96.	Winona, Minnesota	QC-604
46.	Richmond, Indiana	QC-558	97.	Fargo, North Dakota	QC-607
47.	South Bend, Indiana	QC-515	98.	Fargo, North Dakota	QC-596
48.	South Bend, Indiana	QC-520	99.	Fargo, North Dakota	QC-591
49.	South Bend, Indiana	QC-559	100.	Hinsdale, Illinois	QC-605
50.	South Bend, Indiana	QC-533	101.	McCormick Works	QC-622
51.	South Bend, Indiana	QC-544	102.	Kansas City, Missouri	QC-594

First 200 Farmalls, 1924
(Location Shipped and Serial Number)

	Location	Serial Number		Location	Serial Number
103.	Watertown, South Dakota	QC-618	153.	Richmond, Indiana	QC-686
104.	Dallas, Texas	QC-655	154.	Salina, Kansas	QC-676
105.	South Bend, Indiana	QC-631	155.	Berma	QC-685
106.	Fort Wayne, Indiana	QC-610	156.	Bismarck, North Dakota	QC-689
107.	Fort Wayne, Indiana	QC-613	157.	Bismarck, North Dakota	QC-624
108.	Fort Wayne, Indiana	QC-614	158.	Grand Forks, North Dakota	QC-632
109.	Fort Wayne, Indiana	QC-669	159.	Grand Forks, North Dakota	QC-643
110.	Dallas, Texas	QC-600	160.	St. Cloud, Minnesota	QC-538
111.	Dallas, Texas	QC-608	161.	St. Cloud, Minnesota	QC-698
112.	Dallas, Texas	QC-616	162.	Indianapolis, Indiana	QC-699
113.	Dallas, Texas	QC-627	163.	Indianapolis, Indiana	QC-700
114.	Peoria, Illinois	QC-628	164.	Indianapolis, Indiana	QC-682
115.	Kankakee, Illinois	QC-606	165.	Indianapolis, Indiana	QC-683
116.	Kankakee, Illinois	QC-611	166.	Sioux Falls, South Dakota	QC-638
117.	Kankakee, Illinois	QC-612	167.	Sioux Falls, South Dakota	QC-694
118.	Kankakee, Illinois	QC-619	168.	Sioux Falls, South Dakota	QC-697
119.	E. St. Louis, Illinois	QC-620	169.	Milwaukee, Wisconsin	QC-595
120.	E. St. Louis, Illinois	QC-621	170.	Milwaukee, Wisconsin	QC-659
121.	E. St. Louis, Illinois	QC-630	171.	Milwaukee, Wisconsin	QC-695
122.	E. St. Louis, Illinois	QC-609	172.	St. Louis, Missouri	QC-615
123.	Council Bluff,*Iowa	QC-660	173.	St. Louis, Missouri	QC-629
124.	Council Bluff,*Iowa	QC-667	174.	Aurora, Illinois	QC-665
125.	Richmond, Indiana	QC-651	175.	Aurora, Illinois	QC-617
126.	Richmond, Indiana	QC-652	176.	Aurora, Illinois	QC-666
127.	Richmond, Indiana	QC-658	177.	Aurora, Illinois	QC-649
128.	Richmond, Indiana	QC-661	178.	Aurora, Illinois	QC-693
129.	Richmond, Indiana	QC-635	179.	Aurora, Illinois	QC-696
130.	Richmond, Indiana	QC-502	180.	Salina, Kansas	QC-663
131.	Baily, Michigan	QC-662	181.	Peoria, Illinois	QC-637
132.	Des Moines, Iowa	QC-675	182.	Cedar Falls, Iowa	QC-678
133.	Kankakee, Illinois	QC-623	183.	Cedar Falls, Iowa	QC-681
134.	Kankakee, Illinois	QC-636	184.	Cedar Falls, Iowa	QC-625
135.	Kankakee, Illinois	QC-645	185.	West Pullman Works	QC-679
136.	Kankakee, Illinois	QC-646	186.	Chicago Transfer	QC-680
137.	Kankakee, Illinois	QC-671	187.	Chicago Transfer	QC-687
138.	Kankakee, Illinois	QC-684	188.	Sioux City, Iowa	QC-654
139.	Peoria, Illinois	QC-670	189.	Sioux City, Iowa	QC-656
140.	Minot, North Dakota	QC-650	190.	Sioux City, Iowa	QC-648
141.	Quincy, Illinois	QC-639	191.	Des Moines, Iowa	QC-674
142.	Quincy, Illinois	QC-692	192.	Kankakee, Illinois	QC-673
143.	Milwaukee, Wisconsin	QC-626	193.	Kankakee, Illinois	QC-653
144.	Springfield, Illinois	QC-601	194.	Memphis, Tennessee	QC-641
145.	Springfield, Illinois	QC-644	195.	Memphis, Tennessee	QC-664
146.	Kankakee, Illinois	QC-690	196.	Memphis, Tennessee	QC-677
147.	Kankakee, Illinois	QC-691	197.	Memphis, Tennessee	QC-668
148.	Kankakee, Illinois	QC-688	198.	Denver, Colorado	QC-640
149.	Kankakee, Illinois	QC-634	199.	Denver, Colorado	QC-647
150.	Kankakee, Illinois	QC-672	200.	(No entry)	
151.	Kankakee, Illinois	QC-657			
152.	Richmond, Indiana	QC-642			

* #123/124 Council Bluff(s), Iowa